Thrust and Nappe Tectonics

Thrust and Nappe Tectonics

edited by

K. R. McCLAY

Department of Geology, University of London, Goldsmiths' College, London

N. J. PRICE

Department of Geology, Imperial College, London

1981

Published for
The Geological Society of London
by Blackwell Scientific Publications
Oxford London Edinburgh
Boston Melbourne

Published by

Blackwell Scientific Publications
Osney Mead, Oxford, OX2 OEL
8 John Street, London, WCIN 2ES
9 Forrest Road, Edinburgh, EH1 2QH
52 Beacon Street, Boston, Massachusetts 02108, USA
214 Berkeley Street, Carlton, Victoria 3053, Australia

First published 1981

© Copyright 1981 The Geological Society.

DISTRIBUTORS

USA
  Blackwell Mosby Book Distributors
  11830 Westline Industrial Drive
  St. Louis, Missouri 63141
Canada
  Blackwell Mosby Book Distributors
  120 Melford Drive, Scarborough
  Ontario, M1B 2X4
Australia
  Blackwell Scientific Book Distributors
  214 Berkeley Street, Carlton
  Victoria 3053

British Library
Cataloguing in Publication Data
Thrust and nappe tectonics. – (Special publication
  No. 9/Geological Society of London).
  1. Nappes (Geology)
  I. McClay, Kenneth R   II. Price, Neville James
  III. Geological Society of London
  551.8'7   QE606
  ISBN 0-632-00614-5

Text set in 9/10 pt Times at
The Universities Press (Belfast) Ltd, Belfast
and printed and bound at
The Pitman Press, Bath

Contents

IV. THRUST AND NAPPE REGIMES. B. 'THE NEW WORLD'

The Americas

Introduction

N. J. Price & K. R. McClay

An International Conference on Thrust and Nappe Tectonics was held, 9–11th April 1979, at Imperial College, London under the aegis of the Geological Society of London and the Geology Department of Imperial College. The conference, which was convened by the editors of this volume, was attended by over 320 participants, of whom less than half came from Britain. The remaining participants came from, or had worked in, every continent in the world (except, as far as we know, Antarctica) so the conference was truly international.

This book contains the proceedings of that conference, the 44 papers given here representing more than 80% of the material presented. The order of the papers in this volume is somewhat different from that in which they were presented at the conference because of the restrictions imposed by having Lecture and Poster Sessions during the meeting.

At the beginning of the conference, it was considered that an attempt should be made to define the structures which were to be the topic of discussion. Consequently, John Dennis took his courage in his hands and proposed, for the consideration of the participants, a definition of the words 'Thrust' and 'Nappe'. The ensuing discussion was lively and entertaining.

An edited version of this discussion and the written contributions which followed are collected by K. R. McClay and presented as the first paper in this volume and deals, in addition to the definition of thrusts and nappes, with other terminology used in this volume.

Then follows the first group of papers which review the environments and modes of emplacements of thrusts and nappes. Bally reviews the characteristics of gravity-glide structures as found in deltas and along continental margins. He concludes that, except in special cases, such as the Heart Mountain Thrust, Wyoming, and 'high-level' structures (see Graham, this volume), gravity-gliding is not the mechanism by which most thrusts and nappes are emplaced. Other authors in this group compare mechanisms or discuss a single mechanism from an analytical point of view. Most of these papers are mainly concerned with the mechanics of thrust emplacement. However, the study by Ramberg ensures that the emplacement of fold

nappes is not completely neglected. We shall comment on this group of papers later in the introduction.

The movement of nappes over their footwall rocks produces 'fault rocks' and fabrics which are the subject of the second group of papers. It is shown that 'fault rock' studies may provide important information regarding the environmental conditions obtaining during thrust emplacement (see Aprahamian & Parais; Behr *et al.* and Sibson *et al.* this volume).

Of the remaining papers, the local evidence adduced often has an important bearing on one or the other of the theoretical aspects discussed in the first group of papers. It was, however, considered that, because a single paper could correlate with more than one theoretical hypothesis or theory, it would be impossible to group and juxtapose the field-orientated studies with the theoretical ones. Consequently, the field studies are, as far as possible, treated on a regional basis. In so doing, we start with the 'Old World' and then move to the Americas, the 'New World'. (Papers relating to areas in Africa and New Zealand are more conveniently placed in the section dealing with fault-rock products.)

In the studies situated in the 'Old World' we have, in general, migrated from NW to SE; from Scandinavia, Britain and the Alps to the East Indies. In the 'New World' the studies which have been carried out in the Canadian Rocky Mountains and the adjacent areas in the U.S.A. form a particularly significant group of papers. From Canada we move via the Appalachians to South America and the southernmost tip of Chile and Patagonia.

The reader will realize that this volume is not a textbook, nor is the coverage of the subject matter encyclopaedic. The contents are dictated by chance in that we had to rely on the topics which were presented. Hence, regional studies are somewhat scattered; reflecting the increased attention which is paid to detailed studies of geometries and mechanisms.

Only the Canadian Rocky Mountains receive a reasonably widespread series of studies. The same problem obviously applies to the theoretical papers. The theoretical mode of emplacement of thrusts and fold nappes is dealt with in a number of papers in this volume. The statements and opinions expressed are sometimes contradictory and may lead to a confused state in the reader's mind. This situation, in part, reflects the state of the art. However, in an attempt to clarify the issue, the editors wish to make a few comments and offer a few opinions.

Mechanisms of thrust-nappe emplacement

The various concepts considered in this volume are that thrusts and nappes result from one another or, possibly, a combination of the following mechanisms:

1. The structures were 'pushed' from behind;
2. the structures were emplaced by gliding down an inclined plane under the action of gravity;
3. the structures are induced by gravitational spreading, possibly accompanied by an initial phase of diapirism.

(A fourth, contributory mechanism, which is not studied theoretically but is demonstrated to be viable (see Winslow), is that of shortening of the basement relative to the cover.)

In all the various theoretical studies, the 'rock masses' forming the nappes are considered to be homogeneous and isotropic and to conform to (1) elastico-brittle (2) Newtonian-viscous or (3) perfect plastic behaviour forms. In fact, the rock mass, particularly in the upper levels of the crust, will be anisotropic and therefore mechanically heterogeneous, so that its behaviour may approximate to none of the ideal types (elastic, viscous or plastic) noted above.

The reader must, therefore, exercise judgement should he wish to apply one of the theoretical models to a specific field example.

In some geological settings, e.g. deformation in deltas (see Mandl & Crans) or the emplacement of some high-level Alpine nappes (see Graham), the gravitational gliding mechanism is an appropriate one. One then needs to consider the mode of behaviour of the emplaced material. For soft sediment deformation of delta material, the viscous model (Wiltschko) or the weak plastic model (Mandl & Crans) may be appropriate; while for emplacements of high-level nappes the elastic-brittle model can be chosen.

Where the basement and glide surfaces slope, for long distances, against the direction of nappe or thrust emplacement, the gravitational gliding mechanism seems inappropriate (Bally, this volume) and one must turn to the

gravitational spreading or the push from the rear mechanisms (Smith, Murrell etc., this volume).

However, even in these situations, one must bear in mind that the increase in vertical loading which takes place as the thrust develops will result in isostatic adjustment and depression of the thrust plane. In these circumstances, because the movement of the thrust block 'up' the basement slope can be largely, or even totally, off-set by the depression of the basement, the centre of mass of an individual thrust wedge, or unit, may remain at the same level, or even be depressed. Hence, an element of gravity-gliding may be maintained in the mode of emplacement even if the dominant mechanism is gravitational spreading, or push from the rear.

The evidence of rock mechanics experiments permits one to infer that most competent rocks at high crustal levels are too strong to flow at the differential stress that is required for the gravitational spreading mode of emplacement. Such a mode of emplacement can only become important where such rocks are hot and therefore ductile.

It can be argued that even in high level environments the rock mass may achieve 'macroscopic' ductility through the existence of a multiplicity of fractures. Such a conceptual model would liken the behaviour to that of dry sand. Each grain exhibits great strength relative to the pile of sand, which possesses 'macroscopic' ductility. However, the analogy is not a good one. The ductility of sand is related to the void spaces, the geometry of the grain contacts and the ability of a large proportion of these contacts to move at any one instant. None of these features is representative of conditions in a thrust belt. Consequently, for the upper level structures, such as those exposed in the Canadian Rockies, one is left with the 'push' mechanism. Immediately one becomes involved in the old debate regarding the permissible length of thrust blocks. The most outstanding papers on the topic of overthrust mechanics were, without doubt, those written by Hubbert & Rubey in 1959. In these companion papers, they draw to the attention of geologists the important role of fluid pressure in reducing the effective stress normal to the thrust plane, so that frictional resistance to shear along the plane was reduced. In the following two decades, the concepts proposed by Hubbert & Rubey were debated and modified. It may come as a surprise to the reader, therefore, that the concept of high fluid pressure receives relatively little emphasis in the papers in this volume. High fluid pressures are not neglected, of course; they are considered by Gretener and by Murrell and are an important element of the arguments presented by Mandl and his co-authors. More often one will note in this volume that the authors require that 'the resistance to shear movement along the thrust plane be small', often of the order of about 10–20 bars.

Nature of the thrust or décollement surface

A low shear resistance at the base, or sole, of a thrust nappe of 10–20 bars can only exist if (a) a high fluid pressure exists below the 'thrust block' or (b) the thrust moves over a very weak material with a shear strength of only 10–20 bars. Such weak materials could include clays or evaporites. Drained clays under high confining pressures are capable of sustaining relatively high shear stresses. Hence, a clay layer will meet the requirement of low shear strength only when it approximates to the undrained state and the interstitial pressure is so high that the effective confining pressure is reduced to a few tens of bars (i.e. $\lambda = p/\sigma_v \approx 0.9$). If slip takes place on evaporites, the gypsum/anhydrite dehydration reaction would also generate a comparable situation with a high interstitial fluid pressure.

The evidence of metamorphism by frictional heating during thrust movement (Apprahamian & Parais) is compatible with moderate, average fluid pressure ($\lambda = 0.7 \rightarrow 0.8$) on the sole thrust. There may, however, be problems if clay minerals are used as indicators of this type of metamorphism, particularly when textural changes are involved.

For the more deep-seated structures, the nappes may glide over a thin layer of fine-grained material, such as 'lochseitenkalk', which exists below the Glarus Nappe (c.f. Schmid *et al.*, this volume). Theoretical (Rutter 1976) and experimental studies (Schmid 1976) have demonstrated that such fine-grained material (in this case calcite) may deform by diffusion/grain boundary sliding processes at low differential stresses and at temperatures greater than 200°C. Hence, there is no inherent reason for invoking high fluid pressures in the deformation of such materials, but it must be noted that the presence of pore fluids tends to accelerate diffusion deformation processes.

The problem of the generation of such weak layers is indicated by Murrell (this volume), who suggests that an early phase of cataclasis

may sometimes be involved. Unfortunately, evidence of such cataclasis would be destroyed by subsequent diffusion processes.

Alternatively, initial dislocation creep deformation may give rise to a reduction in grain size by dynamic recrystallization. The new small grains can then deform at low differential stress by diffusion/grain boundary sliding. Such a process, which has been invoked for the formation of mylonites (White 1976), may thus produce a weak plastic layer at the sole of the thrust/nappe.

However, the processes related to high fluid pressure and to crystal plasticity are not mutually exclusive. Indeed, they are probably often complementary. Evidence of such combined effects may be inferred from Ramsay's paper on the Helvetic Nappes (this volume). These Helvetic Nappes deformed in a ductile manner. However, the 'crack' of the 'crack-seal' mechanism can be attributed to hydraulic fracture, and this attests to, at least, moderately high fluid pressures existing during nappe deformation.

Shape and size of thrust units

There is a tendency, followed in various papers in this volume, to consider the displacement of wedge-shaped blocks rather than the rectangular, 'boot-box' type unit originally invoked by Hubbert & Rubey (1959). For a given set of parameters, strength, stress conditions etc., this automatically doubles the size of thrust block (of comparable thickness/average thickness) that can be moved. Moreover, rock mechanics data (see Fyfe *et al.* 1978) permit one to infer that, at high levels in the crust, some massive limestone and arenaceous units are capable of sustaining differential stresses up to, or even somewhat beyond, 1 kbar (the comparable figure for rock strength taken by Hubbert & Rubey was ≈700 bars). If we combine these factors of shape of thrust block and possible differences in rock strength, we may infer that a wedge-shaped thrust block may be between three and four times longer than that of the rectangular blocks postulated by Hubbert & Rubey. Indeed, 'cold, dry crystalline rocks' can support a differential stress of several kilobars so that a wedge of such material could be thrust eight to ten times further than that indicated in Hubbert & Rubey's analysis. Hence, the emplacement of thrust wedges with an extent of 50–100 km is not a great problem, even when the fluid pressure at the base is only moderately high.

Fold nappes

Theoretical models dealing with the emplacement of fold nappes have received relatively little attention in this volume. This reflects both the difficulty of the analytical and model problem and the paucity in the general literature of such studies. Most of the model studies dealing with this problem have been produced by Ramberg and his school. The similarity of geometry between their model structures and natural fold nappes is persuasive. His main thesis is, of course, that fold nappes result from density inversion, instability and diapirism. In this volume he also indicates the possible importance of gravitational spreading as a mechanism of emplacement.

Because he is dealing with the development of relatively deep-seated structures, the physical properties of rocks are likely to be such that they will flow under low differential stresses: which is one of the requirements of the gravitational spreading mechanism.

However, high ductility and low strength will only be maintained in the so-called competent rocks while they are at high temperatures and confining pressures. That is, we are not dealing with surface extrusion but possibly a form of intrusion. Are fold nappes analogues of laccoliths? Certainly the fold nappe flows over the 'floor'. Of course, it may also displace the floor, so that a succession of nappes are formed 'piggy back' fashion (see Ramsay, this volume). What happens at the roof of the nappe? Does differential movement between fold nappe and roof take place, or does the fold nappe carry the roof with it, so giving rise to considerable extension of the cover rocks?

There is certainly abundant evidence of normal fault development in and above fold nappes (see for example the Glarus Nappe). These normal faults are often of very small displacement and are, therefore, more likely to have developed during subsequent uplift rather than during the emplacement of the fold nappe. In addition, it is often difficult to relate these extensional events directly to the thrusting.

It is probable, therefore, that differential movement of the nappe relative to its roof has occurred. Cleavage in the upper region of the nappe is sometimes inclined away from the 'root' (Hossack, pers. comm.) and this can be explained in terms of differential movement of the nappe relative to the roof. Even a lack of evidence for such differential movement does not necessarily negate the concept. High level thrust nappes can be emplaced without granulation etc., provided that the fluid pressure below the nappe is high. Fold nappes may similarly be emplaced without granulation etc., if the fluid pressure at the upper interface of the nappe is high. Such conditions are not incompatible with the evidence adduced by Ramsay in this volume.

Hence, it would appear from these arguments and those presented in this volume by Smith, that both fold and thrust nappes may be driven by the forces associated with diapirism and intrusion.

Basement relationships

One of the key questions in thrust/nappe regimes has often been that regarding the degree of basement involvement and what happens to the structures at depth. Basement involvement is well illustrated in classic Alpine fold nappes. Decoupling within the basement is found in the Moine Thrust Zone (Coward & Kim, this volume). Decollement above an unaffected basement is well defined in the Canadian Rocky Mountains (Price, this volume). In many situations, however, the relationships regarding the nature of the faults at depth are uncertain.

Deep seismic reflection profiling, cf. the COCORP project, (see Brewer *et al.*, this volume) may provide some exciting answers to these questions. The Wind River Thrust (Wyoming) has been shown to be a relatively steeply dipping structure extending to 30–35 km depth. In contrast, results of seismic work across the Appalachians (Brewer *et al.*, this volume and Cook *et al.* 1979) indicate that the Piedmont is allocthonous with thrust displacements of at least 250 km. Clearly, more exciting discoveries are at hand and the application of geophysical techniques to the study of thrust belt geometries promises new information which may, in certain areas, (cf. the Moine Thrust Zone) resolve the thick versus the thin-skinned debate.

The reader will most likely conclude from the collection of papers presented in this volume, that our knowledge of the geometry and the mechanics of thrusts and nappes still needs to be improved. Nevertheless, it is apparent that the problem is now tractable and we have the elements necessary for its solution within our grasp.

ACKNOWLEDGMENTS. We wish to thank the Geological Society of London and the Geology Department, Imperial College, for financial support for the conference. The technical and clerical support was generously provided by the Geology Department, Imperial College. In particular, we should like to express our gratitude to Mrs Betty Clements and Miss Juliet Hornsby for all their cheerful assistance in preparing for, and in running, the conference. Mr David Clayton, executive secretary of the Geological Society is thanked for his help and guidance in overcoming many obstacles encountered in organizing the conference. Finally, we should like to thank the many reviewers who scrutinized the manuscripts and, in particular, Mrs Joan Price for her considerable editorial help.

References

COOK, F. A., ALBAUGH, D. S., BROWN, L. D., KAUFMANN, S. D., OLIVER, J. E. & HATCHER, R. D. 1978. Thin-skinned tectonics in the crystalline S. Appalachians. COCORP seismic reflection profiling of the Blue Ridge and Piedmont. *Geology*, **7,** 563–7.

FYFE, W., PRICE N. J. & THOMSON, A. 1978. *Fluids in the Earth's Crust*, Elsevier, Amsterdam, 383 p.

HUBBERT, M. K. & RUBEY W. W. 1959. Role of fluid pressure in mechanics of overthrust faulting Pt.I. Mechanics of fluid-filled porous solids and its application to overthrust faulting. *Bull. Geol. Soc. Am.* **70,** 115–66.

RUBEY, W. W. & HUBBERT M. K. 1959. Role of fluid pressure in mechanics of overthrust faulting Pt.II Overthrust belt in geosynclinal area of W Wyoming in light of fluid-pressure hypothesis. *Bull. Geol. Soc. Am.* **70,** 167–206.

RUTTER, E. H. 1976. The kinetics of rock deformation by pressure solution, *Philos. Trans. R. Soc. London*, **A283,** 203–19.

SCHMID, S. 1976. Rheological evidence for changes in the deformation mechanism of Solnhofen limestone towards low stresses. *Tectonophysics*, **31,** 21–8.

WHITE, S. 1976. The effects of strain on the microstructures, fabrics and deformation mechanisms in quartzites. *Philos. Trans. R. Soc. London*, **A283,** 69–86.

N. J. PRICE, Department of Geology, Imperial College, London SW7 2BP.
K. R. McCLAY, Department of Geology, University of London Goldsmiths College, New Cross, London SE14 6NW.

What is a Thrust?   What is a Nappe?

Discussion with edited contributions from: J. G. DENNIS, R. A. PRICE, J. K. SALES, R. HATCHER, A. W. BALLY, W. J. PERRY, H. P. LAUBSCHER, R. E. WILLIAMS, D. ELLIOTT, D. K. NORRIS, D. W. HUTTON and T. EMMETT.

SUMMARY: The definitions of thrusts and nappes are discussed and the criteria used to define these structures are analysed. A 'thrust fault' is defined as a map-scale contraction fault. A 'thrust nappe' is an allochthonous tectonic sheet which has moved along a thrust fault. Suggested definitions are also given for, a fold nappe; extension fault; contraction fault; listric normal fault; reverse listric fault; klippe; tectonic slide; ramps and flats; duplex structure; blind thrusts.

At the outset of the conference, Professor Dennis took the bull by the horns and proposed the following definitions of a thrust (or overthrust) and of a nappe:

Thrust or overthrust (synonyms): A surface of displacement with predominantly low dip (observed or inferred) along which rocks have been displaced for more than 5 km horizontally. Thrust sheet: the tectonic unit overlying a thrust.
Nappe: A large, essentially coherent allochthonous, sheet-like tectonic unit that has moved a distance several times its thickness and in excess of 5 km along a predominantly subhorizontal floor."
A lively discussion ensued and this contribution represents an edited version of verbal and written comments. The proposed definitions are those which were thought to be the most appropriate by the editor and wherever possible the contrasting and conflicting viewpoints are given.

Thrusts—Thrust Nappes—Fold Nappes

Overwhelming agreement was reached on one point, the definitions of thrust and of nappe (as outlined above) should imply no minimum displacement. Several contributors (R. A. Price, Queens Ontario; D. Elliott, John Hopkins; D. K. Norris, GSC Calgary; R. Hatcher, Florida) emphasized the difficulty of assessing the magnitudes of displacement on thrust faults/and of nappes, particularly where they die out along strike (e.g. southern Canadian Rockies, Price, this volume). Professor Dennis, however, also points out that the 5 km minimum for nappe displacement seems to be entrenched in Alpine literature (e.g. Pfiffner 1977). In addition, Price, Elliott, Norris and others argued that many thrust faults vary significantly in dip particularly where they are folded. J. K. Sales (Mobil Research & Development Corp., Dallas) noted that many basement involved thrusts of the Wyoming-Colorado foreland (cf. Wind River Mountains—Brewer *et al.* this volume) are relatively high angle structures. Hence it is apparent that strict limitations of dip (i.e. 'low angle') would rule out many significant 'thrust' structures in this definition. In addition most contributors to the discussion agreed that there should be no limitation on the size of a thrust fault. J. K. Sales emphasized that the size of individual thrusts is not so much a function of overall shortening but of the thickness and competence of the section being thrust. In thin incompetent sections the individual thrusts are small (e.g. Woodcock & Robertson, and Coward & Kim, this volume). Although some contributors favour a distinction between 'thrusts' and 'overthrusts', others (Elliott & Norris, R. Williams, John Hopkins) preferred to use the term 'contraction' fault for all classes of reverse—thrust—overthrust faults. It may be, therefore, appropriate to simply define—*thrust fault* according to Elliott & Norris.
A THRUST FAULT is a map scale *contraction fault.* This definition has no value of dip mentioned nor are amounts of slip specified. Central to the definition is a 'contraction fault' (Norris 1958) which shortens an arbitrary datum plane (normally bedding). A. W. Bally (Shell Oil Co., Houston) favoured the term 'listric reverse fault' (LRF—defined later in this discussion), but this term does not apply to such steep angled thrusts as the Wind River Uplift (see Brewer *et al.* this volume).
In the context of 'nappe' displacement there also seemed to be general agreement to avoid

the 5 km limitation in any definition. Professor H. P. Laubscher (Basel) noted that the term 'nappe' historically refers to a thrust mass or thrust sheet of a certain lithology which characterizes a palaeo-geographic affiliation (e.g. facies belts of the 'Alpine geosyncline'). He pointed out that in certain contexts (e.g. the Alps) it is more meaningful to refer to 'nappes' rather than to the thrusts (often many) which separate them (e.g. préalpes nappes). The following definition is, therefore, suggested for a thrust nappe.

A *THRUST NAPPE is an allochthonous tectonic sheet which has moved along a thrust fault.* Professor Dennis remarked that the linking of tectonic nappes with recumbent folds is well known in the context of Alpine tectonics. T. Emmett (University of Newcastle U.K.) suggested that the term 'nappe' be reserved for structures which showed large-scale inversion of strata—a feature often associated with nappes which perhaps initiate as recumbent folds. It may be, therefore, appropriate to define 'fold nappe' in the following manner.

'A FOLD NAPPE' is an allocthonous tectonic unit which exhibits large-scale stratigraphic inversion and may have initiated from large recumbent folds. The underlying limbs of these folds may be sheared out into thrust faults.

Contraction and Extension Faults

Central to the suggested definition of a thrust and implied in that for thrust nappes is the concept of a contraction fault. Norris (1958) defines a '*contraction fault*' as a fault which shortens bedding. Its opposite—an '*extension fault*' extends bedding. In more complex and highly deformed terranes, bedding may not be an appropriate datum plane and hence it is probably best to leave the definition of these types of faults to those given below.

A '*CONTRACTION FAULT*' *is a fault which shortens an arbitrary datum plane.* Note that this plane is normally bedding (cf. Norris 1958) but in the case of thrusts developed in crystalline rocks recognition of bedding may be more difficult. Conversely to the definition outlined above.

An *EXTENSION FAULT is a fault which extends an arbitrary datum plane.* Professor R. Price comments that in the case of gravity glide (slide) structures the faults change character from being extensional at the trailing edge of the structure and contractional at the leading edge (see also Mandl & Crans, this volume).

Listric Faults

Considerable discussion centred on the use of 'listric' in describing faults which are concave upwards and whose plane flattens out at depth, see Bally and Mandl & Crans, this volume). A. W. Bally has suggested the following definitions:

REVERSE LISTRIC FAULT (RLF) is a curved fault (concave upwards) in which, the steep-often sub-vertical segment is a high angle reverse fault, the middle segment is a medium angle reverse fault and the sole is a bedding plane fault. In both the steep and middle segments, older rocks overlie younger rocks whereas there is little or no repetition of beds by the sole fault.

LISTRIC NORMAL FAULT (LNF) is a curved fault (concave upwards) which may be divided into high angle normal fault, medium angle normal fault and bedding plane or sole fault segments. With the high and medium angle normal faults stratigraphic section is omitted and younger rocks overlie older rocks.

Other Pertinent Definitions

It is perhaps appropriate to provide a short glossary of terms used in the contributions to this volume. The suggested definitions are a compilation of concepts expressed in both the verbal and written discussion.

KLIPPE—A small detached and isolated portion of a nappe or thrust sheet.

TECTONIC SLIDES are faults that form in metamorphic conditions in metamorphic—orogenic belts. This term (suggested by D. Hutton, Trinity College, Dublin) does not imply any geometrical/movement sense (see also Hutton, this volume).

Rich (1934) first proposed the concept of a ramp to describe thrust faults with a staircase geometry. He noted that long bedding plane thrusts in incompetent units (FLATS) were joined by short steep angle thrusts (RAMPS) which cut up section through the more competent units, hence a staircase geometry.

FLATS are bedding plane thrust segments within a stepped thrust plane. (i.e.) The thrust plane is parallel to the datum plane.

RAMPS are thrusts which cut up stratigraphic section between FLATS in a stepped thrust plane. Excellent examples of this staircase geometry are shown in the sections of Price (this volume).

DUPLEX is a thrust sheet (mass) which is bounded by a 'floor thrust' and a 'roof thrust'.

Often duplex structures are imbricated—examples can be seen in Price (this volume) and also Elliott & Johnson (in press).

BLIND THRUSTS are thrusts which are below the erosion surface but their presence is indicated by shortening in the overlying sequence which is achieved by disharmonic detachment folding. This concept is illustrated by Thompson (this volume).

Discussion

The suggested definitions given above are tentative and should be regarded as a basis for further discussion and modification. As pointed out by R. E. Williams, individual authors should define and state precisely what they mean in any particular context.

This contribution represents the edited discussion of the contributors mentioned above. The compilor accepts responsibility for any subtle nuances or changes which may have occurred in the process of editing the discussion.

K. R. McCLAY

References

ELLIOTT, D. & JOHNSON, M. R. W. 1980. Structural evolution in the Northern part of the Moine Thrust Belt. *Geol. Trans. Roy. Soc. Edinburgh.* (in press).

NORRIS, D. K. 1958. Structural conditions in Canadian Coal Mines. *Bull. geol. Surv. Can.* **44.**

PFIFFNER, O. A. 1977. Tectonische Untersuchungen im Infrahelvetikum der Ostschweiz. *Mitt. Geol. Inst. E.T.H. Zurich, Neue Folge,* **217,** 432 p.

RICH, J. L. 1934. Mechanics of low-angle overthrust faulting as illustrated by Cumberland thrust block, Virginia, Kentucky and Tennessee. *Bull. Am. Assoc. Petrol. Geol.* **18,** 1584–96.

I.
MECHANICS OF THRUSTS AND NAPPES

Thoughts on the tectonics of folded belts

A. W. Bally

SUMMARY: Balanced cross sections and their palinspastic reconstruction in structurally simple external zones of folded belts suggest that a limited amount of continental lithosphere was subducted (Ampferer or A-subduction). This process appears to be associated with preceding or synchronous basement remobilization. Therefore, the rigid or ductile nature and the timing of basement deformation remain as some of the most important orogenic problems. Decoupling and ductility contrasts within the lower continental crust and within the overlying sedimentary sequences are responsible for varying structural styles in mountain ranges.

Gravity gliding as an important factor for mountain building is examined in some detail. Soft sediment gravity tectonics on passive continental margins are dominated by listric normal growth faults. This style contrasts with observed styles of deformation in folded belts. Gravity tectonics induced by stretching of the underlying basement area is commonly observed during the rifting phase of passive continental margins and in episutural basins associated with orogenic systems.

Three opposing schools of thought are today proposing their images of mountain ranges:

The *fixists* (Beloussov 1962, 1975, 1977) visualize mountain building as the product of asthenospheric and related lithospheric diapirism. In their view, widespread thrusting and folding in mountain ranges is explained in terms of either gravity gliding or else gravity spreading (as defined by Price 1971, 1973).

Adherents of an *expanding earth* (Carey 1975, 1977) view mountain building as the fixists do, but essentially as an ensialic process; they differ from fixists because they see the origin of the oceans not by a process of oceanization but instead by accretion and spreading processes along mid-ocean ridges that record the vicissitudes of an expanding earth.

Finally, *plate tectonic* devotees see mountains as the product of subduction processes on converging plate boundaries; overthrust and folded belts are, in essence, of compressional origin and represent excess sediments and slices of the underlying crystalline crust that have been scraped off and decoupled from subducting lithospheric slabs. A large number of observations in mountain ranges can be well fitted into a plate tectonic frame of reference. However, it is only fair to state that despite the brilliant early intuitions of Ampferer (1906), Argand (1924), Staub (1928), and other alpine geologists, plate tectonics are not easily directly deduced from observations that are limited only to mountain ranges. The plate tectonics hypothesis remains anchored mainly in geophysical and marine geological observations.

Deep-sea sediments and possible remnants of oceanic floor (ophiolites) occupy, areally, only minor portions of folded belts. Consequently, a plate tectonic origin of mountain ranges is not all that obvious to an unbiased observer. Much of what we see today in mountain ranges suggests widespread mobilization and 'ductilization' of an earlier rigid sialic lithosphere. In other words, while the continental lithosphere of cratons remains rigid, the continental lithosphere of mountain ranges shows pervasive remobilization during orogenic processes, suggesting repeated lithospheric 'softening'.

In this paper I attempt to provide a perspective of the evidence for, and the relative roles of, normal faulting, thrust faulting, and folding in mountain ranges. Such a perspective may help in judging the realism of some of the geotectonic images mentioned previously. It must be realized, however, that the phenomena on which I propose to concentrate are but the near-surface expression of deeper seated igneous and metamorphic processes, which are much more difficult to unravel but so much more important for an understanding of orogeny.

Although this paper deals mainly with compressional tectonics and thrust faulting, most figures illustrate normal faulting. It is assumed that specialists in thrust faulting and nappe tectonics are familiar and have ready access to the relevant illustrations. However, the seismic examples of gravity-induced normal faulting included in this paper may suggest to folded belt specialists what to look for when they attempt to differentiate gravity from compressional tectonics.

Thrust and Nappe Tectonics. 1981. The Geological Society of London

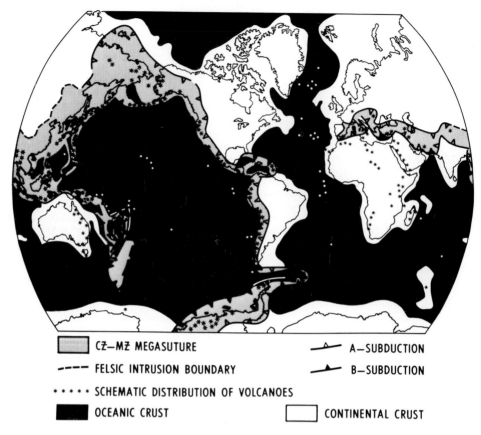

CZ—MZ MEGASUTURE   △ A—SUBDUCTION

---- FELSIC INTRUSION BOUNDARY   ▲ B—SUBDUCTION

* * * * * SCHEMATIC DISTRIBUTION OF VOLCANOES

OCEANIC CRUST   CONTINENTAL CRUST

FIG. 1. Cenozoic–Mesozoic megasuture of the world and its boundaries. B-subduction zones face oceans; A-subduction boundaries face continental cratonic areas. They are characterized by widespread décollement folding and thrust faulting. In China the boundary is an ill-defined envelope around Mesozoic and Cenozoic granitic intrusives (after Bally & Snelson 1980, with permission of Canadian Society of Petroleum Geologists).

Without entering into detailed descriptions, Fig. 1 may serve to show a number of orogenic configurations. In earlier publications I proposed the term megasuture for foldbelts *and* sedimentary basins that are included in them (Bally 1975; Bally & Snelson 1980). For instance, the Mesozoic–Cenozoic megasuture includes all regions of intensive Mesozoic–Cenozoic mountain building and sedimentary basins involved in these processes. In plate tectonics jargon, the megasuture is the integrated product of all subduction-related processes which form the counterpart of the Mesozoic–Cenozoic ocean-spreading processes. The megasuture was introduced primarily to help in classifying sedimentary basins. The term also emphasizes the point that the bottoms of sedimentary basins within the megasutures are typically as deep as the adjacent

mountains are high; and that the evolution of such basins has be be viewed as part of the total evolution of mobile belts (see Fig. 2).

Four types of megasuture boundaries are: B- (or Benioff) subduction boundaries where oceanic lithosphere is subducted; A- (or Ampferer) subduction boundaries where continental lithosphere is subducted; transform fault system boundaries; and—in China—a boundary which is an envelope around felsic intrusives. This fourth boundary type is required because in China the continent facing boundary of the Mesozoic–Cenozoic megasuture is not associated with obvious external foldbelts involving former passive margin sequences and overlying foredeep sequences. Instead one can trace an ill-defined outline of Mesozoic and Tertiary intrusives which invade deeply into China and Mongolia.

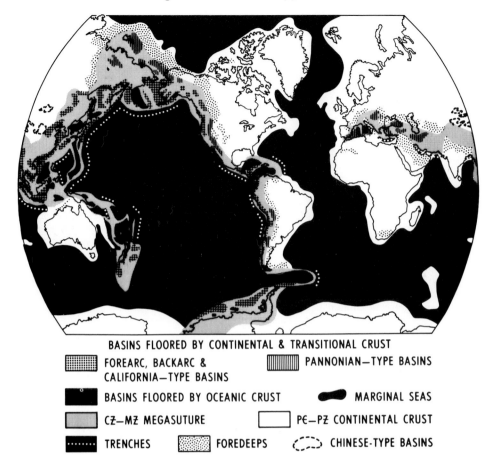

BASINS FLOORED BY CONTINENTAL & TRANSITIONAL CRUST

FOREARC, BACKARC & CALIFORNIA–TYPE BASINS

PANNONIAN–TYPE BASINS

BASINS FLOORED BY OCEANIC CRUST

MARGINAL SEAS

CZ–MZ MEGASUTURE

PЄ–PZ CONTINENTAL CRUST

TRENCHES   FOREDEEPS   CHINESE-TYPE BASINS

FIG. 2. Sedimentary basin families associated with the Cenozoic–Mesozoic megasuture (after Bally & Snelson 1980, with permission of Canadian Society of Petroleum Geologists).

With respect to the Mesozoic–Cenozoic megasuture, we differentiate four major 'orogenic' or megasuture types:

(1) *The SW Pacific type* contained between B-subduction and transform boundaries; a system of island arcs and marginal seas.

(2) *The NW Pacific type* contained between B-subduction and transform boundaries on the Pacific side and the felsic intrusion boundary of China. Within this orogenic type, marginal seas are opened and closed and continental fragments are captured (e.g. Indochina, South China platform, or the Lut Block of Iran).

(3) *The Cordilleran type* contained between a seaward B-subduction and/or transform boundary and a landward A-subduction boundary. The opening and closing of marginal seas appears to be less dominant in the history of the Cordilleras and it would appear that strike-slip rifting of continental fragments plays a major role.

(4) *The Alpine–Himalayan type* is contained within two A-subduction boundaries facing the Eurasian craton to the N and the African–Arabian and Indian continents to the S. This type is the end product of continental collisions.

Note that widespread overthrusting of former passive margin sediments and widespread regional basement remobilization and metamorphism is characteristically associated with A-subduction boundaries. B-subduction boundaries exhibit some imbricate thrusting, and deformation of oceanic sediments in the accretionary wedges of island arcs. Finally there is some thrusting associated with transform systems.

The case for compression and subduction in the external zones of foldbelts

External zones of foldbelts (the Externides of Kober 1928) are the accretionary wedges associated with Benioff subduction zones and more important, they are the folded belts that are associated with A-subduction zones.

The seismic record of Benioff zones favours extension and normal faulting in the peripheral bulge that is formed on the oceanward side of a deep-sea trench and compression in the shallow portions of the subduction zones and the associated accretionary wedge. Reflection seismic data on inner walls of deep-sea trenches suggest accretionary structures formed by 'offscraping' of oceanic sediments that overlie a gently dipping oceanic crust (Fig. 3). Scholl *et al.* (1977) noted that large volumes of pelagic sediments should be, but are not, exposed in Palaeozoic and Mesozoic Circum-Pacific moun-

tain systems. These authors suggest that accretionary wedges may represent mostly deformed slope deposits and that much of the pelagic sediments were subducted with the oceanic crust.

Of course, one is tempted to construct balanced cross-sections (Dahlstrom 1969, 1970) in such a setting. However, the premises for the method are not easily fulfilled, because in most cases, the sediments that form the accretionary wedges are not dated by drilling, and further, because penetrative fabrics and the style of deformation indicates dominance of ductile flow and shear (for details, see von Huene *et al.* this volume). High ductility is suggested by outcrop studies of mélanges and the high pore pressures reported in some wells that are associated with subduction zones (Shouldice 1971). The situation is further complicated by an overprint of gravitational sliding and normal growth faults that show up on a number of reflection lines (see Colombia section, Fig. 3).

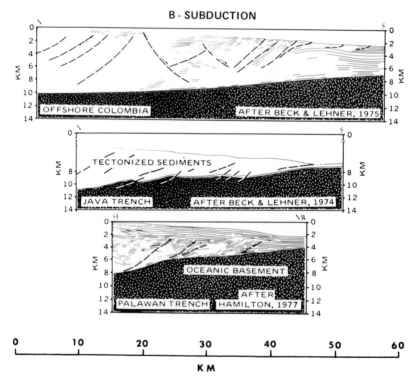

FIG. 3. Sketches of typical accretionary wedges associated with B-subduction zones. (a) Offshore Columbia (after Beck & Lehner 1975); (b) Java Trench (after Beck & Lehner 1974); (c) Palawan Trench (after Hamilton 1977); Drawings after Bally & Snelson (1980, with permission of Canadian Society of Petroleum Geologists).

Although one may rightly question the advisability of using balanced cross section techniques in Franciscan terranes, a recently published reconstruction of northern California by Suppe (1979) suggests some 175 km of shortening of Franciscan, a far cry from the shortening one would expect from offscraping of sediments during the subduction of an oceanic slab that was several thousands of kilometres wide.

One is forced to conclude that the current state of knowledge is inadequate to assess the amount of shortening associated with accretionary wedges of island arcs. The amount of underthrusting can only be derived from reconstructions that are based on magnetic stripe interpretations of the ocean floor. To understand structural deformation in accretionary wedges of island arcs and their ancient equivalents, it is increasingly more important to develope criteria that differentiate the effects of superficial gravitational sliding from the effects of compression and/or extension caused by the sinking oceanic lithospheric slab.

Shortening in folded belts associated with A-subduction boundaries has been studied for a number of years. In fact, the original concept of subduction in the Alps was based on such studies (Ampferer 1906; and later documented by more specific reconstructions: Spengler 1953–59; Trümpy (1969) has provided a detailed palinspastic reconstruction of the Glaronese Alps).

More accurate approximations to palinspastic reconstructions became possible with the aid of structural sections that were based on reflection seismic data. These data allow us to map the basement underlying the frontal folded belts in the Rocky Mountains (Bally *et al.* 1966; Price & Mountjoy 1970; Gordy *et al.* 1975; Royse *et al.* 1975) and in the Appalachians (Gwinn 1970; Roeder *et al.* 1978). A gentle mountainward dipping basement surface observed on numerous reflection seismic sections constrains possible interpretations and leads to more rigid 'balancing' of cross sections as outlined by Dahlstrom (1969), Gwinn (1970), and Roeder *et al.* (1978).

Following Dahlstrom, balanced cross sections are only justified in a 'concentric regime', and the method needs modification if applied in a 'similar fold' regime. Bearing all cautions in mind, shortening in the Canadian Rockies exceeds 160 km and may reach 270 km (Bally *et al.* 1966; Price & Mountjoy 1970; also see Price this volume). For the Helvetic Nappes of the Alps and allowing for the uncertainties due to internal deformation, the accurate nature of

tectonic units, and the estimation of eroded and buried parts, Trümpy (1969) estimates shortening in the order of 30–40 km. Spengler (1953–59) offers estimates typically in the order of 100–150 km for the northern Calcareous Alps.

Gwinn (1970) derives about 80 km for the Central Appalachians, a figure which is increased by Roeder *et al.* (1978) to about 140 km and which is to be further modified to in excess of 200 km in view of the new COCORP data in the area (Cook *et al.* 1979; Hatcher 1972).

For the Scandinavian Caledonides, which are at an erosional level that is particularly favourable for tracing the authochtonous foreland underlying higher thrust sheets, Gee (1975) postulates a total shortening in excess of 500 km. Similar amounts are postulated by Binns (1978) for the Caledonides of nothern Scandinavia. Note that Gee's figure is based mostly on credible inference from surface geology, without reflection seismic data. In the Caledonides like elsewhere, shortening estimates are critically dependent on resolving the penetrative strain recorded in allochthonous sequences, a point properly emphasized by Hossack (1978).

This author computed for the Jotun Nappe 65% vertical shortening and a transverse elongation of 160%. To restore this flattened nappe, its stratigraphic thickness needs to be multiplied by 2.15 to arrive at the original thickness. Even so, the displacement of the Jotun Nappe alone exceeds 290 km.

In other words, the amounts of shortening in external folded belts that are based on reasonably accurate geometric reconstructions and in some cases on reflection seismic data are typically in the range of 50–500 km. Even though in some folded belts of the world the amounts of shortening may be two or three times larger, the figures still are short of the several thousand kilometres that may be deduced from plate motions based on magnetic stripe reconstructions or else on palaeomagnetic data. This suggests either that plate tectonic reconstructions are basically incorrect or else that the subduction mechanism is most efficient in destroying much of the evidence which could be used for a quantitative kinematic check of reconstructions that are based on palaeomagnetics. Because of the convincing nature of the palaeomagnetic data, I favour the second alternative.

For an understanding of mountain building and the genesis of continental crust, it is desirable to examine the fate of the basement which was originally underlying the excess sediment now piled up in thrust sheets, nappes and folds. All authors who have actually carried out quantitative reconstructions in the external zones of folded belts agree that the crust underlying the excess sediments remained in the subsurface: that is, nowhere has a corresponding tectonically denuded surface been exposed, nor is there evidence for subaerial exposure of such a surface that was followed by subsequent burial. Consequently, gravitational gliding will have to be ruled out as a major factor in mountain building.

The concept of gravitational spreading as developed by Price & Mountjoy (1970), Price (1971, 1973), and Elliott (1976a, b) suggests that gravitational forces dominate the emplacement of thrust sheets and, following Elliott, that significant surface slopes are required to form thrusted and folded mountain belts. The linkage of folding in the external zones with the emplacement of metamorphic folds of the Pennine Nappe type is not clear and adequately documented because in a number of cases, such metamorphism precedes the deformation in the external foldbelts.

To conclude: the basement originally underlying excess sediments of external foldbelts remained at depth either to form a mountain 'root' leading to formation of a thickened lithosphere or else it was engulfed in the overall lithospheric subduction process which led to the formation of mountains. In all cases the apparent disappearance in depth of continental lithosphere (A-subduction) is limited to hundreds of kilometres and contrasts with B-subduction involving disposal of thousands of kilometres of oceanic crust. There is little doubt that surface slopes are increased during both A- and B-subduction processes. Such slopes may facilitate gravity spreading. However, the proof for gravity spreading rests on demonstrating that diapir-like metamorphic structures in the internal zones of folded belts formed at the same time as the foreland folds and thrusts which record substantial shortening, and also on a demonstration that extensional tectonics in more brittle overlying sequences are synchronous with the shortening in the foreland. To my knowledge, such conclusive proofs have yet to be published.

This paper is not concerned with the mechanics of the A-subduction process. Conceptual and mechanical difficulties of subduction of substantial portions of continental lithosphere are in part overcome by the simple observation that in all cases we deal with a presumably attenuated continental crust of the

lithosphere of a former passive margin. Nevertheless, until recently, there was a great deal of reluctance by plate tectonic experts to accept A-subduction. It has been argued that the high buoyancy of continental crust would prevent significant subduction of the continental lithosphere. Molnar & Gray (1979) calculate that significant fractions of the continental crust may be subducted if these could be detached from their upper part. Furthermore, these authors suggest that the gravitational force acting on sinking oceanic lithosphere may pull continental lithosphere into the asthenosphere. Such a pull is counteracted by the buoyancy of the light continental crust. Under these circumstances and using varying assumptions, typical values between a few kilometres and up to 330 km in length of subducted continental crust appear to be reasonable. These calculations depend on the thicknesses of lower continental crust that may be detached during the subduction process. If somewhat more extreme assumptions are used, much greater lengths of continental lithosphere may be subducted.

The model of Bird et al. (1975) and Bird (1978) provide a thermal and mechanical scenario which leads to the 'delamination' of sub-crustal lithosphere by insertion or wedging of less viscous asthenosphere between an upper crustal layer and the underlying denser subcrustal lithosphere.

While there is little to add to these interesting models, it is of some comfort to know that subduction of continental lithosphere (A-subduction) which for some time was repulsive to theoretical plate tectonicians has now been accepted in principle. Thus, as geologists, we may now continue to gather observations that may bracket the actual amount of shortening observed in mountain ranges.

The phenomenology of gravity tectonics of sedimentary sequences

Although all preceding considerations seriously limit the role and significance of gravity gliding processes for mountain building, it still may be useful to develop criteria for recognition of gravity tectonics by looking at some obvious examples.

Reviews of gravity gliding have been offered by de Sitter (1954) and North (1964). Various aspects of gravity tectonics are dealt with in a book dedicated to van Bemmelen (de Jong &

Scholten 1973). While many of these authors spend a great deal of effort to convince the readers of the correctness of their mountain building images, very little is offered by way of description of large regions that are unambiguously dominated by gravity tectonics. Two examples of such areas are the Niger Delta and the northern Gulf of Mexico.

The Niger Delta, as described by a number of authors (e.g. Delteil *et al.* 1976; Weber & Daukoru 1976; Lehner & de Ruiter 1977), is prograding on a foundation of high pore pressure shales that overlies an oceanic crust. It is characterized by extensive growth fault systems and shale diapirism. Particularly the toe of the Delta is characterized by imbrications that are similar to features often observed in folded belts (Lehner & de Ruiter 1977).

Like the Niger Delta, the Gulf Coast Tertiary is also prograding on a high pore pressure shale substratum that in turn appears to be underlain by Mesozoic carbonates and a basal salt-bearing sequence which provides an additional unstable base. Where penetrated by the drill, the basement appears to be continental

and an extension of the Palaeozoic mountain system of the Ouachitas and the Appalachians. However, moving towards the Gulf, the crust changes from continental to transitional and/or oceanic (Fig. 4). The structural evolution of the Gulf of Mexico is far from being unraveled, but a few characteristic details shown in reflection seismic lines may offer useful reminders for geologists interested in gravity tectonics in folded belts and may suggest what to look for in support of gravity-gliding concepts.

As suggested on Fig. 4, the edge of the salt mass appears an allochthonous glacier-like tongue overlying very young Tertiary sediments (Watkins *et al.* 1978; Humphris 1978). Widespread pre-Cretaceous listric normal growth faults are restricted to the sedimentary sequence and flatten out at the base of the salt (Figs 5, 6, & 7). Farther up in the sequence and towards the Gulf of Mexico, extensive listric normal growth faults dissect Tertiary clastics and flatten within the high pore pressure shale section at depth. Diapiric salt movement and questionable shale diapirs are intimately associated with these growth fault systems (Figs

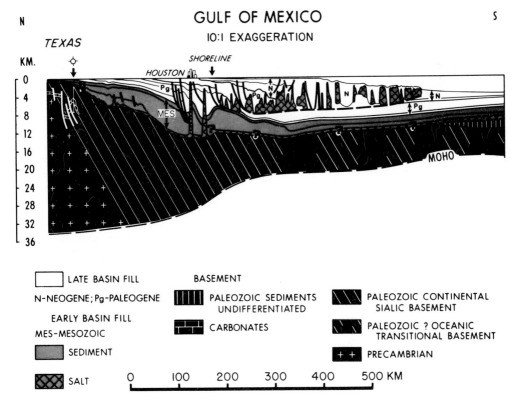

FIG. 4. Schematic section across the Gulf of Mexico.

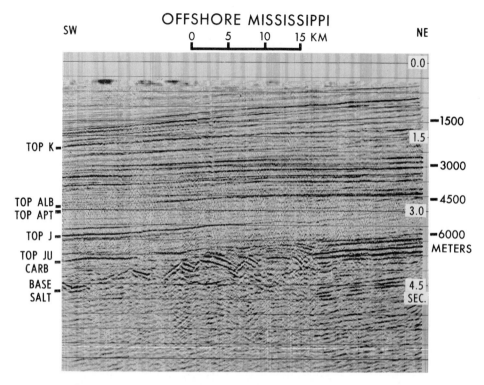

FIG. 5. Offshore Mississippi, reflection seismic section. Note listric normal faults separating salt rollers involving Jurassic carbonates.

8 & 9). The interaction of sedimentation and growth faulting in this region has been summarized by Curtis (1970) and Curtis & Picou (1978), and its relevance for the genesis of hydrocarbon deposits is well illustrated by Curtis (1979). Detailed studies of listric normal faulting and sedimentation are also known from western Ireland (Rider 1978) and Spitzbergen (Edwards 1976).

Gravity tectonics of the type indicated are typical in areas underlain by soft sediments, unstable high pore pressure shales and salt that are associated with high rates of subsidence. Listric normal growth fault systems can be observed in depths in excess of 20 000 ft (6000 m).

An example which shows listric normal faulting that is more or less synchronous with compressional folding is seen on Mexico's eastern offshore (Buffler et al. 1979; Watkins et al. 1976; Fig. 10). Although more data and calibration by drilling are needed, it appears possible that the amount of shortening represented in the folds of the Mexican ridges may correspond roughly to the amount of stretching by

listric normal faulting underlying the Mexican shelf. On the other hand, if the amount of shortening of the linear folds substantially exceeds the postulated stretching, we may interpret the data as a much younger equivalent (i.e. Pleistocene) of the Laramide Sierra Madre Oriental folds, onshore to the W.

Friends of gravity gliding will be quick to point out that—contrary to the Gulf of Mexico example—much of the deformation occurring in folded belts affects already lithified sediments and in several cases the underlying basement. Consequently, it is also of some importance to characterize clearcut gravity tectonics in 'hard' rocks.

Some very well documented examples of local superficial gravitational gliding have been given by Pierce (1957, 1963, 1973) for the Heart Mountain area of Wyoming and by Reeves (1946) for the Bearpaw Mountains of Montana.

Normal faults responding to extension of the upper crust are most common in the western Cordillera of the USA and the southernmost segment of the Canadian Rocky Mountains.

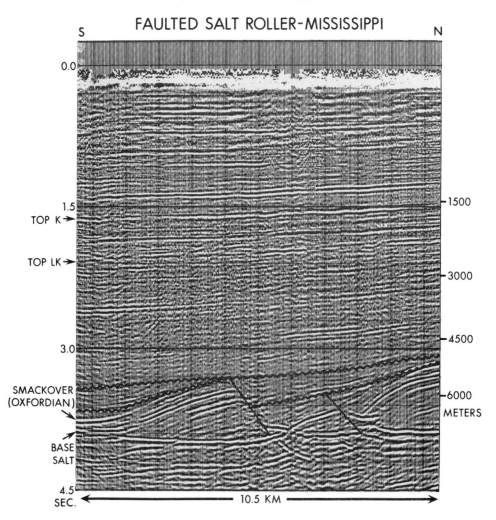

Fɪɢ. 6. Gulf Coast in Mississippi, reflection seismic section. Salt rollers, bounded by normal faults which flatten and merge with base of the salt.

Here again, reflection seismic data indicate the listric nature of the faults. The evidence for this is the presence of continuous reflections underlying obvious normal faults that are post-thrusting in age and can be mapped on the surface. The presence of such reflection data does not permit the direct straight-line projection into the subsurface of the large fault offsets seen at the surface; instead the normal faults have to flatten quickly at depth (see Fig. 11; Bally *et al.* 1966; McDonald 1976).

Another expression of the listric nature of these normal faults is the widespread rotation into the fault plane of beds that were deposited while the fault was active (Fig. 12). In the

western Cordillera the evidence for the listricity of normal faults ranges from superficial low-angle normal faults that simulate the base of a major landslide system to intermediate depth fault systems and exhumed, formerly deep fault systems that separate the more ductile deformation realms of metamorphic core complexes from the brittle overlying sediment cover (Davis & Coney 1979; Davis in press; Effimoff & Pinezich, 1980).

The normal fault systems in the western Cordillera are part of a very complex megashear system that—most unfortunately for 'gravity gliders'—clearly postdate the major overthrusting events of the western

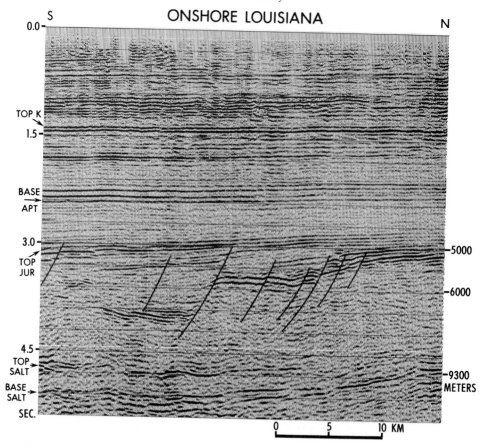

FIG. 7. Onshore Louisiana, reflection seismic section. Note pre-Cretaceous listric normal faults.

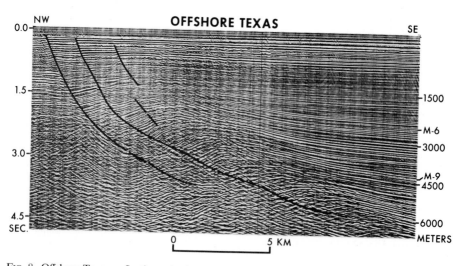

FIG. 8. Offshore Texas, reflection seismic section. Note extensive listric normal growth faults in Miocene section. M-6, M-9 are Miocene marker beds.

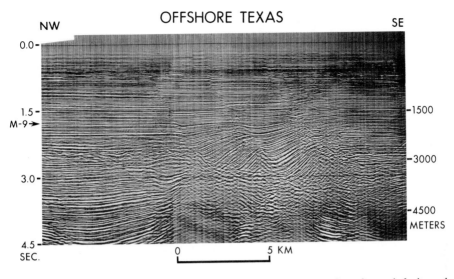

FIG. 9. Offshore Texas, reflection seismic profile showing the interaction of growth faults and diapiric structures. M-9 is a Miocene marker bed.

Cordillera. Note, however, that in a somewhat similar setting, extensional gravity tectonics and normal faulting are also common in the Vienna and the Pannonian Basins (Prey 1974). There, however, the normal faulting roughly occurs during the same time brackets as the last phase of overthrusting in the adjacent Carpathians. However, traditional gravity gliding is precluded by the simple fact that inner portions of the Carpathians are typically subsiding during the Tertiary, instead of furnishing an elevation from which nappes could glide towards the adjacent foredeep.

We may conclude that if we are to explain extensive thrusting and the formation of nappes by gravity gliding, we ought to search for extensive listric normal faulting that is synchronous and directly associated with the overthrust phenomena we observe. The amount of extension of these faults should be comparable to the amount of compressional shortening in the associated foldbelt. So far, I have failed to find in any mountain ranges evidence that would so link the emplacement of overthrust sheets with commensurate extensional fault systems in the inner portions of orogenic belts.

Thrust faulting involving the crystalline basement

So far, the discussion has been concerned with the evidence for the relative role of gravity gliding versus shortening by subduction-related compression. Support has been obtained by studying surface data and reflection seismic data that illustrate décollement tectonics of sedimentary sequences. A few words concerning the involvement of continental crystalline basement in orogenic processes is now in order.

One group of examples of orogenic basement involvement includes cases where slabs of varying thicknesses of, more or less, rigid crystalline basement rocks form thrust sheets. Examples are the eastern Alpine thrust sheets, the Main Central Thrust of the Himalayas, the Blue Ridge of the Appalachians, the Caledonides of Norway, and many others. In this first group, the basement has not been pervasively remobilized and contrasts with a second group of examples where the crystalline basement was extensively remobilized as in the Penninic Nappes of the Alps or the Shuswap complex of the Canadian Cordillera. Both groups can be viewed as end members for transitions showing varying degrees of basement mobility have been mapped across many folded belts. Instead of reviewing in detail the structural deformation of crystalline basement in folded belts, only the following points will be re-emphasized:

The involvement of crystalline continental basement in folded belts is characteristic and

24   A. W. Bally

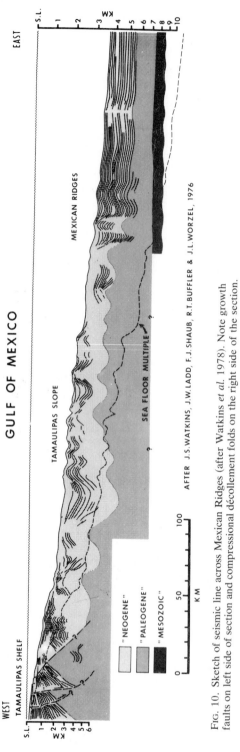

Fig. 10. Sketch of seismic line across Mexican Ridges (after Watkins *et al.* 1978). Note growth faults on left side of section and compressional décollement folds on the right side of the section.

constitutes the main reason why folded belts are often regarded as the product of ensialic orogenies. Some authors see a contradiction between a purely ensialic orogeny and orogenies that are related to plate tectonic processes. It is true that a number of mobile belts involve oceanic crust or ophiolites in suture zones. These permit us to postulate oceans of unknown width in plate tectonic reconstructions. However, in other cases, the evidence for such oceans is not so obvious, and at least in one case, folding and associated basement remobilization is entirely ensialic (Amadeus Basin of central Australia: Wells *et al.* 1970). Admittedly, the last example is unusual, because it affects a relatively small inverted basin located in the foreland of the Tasmanides. Nevertheless, the Amadeus Basin appears to offer an unambiguous case of ensialic deformation with décollement folding accompanied by the formation of small crystalline nappes.

Thrust faulting involving basement clearly indicates the existence of decoupling levels within the continental lithosphere. These may be mostly in the lower crust or may be in the upper mantle. Recent geophysical work in the Alps and Appennines (Angenheister *et al* 1972; Giese *et al.* 1973, 1978; Mueller *et al.* 1976; Mueller 1977) gives evidence for widespread low-velocity layers within the crust that extend well into the foreland. Thus the case for a layered crust with potential intracrustal decoupling levels is reinforced. The rheologic characteristics of these low-velocity layers are as yet poorly defined and consequently, the genesis of crustal low-velocity layers remains a matter for speculation. Some of the geological consequences of this problem are discussed by Hsü (1979).

There is also evidence for widespread crustal decoupling in the foreland of folded belts. A recent reflection line across the Wind River Mountains of Wyoming (Smithson *et al.* 1978, 1979; Brewer *et al.* in press) indicates that this basement uplift is underlain by a thrust fault which can be followed to a depth of about 35 km (see Fig. 13). If—as I believe—this line is characteristic for foreland block faulting, then it would follow that a major Laramide decoupling zone occurring at or near the base of the continental crust was underlying the Cordilleran foreland or the central and southern Rockies of the USA.

In a more speculative vein, attention should be called to Ziegler's (1978) observation that the well-known inversions observed in northwestern Europe (e.g. Wealden Anticlinorium,

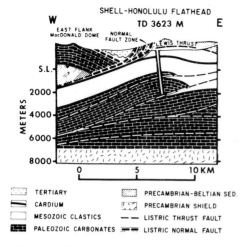

FIG. 11. Post-orogenic normal faults in Flathead area of British Columbia (from Bally *et al.* 1966, with permission of Canadian Society of Petroleum Geologists).

W Netherlands Basin, Lower Saxony Basin, and the Polish Anticlinorium, etc.) occur during the Meso-alpine deformation. This may well mean that with the incipient alpine collision, stresses are transmitted over more than 500 km across a rigid basement plate that overlies a deeper, less competent decoupling level. Such a level may well be located within the lower crust or the upper mantle. The concept is further supported by structural observations (horizontal stylolites, joints, minor re-

verse and strike-slip faults) in the sediment cover of the intervening platforms (Wagner 1974; de Charpal *et al.* 1974; Wunderlich 1974; for an updated review, see also Letouzey & Tremolières 1980).

There is a great deal of similarity between the foreland tectonics described in the preceding paragraphs and the continental collision processes that were described by Molnar & Tapponier (1978) and Tapponier & Molnar (1976) for Central Asia. There the late Palaeogene–Neogene collision of India with Eurasia caused extensive strike-slip faulting, thrust faulting, and normal faulting in Central Asia, which according to Molnar & Tapponier led to much of China being squeezed in an eastward direction. It should be noted that the collision also led to the emplacement of basement thrusts in the Himalayas, and it appears likely to me that some thrust faults associated with the Tien Shan and the Nan Shan uplifts involve thick segments of the continental crust in a manner comparable to the Rocky Mountain foreland.

It is concluded that decoupling within the lower crust and perhaps in the upper mantle is essential to explain thrust faulting of continental basement slabs. More geophysical information is needed to map such decoupling levels. These may well coincide with low-velocity layers that have been determined in a number of crustal studies. We are accustomed to explaining varying styles of deformation in folded and thrust-faulted sedimentary sequences as a function of ductility contrasts that are inherent

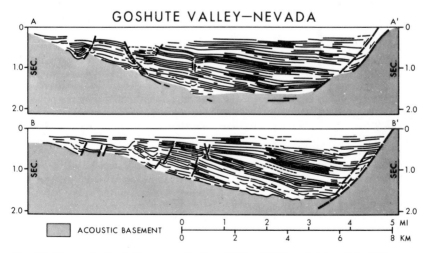

FIG. 12. Sketch of seismic line across Goshute Valley, NE Nevada (after Bally & Snelson 1980), with permission of Canadian Society of Petroleum Geologists).

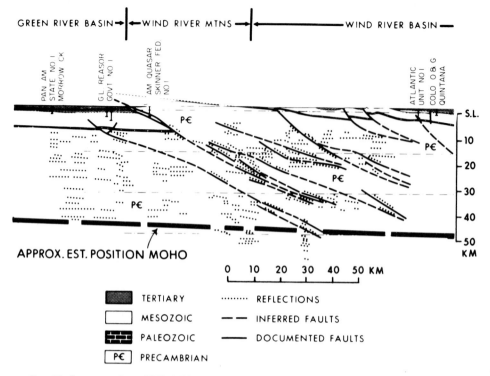

FIG. 13. Interpretation of Wind River Mountains, Wyoming, based on COCORP line (Smithson *et al.* 1978).

in the stratigraphic layering of the deformed sequences. By analogy, the style of deformation of basement slabs is dependent on ductility contrasts within the crystalline basement.

A number of plate tectonic models imply crustal decoupling (Armstrong & Dick 1974; Oxburgh's flake tectonics 1972; Bird's delamination 1978; Molnar & Gray 1979). A significant increase in understanding requires that future work concentrates on getting more detailed geological and geophysical documentation of deep crustal decoupling.

Turning to basement mobilization in the inner folded belts, it may be said that the causes for widespread regional remobilization and metamorphism of the basement remain obscure and may be due to burial and loading by higher thrust sheets or possibly due to thermal uplifts.

Overthrusting and strike-slip faulting

In recent years a number of authors have discussed the nature of thrust faulting as-

sociated with strike-slip faulting (Lowell 1972; Wilcox *et al.* 1973; Harding 1973, 1974, 1976; Sylvester & Smith 1976; Harding & Lowell 1979). These authors document and systematize the phenomenology of wrench faulting with surface, subsurface examples and clay model studies. An important problem relates to the scale and importance of thrust faulting, associated with strike-slip faulting. Clearly *en échelon* faults and thrust faults occur in a wrench fault regime. The upthrust interpretation proposed by various authors needs more verification by reflection seismic data. There remains, however, the question of how much shortening of sediments can be taken up by strike-slip faulting.

A schematic cross section and reconstruction made by my colleague, R. E. Farmer, illustrates the problem (Fig. 14). The Taiwan foldbelt has a structural style that appears to be similar to the Rocky Mountain Foothills of Canada and the outer Carpathians of Rumania. Although no seismic data concerning the underlying basement are published, one may assume gentle eastward dip by the reconstruction of the stratigraphic wedge that

TAIWAN

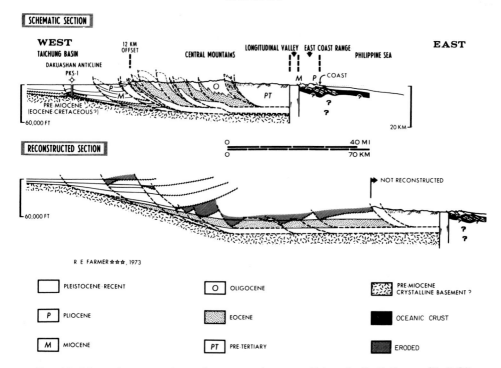

FIG. 14. Schematic cross section and reconstruction across Taiwan by R. E. Farmer (Shell Oil Company). *** Indicates quality.

is involved in the deformation. As a 'denuded' basement does not outcrop in the adjacent mountains, conventional gravity gliding may be precluded.

Accepting the admittedly shaky premises of the cross section, one has to conclude that a strip more than 50 km wide of pre-Tertiary basement apparently was subducted to form a deep 'root' under Taiwan. The crustal character of that basement is unknown. The subduction of the basement could have preceded the strike-slip displacement along the fault of the Longitudinal Valley or else the subduction process occurred during the deformation of that fault and during the folding in western Taiwan. Phases of subduction alternating with strike-slip faulting over short geological time spans can also be imagined.

The conclusion is that a substantial room problem may occur in palinspastic reconstructions of balanced cross sections across foldbelts that appear to be related to or later modified by strike-slip fault systems. Obviously, more reflection seismic data are needed to gain a better feeling for the dimension of the prob- lem. Plate tectonic reconstructions based on palaeomagnetic data frequently suggest the location of orogenic systems in an overall strike-slip/shear context and therefore it becomes increasingly more important to differentiate and determine the scale of thrusting related to strike-slip faulting, A-subduction and B-subduction.

Folded belts, basement mobilization and plate tectonic reconstructions

A corollary of many of the preceding comments and the megasuture concept is that the crystalline basement of folded belts did not behave as part of a rigid lithosphere during orogenic processes. Consequently, it is of some importance to separate relatively more rigid lithospheric realms from basement that has been remobilized and subjected to regional metamorphism and from basement fragments that were overthrust or else were rifted by complex strike-slip movements.

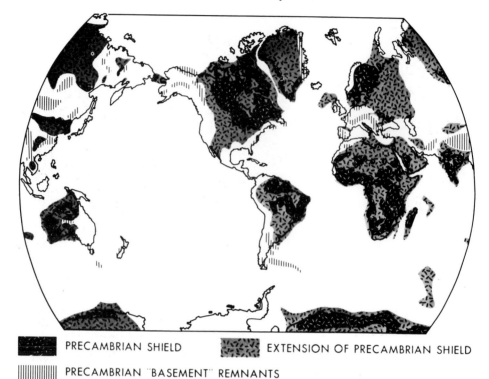

| PRECAMBRIAN SHIELD | EXTENSION OF PRECAMBRIAN SHIELD |

PRECAMBRIAN ¨BASEMENT¨ REMNANTS
INVOLVED IN PHANEROZOIC FOLDED BELTS

FIG. 15. Preserved Precambrian plate remnants. Precambrian 'basement' remnants that have been remobilized within Phanerozoic foldbelts do not qualify as 'rigid' microplates.

Superficial décollement folds and thrust sheets of Externides (Kober 1928) are probably in most cases underlain by a gently dipping basement ramp which represents unambiguous rigid lithosphere. The inner remobilized and metamorphosed portions of folded belts and small interior basement blocks captured during the orogenic process obviously represent either 'ductilized' lithosphere or else stray crustal fragments.

Plate tectonic reconstructions that are based on palaeomagnetic or stratigraphic points of control which are located within folded belts obviously have to be contrasted and related to lithospheric 'cratonic' segments that are now adjacent to these foldbelts. Therefore, there is an urgent need for reasonably accurate structural reconstructions of folded belts. At the same time, it is desirable to map the outlines of pre-Mesozoic and Precambrian continental lithospheric remnants to provide some of the building blocks for plate tectonic reconstructions. Outlines of the different types of building blocks are shown on Fig. 15 for the beginning of the Palaeozoic and on Fig. 16 for the beginning of the Mesozoic. The extensive occurrence of Precambrian and Palaeozoic basement remnants in later folded belts again emphasizes the 'ensialic' aspects of mountain building.

Conclusions

Normal faulting in folded belts and their foreland may be: —listric normal faulting involving the basement and related to the passive margin phase preceding orogenic deformation (for analogue, see de Charpal *et al.* 1978); —surficial soft-sediment listric normal faulting related to the drifting phase preceding orogenic deformation; —listric normal faulting related to the genesis of synorogenic accretionary wedges of B-subduction zones; —synorogenic normal faulting in the foreland related to the foreland bulge associated with subduction zones (Buchanan & Johnson 1968; Hopkins 1968; Laubscher 1978); —syn or

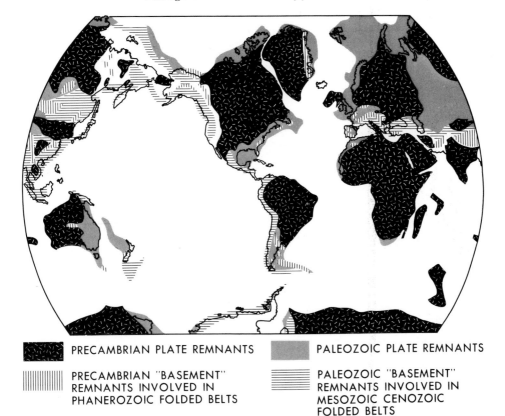

PRECAMBRIAN PLATE REMNANTS

PALEOZOIC PLATE REMNANTS

PRECAMBRIAN "BASEMENT" REMNANTS INVOLVED IN PHANEROZOIC FOLDED BELTS

PALEOZOIC "BASEMENT" REMNANTS INVOLVED IN MESOZOIC CENOZOIC FOLDED BELTS

FIG. 16. Preserved Precambrian and Palaeozoic plate remnants. Palaeozoic and Precambrian outcrops that have been remobilized within Phanerozoic foldbelts do not qualify as preserved "rigid" microplates.

postorogenic listric normal faulting associated with stretching and shearing of the orogenic system (e.g., Great Basin, Vienna and Pannonian Basins).

Thrust faulting in the folded belts may be:
—minor preorogenic thrust faulting at the toe of deltaic systems of passive margins (for analogue, see Lehner & de Ruiter 1977);
—synorogenic listric thrust faulting involving the continental basement within the mountain range (e.g. Himalayas and eastern Alpine Nappe) and in the foreland of mountain ranges (e.g. Wind River Mountains); —synorogenic thrust faulting or sedimentary sequences related to A-subduction processes (e.g. Canadian Rocky Mountains, Appalachians, and Externides of the Alpine system); —synorogenic thrust faulting of sedimentary sequences related to B-subduction processes (see Fig. 3);
—synorogenic thrust faulting related to strike-slip faults (Fig. 14).

All information on folded belts permits and supports their plate tectonic origin at subduction or else at transform plate boundaries. However, much of what we actually observe in mountain ranges involves décollement of and within sedimentary sequences, as well as significant decoupling within the deeper continental crust. Normal faulting and thrust faulting due to gravity gliding is not important for mountain building. This and the absence of wide-spread tectonically denuded basement argues strongly against a major role for gravity gliding.

Future geological and geophysical work should aim at defining and mapping such decoupling levels, particularly those that occur within the crust. Seismic crustal studies are a particularly promising aid in mapping intracrustal decoupling levels.

ACKNOWLEDGMENTS. I would like to thank my colleagues R. E. Farmer for providing the geological cross section of Taiwan, R. L. Nicholas for providing the Gulf Coast reflection lines, and K. Arbenz and S. Snelson for reviewing the paper and for their helpful suggestions. I also thank Shell Oil Company for permission to publish the seismic sections and the paper.

References

AMPFERER, O. 1906. Über das Bewegungbild von Faltengebirgen, Austria. *Jahrb. geol. Bundesanst,* **56,** 539–622.

ANGENHEISTER, G., BÖGEL, H., GEBRANDE, H., GIESE, P., SCHMIDT-THOME, R. & ZEIL, W. 1972. Recent investigations of surficial and deeper crustal structure of the eastern and southern Alps. *Geol. Rdsch.* **61,** 349–95.

ARGAND, E. 1924. La tectonique de l'Asie, *Compt. Rend IIIe. Congr. Int. geol. Liège,* Imprimerie Vaillant-Carmanne (transl. & ed. by Carozzi, A. V.). Hafner Press, New York, 218 pp.

ARMSTRONG, R. L. & DICK, H. J. B. 1974. A model for the development of thin overthrust sheets of crystalline rock. *Geology,* **2,** 35–40.

BALLY, A. W. 1975. A geodynamic scenario for hydrocarbon occurrences. *Proc. Ninth World Petrol. Congr. Tokyo,* **2,** Applied Science, Essex, 33–44.

—, GORDY, P. L. & STEWART, G. A. 1966. Structure, seismic data, and orogenic evolution of Southern Canadian Rocky Mountains. *Bull. Can. Pet. Geol.* **14,** 337–81.

—— & SNELSON, S. 1980. Realms of subsidence. *In:* Facts and Principles of World Oil Occurrence. Mem. Can. Soc. Pet. Geol. **6,** (in press).

BECK, R. H. & LEHNER, P. 1974. Oceans, new frontier in exploration. *Bull. Am. Assoc. Petrol. Geol.* **58,** 376–95.

—— & ——, with collab. of DIEBOLD, P., BAKKER, G. & DOUST, H. 1975. New geophysical data on key problems on global tectonics. *Proc. Ninth World Petrol. Congr. Tokyo,* **2,** Applied Science, Essex, 3–17.

BELOUSSOV, V. V. 1962. *Basic Problems in Geotectonics.* McGraw Hill, New York, 809 pp.

—— 1975. *Foundations of Geotectonics* (in Russian). Nyedra, Moscow, 260 pp.

—— 1977. Gravitational instability and the development of the structure of continents. *In:* SAXENA, S. K. & BATTACHARJI, S. (eds). *Energetics of Geological Processes.* Springer, New York, 3–18.

BINNS, R. E. 1978. Caledonian Nappe correlation and orogenic history in Scandinavia north of lat. 67°N. *Bull. geol. Soc. Am.* **89,** 1475–90.

BIRD, P. 1978. Initiation of intracontinental subduction in the Himalaya. *J. geophys. Res.* **83,** 4975–87.

——, TOKSÖZ, M. N. & SLEEP, N. H. 1975. Thermal and mechanical models of continent–continent convergence zones. *J. geophys. Res.* **80,** 4405–16.

BREWER, J., SMITHSON, S. B., KAUFMAN, S., & OLIVER, J. in press. The Laramide orogeny: evidence from COCORP deep crustal seismic profiles in the Wind River Mountains, Wyoming. *J. geophys. Res.*

BUCHANAN, R. S. & JOHNSON, F. K. 1968. Bonanza gas field—a model for Arkoma Basin growth faulting. *In:* CLINE, L. M. (ed). *A Guidebook to the Geology of the Western Arkoma Basin and Ouachita Mountains, Oklahoma.* Okla. City Geol. Soc. 75–85.

BUFFLER, R. T., SHAUB, F. T., WORZEL, J. L. & WATKINS, J. S. 1979. Gravity slide origin for Mexican ridges foldbelt, southwestern Gulf of Mexcio. *Bull. Am. Assoc. Petrol. Geol.,* **63,** 426.

CAREY, S. W. 1975. The expanding earth—an essay review. *Earth Sci. Rev.* **11,** 105–43.

—— 1977. The Expanding Earth: *Development in Geotectonics Series,* **10.** Elsevier, Amsterdam, 488 pp.

COOK, F. A., BROWN, L. D., HATCHER, R. D., KAUFMAN, S. & OLIVER, J. E. 1979. Preliminary interpretation of COCORP reflection profiles across the Brevard zone in northwest Georgia. *Abstr. Spring Meeting Am. Geophys. Un.*

CURTIS, D. M. 1970. Miocene deltaic sedimentation Lousiana Gulf Coast. *In:* MORGAN, JAMES P. (ed). *Deltaic Sedimentation Modern and Ancient.* Spec. Publ. Soc. Econ. Paleo. Miner. **15,** 293–308.

—— 1980. Source of Oils in Gulf Goast Tertiary. *J. Sediment. Petrol.* (in press).

—— & PICOU, JR., E. B. 1978. Gulf Coast Cenozoic: A model for the application of stratigraphic concepts to exploration on passive margins. *Trans. Gulf Coast Assoc. geol. Soc.* **XXVIII,** 103–20.

DAHLSTROM, C. D. A. 1969. Balanced cross sections. *Can. J. Earth Sci.* **6,** 743–57.

—— 1970. Structural geology in the eastern margin of the Canadian Rocky Mountains. *Bull. Can. Pet. Geol* **18,** 332–406.

DAVIS, G. A. in press. Problems of intraplate extensional tectonics, Western United States. *In:* Nat. Res. Council Continental Dynamics publication.

DAVIS, G. H. & CONEY, P. J. 1979. Geological development of the Cordilleran metamorphic core complexes. *Geology,* **7,** 120–4.

DE CHARPAL, O., GUENNOC, P., MONTADERT, L. & ROBERTS, D. G. 1978. Rifting, crustal attenuation and subsidence in the Bay of Biscay. *Nature,* **275,** 706–11.

——, TREMOLIÈRES, P., JEAN, F. & MASSE, P. 1974. Un example de tectonique de plate-forme: les Causses Majeurs, sud du Massif Central, France. *Rev. Inst. Fr. Pet. Paris* **29,** 641–59.

DE JONG, K. A. & SCHOLTEN, R. 1973. *Gravity and Tectonics.* Wiley-Interscience, New York, 502 pp.

DELTEIL, J. R., RIVIER, F., MONTADERT, L., APOSTOLESCU, V., DIDIER, J., GOSLIN, M. & PAT-

RIAT, P. H. 1976. Structure and sedimentation of the continental margin of the Gulf of Benin. *In*: DE ALMEIDA, F. F. M., (ed). *Continental Margins of Atlantic Type.* Ann. Acad. Brasil **48,** 51–66.

DE SITTER, L. U. 1954. Gravitation gliding tectonics, an essay in comparative structural geology. *Am. J. Sci.* **252,** 321–44.

EDWARDS, M. B. 1976. Growth faults in Upper Triassic deltaic sediments, Svalbard, *Bull. Am. Assoc. Petrol. Geol.* **60,** 314–55.

EFFIMOFF, I. & PINEZICH, A. A. 1980. Tertiary structural development of selected valleys based on seismic data—Basin and Range Province, Northeastern Nevada. *Paper for Roy. Soc. Meeting, London.* (in preparation).

ELLIOTT, D. 1976*a*. The motion of thrust sheets. *J. geophys. Res.* **81,** 949–63.

—— 1976*b*. The energy balance and deformation mechanisms of thrust sheets, *Philos. Trans. R. Soc. London,* **283,** 289–312.

GEE, D. G. 1975. A tectonic model for the central part of the Scandinavian Caledonides. *Am. J. Sci.* **275A,** 468–515.

GIESE, P., MORELLI, C. & STEINMETZ, L. 1973. Main features of crustal structure in central and southern Europe based on data of explosion seismology. *In*: MÜLLER, S. (ed), *Tectonophysics,* **20,** 367–79.

—— & RÜTTER, K. J. 1978. Crustal and structural features of the margins of the Adria Microplate. *In*: CLOSS, H. *et al.* (eds). *Alps, Appennines, Hellenides,* Schweizerbart'sche Verlagsbuchhandlung, Stuttgart, 565–87.

GORDY, P. F., FREY, F. R. & OLLERENSHAW, N. C. 1975. Structural geology of the foothills between Savanna Creek and Panther River SW Alberta, Canada. Guidebook Can. Soc. Petrol. Geol., *Can Soc. Explor. Geophys., Explor. Update* 1975, Calgary.

GWINN, V. E. 1970. Kinematic patterns and estimates of lateral shortening, Valley and Ridge and Great Valley provinces. *In*: FISHER, G. W. *et al.* (eds). *Studies of Appalachian Geology, Central and Southern.* Wiley, New York, 460 pp.

HAMILTON, W. 1977. Subduction in the Indonesian Region. *In*: TALWANI, W. & PITTMAN, W. C. (eds). *Island Arcs, Deep Sea Trenches and Back-arc Basins.* Maurice Ewing Series **1,** Am. geol. Un., 15–31.

HARDING, T. P. 1973. Newport–Inglewood trend, California—an example of wrenching style of deformation. *Bull. Am. Assoc. Petrol. Geol.* **60,** 366–78.

—— 1974. Petroleum traps associated with wrench faults. *Bull. Am. Assoc. Petrol. Geol.* **58,** 1290–304.

—— 1976. Tectonic significance and hydrocarbon trapping consequences of sequential folding synchronous with San Andreas faulting, San Joaquin Valley, California. *Bull. Am. Assoc. Petrol. Geol.* **60,** 366–78.

—— & LOWELL, J. D. 1979. Structural styles, their plate tectonic habitats and hydrocarbon traps in petroleum provinces. *Bull. Am. Assoc. Petrol. Geol.* **63,** 1016–58.

HATCHER, R. D. 1972. Developmental model for the southern Appalachians. *Bull. geol. Soc. Am.* **83,** 2735–60.

HOPKINS, H. R. 1968. Structural interpretations of the Quachita Mountains. *In*: CLINE, L. M. (ed). *A Guidebook to the Geology of Western Arkoma Basin and Ouachita Mountains, Oklahoma.* Okla. City Geol. Soc. 104–8.

HOSSACK, J. R. 1978. The correction of stratigraphic sections for tectonic finite strain in the Bygdin area, Norway. *J. Geol. Soc. London,* **135,** 229–41.

HSÜ, K. J. 1979. Thin skinned plate tectonics during Neo-Alpine Orogenesis *Am. J. Sci.* **279,** 353–66.

HUMPHRIS, C. C. 1978. Salt movement on continental slope, northern Gulf of Mexico. *Am. Assoc. Petrol. Geol. Studies in Geology,* **7,** 69–85.

KOBER, L. 1928. *Der Bau der Erde,* Bornträger, Berlin. 500 pp.

LAUBSCHER, H. P. 1978. Foreland folding. *Tectonophysics,* **47,** 325–37.

LEHNER, P. & de RUITER, P. A. C. 1977. Structural history of the Atlantic margin of Africa. *Bull. Am. Assoc. Petrol. Geol.* **61,** 961–81.

LETOUZEY, J. & TREMOLIÈRES, P. 1980. Paleostress fields around the Mediterranean since the Mesozoic derived from microtectonics: Comparisons with plate tectonic data. *In*: SCHEIDEGGER, A. E. (ed). *Tectonic Stress in the Alpine–Mediterranean region.* Springer Verlag.

LOWELL, J. D. 1972. Spitsbergen Tertiary orogenic belt and the Spitsbergen fracture zone. *Bull. geol. Soc. Am.* **83,** 3091–102.

McDONALD, R. E. 1976. Tertiary tectonics and sedimentary rocks along the transition basin and range province to plateau and thrust belt province, Utah. *Rocky Mtn. Assoc. Geol. Guidebook,* 281–371.

MOLNAR, P. & GRAY, D. 1979. Subduction of continental lithosphere: some constraints of certainties. *Geology,* **7,** 58–62.

—— & TAPPONIER, P. 1978. Active tectonics of Tibet. *J. geophys. Res.* **83,** 5361–75.

MUELLER, S. 1977. A new model of the continental crust. *Monogr. Am. Geophys. Un.* **20,** 289–317.

——, EGLOFF, R. & ANSORGE, J. 1976. Struktur des tieferen undergrundes Entlang der Schwizer geotraverse. *Schweiz. mineral. petrogr. Mitt.* **56,** 685–92.

NORTH, F. K. 1964. Gravitational tectonics. *Bull. Can. Pet. Geol.* **12,** 185–225.

OXBURGH, E. Z. 1972. Flake tectonics and continental collision. *Nature,* **239,** 202–4.

PIERCE, W. G. 1957. Heart Mountain and South Fork detachment thrusts of Wyoming. *Bull. Am. Assoc. Petrol. Geol.* **41,** 519–626.

—— 1963. Reef Creek detachment fault, northwestern Wyoming. *Bull. geol. Soc. Am.* **74,** 1225–36.

—— 1973. Principal features of the Heart Mountain fault and the mechanism problem. *In*: DE JONG, K. A. & SCHOLTEN, R. (eds). *Gravity and Tec-*

tonics. Wiley-Interscience, New York, 457–71.

PREY, S. 1974. External zones. *In*: MAHEL, M. (ed). *Tectonics of the Carpathian Balkan Regions—Explanation to the Tectonic Map of the Carpathian–Balkan Regions and their Foreland*. Geol. Inst. Dionyz Stur. Bratislava, 75–84.

PRICE, R. A. 1971. Gravitational sliding and the foreland thrust and fold belt of the North American Cordillera: Discussion. *Bull. geol. Soc. Am.* **77**, 1133–38.

—— 1973. Large-scale gravitational flow of supracrustal rocks, southern Canadian Rockies. *In*: DE JONG, K. A. & SCHOLTEN, R. (eds). *Gravity and Tectonics*. Wiley-Interscience, New York, 491–502.

—— & MOUNTJOY, E. W. 1970. Geologic structure of the Canadian Rocky Mountains between Bow and Athabasca Rivers: a progress report. *Spec. Pap. geol. Assoc. Can.* **6**, 7–25.

REEVES, F. 1946. Origin and mechanics of the thrust faults adjacent to the Bear-paw Mountains, Montana. *Bull. geol. Soc. Am.* **57**, 1033–48.

RIDER, M. H. 1978. Growth faults in carboniferous of western Ireland, *Bull. Am. Assoc. Petrol. Geol.* **62**, 2191–213.

ROEDER, D., GILBERT, JR., D. E. & WITHERSPOON, W. D. 1978. Evolution and macroscopic structure of Valley and Ridge thrust belt. Tennessee and Virginia. *Univ. Tenn. Geol. Sci. Studies in Geology*, **2**, Knoxville, 25 pp.

ROYSE, JR., F., WARNER, M. A. & REESE, D. C. 1975. Thrust belt structural geometry and related stratigraphic problems, Wyoming–Idaho–northern Utah. *Rocky Mtn. Ass. Geol. Symp.* Deep Drilling Frontiers in Central Rocky Mtns., 41–54.

SCHOLL, D. W., MARLOW, M. S. & COOPER, A. K. 1977. Sediment subduction and offscraping at Pacific Margins. *In*: TALWANI, M. & PITTMAN, W. C. (eds). *Island Arcs. Deep Sea Trenches and Back-Arc Basins*. Maurice Ewing Series **1**, Am. geophys. Un., 199–210.

SHOULDICE, G. H. 1971. Geology of the western Canadian continental shelf. *Bull. Can Pet. Geol.* **19**, 405–36.

SMITHSON, S. B., BREWER, J. A., KAUFMAN, S., OLIVER, J. & HURICH, C. 1978. Nature of the Wind River thrust, Wyoming, from COCORP deep reflections and gravity data. *Geology*, **6**, 648–52.

——, ——, —— & —— 1979. Structure of the Laramide Wind River uplift, Wyoming, from COCORP deep reflection data and from gravity data. *J. geophys. Res.* **84**, 5955–72.

SPENGLER, E. 1953-59. Versuch einer Rekonstruktion des Ablagerungsraumes der Decken der nördlichen Kalkalpen I-III. *Jahrb. geol. Bundesanst.* 1953, 1956, 1959.

STAUB, R. 1928, *Der Bewegungsmechanismus der Erde*, Bornträger, Berlin, 270 pp.

SUPPE, J. 1979. Cross Section of southern part of northern coast ranges and Sacramento Valley, California. *Geol. Soc. Am. Map & Chart Series* **MC–28B.**

SYLVESTER, A. G. & SMITH, R. R. 1976. Tectonic transpression and basement-controlled deformation in the San Andreas fault zone, Salton trough, California. *Bull. Am. Assoc. Petrol Geol.* **60**, 2081–102.

TAPPONIER, P. & MOLNAR, P. 1976. Slip-line theory and large-scale plate tectonics. *Nature*, **264**, 319–24.

TRÜMPY, R. 1969. Die Helvetischen Decken der Ostschweiz: Versuch einer palinspastischen Korrelation und Ansätze zu einer kinematischen Analyse. *Eclog. geol. Helv.* **62**, 105–38.

VON HUENE, R., ARTHUR, M. & CARSON, B. *this volume*. Ambiguity in interpretation of seismic data from modern convergent margins: an example from the IPOD Japan trench transect.

WAGNER, G. H. 1964. Druckspannungsindizien in den Sedimenttafeln des Rheinischen Schildes. *Geol. Rdsch.* **56**, 906–13.

WATKINS, J. S., LADD, J. W., SHAUB, F. J., BUFFLER, R. T. & WORZEL, J. L. 1976. Southern Gulf of Mexico, east–west section from Tamaulipas shelf to Campeche Scarp. *Am. Assoc. Petrol. Geol. Seismic sec.* **1.**

——, ——, BUFFLER, R. T., SHAUB, F. G., HOUSTON, M. H. & WORZEL, J. L. 1978. Occurrence and evolution of salt in deep Gulf of Mexico. *Am. Assoc. Petrol. Geol. Studies in Geology*, **7**, 43–65.

WEBER, K. J. & DAUKORU, E. 1976. Petroleum geology of the Niger delta. *Proc. Ninth World Petrol. Congr. Tokyo*, **2**, Applied Science, Essex, 209–221.

WELLS, A. T., FORMAN, D. J., RANFORD, L. C. & COOK, P. J. 1970. Geology of the Amadeus Basin, central Australia. *Bull. Bur. Miner. Resour. Geol. Geophys. Melbourne*. **100**, 222 pp.

WILCOX, R. E., HARDING, T. P. & SEELY, D. R. 1973. Basic wrench tectonics. *Bull. Am. Assoc. Petrol. Geol.* **57**, 74–90.

WUNDERLICH, H. G. 1974. Die Bedeutung der Süddeutschen Gross-scholle in der Geodynamik Westeuropas. *Geol. Rdsch.* **63**, 755–72.

ZIEGLER, P. A. 1978. Northwestern Europe: tectonics and basin development. *Geol. Mijnbouw*. **57**, 589–626.

A. W. BALLY, Shell Oil Company, P.O. Box 481, Houston, Texas 77001, U.S.A.

Pore pressure, discontinuities, isostasy and overthrusts

P. E. Gretener

SUMMARY: Thrusting represents the shifting of large loads. This has the following consequences: (a) in the overridden sequence high pore pressures develop initially due to rapid loading and later due to aquathermal pressuring caused by slower thermal adjustment. This leads to the activation of deeper and more outward emerging thrust planes: (b) the isostatic response to the loading in front and the simultaneous unloading in the back produces the *wandering bulge*.

These two processes tend to make thrust faulting a self-perpetuating process once it has been initiated.

It is first appropriate to establish a few fundamentals about major overthrust plates (nappes or Decken) as recognized by field geologists.

Such plates show displacements which are measured in tens of kilometres. Plate thicknesses are in the order of several kilometres, and the lateral extent may well be in excess of 100 km. These numbers have been well documented by many authors in different thrust belts all around the world (Gretener 1972). The conclusion is, therefore, inescapable that the telescoping of the sedimentary wedge in the outer part of a thrust belt constitutes a drastic shift of large loads. This has a number of consequences, and their discussion forms the core of this paper.

The velocity of thrusting, or the time required for the emplacement of a single major thrust sheet, is usually not well defined. Elliot (1976) gives an average minimum velocity for the McConnell Thrust in Canada of 5 mm/yr. Hsü (1969) estimates the average advance of the Glarus Thrust in Switzerland to be between 2 and 100 mm/yr. Royse et al. (1975) give the overall shortening in the Idaho–Wyoming thrust belt as about 100 km, accomplished in 100 Ma, which leads to an average speed of 1 mm/yr. This value refers to a thrust belt as a whole and, since thrusting is almost certainly an intermittent process (section 3), it tends to support the figures given by Elliot (1976) and Hsü (1969). Accepting the somewhat arbitrary value of 10 mm/yr results in an advance of 10 km/Ma, and puts the total time for the emplacement of a single major thrust sheet in the order of 1–5 Ma. It is, however, not necessary for a major thrust plate to be completely emplaced in order for the underlying sequence to 'feel' the additional load. Any point about 5 km behind the front of the thrust will be essentially fully loaded. Tectonic loading of several kilometres in no more than one million years results in loading rates of several millimetres per year (X mm/yr). Hubbert & Rubey (1959, p. 171, table 1) have shown that sedimentation rates of several tenths of a millimetre per year (0.X mm/yr) are sufficient to cause severe overpressures. The conclusion is unavoidable that *thrusting constitutes an act of rapid loading*. This remains true even if the adopted estimate of thrust-velocity should turn out to be too high by an order of magnitude.

The direction of the progression of thrusting has not been universally established, but at least in two cases good evidence seems to exist. The outer portion of the southern Canadian Rocky Mountains is among the best explored thrust belts in the world, not owing to the superior talent of the Canadian geologists but because this thrust belt is an attractive area for hydrocarbon exploration. The opinion of the field observers, based on detailed surface geological work, and extensive seismic and drilling data, is essentially unanimous that thrusting progressed outward (Bally et al. 1966; Dahlstrom 1970). Certain exceptions on the more detailed scale, such as the back-limb thrusts of Douglas (1950) cannot detract from the general validity of the outward progression. Royse et al. (1975) have recently demonstrated that much the same case can be made for the Idaho–Wyoming thrust belt. As will be shown later this postulate of the field geologists seems also mechanically most attractive.

One must keep in mind that the following discussion addresses itself primarily to the deformation of the layered sequence, the sedimentary wedge, such as occurs commonly in the outer part of a thrust belt. For the interior thrust sheets, with their crystalline basement cores, different mechanisms than those discussed here must be invoked.

Low angle discontinuities (bedding planes) and high pore pressure

The Mohr diagram of Fig. 1 predicts the mechanical behaviour of a rock in the presence of discontinuities (planes of weakness) and high pore pressure. Raising the pore pressure makes possible the activation of an ever wider orientation of discontinuities with low or zero cohesion. In particular the diagram lets one anticipate the activation of such planes subparallel to the σ_1-axis (δ_{min}).

Experiments by Jaeger (1959), Handin (1969) and others have shown that the above prediction is correct. These authors have investigated samples with sawcuts 'healed' with plaster of Paris (weak cohesion) and open cuts (no cohesion), oriented at angles higher than the angle of natural fracture to the σ_1-axis. Full confirmation of the above prediction was obtained, and the concept of the plane of weakness was fully rehabilitated, inspite of some earlier dissenting opinions of a few theoreticians. Cuts with angles less than that of natural fracture ($\sim 30°$) were not tested since such cuts will intersect the end faces of the specimen and will, therefore, be artificially confined by the platens. This, however, does in no way demonstrate that such fractures cannot be activated in nature and, in fact, movement along such discontinuities is predicted by the Mohr diagram of Fig. 1. The subhorizontal attitude of thrust faults following bedding planes in a stress field where the maximum principal stress is also near horizontal thus finds a convincing explanation.

The fact that natural discontinuities profoundly affect rock behaviour is well known to the engineer. It is supported by the observations on many major land slides, where discontinuities subparallel to the surface slope have played an important role. Examples include: the Flims and Goldau slides in Switzerland, the Vaiont slide in Italy, the Gros Ventre slide in U.S.A., and the Frank slide in Canada, to mention just a few.

The activation of existing faults due to an increase in pore pressure has been experienced in the case of the so-called 'Denver Earthquakes' (Evans 1966). Subsequent experiments by the U.S.G.S. in the Rangely Oilfield in Utah/Colorado (Raleigh *et al.* 1972) fully confirmed the applicability of the theory as presented in Fig. 1. In the case of the Rangely experiments, depth of action is in the order of 2 km, and for the Denver Earthquakes hypocentres ranges from 5 to 15 km in depth. Note that this *is* the depth realm of overthrust faulting. While it is true that the effect of discontinuities is most pronounced under near-surface conditions, as in the case of landslides, the above observations demonstrate that the effect is not to be ignored in the case of major sole thrusts which usually occur at depths less than 10 km. One must also not forget that the presence of high pore pressures restores near-surface conditions at least as far as the rock stresses are concerned.

There is little doubt that the 'Hubbert and Rubey Theory' (1959) constitutes a possible viable mechanism for the 'easy gliding' of large thrust plates. It may well not be the only mechanism as pointed out by Laubscher (1961), Hsü (1969), Kehle (1970) and others.

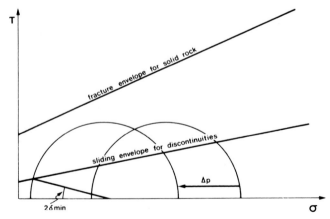

FIG. 1. The presence of discontinuities with low or zero cohesion in zones of high pore pressure allows the activation of those discontinuities which are inclined at a very low angle (δ_{min}) to the maximum principal stress axis (σ_1).

It is also certainly plagued by such unanswered questions as: (a) how are the high pore pressures maintained in space and time in view of the large areal extent of major thrust plates and their long emplacement-time? and (b) can such pressures exist simultaneously over the total length of a major thrust fault in view of the stepped nature of such fault planes (Rich 1934; Douglas 1950)?

A possible solution to these enigmas may be found when one considers the distinct possibility that the high pore pressures may be transient rather than steady state phenomena (Gretener 1972). Segmental movement of these faults, as already envisaged by Oldham (1921), may indeed get us nearer to an acceptable answer, but the details as to how this concept fits into the overall picture remain vague at this time.

One must, however, not forget that the 'Plasticity/Viscosity Theory', originally advanced by Smoluchowski (1909) and recently revived by Laubscher (1961); Hsü (1969) and Kehle (1970), is also not without problems. Investigations of the Lochseitenkalk (the smeared-out base of the Glarus Thrust) by Briegel & and Goetze (1978) lead to a basal shear stress of about 100 MPa. Using the Laubscher formula (1961, p. 244), based on Hubbert & Rubey (1959), and substituting the dimensions of the Glarus Thrust, the maximum permissible basal shear stress is at most 30 MPa. One must note that the Laubscher formula produces values which are almost certainly unrealistically high, and also that the above computation makes no allowance for the tilt of the thrust plane which will further reduce the above value.

Pore pressure, discontinuities, and overthrusts

The outer portion of a thrust belt is a layered sequence, usually in the form of a sedimentary wedge, that is deformed by the thrusting. Present experience shows that in most thick sedimentary sequences abnormal, i.e. higher than normal (hydrostatic), pore pressures are common (Fertl 1974). Abnormally high pressures develop in those parts of the sequence where restrictions to fluid flow prevail. Such restrictions are formed by the thick shales of the clastic facies and/or by the evaporites of the evaporite-carbonate facies. A restriction to flow, not necessarily a perfect seal, is a basic requirement for the development of such excess pressures, regardless of the generating

mechanism. Just how effective the restriction must be depends on the efficiency (speed) of the pressure generating process.

Thus, one can expect the original thrust movement to find zones of high fluid pressure within the undeformed wedge. These zones with the encorporated bedding planes form the situation depicted in Fig. 1. In order to preserve the mechanical strength of the thrust plate itself it is, in fact, necessary that the high fluid pressures be confined to the vicinity of the décollement zones. This again is in accordance with the observations made while drilling in thick sedimentary sequences. There are many cases reported where the pore pressures were found to increase very rapidly in a short depth interval (e.g. Shouldice 1971, p. 432, fig. 18; Hottman & Johnson 1965, p. 722, figs 8 and 9). It is thus both permissible and advantageous to assume that high pore pressures are confined to décollement zones. In contrast to Hubbert & Rubey (1959) the situation is such that:

$$\lambda_{\text{décollement}} > \lambda_{\text{block}}$$

where $\lambda = p/S_z$ with p for pore pressure and S_z for total overburden stress. This leads to the concept of planes of superweakness as defined by Gretener (1972), planes of low cohesion in a high pore pressure environment. The acceptance of different values for λ does, however, have no drastic effect on the original numerical computations by Hubbert & Rubey (1959).

Once the first major overthrust plate has moved into position, the situation is as shown schematically in Fig. 2. As mentioned earlier the extent perpendicular to the line of section may well be over 100 km. Note that the overthrust *is* the toe. Debates about the toe are meaningless insofar as without a toe there is no thrust, unless the front of the thrust mass gives rise to a Jura type fold belt.

Overthrusting results in a major shift of surface loads (Fig. 2). Rapid tectonic loading occurs in the overridden sequence. The conclusion is inescapable that this must lead to a further increase of the pore pressures in the zones of restricted fluid flow in the overridden sequence. For this purpose one must not only assess the effect of pure loading but also that of heating leading to aquathermal pressuring (Barker 1972).

A calculation to explore the possibility of a hypothetical model to put the overburden into a state of floatation ($p = S_z$ or $\lambda = 1$, Terzaghi 1950) might take the following form:

Thickness of the overthurst plate: $z_0 = 4$ km;

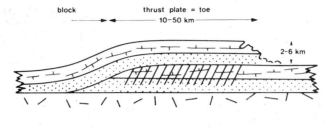

//// realm of expected high pore pressure

FIG. 2. The toe *is* the thrust plate! Major thrust sheets result in rapid loading leading to high pore pressures in the overridden sequence. The effect may be enhanced by aquathermal pressuring, but this effect is lagging the loading process. In view of the dimensions of these plates the isostatic response of the crust is inevitable.

average density 2.55×10^3 kg/m³ leading to a gradient for the total overburden stress of 25 MPa/km. Consider a point 3 km below the overriding plate ($z_0 = 3$ km), located in a future décollement zone. Because of the restrictions to flow prevailing in such a zone one is justified in assuming an initial pore pressure somewhat above normal. Let us arbitrarily set $\lambda_0 = 0.7$ Thus, before the onset of thrusting, the stress condition at $z_0 = 3$ km is as follows:

$$z = z_0 = 3 \text{ km}; \qquad S_z = 75 \text{ MPa};$$

$$p = 0.7 \times 75 = 52.5 \text{ MPa}; \qquad \sigma_z = 22.5 \text{ MPa}$$

For the condition after thrusting, we make the following, arbitrary, but reasonable assumption; namely that 90% of the additional load will be carried by the pore pressure and the remaining 10% will be transferred to the matrix due to slow leakage. Pure tectonic loading thus leads to:

$$z_1 = z_0 + z_0 = 7 \text{ km}; \qquad S_z = 7 \times 25 = 175 \text{ MPa};$$

$$p = 52.5 + 0.9 \times 100 = 142.5 \text{ MPa};$$

$$\sigma_z = 32.5 \text{ MPa}; \qquad \lambda_{0(L)} = 142.5/175 = 0.8$$

It is clearly not possible to produce a condition where $\lambda \sim 1$ at any substantial depth below the thrust plane by pure loading alone. The condition of floating the overburden can only be invoked by calling on an additional mechanism of pressure generation. The most likely candidate is that of aquathermal pressuring as proposed by Barker (1972). According to Barker, a rise in temperature of 1°C leads to an increase in pore fluid pressure of about 1.5 MPa under sealed conditions. In terms of the above example this means: for $\lambda_{0(L+T)} = 1$ we get $\Delta p_T \sim$ 30 MPa or $\Delta T \sim 20$°C.

To evaluate the occurrence of such a temperature increase we may turn to Oxburgh & Turcotte (1974), who have investigated the temperature conditions under advancing thrust

sheets. Their model, being of much different dimensions, does not permit an accurate computation. In view of the various uncertainties, however, an intelligent guess will do. Their computations indicate that the required temperature increase will occur about 0.5–1 Ma after the emplacement of the thrust plate. Such a time lag means that further allowance must be made for some fluid leakage, since perfect seals occur only in models but seldom in nature, with the possible exceptions of salt and overpressured shales. Thus aquathermal pressuring cannot put the overridden beds into a state of floatation until about 1–2 Ma after thrusting has taken place. This implies that *movement on major thrust planes is intermittent.* These are relatively major 'waiting' periods imposed by thermal relaxation and are not to be confused with the postulated segmental movement during active thrusting itself (the caterpillar rests from time to time). It would seem logical that during those 'quiet' periods, while the main thrust is 'stuck', internal deformation might be produced such as the back-limb thrusts of Douglas (1950).

However, following a period of heating, favourable conditions for the advance of the main thrust are produced eventually in the overridden sequence: deeper thrusts are activated, and thrusting progresses outward carrying the old plate piggy-back, just as observed in the southern Canadian Rocky Mountains and the Idaho–Wyoming thrust belts.

If the 'Pore Pressure Theory' is to apply to the inner nappes with their crystalline cores, then it evidently becomes necessary to invoke other pressure generating mechanisms. Possibilities are phase changes such as discussed by Raleigh & Paterson (1965) or metasomatism as mentioned by Platt (1962). Again, as in the case of the sedimentary wedge, such processes should be limited to certain horizons to create the zones of weakness or décollements necessary for thrusting to take its typical form.

Shifting loads and the isostatic response

The shifting of loads during thrusting and the accompanying fast tectonic loading not only creates a situation favourable for the continuation of high pore pressures but must also result in an isostatic response. Fig. 3 describes the situation. Fig. 3a shows the initial undisturbed sedimentary wedge of the outer belt. Figs 3b and 3c show schematically an early stage of

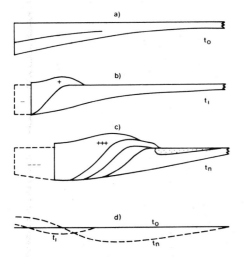

Fig. 3. (a) shows the initial, undeformed sedimentary wedge. (b) shows an early stage of deformation, and (c) gives the final telescoping of the wedge by thrust faulting. (d) shows the expected isostatic response through time due to the successive unloading on the left and the corresponding addition of load on the right. The *advancing isostatic bulge* is the inevitable consequence of this shift of load.

deformation and the final distortion of the crumpled wedge. In the process of thrusting, load has been removed at the back and added in the front. It is well known that the crust is sensitive to the addition and removal of surficial loads and responds by isostatic subsidence or uplift. Scandinavia and northern Canada are still rising due to the removal of the ice caps some 10 000 years ago (Donner 1969; Andrews 1970). The area of Lake Mead in Nevada/Arizona subsided several centimetres in the first 14 years after the man-made lake was impounded (Longwell 1954). According to

Walcott (1970) relaxation time is measured in 10 000 of years which, in terms of thrust faulting, represents an *instantaneous* response. Since major isostatic movements have accompanied man throughout his recorded history the mistaken view still prevails that isostatic movements are slow (Gussow 1963). This is definitely not so, 20 000–40 000 years are insignificant in terms of most geological processes.

Price (1973) has considered the isostatic response due to advancing thrust sheets and correctly postulated the foredeep ('moat') to be the logical consequence of this process. One must note in passing that in terms of the isostatic response and the creation of high pore pressures the rapid sedimentary loading in the foredeep is indistinguishable from the equally rapid tectonic loading further to the rear. However, the total effect is not restricted to a frontal depression of the crust. Load applied in the front has been removed at the back and the resulting isostatic tilt is shown in Fig. 3d. Since both loading and unloading progress outward, the *advancing bulge* results as the inevitable consequence. Regardless of the mechanism favoured—gravity gliding, push-from-the-rear, or spreading in response to a surface slope—the isostatic adjustment will perpetuate them all by depressing the basal sole fault and/or enhancing any existing surface slope. The well informed reader realizes that Wunderlich (1965) has expressed similar, though not identical, ideas.

Conclusions

In the thick portion of a sedimentary wedge high pore pressures are to be expected to exist initially, due to rapid sedimentary loading. Zones of high pore pressure together with the bedding planes with low cohesion form the potential detachment zones along which initial thrusting is anticipated to progress in response to a push-from-the-rear, gravity gliding, a surface slope, or a mechanism yet to be invented.

The 'Hubbert and Rubey Theory' still, as in 1959, offers interesting and promising perspectives. The main difficulties are the maintenance of the high pore pressures over large areas as well as long periods. Also the condition of a continuous plane of weakness (low cohesion) is not easily visualized in view of the step-like nature of most thrust faults.

The acceptance of movements as discontinuous, caterpillar-like, both in time and space may provide a possible way out of this dilemma, but details are far from clear at this time.

The 'Plasticity/Viscosity Theory' is equally beset with difficulties. Detailed investigations of some particular examples indicate basal shear stresses which are much higher than those that can be tolerated in order to preserve the structural integrity of the thrust plate.

Thrusting, once initiated, becomes a self-perpetuating process because: (a) thrusting results in a propagation of the high pore pressures in the overridden sequence due to rapid tectonic loading and heating, (b) thrusting brings about a shift of load which must be accompanied by an isostatic response creating the advancing bulge, which tends to favour further thrusting regardless of the basic mechanism envisaged.

The process of thrusting usually marginally involves the sediments of the foredeep. The process of thrusting comes to rest where the sedimentary cover is reduced below a certain critical minimal thickness and consists primarily of young, high porosity, sediments, an environment unfavourable to the development of high pore pressures.

ACKNOWLEDGMENT. Dr F. Frey has critically read the manuscript and acted as a soundingboard for a number of stimulating discussions. This is not to say that he endorses all the ideas expressed in this paper.

References

ANDREWS, J. T. 1970. Present and postglacial rates of uplift for glaciated northern and eastern North America derived from postglacial uplift curves. *Can. J. Earth Sci.* **7,** 703–15.

BALLY, A. W., GORDY, P. L. & STEWART, G. A. 1966. Structure, seismic data and orogenic evolution of Southern Canadian Rocky Mountains. *Bull. Can. Pet. Geol.* **14,** 337–81.

BARKER, C. 1972. Aquathermal pressuring—role of temperature in development of abnormal-pressure zones. *Bull. Am. Assoc. Petrol. Geol.* **56,** 2068–71.

BRIEGEL, U. & GOETZE, C. 1978. Estimates of differential stress recorded in the dislocation structure of Lochseiten Limestone (Switzerland). *Tectonophysics,* **48,** 61–76.

DAHLSTROM, C. D. A. 1970. Structural geology in the eastern margin of the Canadian Rocky Mountains. *Bull. Can. Pet. Geol.* **18,** 332–406.

DONNER, J. J. 1969. A profile across Fennoscandia of late Weichelian and Flandrian shore-lines. *Comm. Phys.-Math.* **36,** 1–23.

DOUGLAS, R. J. W. 1950. Callum Creek, Langford Creek, and Gap map-areas, Alberta. *Mem. geol. Surv. Can.* **255,** 124 pp.

ELLIOT, D. 1976. The energy balance and deformation mechanism of thrust sheets. *Philos. Trans. R. Soc. London,* **A283,** 289–312.

EVANS, D. M. 1966. The Denver area earthquakes and the Rocky Mountain Arsenal disposal well. *Mt. Geol. Colorado,* **3,** 23–6.

FERTL, W. H. 1976. *Abnormal Formation Pressures.* Elsevier, Amsterdam, 382 pp.

GRETENER, P. E. 1972. Thoughts on overthrust faulting in a layered sequence. *Bull. Can. Pet. Geol.* **20,** 583–607.

GUSSOW, W. C. 1963. Metastasy. *In:* MUNYAN, A. C. (ed), *Polar Wandering and Continental Drift.* Soc. econ. Paleontol. Mineral Tulas. **10,** 146–69.

HANDIN, J. 1969. On the Coulomb-Mohr failure criterion. *J. geophys. Res.* **74,** 5343–8.

HOTTMAN, C. E. & JOHNSON, R. K. 1965. Estimation of formation pressures from log-derived shale properties. *Spec. Trans. Am. Inst. Ming. Eng.* **234,** 717–22.

HSÜ, K. J. 1969. A preliminary analysis of the statics and kinetics of the Glarus overthrust. *Eclog. geol. Helv.* **62,** 143–54.

HUBBERT, M. K. & RUBEY, W. W. 1959. Role of fluid pressure in mechanics of overthrust faulting. *Bull. geol. Soc. Am.* **70,** 115–66.

JAEGER, J. C. 1959. The frictional properties of joints in rocks. *Pure Appl. Geophys.* **43,** 148–58.

KEHLE, R. O. 1970. Analysis of gravity gliding and orogenic translation. *Bull. geol. Soc. Am.* **81,** 1641–64.

LAUBSCHER, H. P. 1961. Die Fernschubhypothese der Jurafaltung. *Eclog. geol. Helv.* **54,** 221–82.

LONGWELL, C. R. 1954. Interpretation of levelling data. *In: First Fourteen Years of Lake Mead,* U.S.G.S. Circular, **346,** 5.

OLDHAM, R. D. 1921. 'Know your faults' (Presidential Address). *Proc. geol. Soc. London,* **LXXVII** lxxvii–xcii.

OXBURGH, E. R. & TURCOTTE, L. D. 1974. Thermal gradients and regional metamorphism in overthrust terrains with special reference to the Eastern Alps. *Schweiz. mineral petrogr. Mitt.* **54,** 641–62.

PLATT, L. B. 1962. Fluid pressure in thrust faulting, a corollary. *Am. J. Sci.* **260,** 107–14.

PRICE, R. A. 1973. Large-scale gravitational flow of supracrustal rocks, Southern Canadian Rockies. *In:* DE JONG K. A. & SCHOLTEN R. (eds), *Gravity and Tectonics.* Wiley, New York, 491–502.

RALEIGH, C. B., HEALY, J. H. & BREDEHOEFT, J. D. 1972. Faulting and crustal stress at Rangely, Colorado. *Mem. Am. Geophys. Union* **16,** 257–84.

—— & PATERSON, M. S. 1965. Experimental deformation of Serpentinite and its tectonic implications. *J. geophys. Res.* **70,** 3965–985.

RICH, J. L. 1934. Mechanics of low-angle overthrust faulting as illustrated by Cumberland thrust block, Virginia, Kentucky, and Tennessee. *Bull. Am. Assoc. Petrol. Geol.* **18,** 1584–96.

ROYSE, Jr., F., WARNER, M. A. & REESE, D. L. 1975. Thrust belt structural geometry and related stratigraphic problems Wyoming–Idaho–Northern Utah. *Rocky Mtn. Assoc. Geol., Symposium,* 41–54.

RUBEY, W. W. & HUBERT, M. K. 1959. Role of fluid pressure in mechanics of overthrust faulting, II. Overthrust belt in geosynclinal area of Western Wyoming in light of fluid-pressure hypothesis. *Bull. geol. Soc. Am.* **70,** 167–205.

SHOULDICE, D. H. 1971. Geology of the Western Canadian continental shelf. *Bull. Can. Pet. Geol.* **19,** 405–36.

SMOLUCHOWSKI, M. S. 1908. Some remarks on the mechanics of overthrusts. *Geol. Mag.* V, 204–5.

TERZAGHI, K. 1950. Mechanism of landslides. *Berkey Volume, Geol. Soc. Am.* 83–123.

WALCOTT, R. I. 1970. Isostatic response to loading of the crust in Canada. *Can. J. Earth Sci.* **7,** 703–15.

WUNDERLICH, H. G. 1965. Zyklischer Bewegungsablauf beim Vorrücken orogener Fronten und derr Mechanismus des Deckschollentransportes nach dem Surf Ridingprinzip. *Geol. Mijn.* **44,** 440–57.

P. E. GRETENER, Department of Geology, The University of Calgary, Calgary, Alberta, Canada, T2N 1N4.

Gravitational gliding in deltas

G. Mandl & W. Crans

SUMMARY: Many cases of faulting in prograding delta slopes can be genetically attributed to submarine gravity gliding (Terzaghi 1956) on slope-parallel slip planes. Essential in this 'thin-skinned' model of gravitational faulting is the overpressuring of the pore fluid, which not only permits the formation of very gently dipping slip planes, but also determines the listric shapes of normal and thrust faults at the head and toe of the gliding path.

The development of the gliding process and the associated primary and secondary structures (antithetic faults, 'roll-over' anticlines) are described for an infinitely long slope and for somewhat idealized pore-pressure profiles, a main parameter being the distance of the overpressure top from the (rising) sediment surface.

Realistic deviations from the idealizing assumptions are discussed in qualitative terms.

The gliding process is 'slow' and controlled by sediment compaction in the slope-parallel direction. Continued sedimentation gives rise to changes in effective stresses and these, in turn, cause active faults to adjust their shapes. Examples of this adjustment are discussed.

Gravity is the cause of various fault and fold structures in deltaic sediment bodies. The well-known trend map of the Niger Delta (Fig. 1), which shows the traces of numerous syn-sedimentary normal faults that dip basinwards and of some counter-regional, i.e. north-hading, normal faults (in the S), may serve as an example. Although these faults and associated fold structures have been produced by the weight of the sediment itself, the genetic processes may differ and various models have been proposed to explain observed phenomena. These models, which may be applicable separately or in combination to different parts of a delta, may be grouped in two classes: 'thin-skinned' and 'thick-skinned' models. In models of the second class, sub-strata beneath a prograding delta slope deform as a result of differential loading, gravitational instability, or divergence of the underlying

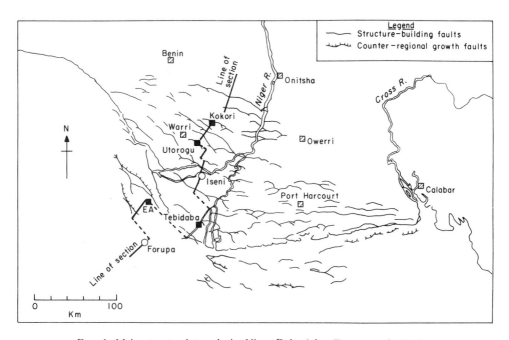

FIG. 1. Main structural trends in Niger Delta (after Evamy *et al.* 1978).

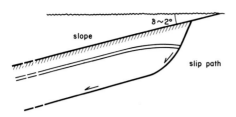

FIG. 2. 'Thin-skinned' submarine sliding (schematic dip section).

crustal basement, and thus form synclinal troughs. The overlying sediments may then slide along normal faults into these troughs, as demonstrated by Rettger (1935).

In contrast, the 'thin-skinned' models—essentially based on Terzaghi's theories of land and submarine slides (Terzaghi 1950; 1956)—envisage gravitional gliding of sediment masses along paths that are not determined by substratal deformations, but run over some distance parallel to the delta slope (Fig. 2). On the gentle delta slopes—with typical slope angles (δ) between 0·5 and 3°—this type of sliding requires pore pressures well in excess of the corresponding pressures of hydrostatic fluid columns. As recognized by Terzaghi in 1925, excess pore pressures in fine-grained sediments reduce the 'effective' weight of the overburden, which is carried by the intergranular contact pressures—the source of the sediment's frictional shearing strength.

The Model

In the following, we shall deal with a 'thin-skinned' model, concentrating on the role of

the excess pore pressures in controlling the development and shape of the sliding paths. We refer to an idealized prograding delta slope (Fig. 3) whose essential features are a very gently dipping, long planar slope, which shifts parallel to itself, and with the top of the pore-water overpressure running practically parallel to the slope. The overpressure top only drops off upslope, where coarser sediments favour drainage and at the base of the slope, where the sedimentation rate is extremely low. The facies boundary remains essentially horizontal during a normal progradation phase.

The assumption of an undeformed 'basement' (shaded in Fig. 3) does not disagree with a downward bending of the substrata (and the lithosphere) under the load of the outbuilding delta, as this flexural deformation is 'smeared out' over much larger distances than the actual slope (e.g. Walcott 1972) and may develop at slower rates than that of the delta progradation. Flexuring of the 'basement' should, therefore, hardly interfere with the stress field at the slope that controls the 'thin-skinned' gravitational gliding process.

To facilitate the stress analysis, it is assumed that all displacements are parallel to the dip section of Fig. 3; hence, no material is flowing sideways into that plane. Secondly, the displacements do not change in strike direction. These 'plane strain' assumptions may approximate reality reasonably well where gravity slides extend along-strike over large distances (Fig. 1), or they may in case of a pronounced 'spoon shape' of the slide at least apply to the midplane. In accord with the 'thin-skinned' character of our model, it seems justifiable to treat the long delta slope as infinitely long.

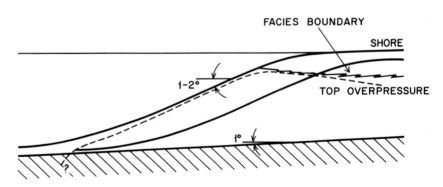

FIG. 3. Prograding delta slope (idealized dip section).

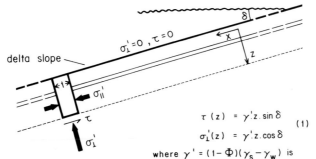

$$\tau (z) = \gamma'.z.\sin\delta$$

$$\sigma_\perp'(z) = \gamma'.z.\cos\delta \qquad (1)$$

where $\gamma' = (1-\Phi)(\gamma_s - \gamma_w)$ is the 'submerged' specific weight with Φ being the porosity and γ_w, γ_s being the specific weight of the pore water and the solid component, respectively.

A) STABLE SLOPE WITH NORMAL FLUID PRESSURE

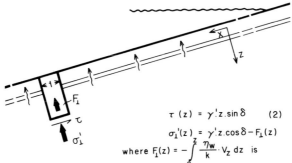

$$\tau (z) = \gamma'.z.\sin\delta \qquad (2)$$

$$\sigma_\perp'(z) = \gamma'.z.\cos\delta - F_\perp(z)$$

where $F_\perp(z) = -\int_0^z \frac{\eta_w}{k}.V_z\, dz$ is

the fluid drag exerted on the sediment inside a column with unit cross-section and extending from the surface to 'depth' z. ($V_z < 0$ seepage rate in negative z-direction, η_w viscosity of water, k permeability in z-direction)

B) OVERPRESSURED STABLE SLOPE

FIG. 4. Gravitational gliding on delta slope.

We consider first a sediment layer on the idealized delta slope (Fig. 4a), assuming that it is in static equilibrium. The downslope pulling weight component of the fluid-filled sediment is balanced by the slope-parallel reactive shear stress τ and the slope-parallel increase in pore pressure. As long as the fluid pressure increases hydrostatically with depth, the effective normal stress $\sigma_\perp'$ (defined as total stress $\sigma_\perp$ minus pore-pressure) that acts perpendicular to the slope will carry the corresponding component of the 'submerged' weight of a sediment column with unit cross section. The expressions for the two stress components are given in Fig. 4a (Eq. 1). They follow rigorously from the equations for static equilibrium of total stresses and body force for an infinite submarine slope, after introducing the effective stress concept.

Since, under hydrostatic pore-pressure con-

ditions, the subvertical effective stress $\sigma_\perp'$ increases linearly with distance z from the sediment surface, the frictional shear strength on slope-parallel planes ($\sigma_\perp' \tan\rho$; ρ being the angle of 'internal friction') also increases linearly with 'depth' z. Therefore, on the gently inclined slope ($\delta \ll \rho$) with hydrostatic pore-pressure conditions the shear stress τ can never reach the limit value defined by the frictional shear strength.

In contrast to this, pore-pressures higher than hydrostatic prevent a continuous linear increase in frictional shear strength with depth and may allow the shear stress τ to reach the limit value. Such excess pore-pressures are quite common in large river deltas where low-permeability sediments are deposited at such rates that incomplete drainage prevents normal compaction and allows excess pressure to build up. Assuming that the compaction behaviour of the sediment is the same everywhere on the slope and that the axes of a possible permeability anisotropy are approximately parallel and perpendicular to the slope, the drainage flow will be driven in the negative z-direction (Fig. 4b) by the negative gradient of the excess pore-pressure. The upward drag $F_\perp$ exerted by this seepage flow on the sediment is determined by Darcy's flow law and specified in Fig. 4b. It reduces the 'effective overburden' stress $\sigma'_\perp$ but leaves the slope parallel shear stress τ unaffected as is expressed by Eq. (2) in Fig. 4b. In Fig. 5a it is schematically shown how the pore-pressure p (solid line), after an approximately hydrostatic increase with depth in a top layer of comparatively high permeability, rises drastically at the transition to very low-permeability sediments in the state of delayed compaction. It is often observed that the gradient of the abnormal pore-pressure quite closely approximates the gradient of the total 'overburden' stress $\sigma_\perp$ ('geostatic' gradient). In the depth interval where this takes place, the 'effective overburden' stress $\sigma'_\perp (= \sigma_\perp - p)$ will maintain the value it attained at the shallower depth Z_{ig} (Fig. 5a). Therefore, in the same interval the frictional shear strength on slope-parallel planes cannot increase in proportion to the actual shear stress τ. Consequently, when the

compacting highly overpressured sediments have reached a certain thickness, the shear stress τ may attain the limiting strength value at the critical 'depth' Z. This is schematically shown in Fig. 5b, where the friction angle ρ is assumed to be constant and the small cohesive strength τ_0 of the deltaic sediment is neglected.

At the critical depth Z, the sediments will start sliding somewhere on a slope-parallel plane (point A in Fig. 6a). To obtain an idea of the magnitude of the 'critical depth', it is convenient to simplify the pore-pressure profile as indicated in Fig. 5a (dotted p-line) and assuming accordingly that $\sigma'_\perp = \sigma'_\perp(Z_{ig})$ for all $z \geqq Z_{ig}$. Equating the shear stress $\tau = \gamma' z \sin \delta$ (Fig. 4a) with the shear strength $\tau_0 + \sigma'_\perp \tan \rho = \tau_0 + \gamma' Z_{ig} \cos \delta \tan \rho$ yields the critical depth:

$$Z = \frac{\tau_0}{\gamma' \sin \delta} + Z_{ig} \frac{\tan \rho}{\tan \delta} \qquad (1)$$

where the strength parameters have been assumed to be constant. For realistic parameters Z becomes about 10 times the depth (Z_{ig}) at which overpressuring started.

Naturally, the exact position of a basal slip plane will also depend on variations of ρ and τ_0 with depth, which, in reality, will make the $\sigma'_\perp \tan \rho$ line in Fig. 5b appear more 'wrinkly'. Obviously, this may even allow for several slip planes being activated at the same time, as the

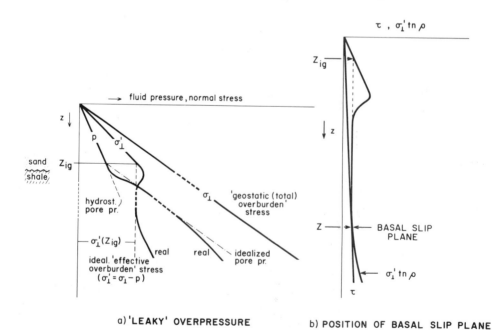

a) 'LEAKY' OVERPRESSURE   b) POSITION OF BASAL SLIP PLANE

FIG. 5. Fluid pressure.

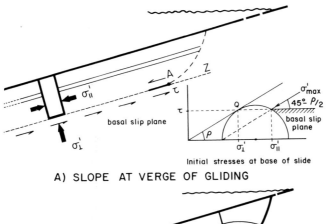

A) SLOPE AT VERGE OF GLIDING

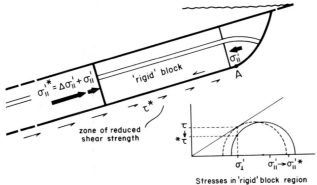

B) PROGRESSIVE SLIDE

FIG. 6. Gravitational gliding on delta slope.

τ-line touches the strength line in more than one point.

Before concluding this introductory section and turning to structures associated with the further development of the gliding process, it is perhaps appropriate to say a few words on the assumed equality of the gradients of pore-pressure and total overburden stress $\sigma_\perp$ in some interval of the compacting low-permeability sediment. Since this implies $d\sigma'_\perp/dz = 0$, it follows from the second Eq. (2) in Fig. 4b and the expression for $F_\perp$ that in the interval considered

$$\gamma' \cos \delta + \eta_w V_z/k = 0 \qquad (2)$$

where γ' is the 'submerged' specific weight, η_w is the fluid viscosity, k the permeability and V_z the seepage rate in the negative z direction ($V_z < 0$). The relation states that within a unit volume of sediment the z-component of the submerged sediment weight is completely balanced by the drag force of the drainage flow. To see how realistic this statement is, let us consider the compaction of a sediment that drains in the upward direction only and let us focus on a slope-parallel 'plane' of sediment which subsides in the z-direction at the rate W. Then, regardless of porosity, the seepage flow V_z crossing a unit bulk area of the subsiding plane per unit time equals $-W$. This can be seen as follows: if the fluid were at rest, the moving cross section with porosity Φ would pass in unit time the fluid volume ΦW. Since, in addition, subsidence at the rate W reduces the pore volume of the underlying sediment by $(1-\Phi)W$ per unit time, an equal volume of fluid has to be squeezed through the moving unit cross section of porosity Φ. (Compressibility of fluid and solid material may be neglected with respect to the much higher compressibility of the bulk material). Adding the two flows and accounting by the negative sign for the upward direction of the flow gives $V_z = -W$.

Measuring the permeability k in cm^2, the water viscosity in poises, the subsidence rate W in mm/yr, and assuming a value of about 0.006 poise for the water viscosity, it follows from Eq. (2) for W/k a value of about 5.10^{13}. Hence, at a subsidence rate of 0.05 mm/yr a permeability of 10^{-15} cm^2 (0.1 micro Darcy) is required to make the fluid carry the weight of the sediment it is seeping through*. For an overpressured deltaic shale this is certainly a realistic value. Furthermore it seems reasonable to expect that eventually, with increasing depth and age of the overpressured sediment, the seepage drag diminishes, giving rise to a gradual increase of the effective overburden stress $\sigma'_\perp$ as schematically shown in Figs 5a,b.

Finally, in case drainage is prevented by impermeable strata (e.g. salt) the pore-pressure can only increase with depth at the hydrostatic gradient, with the exception of the top of the 'sealed' sequence. There a jump-like increase in pore-pressure is accompanied by a corresponding jumplike decrease in $\sigma'_\perp$. If this reduction is sufficient to bring τ—and the strength line in Fig. 5b in contact, slip will start at the top of the sealed, overpressured sequence.

The gliding process

Initiation of gliding at the critical depth Z and further development of the gliding path are controlled by the effective stresses of the slope. For the idealized slope considered and a pre-scribed pore-pressure profile, the effective stresses that act on any slope-parallel plane are known from considering static equilibrium (Figs 4a,b). Not known, in general, is the third stress component $\sigma'_\parallel$ that is required to define the stress state in a dip section. This slope-parallel effective compressive stress builds up as the material's tendency to expand laterally under the accumulating overburden load is impeded by frictional or cohesive contact with the underlying strata. The value of $\sigma'_\parallel$, therefore, depends on the constitutive behaviour of the material and cannot be ascertained from statical considerations alone.

A particular aspect of the material behaviour of clastic sediments is the existence of limit states of effective stress. In the Mohr diagram (i.e. in the plane of shear and normal stresses) the limit condition maps as a pair of lines. One such limit line—for the sake of simplicity taken as straight—is shown in Fig. 7; the second line would be its mirror image on the side of negative shear stresses. Any stress point in the diagram must lie between or on the limit lines. In other words, for a given effective normal stress acting on a planar element inside the material, the tangential stress on that element cannot exceed the value

defined by the limit lines. Considering all planar elements whose normals lie in the plane of greatest and smallest normal stress (e.g. our dip section), the associated stress points lie on a stress circle. The limit states of stress are therefore represented by stress circles that are tangent to the limit lines. Through each stress point between the limit lines, two limit circles can be drawn, representing respectively the 'active' and 'passive' limit state.

Let us assume, for instance, that the stress point Q in Fig. 7 is associated with a slope-parallel plane at 'depth' $z < Z$. In general, at that depth sediments which are not yet in a gliding state and not affected by tectonic stresses, will not be in a limit state—the corresponding stress circle through Q will not touch the limit lines and the value of $\sigma'_\parallel$ will lie between the limit values $\sigma'^a_\parallel$ and $\sigma'^p_\parallel$ (Fig. 7). It is obvious, however, that a modest reduction in $\sigma'_\parallel$ by some lateral extension will be sufficient to induce the active limit state, whereas a large lateral compressive stress would be required to produce the passive limit state on the slope. Similarly, in the sediment which is still at rest on the slope and tectonically undisturbed, the direction of the maximum compressive stress σ'_{max} lies between the directions of σ'^a_{max} and σ'^p_{max} of the active and passive state, respectively (Fig. 7). These directions, referred to some reference direction in physical space, can be easily determined in the Mohr diagram. A straight reference line drawn through the stress point Q in Fig. 7 intersects the stress circle in a second point—the so-called 'pole'. When connecting the pole by a chord with another stress point Q' on the circle the chord defines the relative direction (in physical space) of the plane that is acted upon by the stresses associated with Q'. For a brief explanation of the 'pole' method the reader is referred to Appendix II of 'Mechanical model of thrust sheet gliding and imbrication' by Mandl & Shippam (this volume). Here it may suffice pointing out that the chord connecting the pole with the point $\sigma'_{max}, \tau = 0$ of the stress circle represents—relative to the reference line through Q—the direction of the element which is therefore perpendicular to this chord. The σ'_{max} direction can also be directly obtained by connecting the pole with the stress point defined by the minimum compressive stress (Fig. 7).

As z approaches the critical 'depth' Z in an overpressured slope on the verge of gravitational gliding, the associated stress point Q in Fig. 7 moves towards the limit line, the two limit circles merge into one circle (Fig. 6a); $\sigma'_\parallel$

---

* This will in general not bring the grains in a 'floating' state, as the intergranular contacts still carry the submerged sediment weight of the layers above 'depth' Z_{ig}.

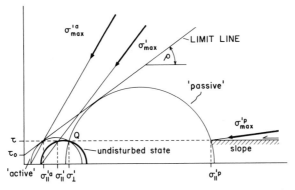

FIG. 7. Limit states on slope (Mohr diagram representation).

attains a well-defined value at $z = Z$ and the principal stress σ'_{max} includes the angle $45° - \rho/2$ with the slope (x-axis).

In general, when the sediment is in the limit state, its deformation will take place by slips along internal surfaces. According to Coulomb's slip concept, which has been found to apply reasonably well to many deformation types of 'frictional' materials, the potential slip elements make an angle of $\pm(45° - \rho/2)$ with the direction of σ'_{max}. Accordingly, for instance on the basal slip plane $z = Z$, the σ'_{max}-direction will be inclined under $45° - \rho/2$ towards the slope.

This inclination may vary in the strata overlying the slip base when the limit state is not confined to this plane but extends some, as yet unknown, distance into the overpressured overburden. The critical stress circles then vary with depth as indicated in Fig. 8 for a 'leaky' overpressure that maintains constant $\sigma'_\perp$. Again, the σ'_{max}-directions can be easily constructed. As clearly shown in the Mohr diagram of Fig. 8, these directions and the associated potential slip elements steepen in an upwards direction (decreasing z). As gliding on the basal slip plane commences in some local area, the overlying sediments will experience sufficient extension to be brought into the active limit state ($\sigma'_\parallel \rightarrow \sigma'^a_\parallel$ in Fig. 7) and the slide can extend from the slip base up-dip towards the slope surface (Fig. 6b) along a Coulomb-type normal fault.

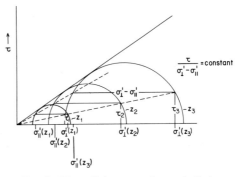

FIG. 9. 'Normally' pressured zone in limit state (unchanged maximum compressive stress direction).

In the overpressured layers the normal fault steepens up-dip. In the normally pressured sediments, however, the fault dip will remain unchanged, provided the cohesive shear strength τ_0 can be neglected with respect to the frictional shear strength and changes in the friction parameter $\tan \rho$ and later compactional flattening of the fault are excluded. This follows from the elementary formula $\tan 2\theta = 2\tau/(\sigma'_\parallel - \sigma'_\perp)$ for the angle which the σ'_{max} direction makes with the slope (x-axis), when taking into account that, as shown in Fig. 9, both τ and $\sigma'_\perp - \sigma'_\parallel$ increases linearly with $z(z_1 < z_2 < \ldots)$.

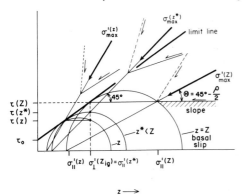

FIG. 8. Overpressed zone in limit state (flattening of maximum compressive stress direction with depth).

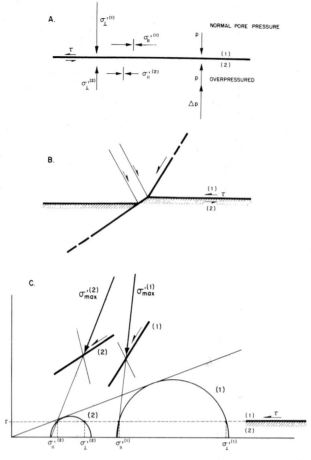

FIG. 10. Normal fault entering overpressured layer under shear stress.

The 'listric' shape of a normal fault on an overpressured slope may, therefore, be attributed to the action of the abnormally high pore pressures which may drastically change the direction of σ'_{max}. To illustrate this further, we consider, in Fig. 10, the case where an inclined interface separates normally pressured sediments from overpressured ones, assuming that the pore pressure increases discontinuously across the interface by an amount Δp ('sealed' overpressure) which affects the effective normal stresses, but leaves the shear stress unchanged. A normal fault entering the overpressured strata flattens abruptly (Fig. 10b) in accordance with the changes in σ'_{max} direction across the interface predicted by the Mohr diagram of Fig. 10c. Similarly, one may show that low-angle thrusts should also suffer an abrupt change in dip at the interface between abnormally and normally pressured sediments; they should steepen when leaving the over-

pressured region. It is also obvious that a gradual change in pore pressure will produce a continuous change in dip angle rather than a kink.

The reason why this pore-pressure effect has not yet found its way into the literature lies probably in the elementary formula for $\tan 2\theta$ used above to determine the σ'_{max} direction. At first sight, any change in pore pressure will leave this direction unchanged, because of the difference in effective stresses in the denominator. In fact, however, the value of the denominator will in general change. This is simply due to the fact that under an increase in pore pressure the strata tend to expand laterally. This stretching is, however, partly or wholly prevented by interstratal friction forces or other lateral constraints. Therefore, in response to these constraints, the total stress $\sigma_{\parallel}$ increases, whereas the 'overburden' $\sigma_{\perp}$ may remain almost unchanged (in case of small dip angles). Hence, the rise in pore-pressure affects the angle θ via imposed deformation constraints.

There is abundant seismic and well evidence for 'listric' fault shapes associated with over-pressured slopes. The reader may be referred to the paper by Bruce (1973). It should be emphasised, however, that overpressures can only produce 'listric' fault shapes when the shear stress τ has a non-vanishing value. Otherwise, the fault will intersect the top overpressure undeflected, as can be seen from Fig. 10c when $\tau \to 0$ and the stresses $\sigma'_\perp$ and $\sigma'_\parallel$ become principal stresses. As a consequence, we should expect a curved synsedimentary normal fault to straighten when still active after the prograding delta edge has been passed.

It should be recalled that our considerations hold for compressive effective stresses. A different approach was followed by Price (1977). When considering a cohesive rock mass gliding down a slope, he postulated temporary excess pressures high enough to render an effective principal stress tensile and thereby bringing the limit state of stress into the transition region between tensile rupture and purely compressive shear failure. In this transition region different limit states may be associated with different fault orientations relative to the same σ'_{max} direction (curved limit line). Referring to this phenomenon, Price interprets the listric shape of a thrust fault branching off the slip base essentially as the result of a gradient in overpressure.

As gliding, which started at some point A (Fig. 6a) on the potential slide base proceeds (Fig. 6b), shear softening will reduce the shear strength of the activated slip plane and, consequently, decrease the value of the basal shear stress $(\tau \to \tau^*)$ which opposes the gliding motion. While the overburden-carrying stress $\sigma'_\perp$ remains constant, the slope-parallel stress $\sigma'_\parallel$ will increase monotonically in downslope direction to compensate for the imbalance in slope-parallel forces caused by the reduction of the basal shear resistance The stress diagram in Fig. 6b demonstrates that for a whole range of increased $\sigma'_\parallel$ values, the stress circle no longer touches the limit line. Therefore, ideally, over a certain length the moving sediment sheet should not be disturbed by faulting and move as a single block.

Of course, the length of the 'rigid' block is limited, since somewhere downslope $\sigma'_\parallel$ may reach a limit value for which the associated stress circle again contacts the limit line (Fig. 11a). This marks the 'toe' of the slide, where

the basal slip plane terminates in one or several low-angle thrusts of the type P indicated in the stress diagram. In addition, $\sigma'_\parallel$ may near the 'toe' exceed the buckling strength of the most competent beds of the sliding sequence and induce folding.

There is no reason why the slope-parallel changes in $\sigma'_\parallel$ should continue across the slip base into the substrata. A discontinuous change of $\sigma'_\parallel$ and $\sigma_\parallel$ (total) across the slip base is perfectly compatible with the equilibrium conditions and is not impeded by an associated jump in slip-parallel strain (e.g. shortening), as the latter can be accommodated by sliding. The compressional 'toe' features should consequently be restricted to the strata above the slip base.

An average distance L between 'head' and 'toe' of the slide has been estimated by W. Crans (cf. Crans *et al.* 1980, p. 278) via equating the unbalanced part of the slope-parallel weight component of the sediment package and the slope-parallel support force resulting from the higher 'slope pressures' $\sigma'^p_\parallel$ in the passive limit state. The actual determination of the support force requires assumptions on the fluid pressure. For the 'leaky' overpressure of Fig. 5 and negligible changes in sediment thickness and Z_{ig} level during the development of the slide it was found that

$$L/Z \doteq 3.5[\Delta \tau](Z)/\tau(Z)]^{-1} \qquad (3)$$

where $\Delta \tau / \tau$ is the relative reduction of the basal shear stress by shear softening, i.e. a kind of 'brittleness index'. Extrapolating from soil mechanical evidence for the shear behaviour of clays which are normally compacted under effective loads, one would not expect $\Delta \tau / \tau$ to exceed a few per cent. Accordingly, the length of the slide could, in general, exceed the thickness by two orders of magnitude.

Naturally, the increase in 'slope pressure' $\sigma'_\parallel$ must be balanced somewhere downslope, since otherwise the whole slope would turn into an accelerating slide. This balance may be accomplished, for instance, by the 'buttressing' effect of a regional decrease of slope angle, or by a decrease in overpressure near the 'foot' of the delta slope, which implies an increased effective overburden and hence an increased frictional strength. One may also consider that real 'toe' structures are of finite extent in the strike direction and will consequently invoke 'buttressing' shear stresses at their lateral boundaries.

The slide model does not provide information as to where the slide starts (point A in Fig.

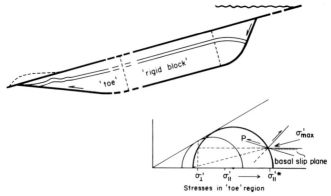

A) COMPLETE GLIDING PATH

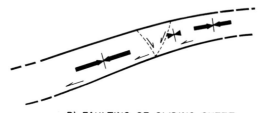

B) FAULTING OF GLIDING SHEET

FIG. 11. Gravitational gliding on delta slope.

6a) and at what rate it proceeds. As to the first question we may argue that at the shelf-edge different compaction regimes exist inside the overpressured sediment (Fig. 12). Onshore, where $\delta = 0$, σ'_{max} is vertically oriented as discussed before, and compaction is therefore also vertical. On the slope, however, the direction of σ'_{max} rotates with depth inside the overpressured zone and so does the direction of maximum compaction. Therefore, at the shelf edge the compacting sediment experiences some stretching and reduction of $\sigma'_\parallel$ which promotes the active limit state ($\sigma'_\parallel \rightarrow \sigma'^a_\parallel$ in Fig. 7). Normal faulting is, therefore, most likely to occur first near the shelf edge. Other factors, such as strength inhomogeneities at the facies boundary (Fig. 3), or local overloading by shelf sediments emerging from a regressing sea, may have a similar effect.

As to the rate of the synsedimentary sliding process, we note that as long as no dramatic drop in basal resistance occurs—e.g. by large-scale liquefaction—stresses and weight remain in equilibrium on the slope even after the onset of sliding. The slide cannot accelerate, furthermore, the distance between the head and a potential toe of the slide on normally consolidated clays (in terms of effective load) may easily exceed the available length of

the slope. Such a slide would therefore remain 'open-ended'. In those parts of the Niger Delta, for instance where the shape of growth faults and associated structures strongly suggest the existence of basal slip planes, corresponding toe structures could not be found. In such slides the rate of sliding will be controlled by the rate of slope-parallel compaction in response to the slope-parallel normal stress (cf. $\Delta\sigma'_\parallel$ in Fig. 6b). This compaction allows the basal slip to spread gradually downslope and it accommodates the influx of new sediment along normal faults at the slide head. When a toe develops, the rate of this sediment influx may become another slide-rate controlling parameter.

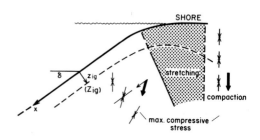

FIG. 12. Onset of faulting at shelf edge.

Some soil mechanical experiments with un-drained loading of normally consolidated clays also suggest that slip plane formation is preceded by considerable continuous deformation of the clay. One might accordingly expect that at the critial depth a zone of continuous simple shearing develops first which, eventually, after a certain amount of shearing concentrates into a basal slip plane. This again could account for a gradual downslope progression of the basal slip.

Whereas, ideally speaking, the slide rate should not increase downslope, one can easily envisage mechanisms which may make it increase in downslope direction, thereby producing a local 'stretching' of the gliding sediment sheet (Fig. 11b). This, in turn, may locally induce the active limit state and corresponding normal faulting and graben-type structures. Mechanisms producing such variations in downslope slide rate may be associated with gently updoming substrata, non-uniformities in basal shear or compaction behaviour, local rise in overpressure, etc.

Structures

At this point it may be instructive to summarize the main features of a complete deltaic gravity slide by a kinematic model that approximates the slide by rigid body motions along a gliding path, composed of segments of circles and straight lines. Fig. 13 shows different stages of a transparent model that was constructed for demonstration by overhead projector. Rotational motion along the curved normal fault produces the typical 'roll-over' structures—but, of course, without synsedimentary thickening of the downthrown beds. To allow for the transition between bodily rotation and the purely translatory motion on the slip base, antithetic faults are generated where the normal or thrust faults connect with the basal slip plane. The successive stages in Fig. 13 show the mobilization and immobilization of the antithetics. (The saw-toothed misfits decrease in size as the spacing of the antithetics is made smaller. In nature the misfits will be accommodated by small-scale slips, compaction etc.). The sense of curvature of the antithetics is not only required for the rigid body motions of the kinematic model, but is also a mechanical necessity. A curved main fault and its antithetics are conjugate Coulomb-slips in the same field of σ'_{max} directions. As the curvature of the synthetic normal fault is caused by a clockwise rotation of the σ'_{max} axis with depth, the associated antithetic

faults must, consequently, steepen with depth. (The phenomenon may be concealed by compaction-flattening or on seismic time sections may be masked by the increase in acoustic velocity with depth.)

As sedimentation continues, stresses and fluid pressure change and the growing structures may have to adjust to these changes. There are essentially two parameters that control the synsedimentary development of the slide structures: sedimentation rate and rate of overpressure relaxation. The first determines the increase in gravitional 'pull' on the slope, the second represents the opposing effect of a re-strengthening of the basal slip plane by an increase in effective overburden. A comprehensive discussion of the interplay of the two factors and of its structural consequences is beyond the scope of this paper. We shall therefore restrict ourselves to a few typical cases.

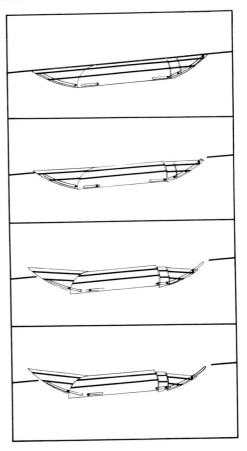

FIG. 13. Perspex model approximating complete gravity slide on delta slope by combination of rigid-body motions.

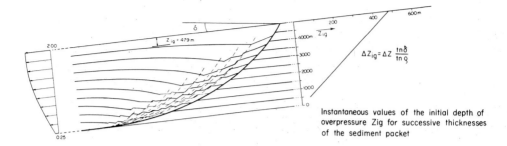

$$\Delta Z_{ig} = \Delta Z \frac{\ln \delta}{\ln \varrho}$$

Instantaneous values of the initial depth of overpressure Zig for successive thicknesses of the sediment packet

Fig. 14. Computer simulation of growth fault and 'roll-over' structures.

First we consider a growth fault as it would develop in a growing sediment package when the pore-pressure distribution is of the ideal 'leaky' type of Fig. 5. The stresses $\sigma'_\perp, \tau$ are those of the 'Rankine state' (Fig. 4b, Eq. (2)), and the head region of the slide is in the active ('extensional') limit state. As to the change in overpressure top, we assume that it rises somewhat less than the sediment surface—the distance between the two levels increasing to such an extent that at any time the growth fault merges tangentially with the active slip base. The result of a computer simulation (Crans *et al.* 1980) of fault growth and development of 'roll-over' anticlines is shown in Fig. 14. The right-hand side of the figure presents the change in Z_{ig}. The result of the computation is noteworthy in two respects. It shows the final fault as the envelope of previous ones and, therefore, bordering a seam of pre-sheared material. Secondly, the regression of the fault causes a drag reversal of the 'roll-over' structures. The deformations of initially slope-parallel bedding planes have been computed by using plastic velocity equations that are based on Coulomb's slip concept (Mandl & Fernández Luque 1979; Spencer 1971) and by prescribing downslope a reasonable creep profile, as shown in Fig. 14. The calculated model might approximately apply to synsedimentary fault growth in a package of overpressured shale.

Next, we consider the case where rapid deposition of very low permeability sediments forces the overpressure top to rise in step with the sediment surface. Since Z_{ig} now remains constant, the effective stress $\sigma'_\perp$ will remain unchanged on the slip base. Consequently, the limit value of the shear stress τ on the slip base will likewise remain unchanged. (The contact between the τ- and $\sigma'_\perp \tan \rho$-curves in Fig. 5b shifts towards higher z-values as the sediment

package grows, and the shear stress τ increases less with depth than in the original 'Rankine' state.) The downslope 'pull' of the accreting sediment can therefore not even partly be balanced by the basal shear stress and induces an extra downslope increase in $\sigma'_\parallel$. Obviously, the passive limit state will then be reached at a smaller distance L from the slide head than predicted by eq. (3). In other words, 'toe' thrusts would tend to migrate upslope. One can, however, see that active and passive regions remain separated by a sheet of sediment that is not in the limit state. When point Q in Fig. 7 represents the stresses on a slope-parallel plane at shallower depth than the slip base, the shear stress on this plane has to increase as sediment accretes, because τ remains fixed at the slip base. The slight upwards shift of Q in the diagram will bring the two limit circles through Q somewhat closer together, leaving, however, still a range of 'slope pressures' $\sigma'_\parallel (\sigma'^a_\parallel < \sigma'_\parallel < \sigma'^p_\parallel)$ associated with non-limit states of stress.

If, however, the relaxation of overpressure dominates, as in the case of very low sedimentation rates or deposition of relatively high permeability sediment, the Z_{ig}-value will increase faster than in the case of Fig. 14. The corresponding increase in $\sigma'_\perp \tan \rho$ will then exceed the increase in τ and the slip base will be re-strengthened. At first this may restore the peak strength and reduce $\Delta \sigma'_\parallel$ (in Fig. 6b). As a consequence, the toe region should migrate downslope. Eventually, the re-strengthening of the slip base will arrest the slide.

In reality, draw-down of the overpressure top may remain restricted to the slide head near the delta edge where coarser sediment is deposited. This will affect the shape of the growth faults while leaving the slip base practically unaffected. This is illustrated in Fig. 15 by

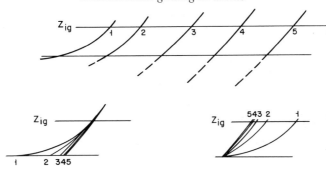

FIG. 15. Synsedimentary fault growth at stationary overpressure level (Z_{ig}).

the calculation of successive growth fault shapes $(1, 2, 3, \ldots)$ for the case of a fixed overpressure top. Typically, the growing faults, which were originally curved in the overpressured region, straighten. Although our simple model does not make allowance for downslope variations in Z_{ig}, it seems plausible enough that the straightening growth fault will 'splinter' when joining the still active slip base and will develop upwards or downwards diverging fault bundles ('horse tails') as sketched in Fig. 15.

Conclusions

Our discussion of gravitional gliding was intended to highlight the role of abnormal pore pressures in determining the shape of gravitional gliding paths, and the control of the sliding rate by slope-parallel compaction. Various interesting features of deltaic sliding remained undiscussed: for instance, the compactional flattening of faults, the interference of neighbouring growth faults, the different types of 'roll-over' anticlines along growth faults, 'multi-storey' sliding, horst and graben features on the slope, and the interaction of deep-seated creep flow with the 'thin-skinned' slides. While the mechanics of these features may be treated within the frame of a two-dimensional approximation, the intriguing 'spoon' shapes of many submarine slides would require an essentially three-dimensional theory, which is long overdue.

In spite of its consistency, the two-dimensional model discussed contains an element that is somewhat debatable. According to Terzaghi, sliding requires that on a slope-parallel plane Coulomb's slip condition is satisfied (Fig. 6a) and that, accordingly, the

maximum compressive stress includes the angle $45° - \rho/2$ with the potential slip base. However, it was found experimentally (Mandl *et al.* 1977) that the thin shear zone, produced in granular material by simple shearing between the rigid plattens of a ring-shear apparatus, is bounded by planes of maximum shear stress rather than by Coulomb slip planes. It was, therefore, concluded that tectonic faults that were forced to develop parallel to competent rock boundaries would be of the 'simple shear' type rather than of the Coulomb (Anderson) type. Typical 'simple shear' faults would be the sole faults in overthrusting, bedding plane faults, and certain types of strike-slip faults.

In view of this, it may seem doubtful whether a long slip base that is forced to develop parallel to the slope can be interpreted as a Coulomb slip, as has been done in determining the critical depth Z of the gravity slide, or whether it should rather be interpreted as a plane of simple shearing. In the latter case the critical stress conditions would be represented by the intermediate circle in Fig. 8, which applies to a slope-parallel plane at depth $z^*(z^* < Z)$. Fortunately, the difference between the alternative positions of the slip base is small. Applying elementary trigonometry to the stress circles in Fig. 8 shows that the critical depth z^* could be obtained from formula (1) for Z by replacing τ_0 by $\tau_0 \cos \rho$ and $\tan \rho$ by $\sin \rho$.

ACKNOWLEDGMENTS. The authors are indebted to Dr S. B. Spijer, Koninklijke/Shell Exploratie en Produktie Laboratorium, Rijswijk, and Mr R. Harkness, University of Southampton, for their criticism and helpful discussions.

References

BRUCE, C. H. 1973. Pressured shale and related sediment deformation mechanism for development of regional contemporaneous faults. *Bull. Am. Assoc. Petrol. Geol.* **57**, 878–66.

CRANS, W., MANDL, G. & HAREMBOURE, T. 1980. On the theory of growth faulting: a geomechanical delta model based on gravity sliding. *J. Petr. Geol.* **2**, 265–307.

EVAMY, B. D. *et al.* 1978. Hydrocarbon habitat of tertiary Niger delta. *Bull. Am. Assoc. Petrol. Geol.* **62**, 1–39.

MANDL, G. & FERNÁNDEZ LUQUE, A. 1970. Fully developed plastic shear flow of granular materials. *Géotechnique London*, **20**, 277–307.

——, DE JONG, L. N. J. & MALTHA, A. 1977. Shear zones in granular material. *Rock Mechanics* **9**, 95–144.

PRICE, N. J. 1977. Aspects of gravity tectonics and the development of listric faults. *J. geol. Soc.* London **133**, 311–27.

RETTGER, R. E. 1935. Experiments on soft-rock deformation. *Bull. Am. Assoc. Petrol. Geol.* **19**, 271–92.

SPENCER, A. J. M. 1971. *Géotechnique London* **21**, 190–2.

TERZAGHI, K. v. 1950. Mechanics of landslides, Application of geology to engineering practice. Berkey Volume, *Mem. geol. soc. Am.* 83–123.

——, 1956. Varieties of submarine slope failures. *Eighth Texas Conf. on Soil Mechanics Found. Engineering*, paper **3**.

WALCOTT, R. I. 1972. Gravity, flexure, and the growth of sedimentary basins at a continental edge. *Bull. geol. Soc. Am.* **83**, 1845–48.

G. MANDL, Koninklijke/Shell Exploratie en Produktie Laboratorium, Rijswijk, The Netherlands.

W. CRANS, formerly same address.

Thrust sheet deformation at a ramp: summary and extensions of an earlier model

D. V. Wiltschko

SUMMARY: A previous model for the equilibrium of a linearly viscous thrust sheet at a ramp shows that fault-zone drag is the most important energy sink, though bending can be an important resisting force and gravity can be a moderate driving force. The model was developed for the Pine Mountain block of the southern Appalachians, though it is general and may be adapted to other geometries.

Increasing the viscosities, ramp dip and thickness of the sheet each impedes forward motion whereas increasing the dip of the erosional surface and fraction of incompetent material and including the effect of an overriding thrust sheet aid movement. Doubling the viscosities doubles the bending resistance. Doubling the block thickness increases bending resistance as well, but since the force required to overcome this added resistance acts over twice the surface area, the net traction is reduced. Doubling the ramp dip greatly increases bending resistance, but if the length of the ramp is adjusted to maintain the same stratigraphic climb, this increase is lessened. The dip of the erosional surface is linearly related to the traction due to gravity in the 'glacier analogy' model. However, gravity cannot overcome all other sources of resistance for a sheet of the dimensions of the Pine Mountain block unless the surface slopes at 16° in the direction of transport. Increasing the fraction of incompetent material decreases bending stresses and therefore reduces the net traction necessary for movement. Finally, in the case of an overriding thrust sheet, if the upper fault zone is equal in shear strength to the lower fault zones, the resistance to movement of the lower one is cancelled; only bending resists motion. Successively overriding thrust sheets is a documented kinematic scheme in major thrust belts and the resulting applied shear stresses may be one mechanism by which stress and displacement are transferred from higher to lower sheets.

The overthrust paradox states that for a thrust sheet to overcome the shear resistance along its base, higher stresses are required than the sheet itself can withstand. However, motion of a thrust sheet is more difficult to achieve than this statement implies. Many major thrust faults are curved in cross section. Thrust sheets overlying these curved faults must deform to conform to them while moving. This bending resists motion.

The model summarized here provides a solution for the stresses within a thrust sheet travelling over a curved fault ramp. The model geometry is taken from the Pine Mountain block of the southern Appalachians; the area where the concept of a ramp was first proposed (Rich 1934).

In the first part of this paper the model is briefly summarized, after which the consequences for both known and hypothetical thrust sheets are explored.

Précis of Model

The strategy in developing the model was to recast folding theory in such a way as to account for the fact that the stress regime in a thrust sheet stays fixed with respect to the lower plate, while the material of the sheet moves through it. In a fold, a particular material element may experience the same sign of stress throughout its development even though the shape of the fold changes. For instance, an element in the inner arc of a fold hinge will remain in compression throughout its entire history. This element will be carried along as the shape of the stress field changes, that is, as the fold gains amplitude. On the other hand, a material element on the lower surface of a thrust sheet will first experience extension as it is bent into the lower hinge of the ramp, then shortening as it is unbent to conform to the limb of the ramp and then compressed further to conform to the top hinge. At the top of the ramp, the element is finally extended once more as it is made to conform to the flat. Thus, an element of a thrust sheet moves through a fixed stress regime whereas an element of a fold stays fixed in a moving stress regime.

The details of the mathematical formulation have been described elsewhere (Wiltschko 1977, 1979). Briefly stated, the model was developed using the Pine Mountain block as an analogue, thereby assuming the Pine Mountain block's ramp geometry. With this geometry, neutral-surface bending was assumed and viscous plane-strain stresses computed, by allowing the model sheet to partition its deformation between pure bending and shear in such a way as to satisfy equilibrium of moments. Since stress still must be applied to the sheet if it is to move, even if a ramp is not present, uniform (non-bending) normal and shear stresses were computed by satisfying equilibrium of tangential forces. The final step was to fix the viscosities so that the observed strains within the Pine Mountain block were not exceeded in the model.

Elliott (1976a,b) and Chapple (1978) have shown that the erosion profile over a thrust terrane is potentially important mechanically. For the model presented here, it was assumed that other thrust sheets stack up and erode in such a way as to produce an erosional profile dipping in the direction of transport over the thrust sheet being considered. This geometry favours forward motion.

The expression for the net force, P, necessary to overcome those forces caused by fault-zone drag, P_{fz}, being resistance at ramps, P_b, and gravity, P_g, is given symbolically by:

$$P = P_{fz} + P_b + P_g \qquad (1a)$$

Specifically,

$$P = 2qS_0 + JS_0 - \int_0^{2S_0} \rho g h \tan\alpha \cos[\theta(s)]\,ds \qquad (1b)$$

where q is the shear strength of the fault zone, S_0 is half the arclength of the ramp, J the bending parameter given by:

$$J = \tfrac{1}{12}\eta_n h^3 A V \theta_0^2 \beta^4 \qquad (2)$$

where η_n is the compressional viscosity (Biot 1965, p. 252), h is the thickness of the sheet, A the fraction of the total bending at a ramp accomplished by pure bending, given by:

$$A = \cfrac{1}{1 + \cfrac{h^2\beta^2}{6}\cfrac{\eta_n}{\eta_t}}. \qquad (3)$$

V is the velocity, θ_0 the maximum ramp dip, η_t the sliding viscosity (Biot 1965, p. 252) and $\beta = \pi/S_0$. Finally, for the gravitational term (last on right in Eq. 1b), ρ is the density, g the acceleration due to gravity, α the slope of the erosional surface and $\theta(s)$ the function describing the shape of the neutral surface in terms of arclength, s. Note that if there is no ramp, that is if $\theta_0 = \theta(s) = 0$, then

$$P = 2qS_0 + 2S_0\rho g h \tan\alpha \qquad (4)$$

the familiar expression for the force necessary to overcome fault-zone drag for a fault of length $2S_0$ (first term) including the effect of a sloping erosional surface (second term), α reckoned negative (see Nye 1952, Eq. 2; Elliott 1976a, Eq. 4).

Results for the Pine Mountain block

The numerical consequences of Eq. 1 are shown in Table 1, calculated using representative parameters for the Pine Mountain block (Table 2). The key result is that for fault-zone strengths greater than about 300 bars (30 mPa), the net traction (P/h) necessary to move the Pine Mountain block is greater than the laboratory crushing strength of dolomite, one of the major constituents of the Pine

TABLE 1. *Results for Pine Mountain block.* q *is the shear strength of the fault zone in bars. Entries for the flat and ramps are the tractions (force divided by thickness of sheet) that must be exerted at the trailing edge of that part of the sheet to overcome the resistance offered by that part. The columns under totals are the net tractions in bars which must be applied to the trailing edge of the block. The last column on the right is the maximum stress attained within the sheet in bars.*

			Ramp 2			Flat		Ramp 1			Total tractions				Maximum stress
q	η_1	η_1/η_2	fault zone	bending	gravity	fault zone	gravity	fault zone	bending	gravity	fault zone	bending	gravity	Total	
10	0.628	38.00	40.2	29.8	−31.6	72.5	−90.2	28.2	23.9	−44.2	120.8	38.75	−150.2	9.316	126.3
50	11.24	140.8	201.2	175.6	−31.6	362.5	−90.2	140.8	130.1	−44.2	603.9	217.9	−150.2	671.6	1310.
150	37.60	157.2	603.5	503.7	−31.6	1088.	−90.2	422.5	391.7	−44.2	1812.	657.1	−150.2	2319.	4240.
300	77.10	161.2	1207.	1063.	−31.6	2175.	−90.2	844.9	784.2	−44.2	3563.	1376.	−150.2	4789.	8635.1

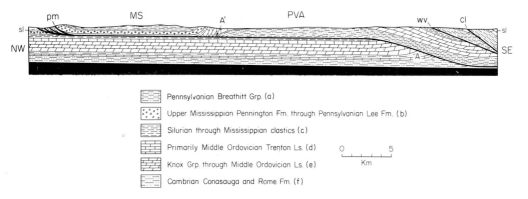

FIG. 1. Cross section through the SW end of the Pine Mountain block. The geometry of the model mimics the ramp geometry of this cross section. Ramp 1 is the SE ramp, the flat is the region between Ramp 1 and the NW ramp, Ramp 2. Symbols: PVA, Powell Valley anticline; Ms, Middlesboro syncline; sl, sea level, pm, Pine Mountain fault; wv, Wallen Valley fault; cl, Clinchport fault. Points A and A' coincided before movement.

TABLE 2. θ_0, *Maximum dip of the ramp*; S_0, *half ramp arclength*; *h, thickness of sheet*; *V, velocity of transport and* f_1, *the fraction of the total sheet composed of competent material (see Biot 1965, p. 252).*

	θ_0	S_0(km)	h(km)	
Ramp 1	20°	5.6	4	$\rho = 2.3$ gm/cc
Flat	1°	29.	4–2	$g = 1000$ cm/sec
Ramp 2	20°	2.5	2	$V = 1.77$ cm/yr
				$f_1 = 0.65$

Mountain block (Wiltschko 1977; 1979). However, the net traction is not the highest stress in the block (see last column, Table 1) and these suggest that crushing will take place if the fault-zone's shear resistance is greater than about 150 bars (15 mPa). A significant portion of the total necessary traction, in either case, is a result of bending resistance, though fault-zone drag is the most important due to the long flat between Ramps 1 and 2 of the Pine Mountain block (Fig. 1). Therefore, the inclusion of the effect of bending resistance at ramps further reinforces the overthrust paradox: for a thrust sheet such as the Pine Mountain block to move, the fault-zone strength must be quite low, lower still than what would be predicted by just accounting for shear resistance along the fault zone.

The predicted principal stress orientations are shown in Fig. 2. If bending stresses were not important, the orientations of the principal stresses would everywhere make the same angle to the neutral surface along a particular perpendicular to the same; in this case they do not. In fact, there are areas within the sheet where the tensile bending stresses are greater than the uniform tangential stresses necessary to overcome the shear resistance along the base of the sheet. This gives rise to areas of predicted extension within areas of shortening. Complex normal and reverse faulting has been documented near the base of some thrust sheets (Harris & Milici 1977) and this may be one explanation for this complexity. An element of material on the lower surface of a thrust sheet could experience first normal and then reverse and then normal faulting once more in travelling from the bottom to the top of a ramp. If the element has travelled over multiple ramps, it may be very complexly deformed.

Other geometries

Although the model above was developed with the Pine Mountain block as its analogue, it has more general applications and may be adjusted to other situations.

It is interesting to consider first the changing state of stress within a thrust sheet overlying an outcropping thrust fault. How do the stresses on the ramp evolve as the length of the outcropping portion of the sheet, or toe, extends with displacement?

The degree of complexity of faulting will change through time. Initially, the rocks on the ramp will not feel the added resistance of an exterior toe. Consequently, bending stresses will predominate initially since a large uniform

h = 4000 m	η_1/η_2 = 157	P/h = 2319 bar
S0 = 5.63 km	η_N/η_T = 36	Max Bending Nrml = 1921 bar
θ = 20 deg.	η_N = 2.45E+23 poise	Max Bending Shear = 1072 bar
V = 1.77 cm/yr	η_T = 6.75E+21 poise	Max. Total Stress = 4240 bar
α = −1. deg.	Flat 1 = 29.0 km	ql = 150 bar
f_1 = 0.65	Flat 2 = 0.0 km	qu = 0.0 bar

Erosion Surface Slopes in Direction of Transport

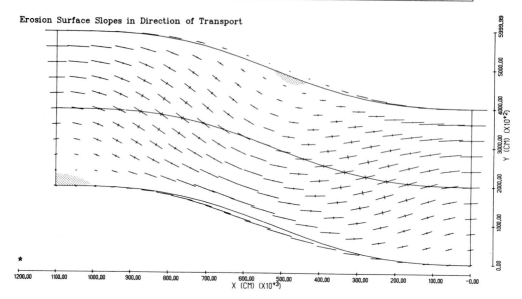

FIG. 2. Principal stress directions. The principal stresses are scaled to the largest value they attain in the sheet. Stippled areas are where the maximum principal stress is tensile. See Table 4 for definitions of parameters.

compression does not yet exist. The geological consequences of this are that an outcropping sheet is initially susceptable to complex faulting; this susceptibility decreasing as the length of the toe increases. In Fig. 3a there is no toe and as a result large areas of tensile stresses. Since only differential stresses are plotted in Fig. 3, the lower right and lower left regions of tension will most likely be in compression in a real sheet because of the hydrostatic component of gravity. The upper region, however, will remain in tension. In Fig. 3b, the toe has extended to 17.7 km and in Fig. 3c to 35.4 km and the regions of tension have decreased progressively. This sequence implies that one may expect early important normal faulting, giving way to more important reverse faulting as the uniform normal stress builds up in the block as a result of increasing flat length. This history of development will be preserved in the sheet itself: its leading edge will be most complexly deformed, giving way towards the interior to a more consistent pattern of internal fault development.

Table 3 lists the results of simply doubling (a) viscosities, (b) sheet thickness and (c) ramp dip as well as (d) increasing the fraction of incompetent material and (e) increasing the slope of the erosional surface from −1 to −3°.

The effect of doubling the viscosities (row 2, Table 3) is simply to double the bending stresses and thus the traction necessary to overcome bending resistance. However, doubling the thickness (row 3) is not so straightforward. Equation 2 contains h^3 and one might intuitively expect a large increase in bending stresses, but this is not so. The reason is that h also appears in the expression for A (Eq. 3), the fraction of the total bending deformation performed as pure bending. Therefore, for larger h, less deformation is due to pure bending and more to shear, so that the net traction only increases slightly. Note, however, that by increasing the block thickness, the traction is less for the flat. The force necessary for movement has remained the same but the stress is less because the area over which this force acts is now twice as great. Therefore, the level of

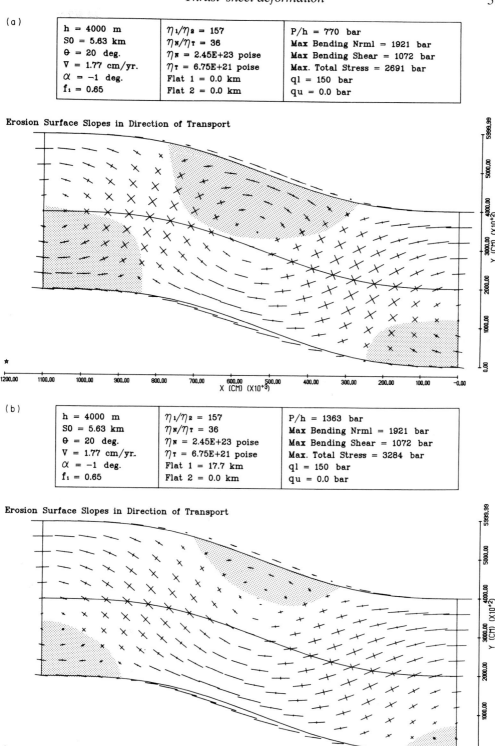

FIG. 3. (a & b)

(c)

h = 4000 m	η_1/η_2 = 157	P/h = 1955 bar
S0 = 5.63 km	η_N/η_T = 36	Max Bending Nrml = 1921 bar
Θ = 20 deg.	η_N = 2.45E+23 poise	Max Bending Shear = 1072 bar
V = 1.77 cm/yr.	η_T = 6.75E+21 poise	Max. Total Stress = 3877 bar
α = −1 deg.	Flat 1 = 35.4 km	ql = 150 bar
f_1 = 0.65	Flat 2 = 0.0 km	qu = 0 bar

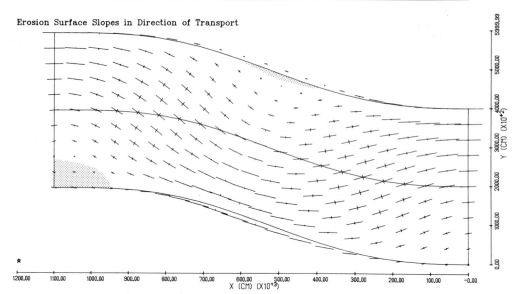

Erosion Surface Slopes in Direction of Transport

FIG. 3. Development of an outcropping thrust sheet. (a) No flat. For equilibrium, one must postulate tractions on the leading edge which equilibrate the stresses within the sheet there. (b) length = 17.7 km. (c) length = 35.4 km. Notice that the areas of tensile stresses (stippled) decrease as the flat extends and as a result requires a greater traction be applied to the trailing edge of the sheet to maintain the same velocity.

stress within the sheet decreases even though the bending portion increases slightly. If everything else is equal, thick thrust sheets will be less likely to lose coherence.

The largest effect on bending stresses arises as a result of the dip of the ramp, θ_0, (row 4).

If the ramp dip is doubled, the bending stresses on the ramp are nearly quadrupled. The mathematic explanation may be found again in the expression for J where θ_0 appears squared. Perhaps surprisingly, though, θ_0 does not appear in the expression for A. The fraction of

TABLE 3. *Tractions in bars for fault-zone drag, bending and gravity within a thrust sheet with two ramps and an intervening flat. Each of rows 2 through 7 are discussed in the text. Row 1 is calculated using the geometry of the Pine Mountain block and given for reference.*

	Ramp 2			Flat		Ramp 1			Total Tractions				Maxi-mum stress
	fault zone	bending	gravity	fault zone	gravity	fault zone	bending	gravity	fault zone	bending	gravity	Total	
1.	603.5	530.7	−31.6	1088.	−90.2	422.5	391.7	−44.2	1812.	657.1	−150.2	2319.	4240.
2. η	603.5	1061.	−31.6	1088.	−90.2	422.5	783.5	−44.2	1812.	1314.	−150.2	2976.	6818.
3. h	301.8	557.2	−31.6	543.8	−90.2	211.2	401.4	−44.2	905.9	680.0	−150.2	1435.	2420.
4. θ_0	603.5	530.7	−31.6	1088.	−90.2	422.5	1567.	−44.2	1812.	1832.	−150.2	3493.	7340.
5. f_1	603.5	246.8	−31.6	1088.	−90.2	422.5	183.4	−44.2	1812.	306.8	−150.2	1968.	2868.
6. α	603.5	530.7	−94.8	1088.	−270.9	422.5	391.7	−132.7	1812.	657.1	−451.0	2018.	3939.
7. q_1	0.0	530.7	−31.6	0.0	−90.2	0.0	391.7	−44.2	0.0	657.1	−150.2	506.9	2428.

the bending partitioned into pure bending is not changed for any choice of θ_0 as long as S_0, the other ramp geometry parameter, is held constant (see Eq. 4). Holding S_0 constant while changing θ_0 is probably unrealistic geologically. Given two ramps of different ramp dips but similar stratigraphic climb, the ramp length will be smaller for the larger-dip ramp and larger from the smaller-dip ramp. Therefore, bending resistance will be greater at the high dip ramp although this results from performing the same climb in fault level over a shorter distance. In the numerical examples given above, the ramp length was held constant, so that the stratigraphic climb was increased. θ_0 and S_0 are not independent for a given stratigraphic climb.

Decreasing the fraction of competent material from 0.65 to 0.25 (row 5) has the effect of decreasing the thrust sheet's bending resistance and thereby making movement of the sheet easier. As a result, the principal stress directions are more nearly layer parallel (Fig. 4) and regions of extension do not arise.

The effect of increasing the dip of the erosional surface from -1 to $-3°$ (row 6, Table 3) is straightforward: the gravational tractions are trebled. Notice, however, that gravity is still not sufficient to overcome the other forms of resistance; a tectonic push is also required.

The effect of a shear stress imposed on the top surface of the thrust sheet (row 7), perhaps as a result of an overriding sheet, is profound (Fig. 5). This shear balances the shear resistance of the fault zone of the sheet and makes movement much easier. For the conditions chosen here (150 bar top shear), the net traction is 507 bar (51 mPa) as opposed to 2.3 kbar (230 mPa) without the top shear. If the upper fault-zone's strength had been larger than 150 bar, it would have overcome some of the resistance caused by bending, though adding a component of simple shear to the sheet's deformation. An overriding thrust sheet may have the significant effect of making movement on the lower one much easier. A well documented kinematic scheme in several major thrust belts is a transfer of displacement from upper to

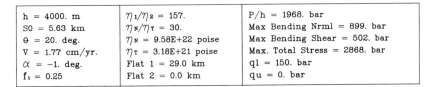

h = 4000. m	η_1/η_2 = 157.	P/h = 1968. bar
S0 = 5.63 km	η_N/η_T = 30.	Max Bending Nrml = 899. bar
θ = 20. deg.	η_N = 9.58E+22 poise	Max Bending Shear = 502. bar
V = 1.77 cm/yr.	η_T = 3.18E+21 poise	Max. Total Stress = 2868. bar
α = −1. deg.	Flat 1 = 29.0 km	ql = 150. bar
f_1 = 0.25	Flat 2 = 0.0 km	qu = 0. bar

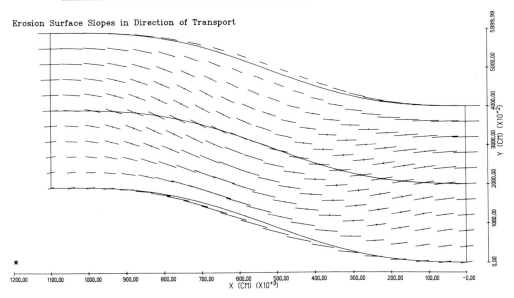

Erosion Surface Slopes in Direction of Transport

FIG. 4. Principal stress directions in a block with a low fraction of competent material. See Table 4 for an explanation of symbols.

TABLE 4. *Definition of symbols used in Figs 2–5.*

H	Block thickness
SO	Half the ramp's arclength (S_0 in text)
θ	Maximum dip of the ramp (θ_0 in the text)
V	Velocity of transport
α	Dip of the erosional surface
f_1	Fraction of competent material
η_1	Competent material velocity
η_2	Incompetent material viscosity
η_n	Compressional viscosity (Biot 1965, p. 252)
η_t	Sliding viscosity (ibid)
Flat 1	Length of flat between ramps 1 and 2 (Fig. 1)
Flat 2	Length of flat out beyond ramp 2
P/h	Net traction necessary to move sheet
Max Bending Nrml	Maximum bending normal stress in sheet
Max Bending Shear	Maximum shear stress due to bending
Max. Total Stress	Largest total stress in the block
q_l	Shear strength of the lower fault zone (base of sheet)
q_u	Shear strength of the upper fault zone (between sheet shown and an overriding sheet, if present)

h = 4000 m	η_1/η_2 = 157	P/h = 507 bar
S0 = 5.63 km	η_N/η_T = 36	Max Bending Nrml = 1921 bar
θ = 20 deg.	η_N = 2.45E+23 poise	Max Bending Shear = 1072 bar
V = 1.77 cm/yr.	η_T = 6.75E+21 poise	Max. Total Stress = 2437 bar
α = −1. deg.	Flat 1 = 29.0 km	ql = 150 bar
f_1 = 0.65	Flat 2 = 0.0 km	qu = 150 bar

Erosion Surface Slopes in Direction of Transport

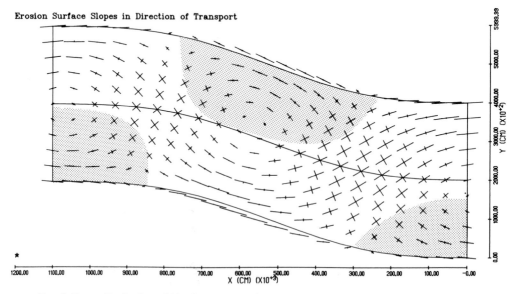

FIG. 5. Stress distribution within the ramp portion of a thrust sheet being overridden by another sheet. The effect of an overriding thrust sheet with a fault zone equal in shear strength to the lower one is to cancel the resistance to movement of the lower fault zone. The only resistance is bending and as a result the net traction is low (compare Fig. 2). Principal stresses are again plotted scaled to the largest value they attain and the stippled areas are where the maximum principal stress is negative.

lower faults. The shear stress arising from an upper sheet overriding the lower one may be one mechanical means by which this is achieved.

Conclusions

Increasing the viscosities, thickness and ramp dip of a linearly viscous thrust sheet will increase the resistance to movement; although in the case of increasing thrust-sheet thickness the net traction will in fact be less. Increasing the dip of the erosional surface and decreasing the fraction of competent material decrease the resistance to movement.

Most of these parameters are most likely nearly constant for a particular thrust ramp through time. What may change, however, is the length of outcropping portion of the thrust and its association with surrounding thrusts. The uneroded toe of a thrust sheet which crops out faster than it is eroded will impose successively higher stresses on the rocks on the most craton-ward ramp as the toe grows successively longer. Moreover, the directions of the principal stresses will be quite complex before appreciable movement but will become more nearly layer-parallel as transport progresses. Since this stress history may be preserved in the form of faults within the uneroded toe, one should expect to find quite complex fault orientations towards the front of the thrust sheet giving way to more consistent orientations internally. Another effect that is likely to develop in thrust terranes is the overriding of one sheet by another. This overriding, or 'stacking,' has an important effect on the equilibrium of the lower sheet. If the fault zones beneath both thrusts have the same shear resistance, then movement on the upper thrust sheet will overcome the shear resistance along the fault zone of the lower one. Therefore, for two thrust sheets, one overriding the other, work must be done against only one fault zone, though both thrust sheets will still resist deformation internally.

References

BIOT, M. A. 1965. Theory of similar folding of the first and second kind. *Bull. geol. Soc. Am.* **76**, 251–8.

CHAPPLE, W. M. 1978. Mechanics of thin-skinned fold and thrust belts. *Bull. geol. Soc. Am.* **89**, 1189–98.

ELLIOTT, D. 1976a. The motion of thrust sheets, *J. geophys. Res.* **81**, 949–63.

—— 1976b. The energy balance and deformation mechanisms of thrust sheets, *Proc. R. Soc. London*, **A283**, 289–312.

HARRIS, L. D. & MILICI, R. C. 1977. Characteristics of thin-skinned style of deformation in the southern Appalachians, and potential hydrocarbon traps, *Prof. Pap. U.S. geol. Surv.* **1018**, 40 pp.

NYE, J. F. 1952. A comparison between the theoretical and the measured long profile of the Unteraar Glacier, *J. Glaciol. London*, **2**, 103–97.

RICH, J. L. 1934. Mechanics of low-angle overthrust faulting as illustrated by Cumberland thrust block, Virginia, Kentucky, and Tennessee, *Bull. Am. Assoc. Petrol. Geol.* **18**, 1584–96.

WILTSCHKO, D. V. 1977. *Mechanics of Appalachian Plateau Structures*, Ph.D. thesis, Brown University, Providence, R. I., 137 pp. (unpubl.).

—— 1979. Mechanical model for thrust-sheet deformation at a ramp, *J. geophys. Res.* **84**, 1091–104.

D. V. WILTSCHKO, Department of Geological Sciences, University of Michigan, Ann Arbor, Michigan 48109, U.S.A.

Deformation and secondary faulting near the leading edge of a thrust fault

D. A. Rodgers & W. D. Rizer

SUMMARY: Elastic dislocation models are used to calculate the displacements of the ground surface produced by a thrust fault climbing section. The models show that the surface uplift is asymmetrical with the steepest slope above and ahead of the fault. The gradient of the surface uplift becomes steeper and the magnitude of the uplift increases as: (1) the fault dip increases; (2) the fault becomes shallower; and (3) the shear modulus of the material above the fault decreases relative to the shear modulus of the material containing the fault. Elastic dislocation, photoelastic, and clay models are used to predict the orientation of secondary faults which might be produced by a thrust fault climbing section. In general, the secondary faults strike parallel to the master fault, but the dislocation models show that there are regions in both the hanging and foot walls where the secondary fault strikes are not parallel to the master fault. The models suggest that a thrust fault in a homogeneous medium is likely to extend itself with about the same dip, while a thrust fault moving from a stronger material into a weaker material is likely to flatten and become layer-parallel. High-angle antithetic faults or back thrusts in the hanging wall are associated with a thrust fault propagating through a homogeneous medium, but layer-parallel antithetic faults are more likely than high-angle antithetic faults in the hanging-wall when a thrust fault is propagating from a stronger to a weaker medium.

One of the major characteristics of overthrust belts is that the major thrust faults are nearly bedding-parallel in incompetent units and are bedding-transverse in competent units (Dahlstrom 1970). The areas where the faults are bedding-transverse are called tectonic ramps or simply ramps, by Harris & Milici (1977) and Serra (1977, 1978). Rich (1934), Serra (1977, 1978), Morse (1977), and Gallagher & Rizer (1978) have considered the structural consequences of ramps in some detail. In particular, they have looked at the development of structures in the hanging-wall of a ramp. However, all the published analyses of ramps assume that the ramp is fully developed. To our knowledge, only Jacobeen & Kanes (1974, 1975) and Gallagher & Rizer (1977) have discussed, in any detail, the processes which might initiate a ramp. Gallagher & Rizer (1977) briefly discussed the problem of a fault propagating up a ramp.

This problem is important for several reasons. First, the secondary structures and fractures produced by the propagating fault will remain in the region initially near the fault tip long after the fault tip has propagated out of the region. Second, it would be useful to be able to predict when a dipping fault will steepen or flatten. Third, the model can be used to estimate ground deformation produced by earthquakes on thrust faults.

In this paper we shall use mathematical, photoelastic, and clay models to investigate the deformation and secondary faulting near the leading edge of a thrust fault propagating through both a homogeneous medium and a layered medium. In particular, we shall look at a fault tip at two different depths below the ground surface. The fault will have dips of 30 and 60°. This present work is different from that of Gallagher & Rizer (1977) in that we are using dislocation and clay models as well as a more sophisticated photoelastic model.

Mathematical models

The mathematical fault model is based on elastic dislocation theory (Steketee 1958a, b). It has been shown that elastic dislocation models produce displacement fields which are similar to the ground displacements observed after earthquakes (Savage & Hastie 1969; Alewine 1974; Chen et al. 1975) and the ground displacements which result from fault creep (Goulty & Gilman 1978; McHugh & Johnston 1978; Rodgers 1979). For strike slip faults there is good qualitative agreement between the structures predicted by dislocation theory and those observed in clay models (Rodgers 1976; Groshong & Rodgers 1978). Thus, elastic dislocation theory is a reasonable tool for modelling faults.

Ben-Menahem & Singh (1968) developed elastic dislocation theory for the case of the surface deformation produced by a point source in a system consisting of a layer over a half space. Their solutions contained integrals which appeared to be impossible to evaluate, but Ben-Menahem & Gillon (1970) showed how to approximate the integrals. We have extended the solutions of Ben-Menahem & Singh and Ben-Menahem & Gillon to calculate the displacements, strains, and stresses at depth as well as on the surface.

The point source solutions of Ben-Menahem & Singh (1968) are integrated over the surface shown in Fig. 1. A Gauss-Legendre double integration scheme with 20th degree Legendre polynomials in each direction along the surface is used. Numerical experiments show that the 20th degree polynomial is sufficient to yield errors of less than 5% everywhere except very near the fault. The points very near the fault are thus not used in the plots which follow.

We present the vertical displacement of the ground surface for four cases, and we discuss the predicted fault patterns for all four cases. The fault patterns are drawn in the vertical (Y2–Y3) plane of Fig. 1. The cases we consider are: 1) a half-space where the fault tip is 20 km deep and the fault dip is 30°; 2) a half-space where the fault tip is 20 km deep and the fault dip is 60°; 3) a half-space where the fault tip is 50 km deep and the fault dip is 30°; and 4) a layer introduced at 20 km when the fault tip is

20 km deep, the fault dip is 30° and the shear modulus in the half-space is 100 times the shear modulus in the layer. In all four cases Poisson's ratio is 1/4 and the shear modulus in the layer is 3×10^{10} Pa. The fault surface is 200 km^2 (Fig. 1), and the displacement across the fault surface is 1 m. The magnitude of the displacement across the fault affects only the magnitudes of the calculated elastic fields; the shapes of the calculated elastic fields do not change as the displacement across the fault changes. The above dimensions can be scaled by any convenient factor, and so the conclusions drawn from the particular dimensions used here are in fact applicable to any problem.

Only the changes in pre-existing elastic fields produced by the specified displacement across the fault can be calculated from elastic dislocation models. In this paper we have not attempted to add in a pre-existing stress field for the dislocation models, for the nature of the stresses required to produce thrust faulting is still being debated. Hydrostatic overburden pressure will not affect the calculated elastic fields and thus is not included. The photoelastic model does show the effect of an applied horizontal compression.

The stress field determined from the dislocation model is three-dimensional. Except at the surface, all three principal stresses are generally non-zero. Therefore, even though the calculated fields are presented in a cross-

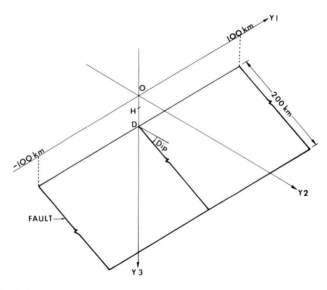

Fig. 1. Sketch of dislocation model. Y1–Y2 plane is the ground surface. D is the depth of the fault tip, and H is the depth of the layer. The fault is 200 km square, and the dip is either 30° or 60°.

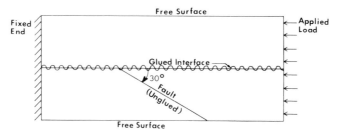

FIG. 2. Sketch of the photoelastic model. The model is 15 cm long, 7.5 cm high, and 0.6 cm thick.

section through the centre of the fault (Y_2–Y_3 plane, Fig. 1), neither a plane strain nor a plane stress condition obtains.

Photoelastic model

Photoelasticity is a technique most commonly used to analyse the state of stress in complex engineering structures. The validity of the technique is amply demonstrated in the engineering literature (see e.g. Coker & Filon 1931; Frocht 1941, 1948; Durelli & Riley 1965). The method has been used in the geologic literature to study brittle fracturing (Bombolakis 1964, 1968; Sowers 1973), folding (Currie *et al.* 1962; Gallagher & Logan 1973); deformation of sandstone-like aggregates (Gallagher *et al.* 1974) and thrust faulting (Gallagher & Rizer 1977).

For this paper, a thrust fault is modelled as a closed rectangular crack in a plate of PSM-5, an elastic, photoelastically sensitive material. The model consists of three pieces of PSM-5 fitted together as shown in Fig. 2. The model is 15 cm long, 7.5 cm wide, and 0.6 cm thick. The mechanical interface between the upper plate and lower two plates is effectively eliminated by bonding with PMC-1, an adhesive with essentially the same elastic modulus as PSM-5. One end of the model is fixed and a load is applied uniformly to the other end as shown in Fig. 2.

Standard photoelastic techniques (Durelli & Riley 1965) are employed to study the stresses in the thrust fault model. The model shown in Fig. 2 is very similar to the vertical $Y1 = 0$ cross section through Fig. 1, and comparisons between the two models will be made.

Calculated vertical displacements

Fig. 3 shows the vertical displacement of the ground surface produced by the four dislocation models. Curves 1 and 2 show that increasing the dip of the fault produces a steeper uplift and moves the peak of the uplift in the hanging-wall direction. Curves 1 and 3 show that moving the fault deeper spreads the

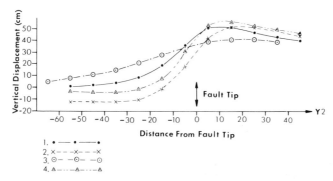

FIG. 3. Vertical displacement in cm of the ground surface calculated from dislocation models with 1 m movement on fault. Displacement from fault tip in km. Curve 1: D = 20 km, dip = 30°, half-space model; Curve 2: D = 20 km, dip = 60°, half-space model: Curve 3: D = 50 km, dip = 30°, half-space model: Curve 4: D = 20 km, dip = 30°, 20 km thick layer with shear modulus = 0.01 of shear modulus of half-space.

uplift over a wider area and decreases the magnitude of the uplift. Finally, curves 1 and 4 show that a fault propagating from a more rigid half-space into a less rigid layer produces a steeper uplift, moves the peak of the uplift in the footwall direction, and somewhat increases the magnitude of the uplift.

The uplift calculated from the models resembles the anticline that forms above a ramp (Dahlstrom 1970; Harris & Milici 1977). The model results imply that the anticline will have varying amplitude and asymmetry depending on the depth and dip of the master fault and the shear modulus contrast between the layer and half-space. In particular, Fig. 3 shows that a low amplitude anticline should form in the hanging wall. This anticline is observed in clay model experiments of thrust faults (R. H. Groshong pers. comm.).

One may infer from these results that the depth and dip of a buried thrust fault can be predicted from geodetic data after an earthquake. Curves 1 and 2 imply that a more steeply dipping fault should produce steeper surface gradients than a shallow-dipping fault when observed by precise levelling surveys, tiltmeters, and gravimeters. From curves 1 and 3 one may infer that a deeper fault should be more difficult to identify than a shallower fault using the above methods since the effects are spread over a larger area. It can be inferred from curves 1 and 4 that a thrust fault in the basement under an alluvial cover should produce larger surface effects than those produced by a fault when the material containing the fault extends to the surface.

Fig. 4a shows the vertical displacement of the ground surface and a plane 12 km deep for the layered model. The two curves diverge between -35 km and $+5$ km, and the 12 km deep curve has a steeper gradient than the surface curve. One may infer from this divergence that there is some thickening between the surface and a plane 12 km deep. Fig. 4b shows a clay model run by R. H. Groshong for a different study which exhibits the same features. A rigid plywood block is moving up a 30° dipping surface into a clay cake. The two lines in the clay cake were originally parallel and horizontal, but the top of the clay cake was not flat originally. The two lines are not parallel now, thus indicating a thickening of the layer in this region. Comparing Fig. 4a and b, we see a similarity between the predicted and observed vertical displacements. Thus, the clay model does thicken in the area predicted by the dislocation model.

Predicted secondary faulting

In this section we present plots of the maximum shear stress distribution (Jaeger & Cook 1969, p. 11–26) and the orientation of planes of potential secondary faulting for the photoelastic and dislocation models. We use the term 'secondary faulting' to refer to faults which can form as the result of a stress field produced by movement on a master (primary) fault. The master fault is either the dislocation surface or the crack in the photoelastic model. The magnitude of the maximum shear stress can be used to indicate areas where secondary faulting can be initiated. In general, secondary faulting is more likely to occur in areas where the maximum shear stress is high than in areas where the maximum shear stress is low. The orientation of possible secondary faulting can be determined from the orientations of the principal stresses (Jaeger & Cook 1969). We use a shear failure criterion for potential failure orientation which assumes that secondary faulting occurs on planes containing the intermediate principal stress and oriented at ±30° to the maximum compressive principal stress. This seems to be a reasonable assumption, since faults do form, in experiments with rocks, at angles which range from 20 to 40° to the maximum compressive principal stress (Jaeger & Cook 1969). The secondary fault trajectories we present are lines which are everywhere parallel to the planes at ±30° to the maximum compressive principal stress. In order to keep our models more general, we do not assume a particular material shear strength. Hence, we do not predict regions of failure.

The secondary fault patterns determined from the photoelastic and dislocation models show only the potential orientations of the initial secondary faults. When failure occurs on a secondary fault, the stress field in the vicinity of the secondary fault is altered. The exact path that the new fault will follow as it grows is determined by the interaction between the initial stress field and the stress field produced by the new fault. Thus, a completely developed secondary fault may, or may not, follow the secondary fault patterns presented in this section. We will present results from a clay model experiment by R. H. Groshong which suggest that the completely developed secondary fault pattern does generally resemble the potential secondary fault pattern predicted here.

Fig. 5 shows the maximum shear stress distribution and secondary fault trajectories in the vertical plane $Y1 = 0$ (Fig. 1) for the dislocation model where the dip is 30° and the tip

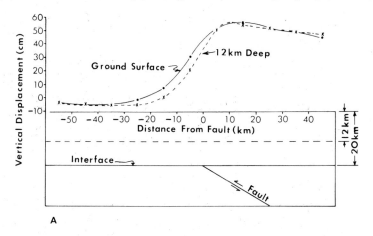

A

B

FIG. 4. **Dislocation** and clay model illustrations of thickening in layer produced by thrust fault. (a) Dislocation model. Solid curve shows vertical displacement of ground surface. Dashed curve shows vertical displacement of plane 12 km deep. Layer above interface has shear modulus 0.01 of shear modulus in half-space below interface. (b) Clay model. Right-hand plywood block moves up 30° incline into clay cake. Lines in cake originally parallel and horizontal. Top of clay cake originally uneven. Photograph by R. H. Groshong.

of the fault is 20 km below the ground surface. The contours shown are drawn by computer. The observation points with more than 5% error are removed from the contoured data set, and the contours are drawn smoothly through the areas near the fault.

As expected, the maximum shear stress is greatest near the tip of the fault due to the fact that the displacement across the fault goes from 1 m to zero at the tip of the fault. In fact, the maximum shear stress should be infinite at

the tip of the fault. However, the maximum shear stress is not calculated at observation points near enough to the fault tip to show this effect, and the hatched zones in Figs 5 & 7 are intended to exclude these singular points from consideration. The maximum shear stress at the ground surface does not reach its greatest value either at the up-dip projection of the fault or in the hanging wall directly above the fault tip but rather peaks somewhere between these two points.

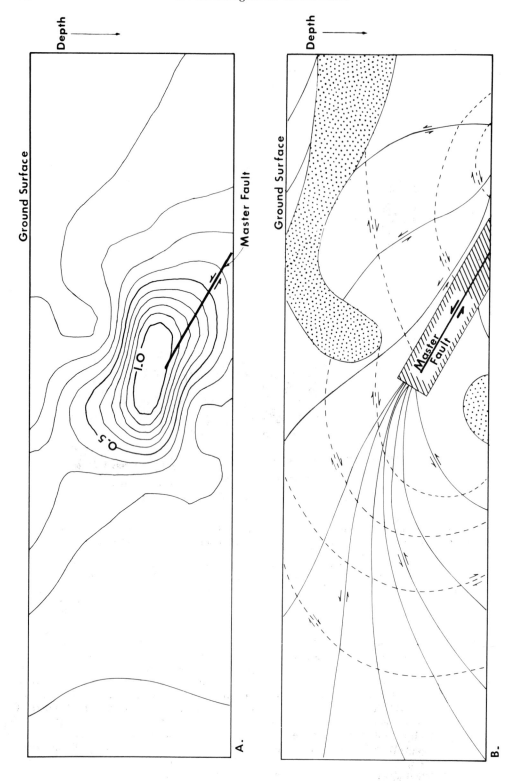

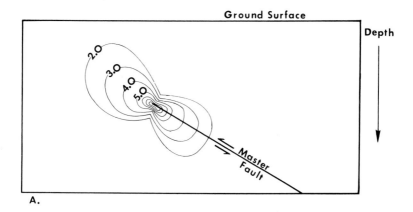

A.

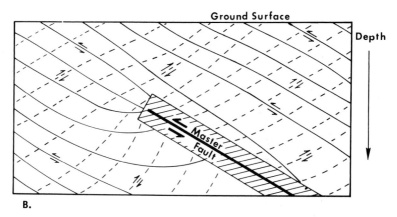

B.

FIG. 6. Stress difference and secondary faulting inferred from photoelastic model. (a) Contours of equal difference between the least and the most compressive principal stresses in MPa (equal to twice the maximum shear stress). The magnitude of the stress difference at a given point is a constant function of the horizontal stress applied at the ends of the model. For this model, the applied stress is 0.5 MPa. (b) Potential ±30° shear fracture trajectories. See Fig. 5 for symbols.

Fig. 5b shows the potential secondary fault trajectories predicted by the same model. The small arrows show the sense of movement on the potential secondary faults. The heavy arrows on the master fault show the sense of the original offset across the master fault. The solid trajectories have the same sense of movement (synthetic) as the initial fault and the dashed trajectories have the opposite sense of movement (antithetic) as the initial fault. The spacing of the trajectories is arbitrary and is not intended to represent fracture intensity. The trajectories shown are only representative

of those faults that could form, and there is nothing to prevent a secondary fault from forming between the trajectories shown.

The numerical integration scheme used does not produce accurate results in the hatched area due to the proximity of the singular points on the fault. Hence, no potential secondary fault trajectories are shown there.

In the region outside the stippled areas the intermediate principal stress is normal to the plane of the figure, thus requiring that the potential secondary fault strikes are also normal to the plane of the figure and parallel to

FIG. 5. Maximum shear stress and secondary faulting in vertical plane Y1 = 0 for half-space dislocation model with D = 20 km and dip = 30°. (a) Contours of equal values of maximum shear stress in megapascals. Magnitude of maximum shear stress depends on the displacement on the master fault and the elastic constants of the half-space. (b) Potential secondary fault trajectories. Solid lines have same sense of shear (synthetic) as master fault and dashed lines have opposite sense of shear (antithetic) as master fault. Strippled areas have out of the plane faulting (see text). Hatched area indeterminate zone around master fault.

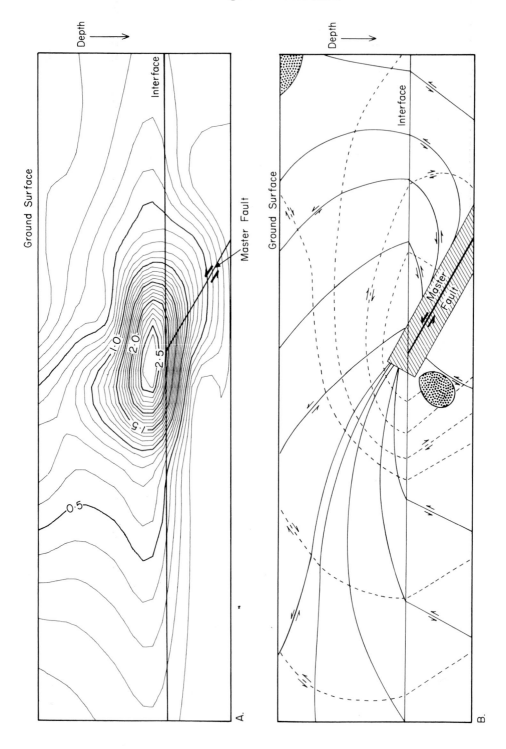

the strike of the master fault. However, in the stippled areas the intermediate principal stress is in the plane of the figure, thus causing either the greatest or least principal stress to be normal to the plane of the figure. This requires the potential secondary faults to strike at an angle to the master fault.

The synthetic potential secondary fault trajectories together with the maximum shear stress distribution suggest that the fault could either propagate to the surface with about the same dip, or extend and become subhorizontal without reaching the surface. Low angle antithetic and high angle synthetic faults can develop in the hanging wall above the master fault. Normal faults do not generally occur in the hanging wall.

The maximum shear stress distribution and potential secondary fault trajectories produced by a 30° dipping thrust fault 50 km deep are essentially similar to Fig. 5 and will not be shown.

The maximum shear stress field produced by a 60° dipping thrust fault again has the same features as Fig. 5a; the major difference is that the field is rotated to a steeper angle than Fig. 5a. The potential secondary fault trajectories for the 60° fault are, as might be expected, much steeper than those for the 30° fault. However the zones of three-dimensional effects are still seen for the 60° fault.

Fig. 6a shows contours of equal difference between the greatest and least principal stresses, and Fig. 6b shows the potential shear fracture trajectories determined for the photoelastic model. The hatched zone near the fault in Fig. 6b indicates an area wherein the stresses are indeterminant. The contours in Fig. 6a have been smoothed in this region. The contour values in Fig. 6a are equal to twice the maximum shear stress. The magnitudes are in MPa and are for an applied horizontal compression of 0.5 MPa. An increase in the applied stress would produce a proportionate increase everywhere in the model. The general shape of the stress distribution, however, would not change. Comparison of Fig. 5a and 6a indicates that the shape of the shear stress distribution is similar for the dislocation and photoelastic models. The difference in inclination of the shear stress pattern is most probably a reflection of the density of grid points at

which the stress field is determined for the dislocation model.

Comparison of Figs 5b & 6b indicates some differences in potential secondary fault trajectories predicted by the two models. Well away from the fault in the photoelastic model the most compressive principal stress is the applied horizontal load, and the secondary fault trajectories form angles of ±30° to the horizontal. Near the fault, the stress changes produced by the fault become larger than the applied load, and the trajectories begin to resemble those determined from the dislocation model (Fig. 5b). The potential secondary fault trajectories predicted from the photoelastic model suggest that the master fault will extend itself to the surface with more or less the same dip. The photoelastic model also shows that low angle antithetic secondary faults can form above the fault. Thus, both the dislocation and photoelastic models predict similar potential secondary fault patterns near the master fault. Note that there are no zones of out of the plane faulting shown in Fig. 6b since the photoelastic model is by definition two-dimensional. The difference in the potential secondary fault trajectories for the two models is due to the presence of the applied horizontal compression in the photoelastic model and the absence of the applied horizontal compression in the dislocation model.

Fig. 7 shows the maximum shear stress distribution and secondary fault trajectories for the case of a 30° dipping fault in a half space which has a greater shear modulus than the overlying 20 km thick layer. Comparing Figs 5a and 7a, it is clear that the layer has an effect on the maximum shear stress contours. The maximum shear stress peak value in the layered case is increased by a factor of about 2.5 over the half-space case, and the contours have been flattened and elongated by the layer. Note particularly that the 0.5 MPa (5 bar) contour has been extended considerably along the interface. This suggests that failure in the layer near the interface to the left of the fault (the footwall) is more likely in the layered case (Fig. 7a) than in the half-space case (Fig. 5a).

Fig. 7b shows the secondary fault trajectories for the layered case. Once again, the master fault can either extend itself to the

---

FIG. 7. Maximum shear stress and secondary faulting in vertical plane Y1 = 0 for layered half-space dislocation model. D = 20 km, layer is 20 km thick, dip = 30°, shear modulus of half-space (below interface) = 100 × shear modulus of layer (above interface). (a) Contours of equal values of maximum shear stress. See Fig. 4a for conventions. (b) Potential secondary fault trajectories. See Fig. 4b for symbols.

surface with more or less the same dip, or the master fault can flatten and curve down toward the interface. There are secondary fault trajectories with an antithetic sense of slip approximately parallel to the interface in the hanging wall above the tip of the master fault, and high angle synthetic faults in the layer above the hanging wall of the master fault. Note that the secondary fault trajectories are refracted at the interface, and normal faulting is predominant in the hanging and footwalls below the interface. Zones of out of the plane faulting seen in Fig. 5b are almost non-existent in Fig. 7b.

Discussion of secondary faulting

The potential secondary fault pattern has several interesting aspects. In both the half-space (Fig. 5) and layered half-space (Fig. 7) cases, the master fault can extend itself either by propagating to the surface with more or less the same dip, or by flattening and curving down. The path that the master fault chooses to follow when extending itself is determined by both the maximum shear stress distribution and the presence or absence of a layer. The photoelastic model suggests that an applied horizontal compression would cause the master fault to extend itself to the surface with about the same dip.

The downward-curved synthetic faults to the left of the master fault in Fig. 7b are seen in high-pressure models of thrust faults in rock (J. H. Spang 1977 pers. comm.) and in clay models of thrust faults (R. H. Groshong 1978 pers. comm.). Fig. 8 shows a clay experiment run by R. H. Groshong for a different study where a rigid block moves up a 30° dipping incline into a clay cake. Note that there are several of the low angle synthetic thrusts in the foot-wall ahead of the master fault, and the master fault finally extends to the surface along a secondary fault with a dip of about 30°. The sequence of formation in clay and rock seems to be that one or more low angle synthetic faults form first, but are later abandoned. The master fault then propagates to the surface along a higher angle synthetic fault with approximately the same dip as the master fault (R. H. Groshong 1978, and J. H. Spang 1977, pers. comm.). The deeper low angle thrusts are therefore older than the shallower higher-angle thrusts.

The above discussion suggests that a thrust fault is more likely to flatten when it passes from a stronger to a weaker layer than when it is moving up through a homogeneous sequence. Thus, the presence of a weak (less competent or more ductile) layer might cause a thrust fault which is climbing section on a tectonic ramp to change into a bedding-parallel fault.

The low angle antithetic secondary faults with reverse slip above the master fault in Figs 6b and 5b are similar to the back thrusts described by Serra (1977, 1978) and Morse (1977). Serra and Morse both suggested that

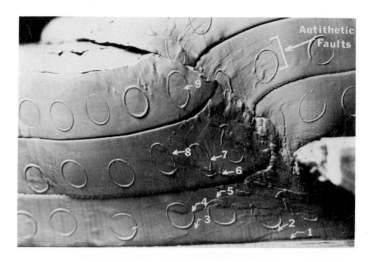

FIG. 8. Secondary faults from clay model experiment. Final stage of experiment shown in Fig. 4. Synthetic faults numbered in order of formation. Photograph by R. H. Groshong.

such antithetic faults form when a thick horizontal competent unit tries to bend to move up an inclined master thrust fault. The low angle, reverse slip, antithetic secondary faults seen in the half-space model (Fig. 5b) leads one to infer that the back thrusts described by Serra and Morse may be features characteristic of an inclined master thrust fault propagating through a thick homogeneous medium. From the lack of low angle antithetic secondary faults with reverse slip above the master fault in Fig. 7b one may infer that back thrusts are not characteristic of a master thrust fault propagating from a more rigid medium into a less rigid medium.

In both Figs 5 and 7 there are antithetic faults above the master fault which are more or less parallel to the ground surface. If there were horizontal bedding, then these secondary antithetic faults could produce bedding-plane slip above the master fault. As Fig. 8 shows, these subhorizontal antithetic faults can also form in a homogeneous clay cake. Movement on these faults is probably a consequence of the material trying to accommodate the bending produced by the vertical uplift (Fig. 3).

Conclusions

The vertical displacement of the ground surface produced by a dipping thrust fault has been calculated from elastic dislocation theory. Four models have been used: (1) a 30° dipping fault with the tip 20 km below the surface of a half-space; (2) a 60° dipping fault with the tip 20 km below the surface of a half-space; (3) a 30° dipping fault with the tip 50 km below the surface of a half-space; and (4) a 30° dipping fault below a 20 km thick layer with a lower shear modulus than the underlying half-space.

The models all show that the surface uplift is asymmetric and is greatest in a zone somewhat behind the vertical projection of the fault tip on the surface. The gradient of the surface uplift becomes steeper as: (1) the fault dip increases; (2) the fault comes closer to the surface; and (3) the shear modulus of the layer decreases with respect to the shear modulus of the half-space. The magnitude of the surface uplift increases as: (1) the fault dip increases; (2) the fault becomes shallower; and (3) the shear modulus of the layer decreases with respect to the shear modulus of the half-space.

The vertical displacements predict that an anticline will form in the hanging-wall of an inclined thrust fault. This anticline is observed both in clay models and in the field. The vertical displacements also predict that the ma-

terial above and ahead of the master fault will thicken slightly, and this effect is seen in a clay model. The fact that the theory predicts features which are found in the clay models increases our confidence in the theory.

Photoelastic and clay models are used together with the four dislocation models to study the potential secondary fault patterns which might be produced by a dipping thrust fault. The potential secondary fault patterns predicted from the photoelastic model and the half-space dislocation model have several features in common. They show that the master fault could extend itself by continuing with more or less the same dip to the surface, and the dislocation model suggests that the master fault could extend itself by flattening and propagating more or less parallel to the ground surface. The photoelastic model suggests that the master fault is likely to extend itself to the surface with about the same dip. This is due to the applied horizontal compression in the photoelastic models which is not in the dislocation models. The models also show that high-angle antithetic faults (back thrusts) could form in the hanging-wall above the master fault. The dislocation models indicate that there are areas where secondary faults could form above and below the master fault that do not strike parallel to the master fault. These out of the plane secondary faults are not seen in the essentially plane stress photoelastic models.

The major difference between the predicted secondary faulting from the 30° dip and 60° dip models is that the fault patterns are rotated. There is essentially no difference between the secondary faults predicted for the 20 km deep and 50 km deep master fault.

The potential secondary fault patterns for a half-space and a layered half-space are quite different. The maximum shear stress in the layered model is increased over the half-space value and elongated parallel to the interface relative to the half-space model, and the master fault is somewhat more likely to flatten as it propagates into a weak layer. This latter conclusion is substantiated by clay and rock models. This is a mechanism that will change a ramp into a bedding-parallel fault. Back thrusts should not be well developed in the layered case, and there are essentially no three dimensional effects in the layered model. The presence of a weak layer may also produce subhorizontal antithetic faults in the layer. These faults would enhance bedding-plane slip in the uplift which forms over the master fault if the bedding is subhorizontal.

The homogeneous dislocation model and photoelastic model predict maximum shear-stress distributions and secondary fault patterns which are similar within the limits set by the different boundary conditions, and the predicted low angle antithetic reverse faults in the hanging-wall of the master fault are seen in nature. The secondary fault pattern predicted by the layered dislocation model resembles the secondary fault pattern which develops in the clay model, and the predicted low angle synthetic reverse faults in the footwall ahead of the master fault are found in nature. The reasonably good qualitative agreement between the three model techniques and the real world gives us a great deal of confidence in using these techniques to study more complex geological problems.

The clay model can also be used to address the problem of the applicability of the small-strain dislocation and photoelastic models to finite strain problems. The presence of the small synthetic faults in the footwall of the clay model and the small sub-horizontal antithetic faults in the hanging wall of the clay model suggests that the secondary faults predicted by the small-strain models do form in finite strain situations.

Finally, the potential secondary fault patterns predicted by the models should be of some interest to earthquake seismologists. The stress field determined from the dislocation models would be similar to that produced by an earthquake on a buried thrust fault. If aftershocks occur in the rocks around the main fault, the aftershocks should have focal mechanisms with orientations similar to the potential secondary fault patterns in Figs 5, 6, and 7. We are not aware of any published studies of focal mechanisms of aftershocks of thrust-type earthquakes which have the necessary station coverage to test the predictions. Thus, we are suggesting this as an area of future research.

ACKNOWLEDGMENTS. The tedious algebraic work and computer programming for the dislocation models were done by Dave Terry and Randy Reed. Martha Withjack and Rick Groshong reviewed the manuscript and provided many helpful suggestions. Pat Lacy prepared the original manuscript on the text editing system at the Cities Service Research Lab. Figs 4b and 8 are from an unpublished experiment run by Rick Groshong in 1977, and he has generously allowed us to use the photographs in this paper. This paper is based on a Cities Service Co. Research Report, and we are grateful to Cities Service for permission to publish the paper.

References

ALEWINE, R. W. III 1974. *Application of Linear Inversion Theory toward the Estimation of Seismic Source Parameters.* Thesis, Ph.D., California Institute of Technology (unpubl.).

BEN-MENAHEM, A. & GILLON, A. 1970. Crustal deformation by earthquakes and explosions. *Bull. seismol. Soc. Am.* **60**, 193–215.

—— & SINGH, S. J. 1968. Multipolar elastic fields in a layered half-space. *Bull. seismol. Soc. Am.* **58**, 1519–72.

BOMBOLAKIS, E. G. 1964. Photoelastic investigation of brittle crack growth within a field of uniaxial compression. *Tectonophysics*, **1**, 343–51.

—— 1968. Photoelastic study of initial stages of brittle fracture in compression. *Tectonophysics*, **6**, 461–73.

CHEN, Y., LIN, Z., LIN, B. & LI, Z. 1975. The focal mechanism of the 1966 Xingtai earthquake as inferred from ground deformation observations (in Chinese). *Acta. geophys. Sin.* **18**, 164–81. Translation in *Chinese Geophysics*, 1978, **1**, 263–88.

COKER, E. & FILON, L. 1931. *A Treatise on Photoelasticity.* Cambridge University Press, London. 720 p.

CURRIE, J. B., PATINODE, H. W. & TRUMP, R. P. 1962. Development of folds in sedimentary strata. *Bull. geol. Soc. Am.* **73**, 655–74.

DAHLSTROM, C. D. A. 1970. Structural geology in the eastern margin of the Canadian Rocky Mountains. *Bull. Can. Pet. Geol.* **18**, 332–406.

DURELLI, A. J. & RILEY, W. F. 1965. *Introduction to Photomechanics.* Prentice-Hall, Englewood Cliffs, New Jersey 402 p.

FROCHT, M. M. 1941. *Photoelasticity*, Vol. 1. John Wiley and Sons, New York. 411 p.

—— 1948. *Photoelasticity*, Vol. 2. John Wiley and Sons, New York. 505 p.

GALLAGHER, J. J., FRIEDMAN, M., HANDIN, J. & SOWERS, G. M. 1974. Experimental studies relating to micro-fractures in sandstones. *Tectonophysics*, **21**, 203–47.

—— & LOGAN, J. M. 1973. Stresses in experimentally produced folds (abstract). *EOS*, **54**, 459.

—— & RIZER, W. D. 1977. Photoelastic model studies of thrust fault initiation. *Wyoming Geological Association Guidebook. 29th Annual Field Conference*, 441–8.

—— & —— 1978. Analysis of thrust-fault mechanisms: III. welded and unwelded photoelastic models of ramps before and after slip (abstract). *Abst. geol. Soc. Am.* **10**, 5.

GOULTY, N. R. & GILMAN, R. 1978. Repeated creep events on the San Andreas fault near Parkfield, California, recorded by a strainmeter array. *J. Geophys. Res.* **83**, 5415–19.

GROSHONG, R. H. & RODGERS, D. A. 1978. Left-lateral strike slip fault model. *In*: WICKHAM, J. & DENISON, R. (eds), *Structural Style of the Arbuckle Region.* Geol. Soc. Am. South Central Section. Guidebook to Field Trip **3**, 1–7.

HARRIS, L. D. & MILICI, R. C. 1977. Characteristics of thin-skinned style of deformation in the southern Appalachians, and potential hydrocarbon traps. *Prof. Pap. U.S. geol. Surv.* **1018**, 40 pp.

JACOBEEN, F. & KANES, W. H. 1974. Structure of Broadtop synclinorium and its implications for Applachian structural style. *Bull. Am. Assoc. Petrol Geol.* **58**, 362–75.

—— & —— 1975. Structure of Broadtop synclinorium, Wills Mountain anticlinorium, and Alleghany frontal zone. *Bull. Am. Assoc. Petrol. Geol.* **59**, 1136–50.

JAEGER, J. C. & COOK, N. G. W. 1969. *Fundamentals of Rock Mechanics.* Methuen, London. 513 p.

McHUGH, S. & JOHNSTON, M. J. S. 1978. Dislocation modeling of creep-related tilt changes. *Bull. seismol. Soc. Am.* **68**, 155–68.

MORSE, J. D. 1977. Deformation in the ramp regions of overthrust faults: experiments with small-scale rock models. *Wyoming Geological Association Guidebook, 29th Annual Field Conference*, 457–70.

RICH, J. L. 1934. Mechanics of low-angle overthrust faulting illustrated by Cumberland thrust block, Virginia, Kentucky, and Tennessee. *Bull. Am. Assoc. Petrol. Geol.* **18**, 1584–96.

RODGERS, D. A. 1976. Mechanical analysis of strike slip faults. II. Dislocation model studies (abstract). *EOS*, **57**, 327.

—— 1979. Deformation, stress accumulation. and secondary faulting in the vicinity of the Transverse Ranges of southern California. *Bull. Calif. Div. Mines Geol.* **203**, 74 pp.

SAVAGE, J. C. & HASTIE, L. M. 1969. A dislocation model for the Fairview Peak, Nevada, earthquake. *Bull. seismol. Soc. Am.* **59**, 1937–48.

SERRA, S. 1977. Styles of deformation in the ramp regions of overthrust faults. *Wyoming Geological Association Guidebook, 29th Annual Field Conference*, 487–98.

—— 1978. *Styles of Deformation in the Ramp Regions of Overthrust Faults.* Thesis. Ph.D., Texas A&M University (unpubl.).

SOWERS, G. M. 1973. Theory of spacing of extension fractures. *In*: H. Pincus, (ed), *Geological Factors in Rapid Excavation*, Eng. Geol. Case Hist. **9**, 27–53.

STEKETEE, J. A. 1958a. On Volterra's dislocations in a semi-infinite elastic medium. *Can. J. Phys.* **36**, 192–205.

—— 1958b. Some geophysical applications of the elasticity theory of dislocations. *Can. J. Phys.* **36**, 1168–98.

D. A. RODGERS, W. D. RIZER, Cities Services Company, Energy Resources Group, Exploration and Production Research Laboratory, Box 3908, Tulsa, OK 74102, U.S.A.

Mechanical model of thrust sheet gliding and imbrication

G. Mandl & G. K. Shippam

SUMMARY: A competent thrust sheet being pushed over incompetent substrata is idealized as an elastic block overriding a stack of perfectly plastic substrata. The stress fields induced in both the plastic substrata and the thrust sheet have been analysed for various thrust sheet dimensions and boundary conditions.

In the case of the plastic substrata the stress analysis accounts for the formation and location of a basal slip plane, its stepping-up to a higher gliding horizon, and for secondary faulting.

For the competent thrust sheets, finite-element analyses have located a well-defined spot where a push force of sufficient magnitude is likely to induce fracturing and, consequently, may control the formation of an imbrication thrust, assuming that faulting is not preceded by compressional folding. Some further conclusions are drawn with respect to the development and spacing of subsequent imbrication thrusts.

The frontal zones of orogenic belts are often characterized by the occurrence of thrust sheets consisting of sediments that have been detached from their substrata. They have been sheared off along basal slip planes formed in beds of low shear strength. The detached sheets may be pulled by their weight or be thrust by a push from the rear over their foreland; the latter case will be discussed in this paper.

The overthrusting sediment, rather than forming a continuous thrust sheet, is likely to be dissected into separate units at an early stage of the process. One possible model is shown very schematically in Fig. 1a, the individual units are in general delimited at front and rear by thrust faults and in the lateral direction by strike-slip faults ('tear faults'). It may be reasonably assumed that these discontinuities define the thrust units not only in a geometrical but also in a mechanical sense, by affecting characteristically the stress transfer through the whole thrust system and breaking the smooth flow of stress trajectories.

A thrust sheet that is pushed from the rear is subject to frictional resistance along its base and to a buttressing force at its front. As overthrusting continues, this resistance may increase to a point where the higher stresses initiate imbrication of the sheet (Fig. 1b). We shall deal with the mechanical aspects of this process in the second part of this paper, considering an idealized thrust sheet of sufficient thickness and 'brittleness' to ensure that imbrication thrusting is not affected by preceding compressive folding.

The incompetent substrata interact mechanically with the overlying competent thrust sheet (Fig. 2) and the analysis of the thrust sheet therefore requires the determination of stresses and deformations inside the substrata. We shall, accordingly, deal first with a stack of substrata subject to shear and compression between two parallel rigid plates representing the base of the thrust sheet and the top of the underlying competent strata, respectively. (Fig. 2). The 'incompetent' material behaviour of the substrata will be idealized as perfectly plastic in the sense of plasticity theory (e.g. Jaeger & Cook 1969, Ch. IX); the most typical features of perfect plasticity being the existence of a yield condition for the stresses and the possibility of deformation by discrete 'slips'. The abundance of slip phenomena observed on a micro and a macro scale at outcrops of overthrusts lends support to this idealization. The shear strength of the material is taken as pressure-independent, but may vary with depth.

The large lateral extent of thrust sheets and substrata permits us to use the further simplifying assumption of 'plane strain', for the main part of the model, which means that the deformations are regarded as being the same for any thrust-parallel vertical cross-section ('plane of deformation'). Furthermore, the plastic strata will be treated as 'infinitely' long; a simplification justified by the high length/thickness ratios encountered in reality.

It should be recalled that the rate of deformation in a perfectly plastic material is not controlled by the stresses and boundary loads,

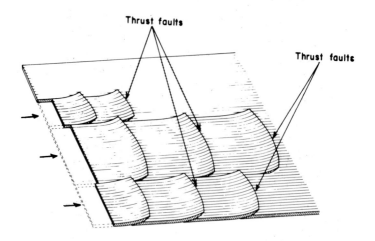

a) THRUST UNITS

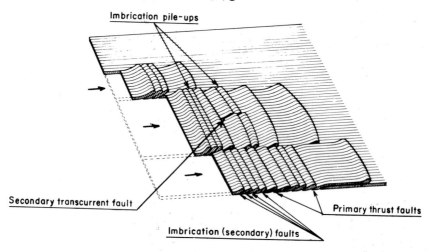

b) IMBRICATION OF UNITS

Fig. 1. Thrust sheets.

but solely by the movements of the outer boundaries. In other words, the rate of deformation in the plastic substrata will be controlled by the rate at which the thrust sheet moves. This 'stress-insensitivity' of the rate of plastic processes constitutes a fundamental difference from viscous flow and precludes the prediction of overthrust rates without introducing additional assumptions. The analysis of the plastic substrata in the following section will, however, provide the stress conditions at the base of the thrust sheet and a mechanical interpretation of various structures such as the sharp smooth thrust planes commonly observed at the basis of thrust sheets, listric subsidiary faults, and 'step-thrusts' joining different gliding horizons.

The plastic substrata

Stresses

The problem of determining the stresses in an infinite strip of layered, perfectly plastic material which is sheared and compressed between parallel rigid platens is illustrated in Fig. 3.

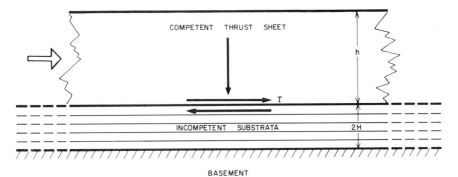

FIG. 2. Incompetent strata loaded by thrust sheet.

The stresses that act in a thrust-parallel vertical cross-section (plane of deformation) are completely known when the two normal stresses σ_x and σ_y—counted as negative when compressive—and the shear stress τ are determined as functions of the coordinates x and y. These stresses must satisfy the equilibrium equations

$$\frac{\partial \sigma_x}{\partial x} + \frac{\partial \tau}{\partial y} = 0, \quad \frac{\partial \tau}{\partial x} + \frac{\partial \sigma_y}{\partial y} = 0 \quad (1)$$

and the quadratic yield condition of perfect plasticity

$$\tfrac{1}{4}(\sigma_x - \sigma_y)^2 + \tau^2 = k(y)^2 \text{ (von Mises' yield} \\ \text{criterion)} \quad (2)$$

where k is the shearing strength. In view of the large boundary loads, gravity is insignificant and is therefore neglected in equation (1).

Since the plastic strip is of infinite extent, it seems appropriate to admit as possible stress fields only those solutions of equations (1) and (2) whose principal stress directions do not vary in the x-direction, i.e. parallel to the horizontal platens. These special solutions are described by the expressions

$$\tau = ay + (\tau_1 + \tau_2)/2, \quad (3a)$$
$$\sigma_y = -ax + \sigma_y^0, \quad (3b)$$
$$\sigma_x = \sigma_y \pm 2(k(y)^2 - \tau^2)^{1/2}, \quad (3c)$$

which for the convenience of the reader are derived in Appendix I. The constant 'a' is defined as

$$a = \mathrm{d}(-\sigma_y)/\mathrm{d}x = (\tau_1 - \tau_2)/2H \quad (4)$$

where $2H$ is the height of the plastic strip and τ_1, τ_2 are the values which the shear stress τ uniformly attains along the upper and the lower boundary ($y = \pm H$), respectively.

The constant $\sigma_y^0 < 0$ denotes the compressive vertical stress exerted upon the strip at the reference points $x = 0$, $y = \pm H$ (Fig. 3).

The class of stress fields described by equations 3a & b contain as special cases the trivial solutions with τ and σ_y constant throughout the plastic strip ($\tau_1 = \tau_2$), and

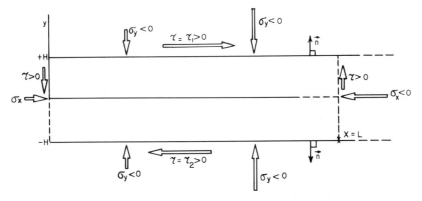

FIG. 3. Shearing of plastic material between rigid parallel platens.

Prandtl's well-known solution to the 'squeezing' problem (e.g. Hill 1960). In Prandtl's case rough parallel walls are either forced together or driven apart, either squeezing plastic material out or allowing it to enter. Prandtl's solution is obtained from equations (3a) and (3b) by imposing $\tau_1 = \tau_2 = k(\pm H)$ which implies, as illustrated in Fig. 4, that both externally applied shear stresses act in the same direction upon the plastic strip—opposing the squeeze flow. According to equation (4) the plastic squeeze flow requires $a > 0$, which further implies by equation (3b) that the compressive boundary stress $-\sigma_y$ increases linearly in the direction of the applied shear stress (Fig. 4). The stress gradient $d(-\sigma_y)/dx = a$ at the same time also defines the critical distance of the two boundary plates in the Prandtl case, for which it follows from (4): $2H = 2k(\pm H)/a$. It will be seen in the next section, however, that during overthrusting large-scale plastic squeeze flow can hardly play a role, since the ratio a/k turns out to reach values so small that the required thickness of the incompetent substrata would amount to tens of kilometres.

The stress field (3a)–(3c) pertinent to our problem will therefore in general be restricted to heights of the plastic strip (Fig. 4)

$$2H < k/a \qquad (5)$$

and subject to the boundary loads

$$\tau(x, +H) = \tau_1 = \text{const} > 0;$$
$$\sigma_y(x, +H) = -ax + \sigma_y^0, \qquad (6)$$

with $a > 0$. The last condition ensures that the compressive boundary stress $-\sigma_y$ increases in the shear direction, this being necessary to achieve static equilibrium of the thrust sheet, as will be discussed later.

The boundary conditions (6) at the upper boundary $y = +H$ also determine the boundary stresses at the lower boundary $y = -H$. In particular, τ_2 is determined by equation (4):

$$\tau(x, -H) = \tau_2 = \tau_1 - 2H \cdot a > 0. \qquad (7)$$

In contrast to Prandtl's solution, both shear stresses τ_1 and τ_2 have the same sign and, according to the sign convention employed,

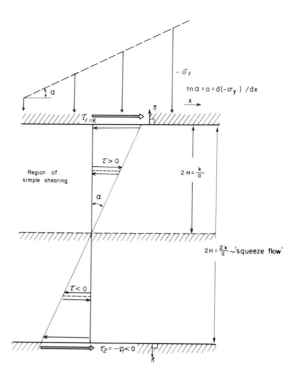

Simple shearing by opposite shear stresses when $2H < \frac{k}{a}$, shearing by equally directed shear stresses when $\frac{k}{a} < 2H < \frac{2k}{a}$, 'Squeezing' when $2H = \frac{2k}{a}$

FIG. 4. Layer thickness and mode of plastic flow (shear strength $k = $ const.).

therefore have opposite directions, as indicated in Figs 3 & 4.

Thus, typically for this plastic solution, the perfectly plastic layers can sustain a difference between top and bottom shear stresses which is independent of the shear strength k, but determined by the gradient 'a' of the boundary 'pressure' $-\sigma_y$.

According to equations (3) the lateral 'confining' stress σ_x is fully determined by the parameters a, σ_y^0, τ_1 and H, except for the double sign in equation (3c). The double sign expresses the typical fact that two different plastic states of stress are compatible with the boundary conditions (6). The plus sign corresponds with the smaller lateral compression $|\sigma_x^+|$ and hence with the smaller compressive mean stress (pressure) $-(\sigma_x + \sigma_y)/2$. This solution characterizes the so-called 'active' plastic state. It may evolve directly from an elastic state (where always $|\sigma_x| < |\sigma_y|$). The negative sign in (3c) is associated with the highest possible lateral compressive stress $|\sigma_x^-| \geq |\sigma_y|$. This 'strong' solution will apply when the flow of the plastic material is obstructed ('passive' state). A noteworthy property of the two solutions is that they give the same state of stress along the plane $y = y^*$, for which the horizontal shear stress τ equals the shearing strength $k = k(y^*)$.

In reality, where we deal with a very long, but finite, plastic strip, the 'confining' stress σ_x will adjust itself on near-end cross-sections to the boundary loads (6) via distortions of the end regions.

Basal thrust planes and secondary faults

It has already been mentioned in the introductory section that slip of material along discrete interior surfaces is the most typical feature of plastic deformation. On a macroscopical, i.e. phenomenological scale the theory of perfect plasticity accounts very successfully for this phenomenon by associating in the plane case two sets of potential slip lines with the plastic stress field. Across these and only these lines (or envelopes of them) the tangential velocity components may change discontinuously ('velocity characteristics'; e.g. Hill 1960). Slip lines or -surfaces in the rock-plastic model therefore impose themselves as mathematical images of tectonic faults—of any magnitude (Odé 1960).

In plane plastic deformation of a material to which v. Mises' yield condition (2) applies, the slip lines coincide with the trajectories of maximum shear stress and consequently bisect at any point the right angle between the principal stress directions. Details of the determination

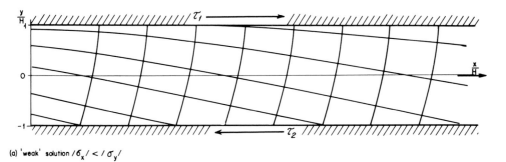

(a) 'weak' solution $/\sigma_x/ < /\sigma_y/$

(b) 'strong' solution $/\sigma_x/ > /\sigma_y/$

FIG. 5. Slip lines in homogeneous layer under shear and compression ($\tau_1 = k$, $aH = k/20$).

and integration of the field of slip directions are given in Appendix I. Two typical solutions are presented in Figs 5 & 6.

In Fig. 5a & b the slip lines are plotted for a case where the tangential stress τ_1 at the base of the thrust sheet, i.e. at the upper boundary $y = +H$ of the plastic strip, equals the shearing strength k of a homogeneous substratum. For both the weak and the strong solution, corresponding with the 'active' and the 'passive' state respectively, the slip lines are cycloids, their radius of curvature being proportional to the parameter k/aH. For a plastic substratum of given height and shearing strength the radius of slip line curvature will therefore according to equation (3b) be inversely proportional to the gradient of the vertical pressure exerted by the thrust sheet. The figures clearly demonstrate the characteristic differences in slip line pattern for the active and the passive state. Both solutions, however, have in common that one set of slip lines is tangential to the upper boundary; in both cases slip can therefore occur along that boundary (thrust base).

In general, the shear strength of the substrata may vary with depth. The solution for such a case is shown in Fig. 6a & b. It is assumed that the variation in shear strength is as indicated in Fig. 7 and that $\tau_1 = 0.6k_\infty$, k_∞ being the value the shear strength attains near

the boundaries of the plastic layer. The weak and the strong solution each give a set of slip lines that intersect a plane SS tangentially. Along this plane SS, whose position is the same for the active and the passive state, the material enclosed between the 'thrust sheet' and the plane will glide as a solid block, since movement along the slip lines is obstructed by the competent boundaries.

The slip plane SS in Fig. 6a & b may be seen as a theoretical representation of real 'thrust planes', like the one shown in Fig. 8. The position y^* of SS is determined in Fig. 7 by the point where the τ-line touches the strength profile. When $a > 0$, i.e. when the vertical compressive stress $-\sigma_y$ increases in the thrust direction, the plane SS will lie above the plane of lowest strength and will shift towards the top of the plastic stratum as the shear strength decreases with depth in a more abrupt manner, as indicated by the dotted strength profile in Fig. 7. The opposite happens of course when the compressive vertical stress $-\sigma_y$ decreases in the thrust direction ($a < 0$).

In general, the strength profile $k(y)$ will have a more irregular shape than in Fig. 7. The thrust sheet may rest in particular on a stack of alternatingly incompetent (i.e. plastic) and competent (i.e. elastic) strata where, as shown in Fig. 9, the horizontal shear stress only varies

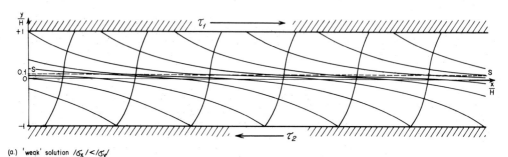

(a.) 'weak' solution $|\sigma_x| < |\sigma_y|$

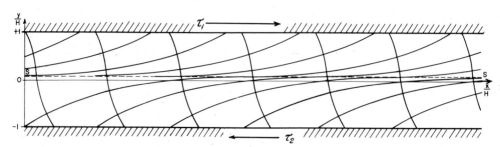

(b.) 'strong' solution $|\sigma_x| > |\sigma_y|$

FIG. 6. Slip lines and 'thrust plane' SS in stratified layer under shear and compression ($k = [1 - \frac{1}{2}\cos^2 y/H]k_\infty$ as shown in Fig. 7; $aH = 0.1k_\infty$, $\tau_1 = 0.6k_\infty$).

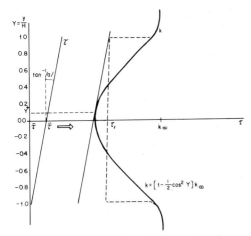

FIG. 7. Critical horizontal shear stress in stratified zone of weakness.

in the incompetent layers, whereas the vertical normal stress remains unchanged with depth throughout the stack of layers.

Since the variation of the horizontal shear stress with depth is determined by the horizontal gradient of the overburden stress $-\sigma_y$ and does not depend on the local shear strength, different overburden gradients may, in a given stack of substrata, mobilize different basal slip planes. As sketched in Fig. 10, a stronger increase of $-\sigma_y$ in the thrust direction will be associated with a slip plane at shallower depth and in a layer of somewhat higher shear strength than in the case of a smaller gradient of $-\sigma_y$. This would suggest 'stepping-up' of a sole fault underneath localities of a drastic increase in the gradient $d(-\sigma_y)/dx$, as for instance caused by thickening of the thrust sheet. The latter is illustrated by Fig. 11. It should be noted that an increased gradient 'a' of the base pressure is not restricted to the transition region between the thinner and the thicker part of the thrust sheet, but will in general, persist, along the base of the thicker part. This is required for the balance of the moment of forces, as will be shown later.

The immobilization of the lower gliding horizon II by shear stress reduction (Fig. 10) is accompanied by change in the slip direction. This is demonstrated in Mohr's stress diagram in Fig. 12, where the new stress state at some point of the original slip plane II is represented by the dotted circle. A simple construction based on the stress 'pole'—for convenience of the reader explained in Appendix II—shows that the former horizontal slip direction is now

FIG. 8. 'Glarus' Overthrust, Tschingelhörner, Switzerland. (Courtesy of Prof. J. G. Ramsay; SS basal thrust plane along top of Malm limestone M, V Verrucano sandstone, F Eocene Flysch).

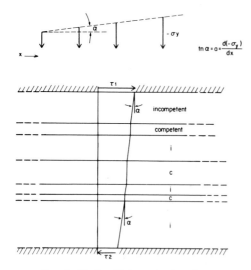

FIG. 9. Stack of incompetent and competent strata under compression and shear.

replaced by a low-angle thrust element. Obviously, the change in dip angle is less abrupt than suggested in Fig. 12, since, in passing along the plane II the transition zone between the two regions of different gradients of $-\sigma_y$, the dip angle of the potential thrust element gradually increases to the value associated with the full τ-reduction indicated in Fig. 10. This allows for a smooth branch-off of a 'step' fault which connects the two gliding horizons (Fig. 11). Steepening of the step fault and final flattening near the upper horizon can—at least qualitatively—be established by the construction of Mohr circles which are similar to the dotted circle in Fig. 12, but are tangent to limit lines associated with the different k-values and pass through the proper stress point $(-\sigma_y, \tau)$.

The step faults have to be distinguished from the slip lines that intersect the plastic strata in

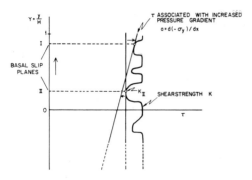

FIG. 10. 'Stepping-up' of basal slip planes.

regions of uniform pressure gradient 'a' as shown in Figs 5 & 6. Slips of these types may occasionally be mobilized, for instance when the base of the thrust sheet deforms or when compaction in the incompetent strata allows for minor slips. Fig. 13 presents the synthetic secondary faults which in the case of Fig. 6 could accompany overthrusting. It is tempting to interpret the lineaments which transect the plastic Malm limestone underneath the 'Glarus' Overthrust in Fig. 8 as secondary thrust faults which are associated with the passive limit state (lower half of fault T' in Fig. 13b). The features would then indicate that at this location the horizontal normal stresses in the plastic limestone have attained values considerably in excess of the overburden stresses.

Frictional plastic substrata

In discussing stresses and faults in the incompetent substrata we assumed ideally plastic behaviour with a stress-independent shear strength ('von Mises plasticity'). Some weak rocks, limestones in particular, may in the pertinent pressure range conform quite closely to this assumption (e.g. Riffault 1969). In this connection reference is made to the plastic microstructures in calcite tectonites of Helvetic nappes that have been discussed by Schmid et al. (this volume). Yet, in many cases of overthrusting the 'weak' rocks that served as 'lubricants' will have a shearing strength which increases with the 'effective' pressure (i.e. the mean normal stress minus pore pressure p). Consequently, in such rocks an increase in pore pressure under unchanged total stress conditions reduces the shear strength. Hubbert & Rubey (1959) employed this concept in their classic overthrust paper and considered the shear strength of the material at the base of the thrust sheet to be linearly related to the effective pressure. Adopting Terzaghi's concept of pore pressure induced landslides (Terzaghi 1950, 1956), Hubbert & Rubey allowed abnormally high pore pressures at the base of a thrust sheet to relieve a good deal of the overburden load carried by the solid rock skeleton and therefore to reduce substantially the frictional resistance along the thrust base.

Taking into account the pressure dependence of the shearing strength when dealing with stresses and deformations of ideally plastic materials would necessitate a more complex variant of plasticity theory ('frictional' or Coulomb-plasticity) than the one employed in this study (e.g. Salencon 1977). In such a

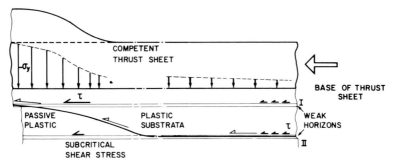

FIG. 11. 'Stepping-up' of basal slip plane underneath overthrust sheet.

theory the right-hand side of the yield condition (2) would have to be replaced by the expression

$$\left[c_0 \cot \phi - \frac{\sigma'_x + \sigma'_y}{2} \right]^2 \sin^2 \phi \qquad (8)$$

ϕ being the 'angle of internal friction' and c_0 the 'cohesive' shear strength; and the total stresses σ_x, σ_y in equations (1) have to be expressed in effective stresses ($\sigma'_x = \sigma_x + p$, $\sigma'_y = \sigma_y + p$; compressive stresses counted as negative).

An analytical solution to this system of equations for Prandtl's compression between rigid parallel platens has so far only been obtained (Marshall 1967) under the simplifying assumptions $\phi = \text{const.}$, $c_0 = 0$, and negligible pore pressure gradients. The stress solution to our simple shearing problem can be 'cut out' from this solution by prescribing along the upper boundary of the frictional plastic strip a constant ratio $\tau/(-\sigma'_y)$, which equals the ratio of the net push force to the total weight of the thrust sheet. (The constancy of the ratio of tangential to vertical normal stress along the boundary follows from the requirement that in

the 'infinite' plastic strip the directions of the principal stresses do not vary in the x-direction.) This may be verified by means of equations (I.1, 2) after K in equation (I.2) has been replaced by the pressure terms in expression (8). It may suffice here to mention that the slip lines are again isogonal cycloids, similar to those in Fig. 5, but now intersecting each other under the acute angle $90° - \phi$. Furthermore, the vertical normal stress $-\sigma'_y$ no longer increases linearly in the thrust direction but exponentially, and so do the other stresses. The decrease of the horizontal shear stress τ with depth inside the plastic layer is also stronger than in the cohesive plastic material considered in the previous section, but a detailed discussion of the solution is beyond the scope of this paper.

Whereas in the cohesive (*v.* Mises) plastic material step-faulting between two gliding horizons (Fig. 11) was controlled by changes in the gradient of the vertical pressure ($-\sigma_y$) and the corresponding changes in the horizontal shearing stress, the pore pressure enters as an additional controlling parameter in the case of a frictional plastic material. Fig. 14a shows a frictional plastic layer enclosed between two parallel gliding horizons (bedding-plane faults). The layer is in the passive limit state, i.e. under high horizontal compression, which permits stepping-up from one gliding horizon to the other. For simplicity, gradients of shear stress and total normal stresses are neglected and changes in effective stresses $-\sigma'_x$ and $-\sigma'_y$ are assumed to be solely caused by pore pressure gradients. We assume that the pore pressure along the main gliding horizons is higher than inside the sheared interlayer (e.g. due to liquefaction at the gliding planes). Consequently, the effective stresses $-\sigma'_y$ decrease towards the bounding gliding planes, as is also indicated for the critical stress circles in the diagram of Fig. 14b, which correspond with the positions 1, 2, 3 in Fig. 14a. The 'poles' of

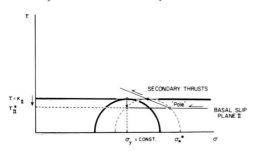

CORD DRAWN FROM POLE TO CONTACT POINT ON LIMIT LINE FORMS SAME ANGLE WITH LINE τ =CONST. AS ACTUAL SLIP WITH BASAL SLIP PLANE

FIG. 12. Immobilization of lower gliding horizon and initiation of secondary thrusts.

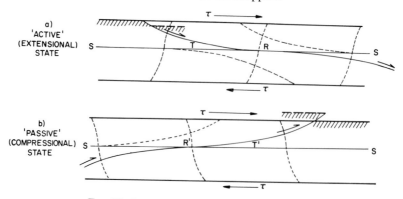

FIG. 13. Secondary faulting in plastic substrata.

the stress circles (cf. Appendix II) lie on the line $\tau = $ const. and the cords drawn from the poles to the respective contact points on the limit line form the same angle with the line $\tau = $ const. as slips inside the interlayer would include with the gliding horizons. One should notice a decrease in dip angle with increasing pore pressure (i.e. decreasing effective compressive stress $-\sigma_y'$) which may account for the sigmoidal shape of step-bedding plane thrusts.

The reader may verify by means of a similar stress diagram that an increase in friction angle ϕ from position 1 to 3 in Fig. 14a, i.e. a corresponding steepening of the limit line in Fig. 14b, would have a similar effect on the shape of the step fault.

The thrust sheet

Stresses and critical strength

Having analysed stresses and fault surfaces in the plastic substrata, we now turn to the analysis of the stresses induced in the overriding thrust sheet. The sheet is idealized as a rectangular block showing a linear elastic behaviour and being propelled by a push force from the rear. Push-stresses and frontal buttressing stresses may by distributed in various ways; the distributions shown in Fig. 15 for a block of 10 km length and 1 km height are taken as a

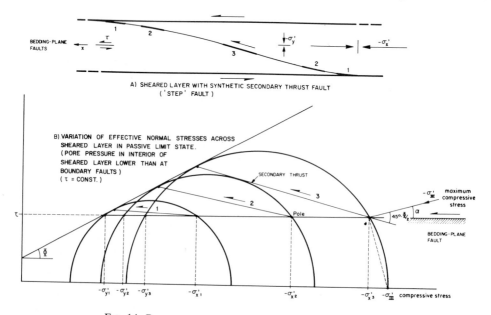

FIG. 14. Pore-pressure control of step-bedding plane thrusts.

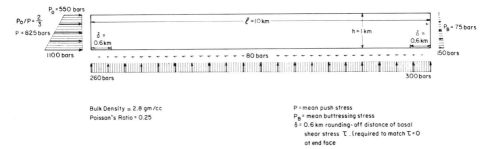

FIG. 15. The reference model.

reference model. One may notice that the net push force and the basal friction force together exert a clockwise moment upon the thrust block which tends to make it topple over. If the weight of the thrust sheet were supported by a uniformly distributed vertical pressure along the base of the sheet, the basal stresses could not provide the countermoment required to keep the thrust block in a horizontal position. As our analysis has shown, however, the plastic substrata, when compressed and sheared by the overriding thrust sheet, will exert a pressure upon the base of the thrust sheet that increases linearly in the thrust direction. Associated with this pressure increase is a counterclockwise moment M_1 whose magnitude with respect to the midpoint of the thrust base is easily determined as

$$M_1 = al^3/12 \qquad (9)$$

where l is the block length. As the moments of basal friction and weight vanish when referred to the chosen reference point, the value of the basal pressure gradient 'a' required to keep the thrust sheet in a horizontal position is found by balancing M_1 with the moment M_2 of the net push stresses. It may be noted here that viscous substrata could not keep the thrust sheet in a horizontal position.

For push and buttressing stresses which increase linearly with depth (Fig. 15) the resulting moment is

$$M_2 = [(P - P_b) + P_0/2]h^2/3 \qquad (10)$$

where P and P_b are the average values of the push and the buttressing stresses respectively, and P_0 is the net push stress at the top of the rear face. The stress gradient 'a' is determined from $M_1 = M_2$ and attains the value of about 4 bar/km in the reference model of Fig. 15. In this model the basal shear stress is 80 bar. With this value taken for the shear strength k of the plastic substratum the ratio k/a becomes 20 km. Referring back to Fig. 4, it may be

noticed that the thickness of the plastic strata required to allow a Prandtl-type of 'squeeze-gliding' would amount to 40 km. As mentioned earlier, it therefore seems impossible that on a larger scale incompetent substrata could be made to 'slip out' from underneath a thrust sheet.

The coupling of thrust sheet and plastic strata under simple shear has allowed us to define the stress problem for the thrust sheet exclusively in terms of boundary stresses. Fig. 16 compares our formulation of the problem with that in earlier work, in particular that by Hafner (1951). In Hafner's formulation the pressure along the thrust base is constant and the necessary anticlockwise force moment is produced by shear stresses at the end faces. In obtaining stress solutions Hafner followed the 'inverse' method, selecting from a whole class of rigorous solutions to the stress equations those which define boundary stresses that looked acceptable from a geological point of

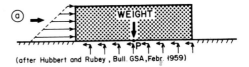

(after Hubbert and Rubey , Bull. GSA, Febr. 1959)

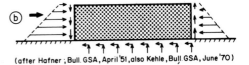

(after Hafner ; Bull. GSA, April '51, also Kehle, Bull. GSA, June '70)

PRESENT MODEL

FIG. 16. Horizontal thrust block (detached).

view. Unfortunately, in this approach the boundary stresses at the front and rear ends cannot be varied in order to establish how typical the special stress solutions are for the tectonic problem. Such variation of the boundary conditions and comparison of the corresponding solutions is, however, necessary in view of the many uncertainties regarding the boundary conditions of the actual tectonic process.

Instead of striving for special analytical solutions we have therefore chosen a numerical approach using a Finite Element program. In about fifty calculated cases the dimensions of the thrust block and the magnitude and distribution of the push and buttressing stresses were systematically varied. The effect of additional

gravity pull on a somewhat tilted block was also studied. The elastic moduli did not require changing, simply because Young's modulus does not enter the statically determined problem, and Poisson's ratio does not affect the in-plane stresses. The pore pressure was assumed to vary linearly with depth, but the ratio pore pressure/overburden stress was varied in some calculations.

Fig. 17 shows the distribution of the effective stresses calculated for the reference model of Fig. 15. The major trends are fairly predictable. In the rear part of the sheet the maximum compressive stress is horizontal, its magnitude declining from the rear to the front edge. The minimum in-plane compressive stress is for the most part simply the overburden stress. In the

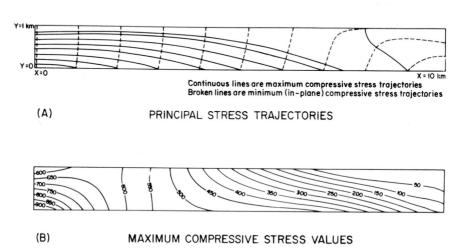

(A)   PRINCIPAL STRESS TRAJECTORIES

Continuous lines are maximum compressive stress trajectories
Broken lines are minimum (in-plane) compressive stress trajectories

(B)   MAXIMUM COMPRESSIVE STRESS VALUES

(C)   MINIMUM (IN-PLANE) COMPRESSIVE STRESS VALUES
(IN THE SHADED REGION THE MINIMUM COMPRESSIVE STRESS IS NORMAL TO THE SECTION)

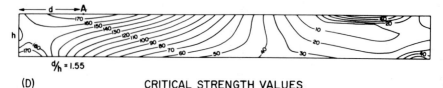

(D)   CRITICAL STRENGTH VALUES

Fig. 17. Effective-stress solution for reference model (in bar).

front part of the sheet, the horizontal component of stress becomes smaller than the overburden stress, and thus transforms from being the maximum to the minimum compressive stress.

Some important exceptions to the above trends are noticeable. Especially in the upper part of the sheet the lateral variation in the horizontal compressive stress $-\sigma'_x$ is not completely linear. In fact, the stress fluctuates almost sinusoidally about a linearly decreasing trend (Fig. 18). This produces two outstanding phenomena—the high concentration of compression at approximately 1.6 km from the rear edge and a region of tension at a similar distance from the front edge.

The peak value of the horizontal compressive stress at the upper surface of the thrust sheet some distance from the rear face is somewhat unexpected and not indicated by Hafner's solution, which rather shows a linear decrease of $-\sigma'_x$ in the thrust direction. In Appendix III it is demonstrated that the existence of a surface peak of $-\sigma'_x$ is not a peculiarity of the stress distribution chosen in our reference model but a quite common phenomenon. Its absence in Hafner's case is due to the very special and seemingly unrealistic distribution of shear stresses at the rear face of the thrust sheet.

The peak value of the horizontal compressive stress component near the upper surface

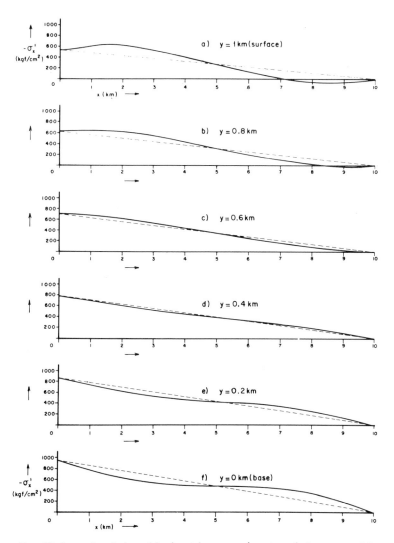

FIG. 18. Lateral variation of horizontal compressive stress (reference model).

of the thrust sheet indicates a location where the rock is likely to fail under shear. This is seen by employing a Coulomb-type failure criterion which, as may be recalled (cf. e.g. Jaeger & Cook 1969; 4.6, eq. 8), can be written as

$$\sigma'_I(1+\sin\phi)-\sigma'_{III}(1-\sin\phi)=2c\cos\phi, \quad (11)$$

where $-\sigma'_I$ and $-\sigma'_{III}$ are respectively minimum and maximum compressive stresses and the 'internal friction angle' ϕ and the 'cohesive' strength c are material parameters. Whereas ϕ varies only little, c may vary over a wide range. Without much loss of generality, we may therefore insert for ϕ a fixed value—choosing for convenience 30°—and rewrite (11) as

$$(3\sigma'_I-\sigma'_{III})/2\sqrt{3}=c. \quad (12)$$

For a given stress field, equation (12) then

defines the minimum cohesive strength the material must possess in order to be capable of withstanding the local stresses without fracturing. Fig. 17d presents the critical strength values calculated for the reference model. Two pronounced peak values of the critical strength can be distinguished: one in the lower rear corner, the other at a surface point A at some distance d from the rear edge. It can be seen that both peak values are far greater than the critical strength values anywhere inside the sheet. Moreover, the position of the surface peak of c was found to be almost insensitive to an increase in push force. We may therefore conclude that fracturing of the thrust sheet under an increased push force will first take place near the surface point A and at the lower rear corner, provided the actual cohesive strength of the rock is not substantially lower at some other location. The assumption therefore suggests itself that, in our reference model, a first

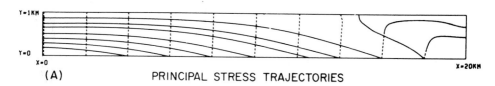

(A)   PRINCIPAL STRESS TRAJECTORIES

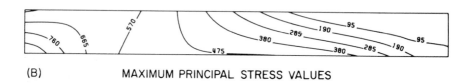

(B)   MAXIMUM PRINCIPAL STRESS VALUES

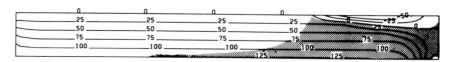

(C)   MINIMUM (IN-PLANE) PRINCIPAL STRESS VALUES

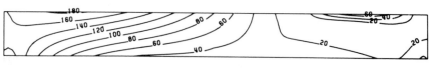

(D)   CRITICAL STRENGTH VALUES

FIG. 19. Effective-stress solution for 20 km × 1 km sheet.

imbrication thrust fault would extend from point A down to the lower rear corner. Testing of this hypothesis is, however, beyond the scope of this paper and reserved for a full elastic/plastic computer simulation of the growth of a fractured zone.

A failable spot or possible 'imbrication nucleus' at the surface was also encountered in all cases considered where the thrust sheet was longer than the reference sheet and the push stress distributed in a similar way as in the reference model or characterized by a higher ratio (P_0/P) between near-surface push stress and mean push stress. A typical example is shown in Fig. 19. For lower P_0/P ratios, i.e. in cases where the push is more concentrated near the base of the sheet, the values of the maximum compressive stress and c are increased in the lower part of the sheet and decreased in the upper part. A typical case is presented in Fig. 20. Although c still shows a maximum at the surface relative to other sur-

face points, the value of c increases in a downward direction. Obviously, in this case, it is unlikely for the thrust fault to start at the surface. Nevertheless, one might speculate that even in this case the upward growing fault zone may approach the location of the surface peak of c by not disturbing the pre-faulting stress state too severely.

In the case of Figs 17–20, only small buttressing stresses have been prescribed along the front edge. Larger buttressing stresses are concomitant with higher thrust forces on the rear edge, which results in higher horizontal stresses throughout the sheet. Fig. 21 shows a solution where the mean buttressing stress amounts to half the mean push stress. Typically, the solution again shows a distinct surface peak of the critical strength value.

Refraining from discussing more cases of our catalogue of calculated models, we should mention an interesting conclusion that has been drawn from an inspection of the results.

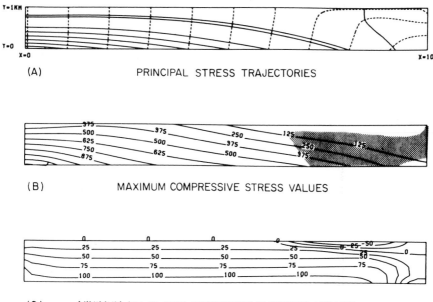

(A)   PRINCIPAL STRESS TRAJECTORIES

(B)   MAXIMUM COMPRESSIVE STRESS VALUES

(C)   MINIMUM (IN-PLANE) COMPRESSIVE STRESS VALUES

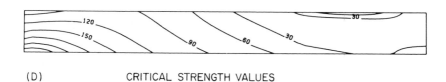

(D)   CRITICAL STRENGTH VALUES

FIG. 20. Effective-stress solution for push stress distribution with $P_0/P = 0.3$ (cf. reference model Fig. 15).

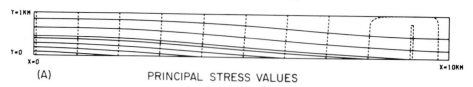

(A)   PRINCIPAL STRESS VALUES

(B)   MAXIMUM PRINCIPAL STRESS VALUES

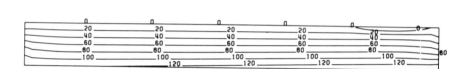

(C)   MINIMUM (IN-PLANE) PRINCIPAL STRESS VALUES

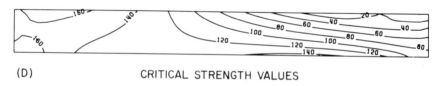

(D)   CRITICAL STRENGTH VALUES

FIG. 21. Effective-stress solution for high buttressing stress ($P_B = 0.5 P$).

The distance 'd' (Fig. 17d) between the rear edge and the surface peak of the critical strength was found to vary mainly with sheet length l and to vary slightly with sheet height and with the ratio P_0/P that characterizes the distribution of the push stresses. This dependence can be approximately represented by the simple relationship

$$d = (1 - \alpha)l \qquad (13)$$

with

$$0.75 < \alpha < 0.9,$$

where α is a lump parameter which accounts for the influence of sheet height and push stress distribution.

Naturally, formula (13) will only apply within reasonable limits. In particular the proportionality with the sheet length will no longer hold if the sheet is very long, its length exceeding its height by say at least a factor 30.

In concluding this section on the stresses set up in a competent thrust sheet, it should be mentioned that the results obtained also hold for a material whose elastic response is delayed by viscous deformation behaviour (Kelvin solid). Since the boundary conditions in the present analysis are formulated exclusively in terms of stresses, the stress state calculated for a perfectly elastic material is also the one asymptotically approached by the visco-elastic Kelvin solid.

Imbrication

As was mentioned in the introduction, individual thrust units are in general bounded by front and rear thrusts rather than by vertical faces (Fig. 22a). Nevertheless, as in the rectangular sheet, increasing basal friction and buttressing effects may raise the push stresses exerted along the rear thrust sufficiently to cause internal faulting as overthrusting continues. To exploit the results of our analysis we

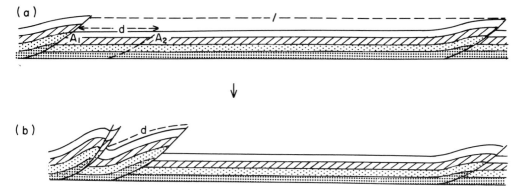

FIG. 22. First imbrication thrust.

restrict ourselves to thrust sheets of such competence and thickness that imbrication faulting is not preceded and controlled by compressive folding. The stress field will then determine the location of a first imbricate thrust which will meet the surface at some distance from the rear (Fig. 22b). As the slab sheared off from the rear of the thrust sheet and is thrust forward, the stresses in the intact remainder of the sheet will be redistributed, and eventually a situation similar to that in the original sheet will be reached, causing a second imbrication fault to form in front of the first. Restricting ourselves to the imbrication style sketched in Fig. 23, which is characterized by the fact that thickness and stiffness of the thrust sheet do not allow individual imbricate shingles to override each other, it becomes obvious that in a reasonably uniform rock mass the process of progressive imbrication should lead to a sequence of fairly regularly spaced imbrication thrusts which developed in succession from rear to front.

Based on the results obtained for our rectangular thrust sheet, we may assume that in the real thrust sheet, too, surface peaks of the critical shear strength will arise, and we may conjecture that these peaks control the position of the imbricate thrusts. As expressed by formula (13), the distance of the youngest thrust fault from its predecessor, measured along the surface of the sheet, will be proportional to the length of the intact part of the original sheet. From this it follows (Fig. 23) that the lengths of successive imbricate shingles form a geometric sequence. A relatively long un-faulted region extends between the last imbrication fault and the front of the thrust sheet (Fig. 23). Once the common factor α of the geometric sequence of imbricate lengths has been determined or estimated from observed surface separations of neighbouring faults, the

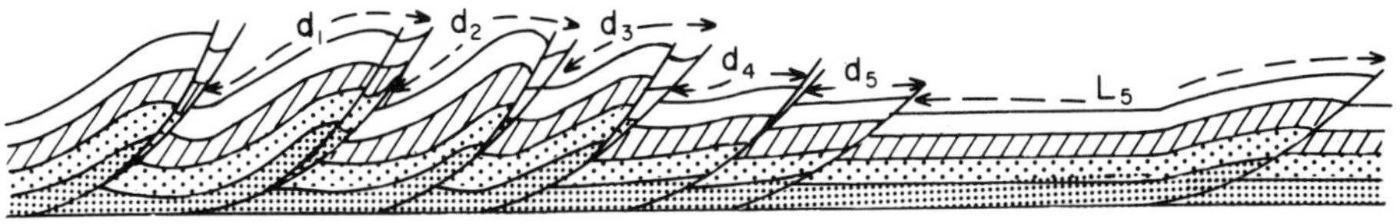

$$d_r = (1-\alpha).\alpha^{r-1}.l \, , \, L_r = \alpha^r.l$$

Thus, $\quad \dfrac{d_2}{d_1} = \dfrac{d_3}{d_2} = \dfrac{d_4}{d_3} = \ldots = \alpha \quad$ (i.e. $d_1 > d_2 > d_3 \ldots$)

and $\quad L_n = \dfrac{\alpha}{1-\alpha}.d_n$

FIG. 23. Progressive thrust sheet imbrication.

length of the unfaulted front region and even the length of the original thrust sheet can be estimated by means of the simple formulae in Fig. 23. Such extrapolations may prove useful in searching for subsurface culminations in simple thrust belts.

Appendix I

Perfectly plastic strip under compression and shear

Stresses

To derive the stresses σ_x, σ_y, τ (Fig. 3) which satisfy the stress equations (1) and (2) and at the same time define principal stress directions which do not vary in the x-direction, we first recall the well-known transformation rules

$$\left.\begin{array}{c}\sigma_x\\\sigma_y\end{array}\right\} = \frac{\sigma_I + \sigma_{III}}{2} \pm \frac{\sigma_I - \sigma_{III}}{2}\cos 2\theta \quad \text{(I.1)}$$

$$\tau = \frac{\sigma_I - \sigma_{III}}{2}\sin 2\theta$$

where σ_I, σ_{III} are the maximum and minimum values the normal stresses attain, and θ is the counter-clockwise angle between the direction of σ_I and the positive x-axis.

If the yield condition (2) is referred to the directions of the principal stresses σ_I and σ_{III} as new Cartesian axes, it takes the form

$$\sigma_I - \sigma_{III} = \pm 2k(y). \quad \text{(I.2)}$$

Since we consider the class of stress fields for which θ is a function of y only, it follows from the last equation (I.1) and equation (I.2) that

$$\tau = \tau(y). \quad \text{(I.3)}$$

Consequently, we obtain from (1)

$$\sigma_y = \sigma_y(x) \quad \text{(I.4)}$$

and from (2)

$$\partial\sigma_x/\partial x = \partial\sigma_y/\partial x. \quad \text{(I.5)}$$

Because of (I.4) and (I.5) the first of the equilibrium equations (1) gives

$$\partial^2\tau/\partial y^2 = 0 \quad \text{(I.6)}$$

and therefore, with reference to Fig. 3,

$$\tau = ay + (\tau_1 + \tau_2)/2. \quad \text{(I.7)}$$

From (I.5, 7) and (1) it follows that

$$\sigma_y = -ax + \sigma_y^0 \quad \text{(I.8)}$$

and from (2)

$$\sigma_x = \sigma_y \pm 2\sqrt{k^2(y) - \tau^2}, \quad \text{(I.9)}$$

where a, σ_y^0 are constants, σ_y^0 always being negative.

Slip lines

Since the potential slip directions coincide with the directions of maximum shear stresses, we first determine the direction field of maximum shear stresses. Introducing the counter-clockwise angle

$$\Phi = \theta + \pi/4, \quad \text{(I.10)}$$

which one of the two maximum shear directions includes with the positive x-axis, and using some well-known trigonometric relations, we may express the slip directions in terms of Φ or θ:

$$(dy/dx)_1 = \tan \Phi = \frac{1 - \cos 2\Phi}{\sin 2\Phi} = \frac{1 + \sin 2\theta}{\cos 2\theta},$$

$$(dy/dx)_2 = -1/(dy/dx)_1. \quad \text{(I.11)}$$

By means of equations (I.1) the slip directions may be expressed in terms of stress components:

$$(dy/dx)_1 = (\sigma_I - \sigma_{III} + 2\tau)/(\sigma_x - \sigma_y) \quad \text{(I.12)}$$

and by employing the yield condition in form (I.2) and (I.9):

$$(dy/dx)_1 = (k(y) + \varepsilon\tau)/\sqrt{k^2 - \tau^2},$$

$$(dy/dx)_2 = -1/(dy/dx)_1, \quad \text{(I.13)}$$

where $\varepsilon = \pm 1$, depending on whether the positive or negative sign in equation (I.9) is chosen (i.e. on whether one is dealing with the 'weak' or the 'strong' solution).

The orthogonal direction fields are finally obtained by substituting from equation (I.7) into equation (I.13):

$$(dy/dx)_1 = \left[1 + \varepsilon k^{-1}\left(ay + \frac{\tau_1 + \tau_2}{2}\right)\right]$$

$$\times \left[1 - k^{-2}\left(ay + \frac{\tau_1 + \tau_2}{2}\right)^2\right]^{-1/2} (\varepsilon = \pm 1) \quad \text{(I.14)}$$

and

$$(dy/dx)_2 = -1/(dy/dx)_1.$$

These formulas are used for the numerical determination of the slip lines in case k is a prescribed function of y. If $k = \text{const.}$ the differential equations (I.14) can be integrated analytically (e.g. Nadai 1950, p. 535) giving the two families of orthogonal slip lines in parameter representation:

$$x_1(2\Phi) = x_1(0) + \frac{k}{a}(\varepsilon \sin 2\Phi + 2\Phi)$$

$$y_1 = y_2(2\Phi) = -\frac{\tau_1 + \tau_2}{2a} - \frac{k}{a}\cos 2\Phi \quad (I.15)$$

$$x_2(2\Phi) = x_2(0) + \frac{k}{a}(\varepsilon \sin 2\Phi - 2\Phi).$$

The two families of slip lines are two orthogonal sets of cycloids. Depending on whether the 'weak' or the 'strong' plastic solution is chosen, one has to substitute for ε the value $+1$ or -1, respectively. When $a \to 0$, the cycloids degenerate into straight lines, as may be seen from equation (I.14).

Appendix II

The pole of the stress circle

A very useful element in Mohr's stress representation is the so-called 'pole'. Suppose a stress circle is given and we know the true orientation in space of the element associated with a stress point A (Fig. 24a). We may then draw the chord from A which is parallel to the trace of the element in physical space, i.e. its intersection with the plane' of the σ_I- and $\sigma_{III}-$ axis. The point where this chord meets the circle is the 'pole'. It has the remarkable property that the chord joining it with any other point B of the circle is parallel to the trace of the element whose stress vector is represented by B. This follows directly from the elementary relation between the angles shown in Fig. 24a). As an illustration Fig. 24b) shows the trace of the element that is acted upon by the major compressive principal stress. $-\sigma_{III}$.

Appendix III

Surface peak of horizontal compressive stress

EQUILIBRIUM EQUATIONS:

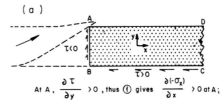

$$\frac{\partial \sigma_x}{\partial x} + \frac{\partial \tau}{\partial y} = 0 \qquad \frac{\partial \tau}{\partial x} + \frac{\partial \sigma_y}{\partial y} = \gamma \quad \text{①}$$

γ specific weight of rock

COMPATIBILITY EQUATION:

$$2\frac{\partial^2 \sigma_x}{\partial x^2} + \frac{\partial^2 \sigma_y}{\partial x^2} + \frac{\partial^2 \sigma_x}{\partial y^2} = 0 \qquad \text{②}$$

(a)

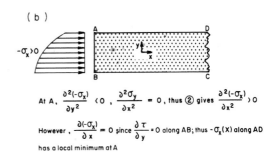

At A, $\dfrac{\partial \tau}{\partial y} > 0$, thus ① gives $\dfrac{\partial(-\sigma_x)}{\partial x} > 0$ at A;

i.e. compressive stress $-\sigma_x$ increases along AD close to A.

(b)

At A, $\dfrac{\partial^2(-\sigma_x)}{\partial y^2} < 0$, $\dfrac{\partial^2 \sigma_y}{\partial x^2} = 0$, thus ② gives $\dfrac{\partial^2(-\sigma_x)}{\partial x^2} > 0$

However, $\dfrac{\partial(-\sigma_x)}{\partial x} = 0$ since $\dfrac{\partial \tau}{\partial y} = 0$ along AB; thus $-\sigma_x(X)$ along AD

has a local minimum at A

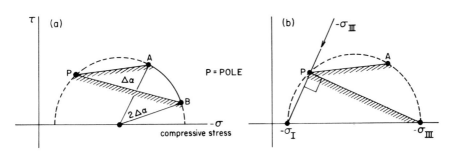

P = POLE

FIG. 24. Pole of stress circle.

References

HAFNER, W. 1951. Stress distribution and faulting. *Bull. geol. Soc. Am.* **62**, 373–98.

HILL, R. 1960. *The Mathematical Theory of Plasticity, VIII.* **5**, Oxford University Press.

HUBBERT, M. K. & RUBEY, W. W. 1959. Role of fluid pressure in mechanics of overthrust faulting. Part I. *Bull. geol. Soc. Am.* **70**, 116–66.

JAEGER, J. C. & COOK, N. G. W. 1969. *Fundamentals of Rock Mechanics*, Methuen & Co., London.

MARSHALL, E. A. 1967. The compression of a slab of ideal soil between rough plates. *Acta Mechanica III*, **2**, 82–92.

NADAI, A. 1950. *Theory of Flow and Fracture of Solids*, **1**, McGraw-Hill, New York.

ODÉ, H. 1960. Faulting as a velocity discontinuity in plastic deformation: in Rock Deformation, *Mem. geol. Soc. Am.* **79**, 293–321.

RIFFAULT, R. (ed.). 1969. *Catalogue des characteristiques geologiques et mechaniques de quelques roches Francaise.* Lab. Central des Ponts et Chaussees.

SALENCON, J. 1977. *Applications of the Theory of Plasticity in Soil Mechanics*; John Wiley & Sons, Chichester.

SCHMID, S. M., CASEY, M. & STARKEY, J. 1981. Microstructure and texture of calcite tectonites in the Helvetic nappes; (this volume).

TERZAGHI, K. V. 1950. Mechanics of landslides. Application of geology to engineering practice. *Berkey Volume, Geol. Soc. Am.* 83–123.

—— 1956. Varieties of submarine slope failures. *Eighth Texas Conf. Soil Mech. Found. Eng.* paper 3.

G. MANDL, G. K. SHIPPAM, Koninklijke/Shell Exploratie en Produktie Laboratorium, Rijswijk, The Netherlands.

The rock mechanics of thrust and nappe formation

S. A. F. Murrell

SUMMARY: Three models of thrust formation have been proposed: sliding opposed by friction, movement by flow in a thin layer, and spreading by more general flow. The field evidence suggests that the shear stresses involved must be low. Experimental and theoretical rock mechanics provide criteria which may be able to distinguish the applicability of the three models, with the constraint of low shear stresses, and the present paper investigates this possibility.

The essential feature of thrusts and nappes is the existence of thrust faults or surfaces of décollement which extend for great distances with an inclination not far from horizontal, and on which have taken place large-scale horizontal displacements of thrust slices and nappes whose thickness is in general small in comparison with their horizontal extent (Table 1).

The fault is in general not a simple geometrical surface but consists of a layer (whose thickness is small compared with that of the thrust rock mass) in which deformation and/or displacement is concentrated.

Discussion of the mechanics of thrusts and nappes has centred around three points.

(1) The nature of the forces resisting movement on the thrust fault; whether these forces arise from sliding friction (Hubbert & Rubey 1959) or from plastic flow in a soft layer (Smoluchowski 1909; Hsü 1969).

(2) The nature of the forces causing movement of the thrust mass; i.e. whether these are surface forces associated with crustal-shortening processes (Oxburgh 1972; Armstrong & Dick 1974); or whether they are gravitational body forces (see Voight 1976; de Jong & Scholten 1973) in which case, if the thrust mass moves as a rigid block it must move down the slope of the thrust fault (except perhaps at the toe, see Lemoine 1973; de Jong & Scholten 1973).

TABLE 1. *Details of large thrusts and nappes taken from the literature*

Thrust/Nappe	Displacement km	Length km	Thickness (Z_1) km	Basal dip (degrees)	Basal rock	Reference
Lewis Thrust, Canadian Rockies	>32·5		>1·4			Hubbert & Rubey 1959
Muddy Mountain Thrust, Nevada	24		7·6			,,
Roberts Thrust, Nevada	>81		8·1			,,
Cumberland Thrust, Applachians	9·8	179	1·63			,,
Jura décollement		80	1·6–2		Gypsum	Hsü 1969
Glarus Thrust	>30		5–6	2–5	Limestone	,,
Bannock Thrust, Wyoming		100	6			,,
Rossberg-Goldau Slide (Switzerland)		1·8	0·1	20		,,
McConnell Thrust, Canadian Rockies	>85		~10	3		Elliott 1976
Papua ophiolite thrust sheet		100	15			,,
Valley and Ridge, Central Applachians			10–22·5	1·5–3	Shale	Chapple 1978
Southern Zagros			9	0·29	Salt	,,

(3) The degree of rigidity of the thrust mass. Fracture and flow within the thrust mass may enable it to spread under the action of surface and gravitational body forces, in which case movement may be up-dip on the thrust faults involved (though, if gravity is involved, movement must be in the down-dip direction of the surface slope, as with glacier flow (Bucher 1956; de Jong & Scholten 1973; Price 1973; Elliott 1976)).

Stability of a thrust block

Detailed quantitative studies have been made by Hubbert & Rubey 1959, Raleigh & Griggs 1963 and Hsü 1969. (See also Jaeger & Cook 1969). These authors consider the problem of a block resting on a horizontal or sloping basal thrust surface and subject to compressive horizontal thrusting forces and/or to gravitational body forces. The limit of equilibrium is reached when either the block moves on the thrust fault or the strength of the thrust block is exceeded.

Following Hubbert & Rubey (1959) we start by considering unit thickness of a rectangular thrust block with cross-section OABC which rests on an inclined thrust fault surface and deforms under plane-strain conditions (Fig. 1). Co-ordinates x and z are taken parallel and perpendicular to the thrust surface respectively and measured from 0. The thrust block has uniform density ρ, and pore pressures $p(z)$ exist in it which are a function of z only. It has an outer layer α which is relatively imperme-

able to pore fluids (and is likely to be relatively stronger therefore because pore pressures are low or absent). The thrust fault surface γ is also relatively impermeable to pore fluids. The boundary tractions applied to the thrust block consist of: (i) a uniform shear traction τ_b along the base BC equal to the shear strength of the basal layer β; (ii) a distribution of normal stress σ_{xx} along the surface OC which is equal to or less than the strength of the thrust block at any given depth z; (iii) a mean normal stress f acting on the surface AB, caused by the toe of the advancing thrust block. In the case of a sub-aerial block the normal and shear tractions acting on the free surface OA are zero. [Ed. note. In this instance the normal stress on the AB surface will not be uniform, see Mandl & Shipham, this volume].

The strength of rock depends on effective confining pressure, and for simplicity, we assume that it follows the Navier-Coulomb criterion with a linear Mohr envelope

$$\tau' = \tau_c + \mu_c \sigma' \tag{1}$$

where τ', σ' are the effective shear and normal stresses, and τ_c and μ_c are the cohesive strength and coefficient of internal friction respectively. In terms of effective principal stresses, equation (1) can be written:

$$\sigma'_{max} = a + b . \sigma'_{min} \tag{2}$$

where σ'_{max} and σ'_{min} are respectively the maximum and minimum effective principal stresses, and

$$\left. \begin{array}{l} a = 2\tau_c . \sqrt{b} \\ b = [\mu_c + \sqrt{(1 + \mu_c^2)}]/[\sqrt{(1 + \mu_c^2)} - \mu_c] \end{array} \right\} . \tag{3}$$

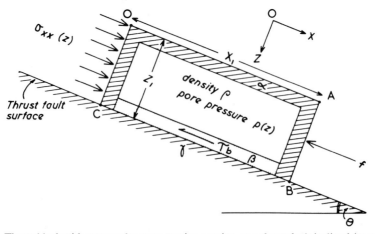

FIG. 1. Thrust block with rectangular cross-section moving on a thrust fault inclined (at angle θ) to the horizontal. θ can take positive values (block moving down-dip) or negative values (block moving up-dip). For explanation see text.

The pore pressure at depth z is taken to be:

$$p = \lambda . \sigma_{zz} \qquad (4)$$

where

$$\sigma_{zz} = \rho . g . z . \cos \theta \qquad (5)$$

and in the case of a horizontal thrust surface λ is the ratio of pore pressure to overburden pressure. The effective principal stresses are thus:

$$\left. \begin{array}{l} \sigma'_{max} = \sigma_{max} - \lambda . \sigma_{zz} \\[2mm] \sigma'_{min} = \sigma_{min} - \lambda . \sigma_{zz} \end{array} \right\} \qquad (6)$$

and

and (2) becomes:

$$\sigma_{max} - \lambda . \sigma_{zz} = a + b(\sigma_{min} - \lambda . \sigma_{zz}). \qquad (7)$$

We shall also assume that the shear strength of the basal layer β follows the Navier-Coulomb relationship, so that:

$$\tau_b = \tau_{bo} + \mu_b . \rho . g . z_1 (1 - \lambda_b) \cos \theta \qquad (8)$$

where τ_{bo} is the cohesive shear strength, μ_b is the coefficient of internal or sliding friction, and λ_b is the value of the pore pressure ratio λ (see equation (4)) in the basal layer (at depth z_1).

As regards the distribution of normal stress at the rear of the thrust block there are two cases to consider. (1) There is the widely accepted view [in accordance, for example, with Anderson's (1951) hypothesis about the dynamics of thrust faulting] that the surface traction pushing the rear of the thrust block is the maximum compressive stress:

$$\left. \begin{array}{l} \sigma_{max} = \sigma_{xx} \\[2mm] \sigma_{min} = \sigma_{zz} = \rho . g . z . \cos \theta \end{array} \right\} \qquad (9)$$

(2) There is the view, held by many others, (e.g. see Hubbert & Rubey 1959) that the thrust block might move under its own weight, or that the rear push is sufficiently small that the normal stress in the z direction (σ_{zz}) is the maximum compressive stress:

$$\left. \begin{array}{l} \sigma_{max} = \sigma_{zz} = \rho . g . z . \cos \theta \\[2mm] \sigma_{min} = \sigma_{xx}, \quad \text{and} \quad \sigma_{zz} > \sigma_{xx} \geqslant 0 \end{array} \right\} . \qquad (10)$$

(Here we take compressive stresses as positive in accordance with the usage of Hubbert & Rubey 1959.)

At the limit of equilibrium, when the thrust block is about to move on the fault surface the forces in the x-direction just balance, and the sum of the surface forces and the component of the gravity force acting on the block in the x-direction is zero. Therefore for unit thickness of the block normal to OABC we have:

$$\int_0^{z_1} \sigma_{xx} . dz - \int_0^{x_1} \tau_{zx} . dx - \int_0^{z_1} f . dz$$
$$+ \rho . g . A . \sin \theta = 0 \qquad (11)$$

where σ_{xx} is the normal traction on OC at depth z, τ_{zx} is the shear traction on CB (independent of x), f is the *mean* normal traction on AB, and A is the cross-sectional area of the block.

Propulsion of thrust block from rear

On carrying through the integrations in (11), for the general case we find:

$$x_1 [\tau_{bo} + \mu_b . (1 - \lambda_b) . \rho . g . z_1 . \cos \theta$$
$$- \rho . g . z_1 \sin \theta] + f . z_1 = \int_0^{z_1} \sigma_{xx} . dz$$
$$\leqslant \left[a . z_1 + \rho . g . \cos \theta \{ b . z_1^2 / 2 \right.$$
$$\left. + (1 - b) \int_0^{z_1} . z . dz \} \right] . \qquad (12)$$

This case applies so long as:

$$\int_0^{z_1} \sigma_{xx} . dz \leqslant \int_0^{z_1} \rho . g . z . \cos \theta . dz$$
$$= (\rho . g . z_1^2 . \cos \theta) / 2 \qquad (13)$$

where the right-hand side of the equation corresponds to a situation of hydrostatic stress ($\sigma_{xx} = \sigma_{zz}$).

In equation (12) the pore-pressure factor λ (where $0 \leqslant \lambda \leqslant 1$) may vary arbitrarily with depth z, depending on the nature of the rocks in the thrust block. Near the upper surface of the block λ may have lower values due to higher permeability (so that $\lambda \approx \rho_w / \rho_r$, where ρ_w is the density of water, and ρ_r that of rock), whereas at lower levels and especially perhaps near the basal surface, if Hubbert & Rubey (1959) are correct, λ may have 'abnormally high' values (approaching 1).

The maximum value of the right-hand side of (12) corresponds to the dry-rock case, with zero pore pressure ($\lambda = 0$), when it takes the value:

$$a . z_1 + \rho . g . \cos \theta . z_1^2 . b / 2 \qquad (14)$$

and the minimum value, corresponding to $\lambda = 1$ (though λ may exceed 1, up to the point when hydraulic, tensile fracturing occurs, see Jaeger & Cook 1971), takes the value:

$$a . z_1 + \rho . g . \cos \theta . z_1^2 / 2. \qquad (15)$$

Equation (12) defines a maximum length for the thrust block, which depends on the strength of the basal layer, the slope of the thrust fault, the effect of the toe, and the strength and thickness of the thrust block.

Weakness of basal layer

Clearly the basal layers of natural thrust blocks are weak, though the causes of this weakness and the reason why it is concentrated in a thin layer are still not entirely clear. We shall discuss these things later. The importance of Hubbert & Rubey's (1959) work is that it quantified the strength of the basal layer and indicated the great importance of abnormally high pore fluid pressures.

In order to bring out the importance of this factor we consider initially the case of a thrust block resting on a horizontal fault ($\theta = 0$), and with no toe effect ($f = 0$).

The thrust block will have its shortest stable length when the basal layer is at its strongest, and the thrust block is at its weakest. The maximum length of the thrust block will be:

$$x_1 = z_1[a + \rho.g.z_1/2]/[\tau_b + \mu_b.\rho.g.z_1].$$
(16)

For example, if we take the values of a, τ_b, μ_b and ρ assumed by Hubbert & Rubey (1959) for the thrust block (i.e. $a = 70$ MPa, $\tau_{bo} = 20$ мpa, $\mu_b = 0.577$, $\rho = 2.31 \times 10^3$ kgm^{-3}), we then find that for a 2.5 km thick thrust block the maximum stable length is 4.7 km, and for a 15 km thick block it is 18.4 km. Longer blocks will deform by fracture and cataclasis.

The thrust block will have its greatest stable length when the basal layer is at its weakest (with the pore pressure factor λ_b taking its maximum value of unity), and the thrust block is at its strongest (with its pore pressure factor λ taking its minimum value of zero). The maximum length of the thrust block will then be:

$$x_1 = z_1[a + \rho.g.z_1.b/2]/\tau_b.$$
(17)

Using Hubbert & Rubey's (1959) values for the material constants (including the value 3 for b) we find that for a 2.5 km thick thrust block the maximum stable length is 19.4 km, and for a 15 km. thick block it is 435 km.

With a weak basal layer the length of a stable thrust block will be determined by the strength of the block, having a minimum value given by:

$$x_1 = z_1[a + \rho.g.z_1/2]/\tau_b$$
(18)

when the pore pressure factor λ has the value

unity throughout the block. A 2.5 km thick thrust block will then have a maximum stable length of 12.3 km, and a 15 km thick block will have a maximum stable length of 180 km.

How large are overthrust blocks? If we may assume that the blocks are pushed from the rear then we can estimate the minimum length of the overthrust block from the overthrusting displacement. Hubbert & Rubey (1959) give examples from Scandinavia (up to 130 km), North America (Roberts Mountain overthrust and Taconic thrust, >80 km), and the Himalayas (>80 km); Schmid (1975) estimates that the main phase of movement on the Glarus overthrust was >35 km; and Elliott (1976) gives examples of several ophiolite nappes, one of which (the Semail nappe in Oman) is believed to have been displaced by > 120 km.

Such large overthrusts clearly require a weak basal layer. Furthermore, from (18) we see that a thrust block of a given length must have a minimum thickness if it is to remain intact during its movement. For a weak thrust block on a weak basal layer (using Hubbert & Rubey's (1959) material constants), we find from equation (18) that a 35 km long thrust block must be 5.4 km thick, and a 130 km long thrust block must be 12.4 km thick.

How weak could the basal layer be? This is a matter which Hsü (1969) has discussed in some detail. Hubbert & Rubey (1959) postulated that the cohesive strength (τ_b) of the basal layer might be zero, and hence if the pore pressure factor λ_b was high (~ 1) the shear strength of the basal layer could be close to zero. Under these circumstances the thrust block could move with only a small push from the rear, or could move by gravity down a basal fault with a very small slope. We will consider later the case when there is a small push from the rear.

Hsü (1969) pointed out that once gravity sliding started on a basal layer of near zero strength then it would become catastrophic, and we would have landslides rather than overthrusts. Indeed Hsü asks whether the Heart Mountain Thrust might not be an example of such a catastrophic slide. In general, however, Hsü took the view that the basal layer must have a finite, but low, shear strength, and that motion of the thrust block involved a creep deformation in this layer. We shall consider this in more detail later.

Thrust block moving up-slope

In this case the angle θ takes a negative

value, and the sign of the $\sin \theta$ term in equation (12) must be changed. As an example we consider the case of a weak basal layer ($\lambda_b = 1$) and a weak thrust block ($\lambda = 1$), then from (12) and (15) (taking $f = 0$) we find:

$$x_1 = z_1[a + \rho.g. \cos \theta.z_1/2]/[\tau_b + \rho.g.z_1. \sin \theta]. \quad (19)$$

The effect of slope is most important in the denominator, where it is of the same order as the τ_b term. The length of a block which is just stable when being pushed up slopes of 3 and 10° is given in Table 2 (from (19) with $\rho = 2.31 \times 10^3$ Kgm^{-3}).

It is seen that cohesionless faults would be permitted in this case, with quite reasonable slopes, contrary to the suggestion of Hsü (1969). Furthermore, in this case the thrust block would not move catastrophically.

Stress differences associated with thrust block movement

These are limited by the strength of the thrust block, and hence by (7) above, from which we find:

$$\sigma_{max} - \sigma_{min} = \lambda(1-b)\sigma_{zz} + a - (1-b)\sigma_{min}. \quad (20)$$

In the present case $\sigma_{max} = \sigma_{xx}$, and $\sigma_{min} = \sigma_{zz}$. We shall consider only a block on a horizontal thrust surface, so $\sigma_{zz} = \rho.g.z$. Hence:

$$\sigma_{xx} - \sigma_{zz} = (1-\lambda)(b-1)\rho.g.z. + a. \quad (21)$$

The maximum stress difference occurs near the base of the thrust block ($z = z_1$), and has a value of 70 MPa if $\lambda = 1$. If $\lambda = 0$ (no pore pressure);

$$\sigma_{xx} - \sigma_{zz} = 70 + 45z_1 \quad (22)$$

where stresses are in MPa, and z_1 is in km.

At depths greater than ~ 2 km the stress differences that would exist in dry rock according to the Hubbert & Rubey (1959) model for the mechanics of a thrust block adopted here would exceed those thought to exist in the crust (a maximum of ~ 150 MPa, see Murrell

1977). This emphasises the importance of pore pressures in the crust, and also points to the significance of creep and flow processes at greater depths in the crust.

Movement of thrust block by gravity gliding

In this case the first term in equation (11) is inessential, and we shall assume that it is zero. The limit of equilibrium is then reached when the left-hand side of equation (12) is zero, and then:

$$\rho.g.z_1. \sin \theta = \tau_b + \mu_b(1-\lambda_b)\rho.g.z_1. \cos \theta + f.z_1/X_1. \quad (23)$$

We discussed previously the case of zero strength of the basal layer ($\lambda_b = 1$, $\tau_b = 0$), when gliding becomes catastrophic, resisted only by the toe effect. We will now look at the effect of finite basal shear strength, assuming negligible toe effect ($f = 0$).

We also assume a high pore pressure factor ($\lambda_b \sim 1$), or that the basal layer flows with a shear strength τ_b independent of confining pressure. Equation (23) then becomes:

$$\sin \theta = \tau_b/\rho.g.z_1. \quad (24)$$

Values of the downward slope (θ) of a thrust fault calculated from (24) are given in Table 3. This emphasises a point made by Hsü (1969) that thin, long thrust blocks (e.g. the Jura décollement) require very low basal shear strengths (~ 3 MPa) if they moved by gravity gliding, but that thicker blocks could slide down very gentle slopes ($\sim 3°$) with basal shear strengths ~ 20 MPa.

In this case, if we take $\sigma_{xx} = 0$, we find from (7) that the maximum value of σ_{zz} above which the thrust block deforms by fracture and flow is:

$$\sigma_{zz} = a/[1 + \lambda(b-1)] = \rho.g.z. \cos \theta. \quad (25)$$

This equation gives the maximum thickness of a gliding block which will remain intact. For

TABLE 2. *Maximum length of a weak thrust block being pushed up a thrust surface on a weak basal layer*

Block thickness, Z_1 (km)	$\tau_b = 20$ MPa		$\tau_b = 0$	
	$\theta = 3°$	$\theta = 10°$	$\theta = 3°$	$\theta = 10°$
2·5	11	8	88	26
15	97	46	212	62

TABLE 3. *Slope required for gravity gliding of a thrust block with a weak basal layer.*

Basal shear strength τ_b (MPa)	Block thickness z_1 (km)	
	2·5	15
20	21°	3·4°
3	3°	0·5°

dry rock ($\lambda = 0$) it is 3.1 km, and for very weak rock ($\lambda = 1$) it is 1.03 km, using the material constants of Hubbert & Rubey (1959).

Wedge-shaped block

In this case (see Fig. 2a) the equilibrium of the block is determined by a modification of equation (12):

$$x_1[\tau_b + \tfrac{1}{2}.\mu_b(1-\lambda_b)\rho.g.z_1. \cos\theta - \tfrac{1}{2}.\rho.g.z_1.\sin\theta]$$
$$= \int_0^{z_1} \sigma_{xx}\, dz \leqslant \left[a.z_1 + \rho.g. \cos\theta \right.$$
$$\left. \times \left\{ \tfrac{1}{2}.b.z_1^2 + (1-b) \int_0^{z_1} \lambda.z.\, dz \right\} \right]. \quad (26)$$

It will be seen that the right-hand side of (26) is the same as in (12), but in general the term in brackets on the left-hand side is reduced. Thus the stable length of a wedge-shaped thrust block is greater than that of a rectangular block.

The main value of this model is that it is a more realistic one for a block being thrust from the rear up a basal thrust surface, and in

this respect it resembles the models discussed by Elliott (1976) and Chapple (1978). In this case the sign of the $\sin\theta$ term in (26) must be changed. If we also assume a constant value of λ in the block and a low basal shear strength ($\lambda_b = 1$) then the maximum value of x_1 will be given by the equation:

$$x_1 = z_1[2a + \rho.g.z_1. \cos\theta\{b + (1-b)\lambda\}]/[2\tau_b + \rho.g.z_1.\sin\theta]. \quad (27)$$

For a strong thrust block ($\lambda = 0$):

$$x_1 = z_1[2a + \rho.g.z_1.b. \cos\theta]/[2\tau_b + \rho.g.z_1.\sin\theta] \quad (28)$$

and for a weak thrust block:

$$x_1 = z_1[2a + \rho.g.z_1. \cos\theta]/[2\tau_b + \rho.g.z_1.\sin\theta]. \quad (29)$$

Calculations of the stable length of wedge-shaped thrust blocks are given in Table 4. Bearing in mind the length of thrust blocks found naturally the calculations suggest that the strength of the weak basal layer is less for the thinner blocks, and that the thinner blocks may also be weaker.

TABLE 4. *Stable length (in km) of wedge-shaped blocks, pushed up thrust faults with a weak basal layer*

Strong block ($\lambda = 0$)

	Slope (θ)	1°		3°		10°	
	τ_b (MPa)	20	3	20	3	20	3
Z_1 (km)							
2·5		19	111	18	86	10·5	19·7
15·0		378	1450	300	725	172	260

Weak block ($\lambda = 1$)

	Slope (θ)	1°		3°		10°	
	τ_b (MPa)	20	3	20	3	20	3
Z_1 (km)							
2·5		12	71	11·5	55	6.7	12.6
15·0		158	606	125	303	72	109

Deformation of thrust block

A number of authors (e.g. Bucher 1956; Price 1973; Elliott 1976; Chapple 1978) have proposed that spreading of the crust in thrust belts due to gravity forces is an important factor. This is comparable with the flow within ice sheets which is necessary to reach an equilibrium thickness and surface form determined by the plastic yield stress of the ice (Nye 1951; Evison 1960). The relation between the maximum height (H) and the radial extent (r) of a sheet of superficial ice showing perfect plasticity (yield stress Y) is:

$$\rho.g.H^2 = 2Y.r. \qquad (30)$$

If this relationship applies to large mountain ranges (e.g. the Himalayas, the Alps) an approximate estimate gives a yield stress of ~ 3 MPa.

For a given horizontal extent (r) equation (30) defines the thickness of a plastic sheet or block, at its culmination, below which gravity spreading will not occur. There is a corresponding surface slope. For greater slopes gravitational spreading will occur. Elliott (1976) and Chapple (1978) have emphasized the significance of the surface slope for gravity

spreading. However, it is readily seen that only if the surface slope in the direction of spreading is significantly greater than the basal slope away from the direction of spreading (Fig. 2b) will the spreading affect the full thickness of the thrust block. If the thrust block was a very viscous liquid (with zero yield stress Y) and had an original surface slope ψ (Fig. 2b) gravity flow would occur in the region of cross-section ABC and the eventual surface (slope zero) would be A′B′. Since the volume of the region of cross-section ABC equals that of the region with cross-section AA′B′C we find:

$$x_{11} = x_{10}.\sqrt{(\tan\psi/\tan\theta + 1)}. \qquad (31)$$

If we take the figures assumed for the McConnell thrust in the Canadian Rocky mountains by Elliott (1976), for which $\psi \approx \theta \approx 3°$ then $x_{11} = 1.41.x_{10}$. The length of this thrust initially (i.e. x_{10}) could have been in the range 85–250 km, so the maximum amount of spreading would have been in the range 35–103 km. The important point, however, is that over most of the basal thrust (in the region OA) there would be no movement.

The chief difficulty with the theoretical treatments so far given of this problem lies in the

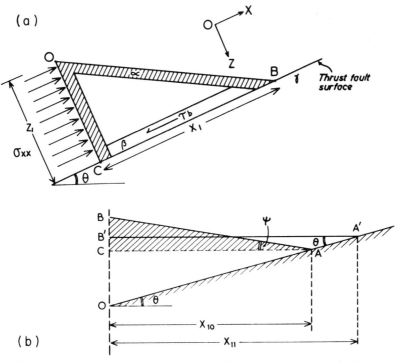

FIG. 2. (a) Thrust block with wedge-shaped cross-section being pushed up an inclined thrust fault. (b) Effect of gravity-spreading on the upper surface of a viscous wedge-shaped thrust block.

assumption of perfect plasticity throughout the thrust block. In general the deformation will actually be brittle and cataclastic, though perhaps with some plastic component. In this respect the treatment of Hubbert & Rubey (1959) is more realistic. However, so far there has been no theoretical treatment of the internal deformation of the thrust block in the Hubbert & Rubey or Hsü model (and of the wedge-shaped block version of it given in this paper). The two consequences of this more realistic rheology are that the thrust block will tend to show a much smaller degree of gravitational spreading, and that the internal deformation will be by faulting and block movements.

To exemplify this factor consider a thrust block on horizontal basal thrust ($\theta = 0$), and assume initially no toe effect ($f = 0$). The front of the thrust block will be weakened by its lack of confinement, but strengthened because it will tend to be drained. Thus the maximum thickness at the front of the thrust block will be limited by the unconfined, drained ($\lambda = 0$) strength. Then from equations (7) and (10) we find:

$$z_1 = a/\rho.g. \qquad (32)$$

Using Hubbert & Rubey's (1959) material constants $z_1 = 3\cdot1$ km.

If $\lambda = 0$ throughout the thrust block the maximum stable length of the block is 27.2 km. However, if the rear of the block is undrained ($\lambda = 1$), then with a thickness $z_1 = 3.1$ km the maximum stable length of block is 16.3 km.

Ramping, toe-effect, crustal thickening

Given a (near-horizontal) weakness plane, when the thrust block is compressed it could form (Anderson 1951) an Andersonian Thrust

fault breaking through to the free surface (with a fault dip of $\sim 20\text{–}30°$), and this fault could then form a ramp up which the thrust block would move (given suitable deformation in the toe region), so that crustal thickening could occur by burial of the pre-existing crustal surface beneath the overthrust block.

This can be represented (Fig. 3) by the Raleigh & Griggs (1963) model for toe effect (see also Jaeger & Cook, 1969). In this model the toe ABD is pushed up the ramp BD (slope ω), and it is assumed that a horizontal thrust force f exists between the thrust block and the toe, but that there is zero shear stress on the surface AB (this is a reasonable approximation if high pore pressures ($\lambda = 1$) exist in the toe region, where substantial deformation must occur as the thrust block changes direction and moves up the ramp). If the total forces acting on the toe are T (parallel to BD) and N (perpendicular to BD) we have:

$$\left. \begin{array}{l} T = f.z_1.\cos\omega - \rho.g.z_1^2.\cos\omega \\ N = f.z_1.\sin\omega - \rho.g.z_1^2\cos\omega.\cot\omega \end{array} \right\}. \qquad (33)$$

The condition for sliding up the ramp, including effects of pore pressure, is:

$$T = (1-\lambda_b)\mu_b N + \tau_{bo}.z_1.\operatorname{cosec}\omega. \qquad (34)$$

Eliminating T and N from (33) and (34) we find the following expression for the mean traction exerted by the toe on AB:

$$f = \operatorname{cosec}\omega[\rho.g.z_1.\cos\omega\{\sin\omega$$
$$- (1-\lambda_b)\mu_b.\cos\omega + \tau_{bo}]/$$
$$[\cos\omega - (1-\lambda_b)\mu_b.\sin\omega]. \qquad (35)$$

In deriving this equation we have assumed that λ_b, μ_b and τ_{bo} are the same on the ramp as at the base of the main thrust block. Initially, however, they might take values closer to those in the thrust block. Once movement has started on the thrust τ_{bo} might go to zero if $\lambda_b = 1$.

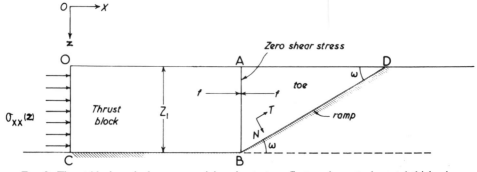

FIG. 3. Thrust block pushed up ramp, giving rise to toe effect, and eventual crustal thickening.

Assuming that $\lambda_b = 1$ and that at the rear of the thrust block $\lambda = 0$ then from equation (12) we find, after inserting the value of f from equation (35) that:

$$x_1 \leq z_1[z_1.\rho.g(b/2, -1)$$
$$+ (a - \tau_{bo}/\sin \omega. \cos \omega)]/\tau_{b0}. \quad (36)$$

If we take a value of 30° for the slope of the ramp, and use Hubbert and Rubey's (1959) material constants we find that the maximum stable length of the thrust block is 6·5 km for a 2·5 km thick block and 145 km for a 15 km thick block.

As thrusting continues and crustal thickening takes place at the front of the thrust block the toe effect could increase, and reach a value twice its initial value (depending on the extent of any erosion). At the same time, however, the forces resisting thrusting on the basal surface may decrease, as τ_{bo} goes to zero and λ_b remains close to unity. Raleigh & Griggs (1963) discussed the effect of an overriding toe in the context of the example of the Pine Mountain thrust.

Mechanism of formation of basal thrust fault

We have seen above that the essential features of the basal thrust are (i) its weakness; (ii) its length; and (iii) its small slopes.

We can envisage two classes of thrust block, one being moved by gravity and the other being propelled by horizontal crustal compression. If the basal faults were produced by an Andersonian (Anderson 1951) brittle faulting mechanism the gravitationally induced faults would be steep normal faults, and the faults produced by horizontal compression would be thrusts dipping at a shallow angle. In order to produce agreement between the Andersonian model and the large-scale basal thrust faults some mechanism is needed by which the forces opposing movement on the fault can be reduced, and the fault itself can be formed at a very shallow angle to the horizontal.

Hubbert & Rubey's (1959) abnormal pore pressure hypothesis offered a means of producing a weak low-angle thrust fault. In particular the hypothesis can explain catastrophic gravity gliding.

Equally if there are thin horizontal or subhorizontal layers of weak plastic or cataclastic rock in the crust (e.g. rock-salt or gypsum) these offer suitable locations and properties for a basal thrust surface.

The higher temperatures at depth may also be an important factor, though with normal geothermal gradients ($\sim 20°$ C/km) the temperature at the base of a thrust will only lie in the range 35–300°C. The higher temperatures are enough to soften rock-salt (especially at low strain-rates), and to weaken gypsum, and chlorite or serpentine bearing rocks by decomposition of hydrous minerals (Murrell 1977) and release of a high pressure pore fluid. The chemical activity of pore water will also be increased. However, the effect of temperatures in this range on the strength of dry, unhydrated silicate rocks is relatively small.

Doubt has however been cast by Hsü (1969) and Schmid (1975) on the adequacy of the high pore-pressure, brittle fault hypothesis in the case of the Glarus Overthrust, where the basal thrust zone is in limestone. Similar doubts must arise in the case of thrust sheets of crystalline rock (see Oxburgh 1972; Armstrong & Dick 1974). Hsü (1969) has proposed that the thin mylonitized layer of the basal thrust zone in the Glarus Overthrust behaves as a weak plastic layer. What remains to be explained is the mechanism of formation of the weak, 'plastic', mylonite layer.

The concentration of shear deformation into a thin fault zone in a substance which was previously isotropic and homogeneous on a macroscopic scale must be accompanied by strain-softening in the fault zone. The mechanism is clear when the deformation is brittle.

However, when the initial deformation is by ductile flow the mechanism by which zones of concentrated shear are formed is not always clear. Where flow involves crystal plasticity by means of dislocations several strain-softening mechanisms exist. A classical example is the formation of Lüders bands in iron and steel, which has been explained (Cottrell 1953; Friedel 1964) by the separation of dislocations from 'atmospheres' of impurity atoms which impede their movement. Other mechanisms are the avalanche-like multiplication of dislocations and adiabatic-softening, which can occur when heat generated by plastic deformation diffuses away sufficiently slowly that the flow stress is able to be reduced. There is no clear evidence at present that these mechanisms operate in crystalline rocks.

On the other hand it is not clear how zones of concentrated shear form in soils and granular substances in which the initial deformation is by homogeneously distributed flow. In the case of natural failure slides in slopes of overconsolidated clay and clay shales there is clear evidence of the progressive development of the failure surfaces over a period of time (Bjerrum

1967), which in the case of the stronger clays may be measured in hundreds of years. This progressive failure is probably associated with chemical processes linked with ground water. It is attractive to hypothesise that large scale natural thrusts in rocks which are even stronger than these clays or shales may also develop by progressive failure mechanism, which in this case may extend over exceedingly long periods of time.

A number of authors have in recent years developed theoretical treatments of slides in soils (Palmer & Rice 1973; Arthur et al. 1977). In most cases, however, a specific strain-softening mechanism is not assumed. Arthur et al. (1977) have developed a strain softening model for granular solids, which involves a competition between localized strain-hardening and strain-softening movements between grains. Even in this case, however, the detailed way in which macroscopic strain-softening takes place is not yet understood, though it seems likely that the development of local anisotropy is an important factor. In the case of clays, the nature of the clay particles suggests that anisotropy is an essential factor in the formation of slides. Furthermore, it appears unlikely that any naturally-formed soil is initially completely isotropic.

Could the phenomena found in soils have any relevance to rocks? I suggest that they will have if cataclasis and cataclastic flow occurs naturally. Cataclastic flow is observed experimentally in dry rocks at high confining pressures and with high shear stresses, when fric-tion prevents sliding on a macroscopic shear fault (Murrell 1966, 1978, Edmond & Murrell 1973, Ismail & Murrell 1976). It involves the widespread cataclasis or fragmentation of a rock by fracturing of grains or grain-boundaries, followed by relative movements (both sliding and separating) of the fractured particles.

Cataclastic flow is unlikely to occur naturally under dry conditions. However, it is suggested that cataclastic flow may occur naturally at much lower shear stresses in fluid-saturated rocks under 'undrained' conditions (Ismail & Murrell 1976). In this case initial dilatancy hardening may inhibit the formation of a brittle shear fault, but a shear fault may develop subsequently, following a period of cataclastic flow, and then the mechanism may be very similar to that found in granular soils. Indeed the basic deformation mechanisms at the microscopic level are very similar: sliding against friction, and dilatancy (but in the case of rocks a substantial part of the dilatancy arises from fracturing processes).

Once a shear zone is formed in rock by cataclastic processes it is possible that new deformation processes may follow. If the rock particles in the shear zone become finely divided in the presence of high, initially 'undrained' pore water pressures, it is possible that grain-boundary diffusion processes at particle contacts could become sufficiently rapid to dominate the deformation process. This would be assisted by elevated temperatures, and high chemical activity of the pore water.

References

ANDERSON, E. M. 1951 The Dynamics of Faulting. Oliver and Boyd. Edinburgh. 2nd ed.

ARMSTRONG, R. L. & DICK, H. J. B. 1974. A model for the development of thin overthrust sheets of crystalline rock. Geology, 2, 25–40.

ARTHUR, J. R. F., DUNSTAN, T., AL-ANI, Q. A. J. L. & ASSADI, A. 1977. Plastic deformation in granular media. Geotechnique, 27, 53–74.

BJERRUM, L. 1967. Progressive failure in slopes of overconsolidated plastic clay and clay shales. Proc. Amer. Soc. civ. Engrs. J. Soil Mechs. Fdns. Div., 93, 3–49.

BUCHER, W. H. 1956. Role of gravity in orogenesis. Bull. geol. Soc. Am. 67, 1295–318.

CHAPPLE, W. M. 1978. Mechanics of thin-skinned fold-and-thrust belts. Bull. geol. Soc. Am. 89, 1189–98.

COTTRELL, A. H. 1953. Dislocations and Plastic Flow. Oxford Univ. Press, Oxford.

EDMOND, O. & MURRELL, S. A. F. 1973. Experimental observations on rock fracture at pres-sures up to 7 kbar and the implications for earth-quake faulting. Tectonophysics, 16, 71–87.

ELLIOTT, D. 1976. The motion of thrust sheets. J. geophys. Res. 81, 949–63.

EVISON, F. F. 1960. On the growth of continents by plastic flow under gravity. Geophys. J. R. astr. Soc. 3, 155–90.

FRIEDEL, J. 1964. Dislocations. Pergamon Press, Oxford.

HSÜ, K. J. 1969. Role of cohesive strength in the mechanics of overthrust faulting and of land sliding. Bull. geol. Soc. Am. 80, 927–52.

HUBBERT, M. K. & RUBEY, W. W. 1959. Role of fluid pressure in mechanics of overthrust faulting. Bull. geol. Soc. Am. 70, 115–66.

ISMAIL, I. A. H. & MURRELL, S. A. F., 1976. Dilatancy and the strength of rocks containing pore water under undrained conditions. Geophys. J. R. astr. Soc. 44, 107–34.

JAEGER, J. C. & COOK, N. G. W. 1969. Fundamentals of Rock Mechanics. Methuen, London.

DE JONG, K. A. & SCHOLTEN, R. 1973. Eds. *Gravity and Tectonics*, John Wiley, New York. Preface pp. ix–xviii.

LEMOINE, M. 1973. About gravity gliding tectonics in the western Alps. In: DE JONG, K. A. & SCHOLTEN, R. (eds), *Gravity and Tectonics*, John Wiley, New York, 201–16.

MURRELL, S. A. F. 1966. The effect of triaxial stress systems on the strength of rocks at atmospheric temperatures. *Geophys. J. R. astr. Soc.* **10,** 231–81.

——, 1977. Natural faulting and the mechanics of brittle shear failure. *J. geol. Soc. London,* **133,** 175–89.

——, 1978. Creep of Engineering materials and of the Earth. (Discussion contributions). *Phil. Trans. R. Soc. London,* **A288.** 47. 94–95, 146.

NYE, J. F. 1951. The flow of glaciers and ice-sheets as a problem in plasticity. *Proc. R. Soc. London,* **A207,** 554–72.

OXBURGH, E. R. 1972. Flake tectonics and conti-nental collision. *Nature,* **239,** 202–4.

PALMER, A. C. & RICE, J. R. 1973. The growth of slip surfaces in the progressive failure of over-consolidated clay. *Proc. Roy. Soc. London,* **A332,** 527–48.

PRICE, R. A. 1973. Large-scale gravitational flow of supracrustal rocks, Southern Canadian Rockies. In DE JONG, K. A. & SCHOLTEN, R. (eds), *Gravity and Tectonics*, John Wiley, New York, 491–502.

RALEIGH, C. B. & GRIGGS, D. T. 1963. Effect of toe in the mechanics of overthrust faulting. *Bull. geol. Soc. Am.* **74,** 819–30.

SCHMID, S. M. 1975. The Glarus overthrust: field evidence and mechanical model. *Eclog. geol. Helv.* **68/2,** 247–80.

SMOLUCHONSKI, M. S. 1909. Some remarks on the mechanics of overthrusts. *Geol. Mag.* **6,** 204–5.

VOIGHT, B. 1976. Ed. *Mechanics of Thrust Faults and Décollement.* Dowden, Hutchinson & Ross, Stroudsburg, Pennsylvania.

S. A. F. MURRELL, University College, London.

Subduction and coeval thrust belts, with particular reference to North America

A. G. Smith

SUMMARY: Although thrust belts at present-day subduction zones are sub-parallel to such zones, several ancient thrust belts dip in the opposite direction to the inferred dip of the contemporaneous subduction zone. Gravity spreading, gravity sliding or compressional stresses transmitted from the subduction zone are unlikely causes of such thrust belts. The driving force is attributed instead to the hydrostatic head of a fluid-like rock welt. If the welt is hot—as in a granitic/metamorphic belt—foreland thrusts may form.

The emplacement stresses are similar in magnitude to those of gravity spreading, but the thrust wedge need not be weak. The essential requirements of a thrust belt created by a fluid welt are a downhill surface slope in the direction of thrust transport and weak decollement horizon(s).

In the Mesozoic foreland thrust belts of western North America, the volume of rock pushed onto the foreland is comparable to the volume of the batholiths in the orogenic core and to the volume of new material added by subduction to the overriding American Plate.

After collision with another continent or an island arc the recognition of thrust belts emplaced by fluid welts is more difficult, particularly when ophiolites are present.

The problem of finding subduction dip directions

In a recent review of plate tectonics and orogeny (Smith 1976), the author concluded that it was difficult to answer one of the most elementry questions in plate tectonics: which way did the subduction zone(s) associated with an ancient orogenic belt dip?

For example, contrast the interpretations of Dewey & Bird (1970) and Ernst (1973) for the Alps with that of Oxburgh (1972) and Oxburgh & Turcotte (1974); for the Apennines, contrast Boccaletti *et al.* (1971) with Laubscher (1971); for the western North American Cordillera, compare Hamilton (1969) with Roeder (1973); or for Newfoundland contrast Bird & Dewey (1970) with Dewey & Bird (1971) and then Dewey (1974).

Until the direction of subduction zone dip can be reliably determined, there is little hope of understanding the relationship between orogenic processes and plate motions beyond that achieved by a thumb-nail sketch. Part of the difficulty stems from uncertainty about the processes that create thrust belts. This paper briefly discusses the problem of the driving forces of foreland thrust belts; presents a simple new model of them and then discusses why these thrusts dip in the opposite direction to the associated subduction zone.

Idealized orogenic belt

Consider first an idealized orogenic belt created at the edge of a continent next to a sinking oceanic slab (Fig. 1), similar to that envisaged by Ernst (1974) and Dickinson (1977). The orogenic belt is bounded on the oceanic side by the undeformed crust of the sinking plate, and on the continental side by the edge of foreland deformation. The deformation near the subduction zone will be referred to as 'trench deformation', whether or not a trench is actually present; that adjacent to the foreland will be referred to as 'foreland deformation'. Dickinson (1977, p. 38 and Fig. 5) refers to this foreland zone as a 'back-arc fold thrust belt'. These, or similar terms, are preferred to others such as 'antithetic' and 'synthetic' that have been suggested to describe the relationship between subduction and material transport (Roeder 1973, p. 5007).

North American Cordillera

Active foreland belts of the kind required by the simple model of Fig. 1 are not known to the writer. The best known fossil example is the foreland belt of the western North American Cordillera. In later Mesozoic and early Cenozoic time, foreland thrusts developed on the E side of plutonic/volcanic arc stretching

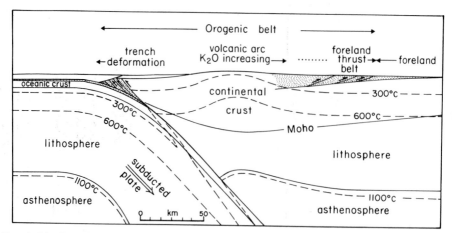

FIG. 1. Idealized Cordilleran orogenic belt prior to collision. Modified from Ernst (1974) and Dickinson (1977). The isotherms below the Moho under the volcanic arc have been raised to give a shallower low velocity channel than that in adjacent regions.

from Alaska to Mexico (Fig. 2). Though broadly contemporaneous, the thrust belts are diachronous along strike. The time difference along the strike is sufficient to show that thrusting ceased at about the same time as did calc-alkaline igneous activity (Armstrong 1974).

Trench deposits and subduction zone dip

Later Mesozoic and earlier Cenozoic subduction complexes have been recognized along much of the Pacific margin of North America. The thrusts in them transport presumed trench sediments toward the Pacific (Jones *et al.* 1978), as required by the idealized model.

The dip of the former subduction zone can be inferred independently by the K-h method of Dickinson & Hatherton (1967). All available data show the subduction zone always had an eastern dip under the North Amercan continent at the time of foreland thrusting, with a trench near the present continental margin (Dickinson 1970; Lipman *et al.* 1972; Coney & Reynolds 1977; Coney 1978; Keith 1978). The subduction zone dip flattened throughout the Mesozoic, in turn causing a general eastward migration of igneous activity, in front of which lay a migrating zone of foreland thrusting.

Foreland thrust belt

In cross-section the thrust belts are wedge-shaped, thickening westward toward the plutonic/volcanic arc. The thrust wedge gener- ally consists of a tectonically thickened sedimentary prism. Prior to deformation the prism was part of a westward-thickening miogeocline and platform deposited on the western North American continent. The rear end of the sedimentary prism had an original thickness generally greater than 10 km. In the southern Canadian Rockies and in the Wyoming Rockies of the United States, thrusts developed progressively from the interior of the orogenic belt outward to the foreland (Armstrong & Oriel 1965, fig. 20, p. 1861; Bally *et al.* 1966, p. 371; Rubey & Hubbert 1959, p. 190; Price & Mountjoy 1970, p. 22–23). Deformation on the eastern margin is by thrusting and/or folding. Towards the arc, deformation becomes penetrative, and near the arc itself may include the generation of schists and gneisses.

The deformation in these areas is 'thin-skinned'. Thrusts merge downwards to a sole thrust that generally does not cut the basement. Shortening in the Canadian Rockies is estimated as an original 370 km shortened to 200 km (Price & Mountjoy 1970, p. 16); further S, an original 280 km has been shortened to 125 km E of the Rocky Mountain Trench (Bally *et al.* 1966, plate 12). In the Wyoming Rockies a minimum of 300 km of section has been shortened to 190 km (Rubey & Hubbert 1959 fig. 7). Further S still, in the Sevier orogenic belt of Utah, a shortening of 100 km is probable (Armstrong 1968, p. 441). The thrusts can best be described as representing stratal rather than crustal shortening: only the sedimentary cover is involved, rather than the whole crust.

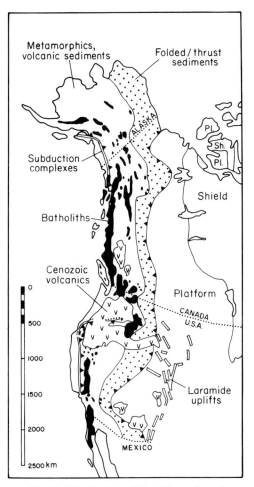

FIG. 2. Distribution of later Mesozoic and early Cenozoic subduction complexes, batholiths and foreland folding/thrusting in the North American Cordillera. Modified from Bally *et al.* (1966) and Jones *et al.* (1978).

In the above areas, thrusting was preceded by uplift of the source area and by igneous activity in the arc. Though providing a surface slope down to the foreland at the time of thrusting, uplift did not give a downhill slope to the décollement horizons: the thrust sheets travelled uphill.

The principal exception to this thin-skinned deformation is in the Mohave Desert of SE California. Here, Burchfiel & Davis (1972) show that the Mesozoic batholith belt truncates the earlier Phanerozoic miogeoclinal facies belts. The foreland thrusts also parallel the batholiths, cutting obliquely across the facies belts and eventually cut the Precambrian basement into thrust slices.

Tectonic thickening in the foreland

Price (1973, p. 493–496) has argued that although rocks on an outcrop scale in the Canadian Rockies have behaved as rigid bodies during thrusting, on the scale of an orogenic belt the deformation is better regarded as a type of penetrative plastic flow. Were the deformation simultaneous throughout the belt, this interpretation would be unavoidable. But as noted above, the thrust belts developed progressively from W to E. It seems therefore possible to adopt an alternative view of their deformation: that at any one time only a few thrusts may have been active. As time passed, this non-penetrative deformation could in the author's view have worked its way eastward in a series of discontinuous stages, producing as an end product only the appearance of penetrative plastic flow (Fig. 3).

The sole thrust eventually cuts up through the entire sedimentary section. It does so by

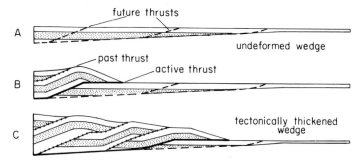

FIG. 3. Successive stages in the deformation of a miogeoclinal wedge (A, B and C). Deformation is envisaged as proceeding from left to right. At any given time only one fault is assumed active. The end result is a tectonically thickened wedge showing apparent penetrative plastic deformation, but at any instant deformation is not penetrative, but is confined to a narrow zone.

forming bedding-parallel thrusts ('flats') in weak rocks such as coal and shale and higher angle, brittle fractures ('steps' or 'ramps') in more competent strata (Dahlstrom 1970, figs 8 & 9, p. 343). Eventually, possibly due to increased loading, the sole thrust creates a new fracture further east, the original fracture becomes inactive and the active deformation moves eastward (Fig. 3).

As several authors have noted, the kinematics of a foreland thrust belt closely resemble that of an accretionary wedge formed at a subduction zone (Karig & Sharman 1975), in which slices of sediment are progressively accreted to its base. However, to describe this as a type of subduction seems inappropriate. As will be argued later, material may well have been added to the upper levels of the crust, rather than being removed to deeper levels as implied by the term subduction.

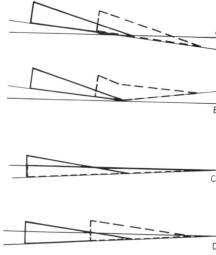

FIG. 4. Sliding, spreading and pushing. In all four cases the horizontal is shown, together with the initial (bold lines) and final (dashed bold lines) shape and position of the thrust wedge. A and B: gravity sliding. B shows apparent sliding uphill at the edge of the wedge, but regionally the wedge has slid downhill. C: gravity spreading for a fluid. At the end of spreading the upper surface is horizontal. Materials with a low yield stress will have low but finite surface slopes once spreading has ceased. D: pushing uphill (without tectonic thickening as in Fig. 3).

Foreland thrusts—emplaced by sliding, spreading or pushing?

Three causes have been suggested for the emplacement of these Cordilleran foreland thrusts: i) gravity sliding, ii) gravity spreading and iii) pushing by tectonic forces (Fig. 4).

Gravity sliding

Gravity sliding of rigid thrust sheets requires a slope down which thrust sheets can slide and leaves behind an area of tectonic erosion or tectonic thinning. Because the basal sliding horizon of the foreland thrusts dipped sourceward at the time of thrusting, and because there is no tectonic gap in the orogenic core in North America (Price 1971), this process can be eliminated.

Gravity spreading

Here the downhill surface slope from the orogenic core to the foreland provides a shear stress that drives the thrust wedge. Price & Mountjoy (1970, p. 18) envisaged the foreland thrusting of the southern Canadian Rockies as being caused by the lateral spreading of an upwelling zone of hot mobile rock from the interior of the orogenic belt. Each local upwelling pulse is believed to have corresponded to a local surge in foreland thrusting. Price (1973, p. 496) uses Bucher's model of solid wax spreading outwards over interlayered wax and grease as an analogy (Bucher 1956, plate 1, fig. 1) and likens the periphery of the Canadian thrust belt to the edge of a large ice-sheet.

Applied compressional stresses

Until the advent of plate tectonics, the source of any compressional stresses was obscure. With the recognition of subduction zones, it is now assumed that compressional stresses at these zones can be transmitted laterally through the crust to the foreland belt (Burchfiel & Davis 1972, p. 15, 1975, p. 391; Armstrong 1974). That westward-directed thrusts at the subduction zone ceased at about the same time as did the eastward-directed foreland thrusts, supports this view. Armstrong (1974) and Armstrong & Dick (1974) argued in addition that zones of anomalously high heat flow were a prerequisite for large-scale crustal deformation. The heated region could then 'be compressed or stretched apart depending on plate motions dictated by processes acting on a global scale' (Armstrong 1974, p. 350). Because the Mohave Thrusts in California cut the Precambrian basement rather than continuing in the sedimentary rocks, and because they then continue to parallel the batholithic belt to the W, Burchfiel & Davis (1972) also believe the gravity spreading model to be inapplicable.

Thrust mechanics

Quite apart from regional considerations, emplacement of a thrust sheet can be regarded as a purely mechanical problem.

Frictional sliding

If the laws of frictional sliding are applied to the problem, we rediscover the 'mechanical paradox of large overthrusts', discussed as long ago as 1909 by Smoluchowski. Essentially, the paradox is that the stress that must be applied at the rear of a large rectangular block to cause it to slide frictionally on a horizontal surface exceeds the strength of most rocks.

High pore-fluid pressures

Hubbert & Rubey (1959) retained the rectangular shape, allowed for an increase in strength with confining pressure, assumed frictional sliding occurred and were still unable to remove the paradox. They solved it ingeniously by postulating that high pore-fluid pressures reduced the normal reaction on the sliding surface during emplacement. In support of their model they cited examples of high pore-fluid pressures in sedimentary sequences. Some aspects of the model were criticized (Laubscher 1960; Birch 1961; Moore 1961), but did not alter its basic features (Hubbert & Rubey 1960, 1961a, b). The toe effect ignored by Hubbert & Rubey, was discussed by Raleigh & Griggs (1963). Later Hsu (1969b, c) and Hubbert & Rubey (1969) discussed the importance of a neglected shear strength term in their original formulation. However, the difficulties of explaining why such sliding is not catastrophic remain (Chapman 1979). Carlisle (1965) argued that the simple laws of frictional sliding may not apply during thrusting. Hanshaw & Zen (1965) discussed the possibility of maintaining high pore-fluid pressures in evaporite sequences by shales acting as semipermeable osmotic membranes. Heard & Rubey (1966) examined several dehydration reactions that could generate transient high pore-fluid pressures in sediments and metamorphic rocks. The problem of how fluids escape from thick piles of sediment was ex-

amined by Bredehoeft & Hanshaw (1968) and Hanshaw & Bredehoeft (1968).

Despite the great interest in the subject, in practice it is usually difficult to demonstrate that high pore-fluid pressures existed during the emplacement of any foreland thrusts, though their local development may be inferred (see Gretener this volume). Such pressures must exist in the interior of an orogenic belt undergoing regional metamorphism because metamorphic petrologists consider the fluid pressure to be essentially lithostatic (e.g. Yoder 1955). Presumably, the enormous volume of water lost during the regional metamorphism of argillaceous sediments takes place under conditions of high pore-fluid pressures (Heard & Rubey 1966).

Viscous sliding

Kehle (1970), noting the prevalence of shales, evaporites and some limestones as decollement zones, suggested that such zones should be regarded as viscous fluids, rather than as frictional discontinuities. Thus the zone of high pore-fluid pressures of Hubbert & Rubey can often, or at least sometimes, be replaced conceptually by a viscous layer. If pushed from the rear, geologically significant movement would occur provided the 'viscosity' was low enough. Hsu (1969a) gave a similar treatment of the Glarus Thrust (here regarded as originating by collision rather than being thought of as a foreland thrust).

Weak thrust wedge

Where thrust sheets have moved uphill, the only possible driving forces are either gravity spreading or some force applied externally to the thrust belt. Elliott (1976a, b) develops a gravity spreading model of thrusting in which the theory developed for glacial flow is applied to deforming rocks. As in glaciers, the surface slope drives the outward flow of the material.

Chapple (1978) criticizes the gravity spreading model on several grounds. In particular, he believes the shear stress caused by the surface slope is an order of magnitude less than the strength of many thrust wedges. Such wedges cannot deform internally as required by gravity spreading.

An additional argument against gravity spreading and also against treating décollement layers as fluids is that many present-day passive continental margins contain thick, unlithified sedimentary sequences similar to those of foreland belts. The average dip of the continental slope of passive continental margins is about 4° (Drake & Burk 1974, fig. 9, p. 8), twice as great as that inferred during emplacement of the Canadian foreland thrusts. The surface dip of some passive continental slopes is greater still. Why then is there so little deformation other than surficial sliding in such sequences? (Moore 1977; Embley & Jacobi 1977; Woodcock 1979).

Strong thrust wedge

Chapple (1978) treats the thrust belt as a strong plastic wedge sliding on a weak layer. The wedge itself thickens by compressive flow during emplacement. The stresses needed to drive the model are determined by the yield conditions.

Fluid push model

The available evidence clearly points to some spatial and temporal relationship between the plutonic/volcanic arc and foreland thrusting in the North American Cordillera. Gravity sliding and gravity spreading are both unlikely: pushing seems the only likely mechanism. But, as Price & Mountjoy (1970), Armstrong (1974), Burchfiel & Davis (1972, 1975) have all argued, the plutonic/volcanic arc is ductile and weak. How can it transmit significant non-hydrostatic stresses to the foreland? Here we encounter what can be regarded as a second

mechanical paradox of foreland thrusting: the most likely source for applied compressional stress appears to be the subduction zone, yet the intervening plutonic/volcanic arc prevents their transmission to the foreland.

Weak zones in the idealized orogenic belt

The strength of rocks decreases as temperature increases. We can assume that the amount by which the temperature in an orogenic zone exceeds the temperature of the equivalent level outside the zone is a crude measure of the weakness of that level (Fig. 5). The weak zone below the volcanic arc is clearly shown, as is the weak zone along the subduction zone. In addition to these thermally weakened zones, the sediments in the accretionary prism, forearc basin and continental miogeosyncline will be mechanically weak, as will be the entire asthenosphere.

The mechanical paradox can then be resolved by postulating that the rocks under the volcanic arc are essentially fluid and that their hydrostatic head drives the foreland thrust belt.

A qualitative model

The author has therefore constructed a thrust emplacement model that explicitly attributes the driving force to the hydrostatic pressure applied by the welt at the rear end of the thrust wedge (Fig. 6).

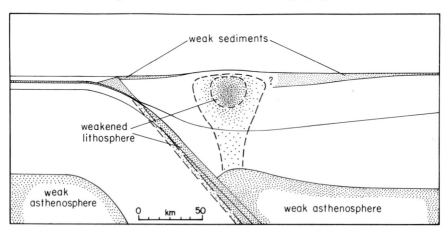

FIG. 5. Zone of weakened lithosphere in the subduction and below the volcanic arc. Density of dots represents temperature excess relative to areas outside influence of subduction zone and plutonic/volcanic zone. Mechanically weak sedimentary wedges present in accretionary prism, forearc basin and continental miogeosyncline. Based on Ernst (1974), Oxburgh & Turcotte (1970), Dickinson (1977) with modifications. The thermally weakened zone below the arc is assumed to be essentially fluid in its stress behaviour. It acts as a stress buffer to any non-hydrostatic stress from the subduction zone.

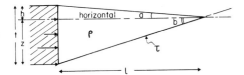

FIG. 6. Idealized fluid welt model. The welt is diagonally shaded and has the same density, ρ, as the wedge. τ is the yield stress of the décollement horizon. Horizontal arrows at rear of wedge indicate fluid pressure applied at rear of wedge.

To bring out its basic properties, the model is exceptionally simple. It deliberately ignores the problems of how the fluid welt originates, of moving thrusts over 'steps', the importance of the toe, whether the thrust wedge is porous and saturated with water, all of which are regarded as problems to be dealt with if the correctness of the general principle can be established. As discussed above ('tectonic thickening'), it is not necessary to postulate penetrative plastic flow during thrusting. The driving force is attributed to a change in mechanical properties brought about by heat, as envisaged by Price & Mountjoy (1970) and Price (1973). Initially, the rocks at the rear of the thrust belt are cold and behave as brittle elastic materials. The stresses in these rocks are assumed to be such i.e., the vertical stress component at a point is the mass of rock above that point; the horizontal component is (vertical stress) $\times$ ($v/(1-v)$), where v is Poisson's ratio (Hafner 1951, p. 380). For most rocks v is about 0.25, giving a horizontal component of one third of the lithostatic load.

When plutonism and/or metamorphism take place, Poisson's ratio increases until the rocks are essentially fluid and the horizontal stress is then equal to the lithostatic load. A yield stress of the order of 1 MPa ($=10$ bars) or less is envisaged for 'fluid' rock below the arc. If rocks on one side of an imaginary vertical surface are liquefied, the fluid rock exerts a hydrostatic pressure equal to the adjacent lithostatic stress on the solid rock. This horizontal stress is sufficient to push a thrust wedge if there is a weak enough layer at its base.

Thus, the essential requirements of the fluid push model are (i) a downhill slope from an area of weakened rock to provide a driving force and (ii) a weak layer within the potential thrust wedge. As soon as the welt is strengthened—by cooling—or the slope vanishes—by subsidence and/or erosion—or the décollement zone becomes stronger—by dewatering, solution of weak material such as halite or loss of fluid pressure—thrusting must cease. Unless surface slope, fluidity and décollement zone are simultaneously present, no thrusting can occur. Thrusts cannot be driven by this mechanism in sequences lacking a weak layer or a means of progressively creating a weak layer in strong rock.

The model cannot distinguish between welts created by diapiric uprise of magmas from the sinking slab or welts created by compressive stresses from the subduction zone (Fig. 7). Gravity spreading does occur, in the welt, but not in the thrust belt. The belt is pushed from behind by the welt.

A fluid welt may consist of rocks undergoing regional metamorphism (here including slates), a magma or a crystal mush. Since all such rocks are probably weak even if they contain only a small amount of fluid (pore water, water from dehydration or igneous melt), the solid densities are taken as good estimates of the densities during flow. These will range from 2.7 for granite to 3.0 for gabbro, and 2.6 for granitic gneiss to 3.0 for amphibolites (Daly *et al.* 1966). The densities of sediments are very variable and a wedge might have a range of average densities from 2.2 for poorly consolidated shales to 2.8 for void-free carbonates (Daly *et al.* 1966).

For convenience, the densities of the wedge and welt are assumed to be equal. Hence a small 'safety factor' is built into the argument.

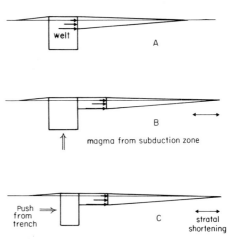

FIG. 7. Fluid pumping by diapiric uprise of magmas from the subduction zone (A) and by compression of the fluid welt (B). Both processes increase the fluid head above its original value; both could occur simultaneously; both cause the same changes in the boundary conditions at the rear end of the thrust wedge.

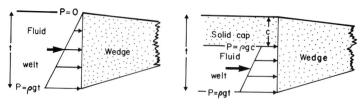

FIG. 8. Pressures and average pressures on the rear of a wedge driven by (A), completely fluid welt; (B), rock-capped fluid welt.

Driving stresses

Mass of wedge $= (tl\rho)/2$, where t = thickness of rear end of wedge, l = length of wedge, ρ = density of wedge assumed equal to the fluid welt. Downslope force $= tl\rho g . \sin(b))/2$, where g = acceleration of gravity, b = dip of base of wedge.

Movement up or down slope is resisted by $(l\tau/\cos(b))$ where τ = shear strength of weak layer

Fluid pressure at top of wedge = zero; fluid pressure at base of wedge = ρgt. Therefore mean fluid pressure = $\rho gt/2$. The force exerted by this pressure per unit width of the thrust wedge is $t.(\rho gt)/2$ (Fig. 8).

If (b) is downslope from foreland then, at sliding, the component of the fluid driving force up the slope $(\rho gt) . t . \cos(b)/2$, must equal the resistance of the weak layer, $l\tau/\cos(b)$, and the downslope component of the mass of the wedge, $tl\rho g . \sin(b)/2$:

$$(\rho t) . tg . \cos(b)/2 = tl\rho g . \sin(b)/2 + l\tau/\cos(b)$$

For small b, $\sin(b) = z/l$, where z is vertical thickness of wedge from horizontal to depth; $\cos(b) = 1$

$$(\rho t) . tg/2 = tl\rho gz/2l + l\tau \qquad (1)$$

$$\tau = g\rho t(t-z)/2l$$

$$= g\rho th/2l$$

$$= gt(a)\rho . (\pi)/360,$$

where (a) = surface slope in degrees.

If τ is in MPa (1 MPa = 10 bars) ρ is 2.7×10^3 kg m^{-3}, t in km and (a) in degrees, then

$$\tau = 0.23t(a) \text{ MPa} \qquad (2)$$

In reality, the fluid welt will be capped by a block of stronger rock which will reduce the driving force. If the cap has a thickness c, then there is no horizontal driving force due to fluid pressure until a depth c, where it is $g\rho c$. At a depth t, the fluid pressure is the same—$g\rho t$. The mean fluid pressure is therefore $g\rho . (t + c)/2$, but it acts over a vertical distance of

$(t-c)$, (Fig. 8B). The mean fluid pressure is therefore $g\rho(t+c) . (t-c)/2$. The available driving force is therefore reduced in the ratio $(1 - c^2/t^2):1$.

Even if the shear resistance on the sliding horizon is zero, the rock-capped fluid column cannot move unless its height exceeds a minimum value. This height is readily found by equating the upslope component of the driving force with the downslope component of the mass of the wedge:

$$\rho(t^2 - c^2) . g . \cos(b)/2 = tl\rho g . \sin(b)$$

For small b, this reduces to

$$c^2 = th.$$

For a 10 km thick thrust wedge rising 2 km in its source area above its toe, the fluid column must rise to within 4.5 km of the surface before any thrusting can take place. Geologically, the solid cap corresponds to the 'superstructure', and the weak rocks below to the 'infrastructure' recognized by structural geologists mapping granitic terrains.

Equation (2) is similar to Elliott's equation 4 (1976a, p. 951). Chapple's equation 35 has an additional term brought in by the slope of the basal layer. The slope of the basal layer is absent in the above derivation because the density of the driving fluid has been equated with that of the thrust wedge and in the small angle approximation terms involving (b) cancel (equation 1 above).

Contrast with other models

Because the boundary stresses at the rear of the wedge are assumed to be essentially hydrostatic, it is impossible to satisfy Chapple's yield criterion (his equation 2). Thus the thrust wedge as a whole cannot yield in compressional flow as a plastic body in the fluid welt model unless its yield stress varies with depth.

The difference between the fluid push and the gravity spreading model is perhaps made clear if we consider a double wedge with a

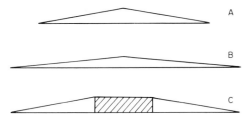

FIG. 9. Essential difference between the spreading of a fluid welt and pushing by a fluid welt. (A), initial state; (B), spreading of a weak double wedge; (C), pushing by injection at rear of a strong wedge.

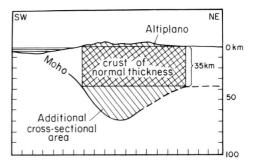

FIG. 10. Accretion under the Altiplano region in the Andes. The diagonally shaded area represents material that exeeds in volume a crust at sea level and 35 km thickness. Based on James (1971).

horizontal base (Fig. 9). According to the gravity spreading model, the shear stress created when the surface slope exceeds a few degrees will bring about internal flow within the thrust wedge. The wedge will spread symmetrically outwards under its own weight, changing shape as it does so (Fig. 9B). If the wedge is strong enough to resist the shear stress due to the sloping surface, then it does not move until a zone of fluid is created, say in a vertical central zone. If the stress generated by this fluid welt exceeds the sliding resistance, the double wedge separates into two halves that maintain their shape (unless they themselves become weakened by heating), the fluid level drops and the movement eventually ceases (Fig. 9C).

Pumping in more fluid, or thickening an existing igneous/metamorphic welt, or providing sufficient additional heating of the existing rock starts the process again. In practice, the deforming wedge does change its shape by the tectonic accretion of new material to its outer underlying edge (Fig. 3), rather than by internal deformation.

Applications of the model

When thrusting takes place, equation 2 is satisfied. The fluid push and gravity spreading models cannot be distinguished by the stresses required for thrust emplacement. These stresses are small and are readily estimated. For the McConnell Thrust, cited by Elliott as an example of emplacement by gravity spreading (Elliott 1976b, fig.1), t, is about 17.5 km, the average surface slope is about 3.5 in 100 km, or 2°. Then τ is about 8.1 MPa.

Elliott estimates an overall strength of 20 MPa for the McConnell Thrust (1976b, p. 301), but believes the basal shear stress during emplacement is lower, as indicated. (Like Chapple, the author considers that a yield stress of 20 MPa is too low an estimate for the

wedge as a whole). The calculated yield stress of the weak layers in three of Chapple's models are 2.5, 9.8 and 25.5 MPa.

The actual yield stress of most weak layers is not known. Halite has a yield stress of about 1.5 MPa at 100°C at a strain rate of $10^{-14}\,\mathrm{s}^{-1}$ (Chapple 1978, p. 1197); rapidly stressed weak rocks have yield stresses of about 10 MPa, which would be much less at geological strain rates of about $10^{-14}\,\mathrm{s}^{-1}$ (Elliott 1976a, p. 950). The cohesive strength of materials parallel to their sliding surfaces when the normal stress is zero $C_o = 0$ in the Coulomb theory) is estimated as 0.07 MPa for the Grand Banks slide off Newfoundland and 0.05 MPa for the Ranger slide off Mexico (Chapman 1979).

Locally, of course, the shear stress resisting motion could be much larger. For example, the McConnell Thrust could have a strong layer 1 km in length that required a stress of 100 MPa to cause movement on it. But this would reduce the average stress on the remaining 99 km of the thrust to about 7.2 MPa, instead of 8.1 MPa. Thus, interconnections of one weak layer up through a strong layer to another weak layer, required by observation (Dahlstrom 1970), are not precluded by the model.

Possible examples

The author believes that a fluid rock welt could have emplaced the Huayhuash Thrusts of the Peruvian Andes (Coney 1971); the Papuan New Guinea Thrusts described by Jenkins (1974)—attributed to gravity sliding; and possibly the Mohave Thrusts of southern California (Burchfiel & Davis 1972)—attributed to crustal compression. The mechanism may not be applicable to basement thrusts such as the

Wind River Thrust of Wyoming (Smithson *et al.* 1978) because a fluid rock welt did not exist in the area at the time of thrusting. However, Molnar & Tapponnier (1978) have suggested that the current seismic activity in the Tien Shan in Soviet central Asia may be due to Tibet acting as a pressure gauge and transmitting stress hydrostatically to the Tien Shan via the intervening Tarim Basin (their fig. 5, p. 5373). If stresses can be transmitted in this way, then the Laramide basement thrusts may have a similar origin.

Why asymmetry?

Although the idealized orogenic belt is two-sided (Fig. 1), the fluid welt is here regarded as flowing principally towards the foreland and generating only one significant thrust belt. The oceanward-directed thrusts are believed to be caused by shear on the subduction zone, rather than representing the oceanward push of the welt. The reason for this asymmetry is attributed partly to block faulting between the welt and the continental margin. Such faulting would create an irregular sedimentary pile lacking the smooth, unbroken profile of foreland wedges and would be more resistant to deformation. In North America an additional factor is the progressive eastward migration of igneous activity in time, due to the flattening of the subduction zone.

Similar asymmetries must exist in the attitude of cleavage and foliation surfaces created by the one-sided outward flow of the fluid welt. It is an alternative to invoking changes in subduction zone dip to account for such asymmetries (Roeder 1973, 1975).

The space problem

The association of batholiths and thrust belts has long been noted (see Hamilton & Myers

TABLE 1. *Thrust wedge volumes, batholith volumes and rates of accretion*

Thrust wedges

Displacement in km	Volume in km^3	Time interval in Ma (Armstrong 1974)	Volume/Ma in km^3
170 (Canadian Rockies, Price & Mountjoy 1970)	1700	*c.* 95	18
155 (Canadian Rockies, Bally *et al.* 1966)	1550	*c.* 95	16
110 (Wyoming Rockies, Rubey & Hubbert 1959)	1100	*c.* 80	14
100 (Sevier Belt, Utah, Armstrong 1968)	1000	*c.* 80	12.5

Batholiths

	Area km^2	Strike length km	Average width km	Average volume km^3	Volume/Ma km^3
	370,000	2900	128	1280	> 18
(Mesozoic batholiths in Canada and Alaska, (Knopf 1955). Assumed 10 km thick, mostly Cretaceous in age—70 Ma interval)					
	182,000	2000	91	910	> 13
(Mesozoic batholiths in United States, (Knopf 1955). Assumed 10 km thick, mostly Cretaceous in age—70 Ma interval)					

Accretion

Assume subduction at 10 cm per year; 500 m oceanic sediment accreted to overriding plate, compacted to 0.6 of original volume. Accretion rate per km of orogenic strike is 30 km^3 per Ma (Oxburgh & Turcotte 1970).

Assume cross-sectional area increase in Andes represents accretion since early Cretaceous time, or 140 Ma. A real increase per km of orogenic strike is about 66 km^3 per Ma. Based on James (1971).

1967 for discussion). They believed the relationship might be causal, with the thrust forming either by sliding off the roof of batholiths or the batholiths shouldering aside the country rock. They noted that field evidence suggested that batholiths had commonly been intruded at relatively high levels; at times having a roof made of their own volcanic products. They suggested that many of them might be relatively thin, less than 10 km, with a mushroom cross-section and a relatively narrow conduit.

In the fluid welt model these batholiths push the foreland thrust belt into place. Thus, the batholith volume per km of orogenic strike should be comparable with the displacement of the foreland thrust multiplied by the thickness at the rear of the thrust wedge (Table 1). The *minimum* batholithic volume per km of orogenic strike will be the present surface area of the batholiths multiplied by their average thickness, here taken as 10 km. Thrust belt volume and batholithic volume are comparable (Table 1).

Quite independently, we can assume that subduction has added material to the base of the North American continent at a rate equivalent to adding 500 m of oceanic sediment, subsequently compacted to 0.6 of its original volume at 10 cm per year (Oxburgh & Turcotte 1970). About 30 km^3 per km of orogenic strike are added per Ma. The sediment then melts and works its way up to the crust as magma, or is added as solid material to the base of the continental crust ('underplating'). The rates are again comparable (Table 1).

A second estimate of accretion rates can be made from the Andes (James 1971). In early Cretaceous time much of the Andes was at, or

below, sea level (Coney 1971). We can assume that the crustal thickness was about that of a normal continent, or 35 km. Today, the crustal thickness is more than 70 km under the Altiplano, an exceptionally high plain in western Bolivia, underlain by one of the thickest continental crustal sections known. The calculated rate of accretion will probably be an upper limit. This area is one in which foreland thrusts might well be active. If we assume that the increase in cross-sectional area is due to accretion since early Cretaceous time (Fig. 10), then the rate of addition of new material is indeed high (Table 1).

To sum up: estimated thrust belt volumes and volumetric transport rates are only 1.1–1.3 times greater than the associated average minimum batholith volumes and rates of generation; about 0.3–0.6 of presumed accretion rates at rapidly moving subduction zones and 0.1–0.2 of presumed exceptionally high accretion rates.

A model in which these figures are integrated into a tectonic flow diagram is given in Fig. 11. In effect, subduction, partial melting and injection provide a fluid reduction drive of some 50:1 from subduction velocities to the thrust velocity.

Dips of thrust belts and associated subduction zones

In the case of a hot welt, the subduction zone dips in the opposite direction to the foreland thrust belt, as is clear from the thrusts of western North America. After collision, the interpretation is more difficult, but providing a thrust belt can be traced continuously from an

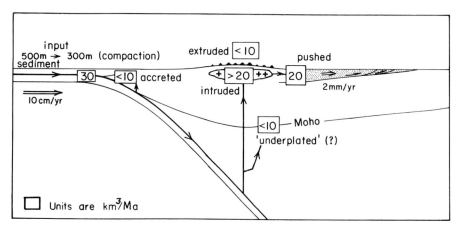

FIG. 11. Tectonic flow diagram linking subduction, accretion, batholithic intrusion and foreland thrusting.

undeformed foreland to a contemporaneous igneous/metamorphic core—without any ophiolites—then such a belt probably dips in the opposite direction to any associated subduction zone.

Ideally, all such foreland thrust belts should have the following properties: i) develop in the sedimentary prisms deposited on continental margins; ii) be traceable continuously across strike from undisturbed foreland to once hot rock; iii) display no evidence of ophiolites; iv) provide evidence of a downhill surface slope from the source area of the thrusts during emplacement; and v) be contemporaneous with plutonism and/or regional metamorphism. Such thrusts develop so that the associated subduction zone dips under the thrust belt and transports material in the same direction as the thrust belt itself (Fig. 1).

Examples may include the Moine Thrust of the Scottish Caledonides (subduction zone dip to NW?); the foreland thrusts of the southern Appalachians (subduction zone dip to the NW?); the Hercynian Thrusts of southern Ireland and South Wales (subduction zone dip to the N?).

Orogenic belts with poorly developed foreland thrusts and with abundant granites include the Hercynian belt in central Europe and the Palaeozoic orogenic belt of eastern Australia. A well-developed thrust belt may be absent because a suitably weak sedimentary prism is lacking in turn caused perhaps by block faulting.

ACKNOWLEDGMENTS. W. B. Harland and J. C. Maxwell first aroused the author's interest in thrust belts. He thanks P. F. Friend and N. H. Woodcock for reading and criticizing the manuscript, and G. King and E. R. Oxburgh for discussions.

References

ARMSTRONG, R. L. 1968. Sevier orogenic belt in Nevada and Utah. *Bull. geol. Soc. Am.* **79**, 429–58.

—— 1974. Magmatism, orogenic timing, and orogenic diachronism in the Cordillera from Mexico to Canada. *Nature London*, **247**, 348–51.

—— & DICK, H. J. B. 1974. A model for the development of thin overthrust sheets of crystalline rock. *Geology*, **2**, 35–40.

ARMSTRONG, F. C. & ORIEL, S. S. 1965. Tectonic development of Idaho-Wyoming thrust belt. *Bull. Am. Assoc. Petrol. Geol.* **49**, 1847–66.

BALLY, A. W., GORDY, P. L. & STEWARD, G. A. 1966. Structure, seismic data and orogenic evolution of southern Canadian Rockies. *Bull. Can. Pet. Geol.* **14**, 337–81.

BIRCH, F. 1961. Role of fluid pressure in mechanics of overthrust faulting: Discussion. *Bull. geol. Soc. Am.* **72**, 1441–4.

BIRD, J. F. & DEWEY, J. F. 1970. Lithosphere plate-continental margin tectonics and the evolution of the Appalachian orogen. *Bull. geol. Soc. Am.* **81**, 1031–60.

BOCCALETTI, M., ELTER, P. & GUAZZONE, G. 1971. Plate tectonic models for the development of the western Alps and northern Appennines. *Nature London*, **234**, 108–11.

BREDEHOEFT, J. D. & HANSHAW, B. B. 1968. On the maintenance of anomalous fluid pressures: 1. Thick sedimentary sequences. *Bull. geol. Soc. Am.* **79**, 1097–106.

BUCHER, W. A. 1956. The role of gravity in orogenesis. *Bull. geol. Soc. Am.* **67**, 1295–318.

BURCHFIEL, B. C. & DAVIS, G. A. 1972. Structural framework and evolution of the southern part of the Cordilleran orogen, western United States. *Am. J. Sci.* **272**, 97–118.

—— & DAVIS, G. A. 1975. Nature and controls of Cordilleran orogenesis, western United States: extensions of an earlier synthesis. *Am. J. Sci.* **275-A**, 363–95.

CARLISLE, D. 1965. Sliding friction and overthrust faulting. *J. Geol. Chicago*, **73**, 271–91.

CARTER, N. L. 1976. Steady state flow of rocks. *Rev. Geophys. Space Phys.* **14**, 301–60.

CHAPMAN, R. E. 1979. Mechanics of unlubricated sliding. *Bull. geol. Soc. Am.* **90**, 19–28.

CHAPPLE, W. M. 1978. Mechanics of thin-skinned fold-and-thrust belts. *Bull. geol. Soc. Am.* **89**, 1189–98.

CONEY, P. J. 1971. Structural evolution of the Cordillera Huayhuash, Andes of Peru. *Bull. geol. Soc. Am.* **82**, 1863–84.

—— 1978. Overview of Mesozoic-Cenozoic Cordilleran plate tectonics. *In.* SMITH, R. B. & EATON, G. P. (eds). *Cenozoic Tectonics and Regional Geophysics of the Western Cordillera.* Mem. geol. Soc. Am. **152**, 33–50.

—— & REYNOLDS, S. J. 1977. Cordilleran Benioff zones. *Nature London*, **270**, 403–5.

DAHLSTROM, C. D. A. 1970. Structural geology in the eastern margin of the Canadian Rocky Mountains. *Bull. Can. Pet. Geol.* **18**, 332–406.

DALY, R., MANGER, G. E. & CLARK, S. P. 1966. In: CLARK, S. P. (ed). *Handbook of Physical Constants.* Mem. geol. Soc. Am., **97**, 19–26.

DEWEY, J. F. 1974. Continental margins and ophiolite obduction Appalachian Caledonian system. *In:* BURK, C. A. & DRAKE, C. L. (eds). *The Geology of Continental Margins,* Springer, Berlin. 933–50.

—— & BIRD, J. M. 1970. Mountain belts and the new global tectonics. *J. geophys. Res.* **75**, 2625–47.

—— & —— 1971. Origin and emplacement of the

ophiolite suite: Appalachian ophiolites in New-foundland. *J. geophys. Res.* **76**, 3179–206.

DICKINSON, W. R. 1970. Relations of andesites, granites and derivative sandstones to arc-trench tectonics. *Rev. Geophys. Space Phys.* **8**, 813–60.

—— 1977. Tectono-stratigraphic evolution of subduction-controlled sedimentary assemblages. *In*: TALWANI, M. & PITMAN, W. C. (eds). *Island Arcs, Deep Sea Trenches and Back-Arc Basins*, Maurice Ewing Series **1**, Am. Geophys. Union, Washington, D.C. 33–40.

—— & HATHERTON, T. 1967. Andesitic vulcanism and seismicity around the Pacific. *Science*, **157**, 801–3.

DRAKE, C. L. & BURK, C. A. 1974. Geological significance of continental margins. *In*: BURK, C. A. & DRAKE, C. L. (eds). *The Geology of Continental Margins*, Springer, Berlin. 3–10.

ELLIOTT, D. 1976*a*. The motion of thrust sheets. *J. geophys. Res.* **81**, 949–63.

—— 1976*b*. The energy balance and deformation mechanisms of thrust sheets. *Philos. Trans. R. Soc. London*, A, **283**, 289–312.

EMBLEY, R. W. & JACOBI, R. D. 1977. Distribution of large submarine sediment slides and slumps on Atlantic continental margins. *Marine geotechnology*, **2**, 205–28.

ERNST, W. G. 1973. Interpretive synthesis of metamorphism in the Alps. *Bull. geol. Soc. Am.* **84**, 2053–78.

—— 1974. Metamorphism and ancient continental margins. *In*: BURK, C. A. & DRAKE, C. L. (eds). *The Geology of Continental Margins*, Springer, Berlin. 907–19.

HAFNER, W. 1951. Stress distributions and faulting. *Bull. geol. Soc. Am.* **62**, 373–98.

HAMILTON, W. 1969. Mesozoic California and the underflow of the Pacific mantle. *Bull. geol. Soc. Am.* **80**, 2409–29.

—— & MYERS, W. B. 1967. The nature of batholiths & *Prof Pap. U.S. geol. Surv.* **554-C**, 30 p.

HANSHAW, B. B. & BREDEHOEFT, J. D. 1968. On the maintenance of anomalous fluid pressures: 2. Source layer at depth. *Bull. geol. Soc. Am.* **79**, 1107–22.

—— & ZEN, E-AN. 1965. Osmotic equilibrium and overthrust faulting. *Bull. geol. Soc. Am.* **76**, 1379–86.

HEARD, H. C. 1976. Comparison of the flow properties of rocks at crustal conditions. *Philos. Trans. R. Soc. London*, A. **283**, 173–86.

—— & RUBEY, W. W. 1966. Tectonic implications of gypsum dehydration. *Bull. geol. Soc. Am.* **77**, 162–95.

HSU, K. J. 1969*a*. A preliminary analysis of the statics and kinetics of the Glarus overthrust. *Eclog. geol. Helv.* **62**, 143–54.

—— 1969*b*. Role of cohesive strength in the mechanics of overthrust faulting and of landsliding. *Bull. geol. Soc. Am.* **80**, 927–52.

—— 1969*c*. Role of cohesive strength in the mechanics of overthrust faulting and of landsliding: reply. *Bull. geol. Soc. Am.* **80**, 955–60.

HUBBERT, M. K. & RUBEY, W. W. 1959. Role of

fluid pressure in mechanics of overthrust faulting. *Bull. geol. Soc. Am.* **58**, 362–75.

—— & —— 1960. Role of fluid pressure in mechanics of overthrust faulting: A reply. *Bull. geol. Soc. Am.* **71**, 617–628.

—— & —— 1961*a*. Role of fluid pressure in mechanics of overthrust faulting : reply to discussion by Francis Birch. *Bull. geol. Soc. Am.* **72**, 1445–52.

—— & —— 1961*b*. Role of fluid pressure in mechanics of overthrust faulting : A reply to a discussion by Walter C. Moore. *Bull. geol. Soc. Am.* **72**, 1587–94.

—— & —— 1969. Role of cohesive strength in the mechanics of overthrust faulting and of landsliding: discussion. *Bull. geol. Soc. Am.* **80**, 953–4.

JAMES, D. E. 1971. Plate tectonic model for the evolution of the central Andes. *Bull. geol. Soc. Am.* **82**, 3325–46.

JENKINS, D. A. L. 1974. Detachment tectonics in western Papua New Guinea. *Bull. geol. Soc. Am.* **85**, 533–48.

JONES, D. L., BLAKE, M. C., BAILEY, E. H. & McCLAUGHLIN, R. J. 1978. Distribution of upper Mesozoic subduction complexes along the west coast of North America. *Tectonophysics*, **47**, 275–94.

KARIG, D. E. & SHARMAN, G. F. 1975. Subduction and accretion in trenches. *Bull. geol. Soc. Am.* **86**, 377–89.

KEHLE, R. O. 1970. Analysis of gravity sliding and orogenic translation. *Bull. geol. Soc. Am.* **81**, 1641–64.

KEITH, S. B. 1978. Paleosubduction geometries inferred from Cretaceous and Tertiary magmatic patterns in southwestern North America. *Geology*, **6**, 516–21.

LAUBSCHER, H. P. 1960. Role of fluid pressure in mechanics of overthrust faulting: A discussion. *Bull. geol. Soc. Am.* **71**, 611–6.

—— 1971. The large-scale kinematics of the western Alps and the northern Apennines and its palinspastic implications. *Am. J. Sci.* **271**, 193–226.

LIPMAN, P. W., PROTSKA, H. J. & CHRISTIANSEN, R. L. 1972. Cenozoic volcanism and plate-tectonic evolution of the western United States. 1. Early and Middle Cenozoic. *Philos. Trans. R. Soc. London*, A. **271**, 217–48.

MOLNAR, P. & TAPPONNIER, P. 1978. Active tectonics of Tibet. *J. geophys. Res.* **83**, 5361–75.

MOORE, D. G. 1977. Submarine slides. *In*: VOIGT, B. (ed.). *Rockslides and Avalanches*, **1**, Natural Phenomena, *Developments in geotechnical engineering*, **14A**, 563–604.

MOORE, W. L. 1961. Role of fluid pressure in overthrust faulting: A discussion. *Bull. geol. Soc. Am.* **72**, 1581–6.

OXBURGH, E. R. 1972. Flake tectonics and continental collision. *Nature London*, **239**, 202–4.

—— & TURCOTTE, D. L. 1970. Thermal structure of island arcs *Bull. geol. Soc. Am.* **81**, 1665–88.

—— & —— 1974. Thermal gradients and regional metamorphism in overthrust terrains with special reference to the Eastern Alps. *Schweiz. mineral. petrogr. Mitt.* **54,** 641–662.

PRICE, R. A. 1971. Gravitational sliding and the foreland thrust and fold belt of the North American Cordillera: Discussion. *Bull. geol. Soc. Am.* **82,** 1133–8.

—— 1973. Large-scale gravitational flow of supracrustal rocks, southern Canadian Rockies. *In:* DEJONG, K. A. & SCHOLTEN, R. (eds). *Gravity and Tectonics.* Wiley, New York, 491–502.

—— & MOUNTJOY, E. W. 1970. Geologic structure of the Canadian Rocky Mountains between Bow and Athabasca Rivers—a progress report. *Spec. Pap. geol. Assoc. Can.* **6,** 7–25.

RALEIGH, C. B. & GRIGGS, D. T. 1963. Effect of the toe in the mechanics of overthrust faulting. *Bull. geol. Soc. Am.* **74,** 813–30.

ROEDER, D. H. 1973. Subduction and orogeny. *J. geophys. Res.* **78,** 5005–24.

—— 1975. Tectonic effects of dip changes in subduction zones. *Am. J. Sci.* **275,** 252–64.

RUBEY, W. W. & HUBBERT, M. K. 1959. Role of fluid pressure in mechanics of overthrust faulting. II. Overthrust belt of western Wyoming in light of fluid-pressure hypothesis. *Bull. geol. Soc. Am.* **70,** 167–206.

SMITH, A. G. 1976. Plate tectonics and orogeny: a review. *Tectonophysics,* **33,** 215–85.

SMITHSON, S. B., BREWER, J., KAUFMAN, S. & OLIVER, J. 1978. Nature of the Wind River thrust, Wyoming, from COCORP deep-reflection data and from gravity data. *Geology,* **6,** 648–52.

SMOLUCHOWSKI, M. S. 1909. Some remarks on the mechanics of overthrusts. *Geol. Mag.* **6,** 204–5.

WOODCOCK, N. H. 1979. Sizes of submarine slides and their significance. *J. struct. Geol.* **1,** 137–42.

YODER, H. S. 1955. Role of water in metamorphism. *Spec. Pap. geol. Soc. Am.* **62,** 505–24.

A. G. SMITH, Department of Geology, Sedgwick Museum, Downing Street, Cambridge CB2 3EQ, England.

The role of gravity in orogenic belts

H. Ramberg

SUMMARY: The diapiric and nappe structures of the Caledonides in Scandanavia are briefly discussed and compared with similar structures in other orogenic belts. The buoyancy of sialic basement is discussed and a theoretical treatment of basement buoyancy is outlined. The gravitational spreading of nappes is then considered. Two theoretical models are presented: the first considers the condition of free slip on the base and the second deals with the more realistic situation when the base exhibits coherence.

The primary energy which drives the evolution of orogenic belts is probably to be found in the Earth's mantle. Convection currents and/or mantle diapirism are likely driving mechanisms for the tectonism of orogenic belts. However, the detailed connection between these deep-seated phenomena and orogenesis is not yet documented by geophysical-geological observations, and convincing experimental or numerical models have not been devised. The models to be discussed in the present paper are consequently of less ambitious character. We shall investigate to what extent the kinds of deformation structures and movement patterns which are encountered in orogenic belts can be related to forces originated within the orogenic architecture itself, that is, forces which are more accessible for study than the unknown forces hidden deep in the Earth's mantle.

Within most orogens, including the Scandinavian Caledonides, three types of structures belonging to this second category can be recognized, viz. (1) domes, diapirs and horsts consisting chiefly of more or less activated sialic basement which have risen into the cover of supracrustals and nappes, (2) nappes spread plastically over their substratum and (3) rock masses which have slid down inclined surfaces (Fig. 1).

These are phenomena whose immediate cause—that is, immediate driving energy—is found in the orogenic architecture itself.

The structures mentioned are the results of the dissipation of gravity potential on a regional or local scale.

The protuberances of basement into the cover are driven by buoyancy of the granitoid basement which generally is less dense than the column of metalavas and metasediments. The rise of the basement is compensated by the descent of the more dense overburden. This means decreasing gravity potential during the process, the potential energy being partly dissipated to heat; partly, perhaps, changed to chemical energy in the form of new mineral assemblages.

The energy behind the vertical sagging and complementary horizontal spreading recorded in some nappes is also a decreasing gravity potential. When a nappe thins, its centre of gravity descends. This is equivalent to saying that the gravity potential of the nappe decreases as it moves.

In contrast to a plastically collapsing nappe, a rock-mass sliding down an inclined substratum may exhibit no indication of internal sagging or plastic collapse. The rock may move as a rigid unit. Again, it is evident that the gravity potential decreases during the slide.

Basement diapirism in orogens

As far as the structural relationship between basement and cover goes—the latter also including thrust sheets—there are noteworthy similarities between a number of orogenic belts. The similarities stem partly from the fact that the mobility of the sialic basement increases from the edge of the orogen to its core. The increase of basement mobility coincides with the change in grade of regional metamorphism and with the rise in temperature across the orogenic belt. In the core zone of orogens the basement often seems to have been more ductile than many of the cover rocks, whereas the opposite is true close to the edges of orogenic belts where the cover sediments are often tightly folded above a rigid, unaffected basement (see Wegman 1930).

However, the characteristic structural relationship between basement and cover is not explicable solely by a changing absolute ductility or a changing ductility contrast between the two structural units. The tendency of the basement to rise in the form of anticlinal cores, domes and diapirs also indicates that the basement is buoyant relative to the cover. (It is necessary to use the modest term 'indicates'

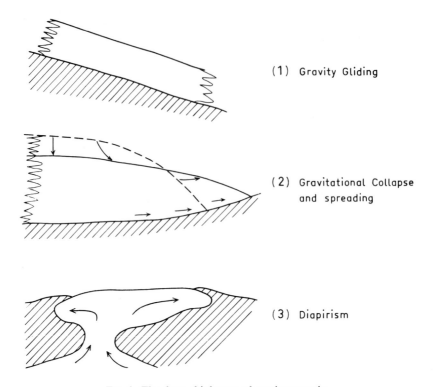

(1) Gravity Gliding

(2) Gravitational Collapse
     and spreading

(3) Diapirism

FIG. 1. The three chief types of gravity tectonics.

because basement anticlines and uplifts in general may also be produced solely by horizontal compression without any buoyant force whatsoever. It is the special shape and structure of the uplifts—in combination with measured gravity anomalies and density contrasts—which show whether they are produced by buoyancy or by horizontal compression.

Let us consider briefly the general character of the basement-cover relationships in the Scandinavian Caledonides, (Fig. 2) in three somewhat different situations; characterized by different ductility of the basement and different metamorphic relationships between cover and substratum.

(1) Along the E and SE border of the Scandinavian Caledonides the sialic Baltic shield dips gently below autochthonous Cambrian and Eocambrian sediments and the overriding Caledonian nappes. Little or no sign of Caledonian metamorphism is visible in the granitoid basement except cataclasis and mylonitization which show that the basement was not completely undisturbed during the Caledonian orogenesis. Hence, wherever the metamorphic nappes—especially the extensive Seve Nappe in Sweden and the Jotun Nappes in

Norway—have spread over the autochthon and basement there is an inverted metamorphic gradient i.e. the grade of dynamothermal metamorphism increases from the base up.

(2) Within the Caledonian belt, but still rather close to its eastern edge, there is a row of uplifts in which the basement is exposed in a series of Precambrian windows extending from Valdres and Atnasjö in S Norway to Raipas in N Norway. In these peripheral uplifts the Precambrian structure and mineral facies are still well preserved and neither Caledonian deformation nor Caledonian recrystallization penetrates deep into the basement. Large portions of the Precambrian granites, gneisses and porphyries are not visibly affected by the Caledonian event. With few exceptions (see Gustavson 1963, 1972) the rise of the peripheral basement windows is generally believed to have occurred in Caledonian time after the main motion of the nappes.

It is not easy to decide whether the often considerable shear strain and flattening of the basement rocks along the contact is due to the motion of the overriding nappes or to the rise of the uplifts. Both processes will give shear strain at the contact, but the symmetry and

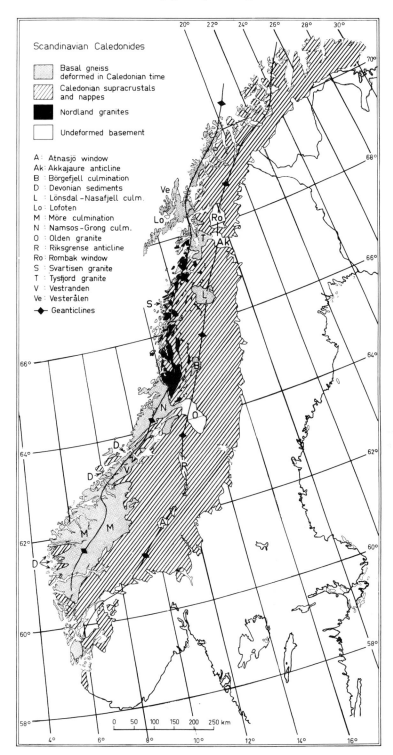

Fig. 2. The Scandinavian Caledonides, simplified and modified from geological map of Norway by Holtedahl & Dons 1960 and the pre-Quaternary map of Sweden by Magnusson *et al.* 1957.

magnitude of the resulting strain will differ in the two unlike processes. This has not as yet been studied sufficiently in the field

(3) Along the coast of Norway, from the Bergen-arc district in the SW to Lofoten in the N the basement is exposed, in what often appears a strongly Caledonized state, within a number of culminations.

The largest of these is the huge Möre culmination which is connected through the NE trending strip of gneisses in Vestranden with the more bulky Namsos–Grong–Olden culmination. Though whole rock Rb–Sr age determinations mostly give ages around 1700 Ma in the Möre gneiss (Pidgeon & Råheim 1972; Råheim 1977, & pers. comm.) much of the metamorphism, intensive folding and other deformations which characterize the Möre–Vestranden–Namsos gneisses and crystalline schists are features gained in Caledonian time. This is shown by mineral age determinations and by the conformity between small and large scale basement structures and the documented Caledonian structures in the cover.

Along the edge of the Möre culmination and along the several synforms of cover which extend into the Vestranden gneisses, the basal gneisses and the cover are intensively co-folded and co-deformed giving rise to complicated geometry. Thus writes Holmsen in Strand & Holmsen (1960) about the cover-basement relations at the E edge of the Möre culmination:

'The large-scale structural picture of the culmination area thus exhibits a number of dome-shaped anticlines, partly overturned in diverging directions. The domes are separated by deeply downfolded elongated and curved synclines, containing the younger rocks and the overturned and inverted parts of anticlines of the basement gneisses.'

These structures of central basement culminations are quite similar to the domal structures produced in our experimental models, see Ramberg (1966) and Ramberg & Sjöström (1973).

N from the Namsos–Grong culmination, the basement penetrates the cover in a number of domes and diapirs—the so-called 'Nordland granites' or the 'bottom granites' as these bodies often are called, Fig. 3. Descriptions by Rekstad (1919 & 1929), Skjeseth & Sörensen (1953), Rutland & Nicholson (1965), Nicholson & Rutland (1969), Nicholson (1973) show that Holmsen's account of the Möre domes can just as well be applied to many of the Nordland 'granites'. There are, however,

exceptions because some of the Nordland 'granites' have a more magmatic appearance than would be expected from a plastically flowing but not molten activated basement. A case in point is the Bindal granite—the southernmost of the Nordland 'granites'. This exhibits a coarse, porphyric massive internal structure, it occasionally cuts across the schistosity of the surroundings and seems to have produced thermal metamorphism in some of the adjacent schists. Mylonites within the contact zone, however, prove that relative motion between the Bindal body and the adjacent schists and gneisses has been considerable even after the granite solidified.

It is worth noting that Rb–Sr age determination of the Bindal granite gives a Caledonian age, viz. 424 ± 26 Ma according to Priem et al. (1975). This young age contrasts with the Precambrian ages (around 1700 Ma) determined for some other Nordland 'granites' (see Wilson 1973).

In the Lofoten–Vesterålen area the zone of Nordland 'granites' is replaced by a basement complex which has been much less active in Caledonian times. Except for minor local Caledonian disturbances within the complex and considerable strain along the contact with the cover in the E (Gustavson 1974a and b), the Lofoten–Vesterålen complex seems to have acted as a rather rigid block—perhaps as a sort of 'Zwischengebirge'—between the Scandinavian and the Greenlandic Caledonides during the orogenesis. The rocks within the complex show a wide spectrum of Precambrian ages varying from 900 to 2700 Ma (Griffin et al. 1978). The weak Caledonian influence is here and there detectable, as indicated by the age 460 ± 12 Ma measured in metasediments (the Leknes group) within the complex (Tull 1977, p. 33).

In two regions, cross culminations extend across the entire Scandinavian Caledonides, exposing the sialic basement continuously from the practically unaffected Baltic craton in the E to the state of maximum Caledonian mobilization in the coastal region of Norway. One cross culmination extends from Olden in Sweden to the Grong–Namsos complex in Norway; another unites the Tysfjord 'granite' (Foslic 1941) in N Norway with the Baltic shield in the region of the Stora Sjöfallet national park on the Swedish side.

In conclusion, then, we find that the basement below the column of supracrustals and nappes in the Scandinavian Caledonides is exposed in two rows of culminations oriented parallel to the trend of the orogenic belt. One

FIG. 3. Distribution of the Nordland granites in the Norwegian Caledonides, see also Fig. 2.

row of peripheral windows rather close to the E boundary of the orogen defines a geanticline extending along the entire edge of the belt. In these windows the Precambrian structure and mineral facies are well preserved, the Caledonian influence being limited to contact zones of variable thickness. The thermal component of the dynamothermal metamorphism has been weak during the rise of the uplifts, and the basal granitoid rocks appear to have behaved rather rigidly, giving rise to geometrically simple anticlines, domes or horsts.

The second row of basement uplifts coincides with the core zone of the orogen, the zone of high grade of dynamothermal metamorphism and great mobility of basement as well as cover.

Similarity between the Scandinavian Caledonides and the Appalachians and the Alps

It is tempting to compare the peripheral uplifts of Precambrian basement in the Scandinavian Caledonides with similar structures in both the Alps and the Appalachians.

The curved row of external massifs in the French and Swiss Alps (the Argentera, the Pelvoux, the Belledonne, the Montblanc and the Aiguilles rouges, the Aare and the Gotthard Massifs) are uplifts of the Alps sialic basement.

These massifs consist essentially of granitoids of Hercynian age and are but moderately affected by Alpine deformation and metamorphism. They seem to play the same role in the Alpine orogenesis as do the peripheral basement uplifts in the Caledonian orogenesis.

A similar situation exists in the Appalachians in North America. Inside the belt, but close to its eastern edge, separating the external zone of weakly metamorphosed strata from strongly metamorphosed rocks in the internal zone, there exists a row of basement anticlines extending from the Blue Ridge in the S to the Green Mountains in the N. Between these two well known uplifts a number of perhaps less well known basement windows include the Reading Prong, the Hudson Massif, the Housatonic Massif and the Berkshire Massif. These windows of basement gneisses of Grenvillian age are but weakly affected by Taconic or Acadian metamorphism and deformation, yet there is good evidence that the rise has occurred during the Appalachian Orogeny. For a modern description of the Appalachians

see Zen *et al.* (1968) and Fisher *et al.* (1970).

For some of the basement massifs, e.g. the Reading Prong complex, a buoyant rise model may be too simple. It has been suggested that thrusting has played an important role in the emplacement of the Reading Prong Precambrian substructure (Drake Jr *In*: Fisher *et al.* 1970). The same may be true for the Blue Ridge.

The row of strongly activated basement culminations described from the core of the Scandinavian Caledonides also finds its counterparts in the Alps and the Appalachians.

In the Alps, the Pennine Nappes and in the Appalachians the Bronson Hill Anticlinorium (Fig. 4), the Baltimore gneiss domes and gneiss structures in the Piedmont compare well with structures encountered in the Möre–Namsos gneiss and among the Nordland 'granites'.

Though radiometric age determinations of some of the Bronson Hill plutons give Ordovician age (Naylor, *In*: Zen *et al.* 1968) much of the core gneiss in the domes and mushrooming diapirs may still be Precambrian, the Ordovician age possibly being due to strontium isotope homogenization during strong dynamothermal Taconic metamorphism. It is also possible that a part of the gneiss below the cover of documented Ordovician sediments and lavas is in fact 'gneissified' acidic lava belonging to the cover rather than to the true basement, see Naylor, op. cit. In this connection, one recalls the Caledonian Rb-Sr age determination of at least one of the Nordland 'granites' and the intensive late Alpine metamorphism in the Hercynian core gneiss of the Pennine Nappes (e.g. Gwinner 1971).

Is the sialic basement buoyant in orogenic belts?

A crucial prerequisite for a model which holds that basement domes and diapirs are not formed in response to horizontal compression but are rather caused by vertical buoyancy forces, is that the basement is less dense than the overburden of sediments, lavas and possible thrust sheets.

First we note that wherever the basement is exposed it is sialic. There is no sign of a extensive simatic substratum even when the basement is exposed outside the culminations. This, of course, is expected since isostatic equilibrium prevents a possible simatic basement from rising high enough to be uncovered by continental erosion.

Basic lavas are more dense than an average granitoid gneiss. But usually the amount of

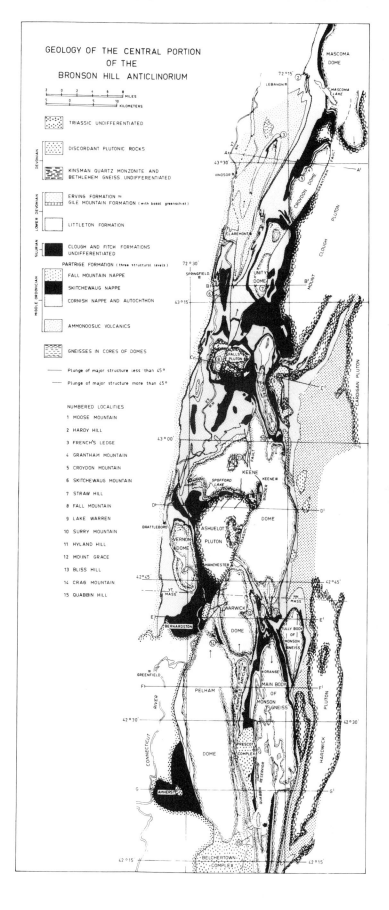

FIG. 4. Gneiss domes within the Bronson Hill Anticlinorium. Reproduced after Zen *et al.* 1968.

sediments greatly exceeds the amount of lavas in the geosynclinal column, and in the Scandinavian Caledonides the gneiss in domes and anticlines is often mantled by metasediments rather than basic lavas.

Unmetamorphosed sediments are less dense than granites, but metamorphic sediments are generally not. Depending upon mineral composition, mica schist, calc silicate schists, marble, metagreywacke etc, are generally significantly more dense than a granitoid gneiss. Thus, for example, Wenk & Wenk (1969) have determined the density of a large number of metasediments in the Alps and find that on an average they show higher density than granitoid gneisses.

Using the values of Wenk & Wenk, an assemblage of 90% schists and 10% amphibolite (greenstone) has a density close to 2.77 g/cm^3 whereas 2.67 g/cm^3 is normal for an ordinary granite. Empiric density data accordingly show

that a granitoid basement may well be buoyant when overlain by metamorphosed sediments and metalavas. This agrees well with the experience that basement diapirism increases in intensity from the outskirts to the core of orogens, both as regards area occupied by basement domes and as regards degree of penetration and lobe-development of the rising masses. The high grade of metamorphism in the core not only changes the sediments to high-density rocks (e.g. garnet mica schists, kyanite-carrying schists etc) but also increases the mobility of the sialic substratum, making the initially rigid basement and the initially soft, unconsolidated sediments approach one another as regard ductility. This change of physical properties implies a strong tendency to develop tectonic conformity between basement and cover, a conformity which often prevails even when the basement protuberances assume intricate geometric shapes, see Fig. 5.

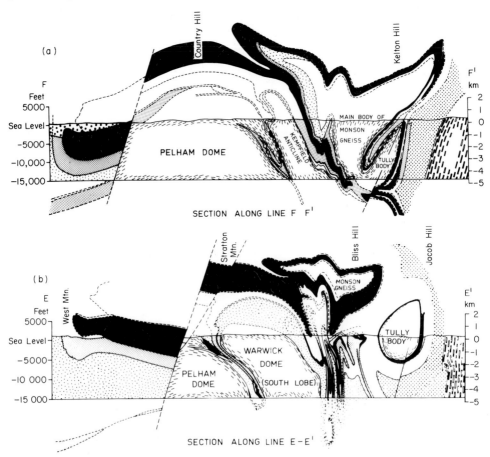

FIG. 5. a & b. Cross sections showing various patterns of the Bronson Hill gneiss domes. For locations see Fig. 4. Reproduced after Zen *et al.* 1968.

Numerical test of the dynamic effect of basement buoyancy

Assuming Newtonian viscosity for the rocks during the conditions of regional metamorphism, and starting with gentle sinusoidal deflections of the boundaries between horizontal layers, it is possible to determine theoretically the velocity of buoyant rise as well as the spacing between spontaneously forming anticlines or domes. Data necessary for the calculations are the densities, the thicknesses and the effective viscosities of all layers in the model. Based on these data we obtain values for the dominant wavelength i.e. the perturbation which grows with maximum velocity and hence the spacing between the resulting anticlines or domes. The theory also furnishes values for the velocity of rise of the domes as long as their amplitude is small relative to the spacing. Information on the stresses and strains within the whole unstable layered model is also obtainable from the mathematical model (Ramberg 1968).

A model consisting of 4 layers has been calculated by the author (Ramberg 1972), Fig. 6. The top layer, called layer 2 in the computer program, consists of unmetamorphosed sediments whose properties are as follows: thickness, $h_2 = 5 \cdot 10^5$ cm ($= 5$ km), density, $\rho_2 = 2.55$ g/cm^3 and effective viscosity, $\mu_2 = 10^{17}$ poise. Below the unmetamorphosed sediments comes layer number 3 consisting of metamorphosed sediments and basic lavas whose composite thickness, h_3 also is $5 \cdot 10^5$ cm, average density, ρ_3, is 2.77 g/cm^3 and effective viscosity, μ_3, is 10^{21} poise. This layer rests directly on layer 4 which is the granitoid basement whose properties are: $h_4 = 5 \cdot 10^5$ cm, $\rho_4 = 2.67$ g/cm^3 and $\mu_4 = 10^{20}$ poise. The granitoid basement rests on sima whose density, ρ_5, is 3.1 g/cm^3 and viscosity, μ_5, is 10^{22} poise. Sima is regarded as an infinite half space in the calculation (Fig. 6).

These properties give rise to a dominant wavelength

$$\lambda_{\text{dominant}} = 4.485 \cdot h_2 = 22.5 \text{ km}$$

which is then the theoretical distance between adjacent domes or anticlines. The above properties give the following expression for the velocity of rise of the anticlines as long as the amplitude is less than 10% of the wavelength, that is $y < 2.25$ km.

$$v_3 = \kappa_1 q_1 y_3. \tag{1}$$

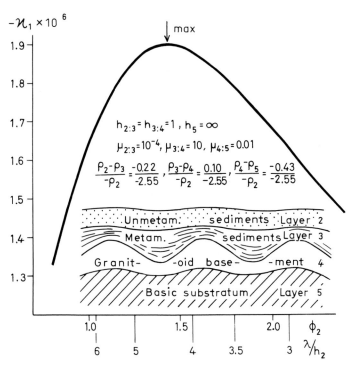

FIG. 6. Kappa function and pertinent dynamical properties of a model consisting of a buoyant granite layer overlain by sediments. Reproduced after Ramberg 1972.

Here v_3 is the velocity of rise of the amplitude of the basement uplifts, y_3 is the amplitude,

$$q_1 \equiv -\frac{\rho_2 h_2 g}{2\mu_2} = -6.2539 \cdot 10^{-9} \sec^{-1},$$

and $\kappa_1 = -1.8996 \cdot 10^{-6}$. κ_1 is a dimensionless quantity characteristic for the layered system under study. At the moment when the amplitude is 10% of the wavelength the velocity of rise is

$$v_3 = 1.8996 \cdot 6.2539 \cdot 10^{-15} \cdot 2.25 \cdot 10^5$$
$$= 26.73 \cdot 10^{-10} \text{ cm/sec} = 0.084 \text{ cm/yr.}$$

Because the amplitude velocity is a function of the amplitude the value of the velocity at an arbitrarily selected amplitude is not very informative when it comes to the rate of evolution of basement diapirs. It is more meaningful to study the time taken to develop anticlines with a finite amplitude $y_3 = 0.1\lambda_{dominant} = 2.25$ km, (the validity limit of eq. (1)) as developed from initial gentle perturbations with a defined amplitude, y_0, to which we can assign reasonable values. Let for example y_0 be 1 m, which of course means very gentle initial perturbations because $\lambda = 22.5$ km.

Integration of eq. (1) gives

$$\frac{y_3}{y_0} = \frac{2250}{1} = e^{\kappa_1 q_1 t}, \quad \text{or}$$

$$t = \frac{\ln 2250}{\kappa_1 q_1} = \frac{7.72}{1.188 \cdot 10^{-14}}$$
$$= 6.5 \cdot 10^{14} \sec = 20.6 \text{ Ma.}$$

In other words, it takes 20.6 Ma for the amplitude to increase from 1 m to 2.25 km.

If the amplitude of the initial deflections is 10 m—which in view of the large wavelength still means very gentle perturbations—the time to reach $y_3 = 2250$ m is less:

$$\frac{y_3}{y_0} = \frac{2250}{10} = e^{\kappa_1 q_1 t}, \quad \text{or}$$

$$t = \frac{\ln 225}{\kappa_1 q_1} = 14.5 \text{ Ma.}$$

When the amplitude exceeds 0.1λ—in this example 2250 m—eq. (1) is not applicable. The velocity increases less rapidly with the amplitude than expressed by the equation. Assuming that the velocity of rise is independent of the amplitude when $y_3 > 0.1\lambda_{dominant}$, we find that the diapir continues to rise at a rate of 840 m per Ma.

It goes without saying that the rates estimated here are only valid for the particular parameters selected in the model. Other thicknesses of the layers, other viscosities and other densities will, of course, change the velocities and thereby the significance of basement diapirism in orogenic evolution.

Spreading nappes

A major structure in the Scandinavian Caledonides is, of course, the famous nappes or thrust sheets which have moved across the belt from the W and NW to the E and SE, the maximum displacement probably being several hundred kilometres (Törnebohm 1888, 1896; Oftedahl 1949, 1956; Gee 1975).

In the later years the idea that gravity plays a major part in the nappe movement has become increasingly acceptable to geologists (see e.g. Bucher 1956; van Bemmelen 1960; Elliott 1976; Price 1973; Ramberg 1967, 1977; Ramberg & Sjöström 1973). The forward movement of a nappe has been compared with the spreading of a lobe of a huge mushroom-shaped dome (Ramberg 1966; Ramberg & Sjöström 1973), or with the spreading of an ice cap (Elliott 1976; Ramberg 1977). The movement pattern of an active ice cap and of a spreading lobe of a rising dome is in principle the same, the chief difference being that the flow in the ice cap is fed from above by precipitation while the spreading dome is fed from below, either from buoyant materials, or from materials which, for other reasons, have been forced upward.

The forward movement of the front of a gravity-driven nappe which moves along a horizontal or upward-sloping base is the result of the shortening of its vertical dimension. This vertical shortening means a lowering of the centre of gravity and hence a decrement of the gravity potential. It is generally associated with a lengthening in the horizontal plane; the result being a forward movement of the front of the nappe relative to sections farther back.

If the material of the nappe was strongly compressible the tendency for horizontal movement would be negligible. Instead of strong compressibility, one could think of the effect of pressure solution: if vertical shortening was completely accounted for by solution along horizontal seams or stylolites, then the gravity-potential decrement would balance energy associated with the dissolution and with the the transport of the dissolved material away from the sites of dissolution. There would be no energy left to move the whole nappe horizontally. There is, however, no grounds for assuming that pressure solution occurs so widely in nappes that a major part of the vertical compression is not ordinarily compensated for by a horizontal extension. Therefore, the rocks in the dynamic model to be discussed are regarded as incompressible viscous or plastic bodies. Any shortening in one direction is automatically compensated for by a volume-preserving lengthening in directions normal to the shortening, and the decrement of the gravity potential associated with the vertical shortening is completely balanced by the strain energy of the collapsing nappe and the frictional energy at the sole. There is accordingly a noteworthy difference between a gravity-driven nappe which moves horizontally or even uphill along a rigid support, and a rock complex which slides downhill because of the force of gravity. In both cases the motion is caused by—or perhaps, more correctly associated with—a decrement of the gravity potential, i.e. a lowering of the centre of gravity. The downhill sliding takes place even if the rocks are completely rigid, but the horizontal or uphill movement of the nappe is only possible, if the rocks are weak enough to spread under their own weight.

The Scandinavian Caledonian belt is quite straight as it extends from SW Norway to the northernmost coast of Finnmark, and the nappes are elongate sheets whose length is much larger than their width. During the collapse, therefore, spreading in a SW–NE direction will be negligible. As a good first approximation we may accordingly regard the movement and strain in the nappe as two-dimensional in the plane normal to the belt, the horizontal lengthening being maximum in a direction more or less normal to the trend of the belt.

It is well established by numerous field studies that the strain in several nappes show a pronounced extension across the trend of the belt in the WNW–SSE direction (Kvale 1953; Strand 1945; Oftedahl 1948; Zachrisson 1964; Ramberg 1966, 1977 and numerous unpublished field observations, Ghosh *et al.* 1979). This is demonstrated by mineral lineation, by boudinage and by the rotation of small-scale fold axes.

It is true that this structural evidence for a stretching in the horizontal direction cannot be taken unconditionally as proof of a vertical shortening, because quasi-horizontal extension will also be produced by a large simple-shear angle generated by a large horizontal displacement of the upper sheets relative to the lower sheets. It is difficult to distinguish between a stretching which is caused by extensive simple shear alone and a stretching caused by a combination of pure shear with vertical shortening and simple shear parallel to the sole.

The reason for believing that there has been a considerable vertical shortening in the Scandinavian Caledonides is that the lineation and other evidence of a horizontal lengthening is a penetrative feature observed throughout some of the nappes and is not limited to the narrow zones of high shear strain between the various thrust sheets. This is particularly evident in the large Seve Nappe. It is difficult to see how the greater part of the column of nappes can be exposed to a penetrative process of simple shear if this was not combined with a simultaneous vertical shortening. A purely simple shearing requires that unknown masses above the column of sheared nappes have been pushed forward in order to transmit shear stress to the nappes below. Of course, this is not impossible, but it seems more acceptable that the horizontal lengthening is caused by a combination of pure-and simple shear, involving both vertical shortening and shear in a quasi-horizontal plane. In this model the primary process is the slow plastico-viscous gravity collapse of the system of nappes.

If there was no friction along the base the collapse will be almost ideal pure shear, viz, a vertical shortening balanced by a horizontal lengthening. Because vertical compressive stress increases with depth the horizontal lengthening also tends to increase with depth. It follows that shear is created parallel to the horizontal plane in the column of nappes, because of drag between the actively spreading deep layers and the more passive layers above.

In the qualitative analysis of the processes we shall assume that the rocks behaved almost as Newtonian substances during the Caledonian Orogeny, or at least that their yield strength was very small in response to stresses which acted over millions of years. For stresses of magnitude between the small yield stress and the ultimate strength of the rocks, the rate of change of strain is considered nearly proportional to the deviatoric stress. We assume that the deviatoric stresses in the nappes are limited to the interval between the yield strength and the ultimate strength of the rocks, the latter defined as the maximum stress which a rock can withstand without discontinuous disruption.

Model with free slip along base

First, the effect of pure shear alone will be discussed. This condition is obtained if the model rests on an ideally frictionless sole. Although the situation is unrealistic, the analysis is important for the understanding of the more complex situation encountered when nappes are welded to the basement along the sole and consequently simple shear becomes an important part of the strain.

For an experimental study of the free-slip model we have found it practical to let a plastic or viscous mass (e.g. silicone putty) rest on a layer of mercury. The great contrast in density causes the silicone putty to float almost on the top of the mercury, and the low viscosity of the mercury means that the friction at the base is negligible relative to the viscous internal friction in the spreading mass. The description and discussion of these experiments are under preparation by R. Häll and the present author.

Consider a rectangular block which is long in the z direction in relation to the width in the direction x. y is the vertical coordinate, Fig. 7. Because of the elongate shape of the parallelpiped the strain will be two-dimensional in the plane x, y. The contact between the body and its base is frictionless, neither is there any shear stress or strain at the three free surfaces of the body. For the present study the air pressure is insignificant and normal stress at the free surfaces can be disregarded.

To determine the strain rate and the velocities u and v in the x and y directions, respectively, the equation valid for Newtonian substances under pure shear is pertinent:

$$\dot{\varepsilon}_x = \frac{\sigma_x - \sigma_y}{4\mu}. \tag{2}$$

Here $\dot{\varepsilon}$ is the strain rate in the direction x, μ the effective viscosity and σ the normal stress.

Since the normal stress, σ_{x0}, at the sides is zero and furthermore the basal contact is frictionless, we conclude that σ_x at any point in the body vanishes (we shall see below that that is not exactly true). The normal stress in direction y at any point in the body equals the weight of the overburden:

$$\sigma_y = -\rho g(H - y) \tag{3}$$

where ρ is density, g is the acceleration due to gravity, H thickness and y distance from the base. (Tensile stress is defined as positive, compressive stress as negative.)

The strain rate at a level at depth y is accordingly:

$$\dot{\varepsilon}_x = \frac{\rho g(H - y)}{4\mu}. \tag{4}$$

The strain is homogeneous at any one given level so the velocity in the x direction is:

$$u = \dot{\varepsilon}_x x = \frac{\rho g(H - y)x}{4\mu} \tag{5}$$

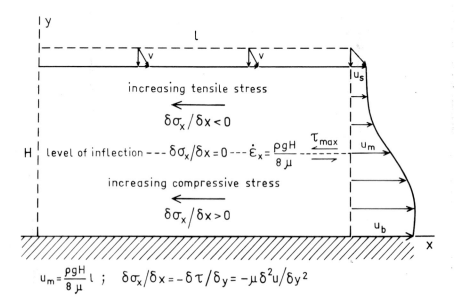

$$u_m = \frac{\rho g H}{8\mu} l \; ; \quad \delta\sigma_x/\delta x = -\delta\tau/\delta y = -\mu\delta^2 u/\delta y^2$$

FIG. 7. The half profile of a symmetric spreading rectangular body at free-slip along base. Stippled lines indicate initial cross section. See text.

where x is the distance from the central section of the body. Since $v = 0$ at $y = 0$ at all x, the vertical velocity component at level y is:

$$v = \int_{0}^{H-y} -\dot{\varepsilon}_x \delta y = -\frac{\rho g}{4\mu}(Hy - \tfrac{1}{2}y^2) \quad (6)$$

because incompressibility means that $\dot{\varepsilon}_y = -\dot{\varepsilon}_x$. The velocity v is thus independent of x in the free-slip model.

According to the above discussion, the horizontal spreading of the rectangular body becomes faster the deeper the level; maximum spreading occurring at the bottom while the uppermost boundary at which σ_x as well as σ_y vanish does not spread at all. (See, however, below.)

As already indicated this simple linear variation of the strains and stresses cannot be entirely correct. The reason is that the increase of the velocity u with depth must be associated with a shear strain and a corresponding shear stress, τ_{yx}, in the direction x. A component of simple shear along x in the horizontal plane shows that x is not a principal direction and hence that the initial assumption of a pure-shear model is not exact. The fast-spreading deep strata in the body create a horizontal pull on the slow-spreading strata above which therefore spread somewhat faster than they would otherwise have done. On the other hand, the horizontal shear stress diminishes the spreading rate of the layers below. The nett result is that the surface spreads more rapidly than expected according to the simple model, while the bottom spreads more slowly than expected.

Since the normal stress σ_y is zero at the surface, a significant conclusion follows, viz.: the stress σ_x within the top layer is tensile. Likewise, since the bottom layers spread less than expected we conclude that σ_x does not vanish in a layer along the frictionless bottom. In other words the gradient $\delta\sigma_x/\delta x$ is not zero in the model.

Taking into account the lack of shear stress at the top surface and at the frictionless base, we conclude that the front boundary of the original rectangular body close to the top, as well as close to the bottom, must be normal to the base and normal to the top surface, respectively, also after deformation. It follows that the originally vertical and plane sides become sigmoid-shaped as indicated on Fig. 7.

The velocity profile for the component u is also sigmoidal. A consequence of the deviation from linearity of the velocity profile is that the

stress σ_x has a gradient in the x direction because the term $\delta^2 u/\delta y^2$ in the equation below does not vanish

$$\delta\sigma_x/\delta x = -\mu(\delta^2 u/\delta y^2). \quad (7)$$

This relationship follows from the condition of equilibrium between the stresses at two dimensional strain in the plane x, y. The equation for equilibrium between the normal-stress gradient in the x-direction and the shear stress τ_{yx} is

$$\delta\sigma_x/\delta x = -\delta\tau_{yx}/\delta y \quad (8)$$

when the motion is so slow that acceleration is negligible. Since x lies in the horizontal plane the body force of gravity does not occur in the equation. For Newtonian materials the relation

$$\tau_{yx} = \mu\dot{\gamma}_{xy} \quad (9)$$

is valid. Moreover, $\dot{\gamma}_{yx} = \delta u/\delta y + \delta v/\delta x$. In our model $\delta v/\delta x$ is much smaller than $\delta u/\delta y$, hence we employ the approximation $\dot{\gamma}_{yx} \approx \delta u/\delta y$, and the relationship $\delta\sigma_x/\delta x = -u\delta^2 u/\delta y^2$ is obtained.

Below the inflection point shown in Fig. 7 the term $\delta^2 u/\delta y^2$ assumes negative values. This requires that σ_x increases from $x = 0$ to the edge at $x = l$. Remembering that compressive stress is negative, this means that the stress becomes less compressive as one goes from $x = 0$ to $x = l$. The condition $\sigma_x = 0$ at $x = l$ means that σ_x becomes increasingly compressive from the edge to the central section of the collapsing body. Above the inflection point, the situation is opposite: $\delta^2 u/\delta y^2$ is positive and the stress is tensile at all x, changing from zero at $x = l$ to a maximum value at $x = 0$.

One notes moreover that the strain is essentially pure shear within a zone close to the top surface and within a zone close to the bottom. At the bottom, the pure shear is caused by the compressive stress, σ_y, being larger than σ_x; at the top, the strain is caused by the stress σ_x being tensile while the stress σ_y vanishes. In the middle zone of the body, on either side of the level of inflection where $\delta^2 u/\delta x^2 = 0$, there is a combination of pure-and simple shear, simple shear reacting maximum value at the level of inflection.

The condition that $\delta^2 u/\delta y^2 = 0$ at a level which is close to the depth $y = \tfrac{1}{2}H$ is significant, because we see here a simple way of determining the velocity of collapse and spreading of the body. At the level of inflection where $\delta^2 u/\delta y^2 = 0$, eq (7) shows that $\delta\sigma_x/\delta x$ vanished and hence that σ_x is zero at all x. It follows that the longitudinal strain rate at the level of inflection is $\dot{\varepsilon}_x = \rho gh/4\mu$ where h is

138   H. Ramberg

the depth of the level of inflection. Experiments with Newtonian substances performed by R. Häll in the Uppsala laboratory show that $h \approx \frac{1}{2}H$. Accordingly, the mean strain rate is $\dot{\varepsilon}_x = \rho g H/8\mu$, and the velocity at the front is $u = \rho g H l/8\mu$.

The above comments on the ideal free-slip model helps to understand the more realistic model in which there is complete coherence between the basement and the model nappe itself.

Model coherent to the base

A condition valid for the coherent-base model is that $u = 0$ at $y = 0$ for all values of x. The same holds for v. A condition valid for both models is that the only driving force is gravity: any horizontal shear stress which may exist is created by the gravitational force.

Gravitational collapse and its complementary spreading, combined with coherence at the bottom, require that u increases from zero at the base to a maximum value at a certain level. Above that level the horizontal velocity component must again decrease because of the drag from the superincumbent layers similarly as explained for the free-slip model. Hence, at the front edge the velocity profile is as shown on Fig. 8.

The fact that shear stress vanishes at the free surface requires that $\delta u/\delta y + \delta v/\delta x = 0$ at the surface. Consequently, there must be an inflection point on the u-velocity profile somewhere between the top surface and the level of maximum velocity, u_{max}. The level at which $\delta^2 u/\delta y^2 = 0$ is probably located approximately midway between the free surface and the level of maximum horizontal velocity. Above the level of maximum velocity, the coherent-base model is dynamically similar to the free-slip model.

It is interesting that the bulge at the level of maximum velocity is well documented by experiments (Häll & Ramberg, in preparation). The discredit which the theory of 'extrusion flow' in ice caps has suffered among glaciologists is, therefore, unfair (see Shumskii 1964, p. 329). It is true, though, that the level of maximum velocity and the associated bulge are located at higher and higher levels in the collapsing body the greater its length relative to its thickness (the larger the slenderness ratio). In other words, 'extrusion flow' decreases in significance with the slenderness ratio. For many ice caps, the process of extrusion may, therefore, be of little consequence. The reason is simple: the larger the distance between level of maximum velocity and the sole, the less the shear-strain rate for a given velocity u_{max}. On the other hand, the longer a nappe is relative to its thickness, the more energy is

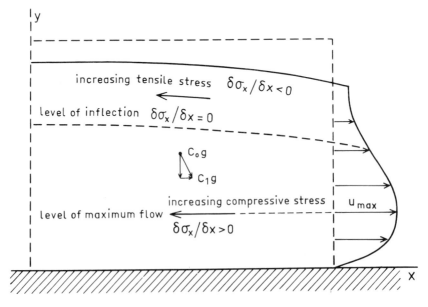

FIG. 8. The half profile of a symmetric spreading rectangular body at coherence along base. Strippled lines indicate initial cross section, full curves outline shape at an early stage of spreading. See text.

dissipated by shear strain. For long, thin nappes and ice caps, therefore, the shear strain energy will be less, if the level of u_{max} is close to the surface. Experiments indicate that, the level of maximum velocity is practically at the surface for slenderness ratios above 5.

The velocity profile for the component u indicates that within the whole region from the zone of inflection to the base there is a non-zero gradient $\delta\sigma_x/\delta x$ so directed that σ_x at $x = 0$ is compressive all the way from the bottom to the level of inflection. (It is safest to say 'indicates' at this point because in the coherent-base model $\delta v/\delta x$ is not insignificant and the correct relation between $\delta\sigma_x/\delta x$ and the velocity variations is

$$\delta\sigma_x/\delta x = \mu(\delta^2 u/\delta y^2 + \delta^2 v/\delta x\delta y) \quad (10)$$

rather than the approximation $\delta\sigma_x/\delta x \approx \mu\delta^2 u/\delta y^2$ used in the free-slip model. Even in the coherent-base model, however, the term $\delta^2 v/\delta x\delta y$ is probably small relative to $\delta^2 u/\delta y^2$.

Above the inflection level at $x = 0$ the stress σ_x is tensile in the coherent-base model, just as it is in the free-slip model. Incidentally, the conclusion that horizontal tensile stress exists at the surface layers of a spreading orogenic

nappe or an active ice cap is in good agreement with the distribution of crevasses in ice caps. For the Scandinavian Caledonides, the erosion level is too deep to enable this theoretical-experimental result to be tested. Model tests, however, verify that the top zone of a spreading body is under tensile stress

The circumstance that the negative gradient $\delta\sigma_x/\delta x$ below the level of inflection is steeper in the coherent-base model (the term $\delta^2 u/\delta y^2$ is numerically larger) than in the free-slip model, and moreover that the stress gradient extends through a thicker zone in the former has a bearing on the contrast in flow behaviour of the two models. The horizontal compressive stress component is higher and, accordingly, the rate of vertical sagging is less in the interior of the coherent-base model than in the interior of the free-slip model. At the front at $x = l$, the stress difference $\sigma_x - \sigma_y$ is practically the same in both models. In the frontal part then, both models sag and spread with practically the same strain rate. It follows that the coherent-base model will develop a gentle anticlinal-shaped profile while the free-slip model spreads out as a sheet with practically even thickness. This is well displayed by the models produced by R. Häll in the tectonic laboratory in Uppsala.

References

BEMMELEN, VAN, R. W. 1960. New views on East-Alpine Orogenesis. *Int. geol. Cong. Rept. 21th Session (Norden)* **XVII**, 99–116.

BUCHER, W. H. 1956. The role of gravity in orogenesis. *Bull. geol. Soc. Am.* **67**, 1295–318.

ELLIOTT, D. 1976. The motion of thrust sheets. *J. geophys. Res.* **81**, 949.

FISHER, G. W., PETTIJOHN, F. J., REED, J. C. & WEAVER, K. N. 1970. *Studies of Appalachian Geology: Central and Southern.* Interscience Publishers, New York, 460 pp.

FOSLIE, S. 1941. Tysfjords geologi. *Nor. geol. Unders.* **149**, 298.

—— & STRAND, T. 1956. Namnsvatnet med en del av Fröyningsfjell. *Nor. geol. Unders.* **196**, 82.

GEE, D. 1975. A tectonic model for the central part of the Scandinavian Caledonides. *Am. J. Sci.* **275 A**, 468–515.

GHOSH, S. K., RAY, N. & TROENG, B. 1979. Superposed folding and metamorphism in the Seve Nappe, Swedish Caledonides. *Geol. Fören Stockholm Förh.* **101**, 85–103.

GRIFFIN, W. L. et al. 1978. Archaean and Proterozoic crustal evolution in Lofoten-Vesterålen, N. Norway. *J. geol. Soc. London*, **135**, 629–48.

GUSTAVSON, M. 1963. Grunnfjellsvinduer i Divida-

len, Troms. *Nor. geol. Unders.* **223**, 92–105.

—— 1966. The Caledonian mountain chain of the Southern Troms and Ofoten areas, Part I. *Nor. geol. Unders.* **239**, 162.

—— 1972. The Caledonian Mountain Chain of the Southern Troms and Ofoten Areas, Part III. *Nor. geol. Unders.* **283**, 1–56.

—— 1974a. Harstad. *Nor. geol. Unders.* **309**, 14.

—— 1974b. Ofoten. *Nor. geol. Unders.* **310**, 15.

GWINNER, M. P. 1971. *Geologie der. Alpen.* E. Schweizerbart'sche Verlagsbuchhandlung, Stuttgart. 477 pp.

HOLTEDAHL, O. & DONS, J. A. 1960. Geologisk kart over Norge. *Nor. geol. Unders.*

KVALE, A. 1953. Linear structures and their relation to movement in the Caledonides of Scandinavia and Scotland. *Q. J. geol. Soc. London*, **109**, 51–73.

MAGNUSSON, N. H. et al. 1957. Karta över Sveriges Berggrund. *Sver. geol. Unders.*

NICHOLSON, R. 1973. The Vatnfjell Fold Nappe complex of Saltdal, north Norway. *Nor. geol. Tidsskr.* **53**, 195–212.

—— & RUTLAND, R. W. R. 1969. A Section across the Norwegian Caledonides, Bodö to Sulitjelma. *Nor. geol. Unders.* **260**, 1–86.

—— & WALTON, B. J. 1963. The structural geology

of the Navervatn-Storglomvatn area, Glomfjord, northern Norway. *Nor. geol. Unders.* **43,** 58 p.

OFTEDAHL, CH. 1948. Deformation of quartz conglomerate in central Norway. *J. Geol. Chicago,* **56,** 476–87.

—— 1949. Skyvedekker i det centrale Norges sparagmitformasjon. *Nor. geol. Tidsskr.* **27,** 164–70.

—— 1956. Om Grongkuliminasjonen og Grongfeltets skyvedekker. *Nor. geol. Unders.* **195,** 57–64.

PIDGEON, R. T. & RÅHEIM, A. 1972. Geochronological investigation of the gneisses and minor intrusive rocks from Kristiansund, West Norway. *Nor. geol. Tidsskr.* **52,** 241–56.

PRICE, R. A. 1973. Large-Scale Gravitational Flow of Supracrustal Rocks, Southern Canadian Rockies. *In.* JONG, J. K. A. DE & SCHOLTEN, R. (eds). *Gravity and Tectonics,* Wiley, New York, 491–502.

PRIEM, H. N. A., BOELRIJK, N. A. I. M., HEBEDA, E. H., VERDURMEN, E. A. TH. & VERSCHURE, R. H. 1975. Isotopic Dating of the Caledonian Bindal and Svenningdal Granitic Massifs, Central Norway. *Nor. geol. Unders.* **32,** 29–36.

RÅHEIM, A. 1977. A Rb, Sr study of the rocks of the Surnadal Syncline. *Nor. geol. Tidsskr.* **51,** 193–204.

RAMBERG, H. 1966. The Scandinarian Caledonides as Studied by Centrifuged Dynamic Models. *Bull. Geol. Inst. Uppala,* **43,** 72 p.

—— 1967. *Gravity, Deformation and the Earth's Crust.* Academic Press, 217 p.

—— 1968. Instability of layered systems in the field of gravity I. *Phys. Earth Planet. Inter.* **1,** 427–47.

—— 1972. Theoretical Models of Density Stratification and Diapirism in the Earth. *J. geophys. Res.* **77,** 877–89.

—— 1977. Some remarks on the mechanism of nappe movement. *Forh. geol Foren. Stockholm,* **99,** 110–17.

—— & SJÖSTRÖM, H. 1973. Experimental geodynamical models relating to continental drift and orogenesis. *Tectonophysics,* **19,** 105–32.

REKSTAD, J. 1919. Geologiske iakttagelser på strek-

ningen Folla-Tysfjord. *Nor. geol. Unders.* **83,** 17 p.

—— 1929. Salta. *Nor. geol. Unders.* **134,** 83 p.

RUTLAND, R. W. R. & NICHOLSON, R. 1965. Tectonics of the Caledonides of a part of Nordland, Norway, *Q. J. geol. Soc. London,* **121,** 73–109.

SHUMSKII, P. A. 1964. *Principles of Structural Glaciology.* Dover, New York, 497 p.

SKJESETH, S. & SÖRENSEN, H. 1953. An example of gravitization in the central zone of the Caledonides in N Norway. *Nor. geol. Unders.* **184,** 154–83.

STRAND, T. 1945. Structural petrology of the Bygdin conglomerate. *Nor. geol. Tidsskr.* **24,** 14–31.

—— & HOLMSEN, P. 1960. Stratigraphy, petrology and Caledonian nappe tectonics of central southern Norway: Caledonized basal gneisses in a northwestern area. *Nor. geol. Unders.* **212,** 31 p.

TÖRNEBOHM, A. E. 1888. Om fjällproblemet. *Forh. geol. Foren. Stockholm,* **10,** 328–36.

—— 1896. Grunddragen av det centrala Skandinaviens berg-byggnad. *K. Sven. Vetenskapsakad. Handl.* **28,** p. 5.

TULL, J. F. 1977. Geology and Structure of Vestvågöy, Lofoten, North Norway. *Nor. geol. Unders.* **333,** 1–59.

WEGMAN, C. E. 1930. Über Diapirismus (besonders in Grundgebierge). *C.R. geol. Soc. Finland* **3,** 1–19.

WENK, H. R. & WENK, E. 1969. Physical constants of alpine rocks. *Beitr. geol. Schweis, Kleinere Mitt.* **45,** 343.

WILSON, M. R. 1973. *Some Age and Isotope Studies in the Scandinavian Caledonides.* Report from the Z. W. O. Laboratory for Isotopen-Geologie, Amsterdam.

ZACHRISSON, E. 1964. The Remdalen Syncline. *Sver. geol. Unders. C.* **596,** 53.

—— 1969. Caledonian geology of Northern Jämtland-Southern Västerbotten. *Sver. geol. Unders. C.* **644,** 33.

ZEN, E-AN, WHITE, W. S. HADLEY, J. B. & THOMPSON, J. B. Jr, 1968. *Studies of Appalachian Geology: Northern and Maritime.* Interscience Publishers, New York, 475 pp.

H. RAMBERG, Geologiska Institutionen, Uppsala Unversitet, Sweden.

II.
ROCK PRODUCTS
OF THRUSTING

Dynamic analysis of a small imbricate thrust and related structures, Front Ranges, Southern Canadian Rocky Mountains

J. H. Spang & S. P. Brown

SUMMARY: The thrust is a hanging-wall imbricate of the Lac des Arcs Thrust within the McConnell Thrust Plate. The small imbricate terminates vertically into a cylindrical, macroscopic kink band and laterally by merging with the Lac des Arcs Thrust. Numerical dynamic analysis of calcite and dolomite twin lamellae gives a near layer parallel maximum principal compression and an extension at a high angle to layering, both in the transport direction. The twinning is considered to be late stage. Reorientation of the principal axes occurs near folds and other minor thrusts in the area.

Detailed field and laboratory studies of a small (15 km²) area in the Front Ranges of the Southern Canadian Rocky Mountains have been done in order to examine the structural evolution of a fold and thrust fault terrain. Detailed study of such structures is necessary in order to understand more fully the mechanical origin of thrusts and folds in an area of thin skinned tectonics. The field component of the study included mapping on a scale of 1:12 000, analysis of fold style, and determination of the macroscopic and mesoscopic deformation mechanisms. In the laboratory, calcite and dolomite twin lamellae have been analysed in order to interpret the study area dynamically. The results of the dynamic analysis are reported here.

Geological setting

The termination of a minor thrust fault examined in this study is located in the Front Ranges structural subprovince of the Southern Canadian Rocky Mountains (Fig. 1). The study area is in the McConnell Thrust Plate, the easternmost of the four major overthrusts which comprise the Front Ranges in this area. The faults are listric and low-angle on the regional scale with locally steep dips associated with steps, folding and imbrication (Dahlstrom 1970). Dahlstrom defines a 'Foothills family' of four structural types common to both the Foothills and Front Ranges: 1. concentric folds (with their attendant décollement); 2. low angle thrust faults (commonly folded); 3. tear faults (usually transverse); and 4. late normal faults (commonly listric).

On the basis of seismic data and field mapping, Bally et al. (1966) and Price & Mountjoy (1970) conclude that the thrusting is 'thin skinned' and does not involve the gently, SW

dipping Hudsonian basement, perhaps as far W as the Rocky Mountain Trench. Corresponding with the SW–NE migration of thrusting and folding was a decrease in intensity of deformation in the same direction. Based on the local structural trends, the transport direction in the study area is 063°. Most of the shortening in the Front Ranges (approximately 140 km) probably occurred between early Cretaceous (100–136 Ma) and early Eocene (49–54 Ma), yielding a gross mean displacement rate of 2 mm/year (Wheeler et al. 1974, p. 598). Similarly, the bulk of the movement along the McConnell Thrust is of the order of 30 km in a time period of post-early Campanian to pre-Palaeocene (10 Ma), which gives a gross mean displacement rate of about 3 mm/year. Based on authigenic minerals in

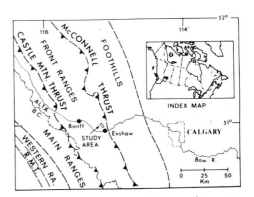

FIG. 1. Location map showing the study area in the Front Ranges of the Southern Canadian Rocky Mountains. The structural subprovinces of the Rocky Mountains are the Foothills, Front Ranges, Main Ranges and Western Ranges. They are boardered on the E by the orogenically undisturbed Plains and on the W by the Rocky Mountain Trench (RMT).

Cretaceous clastics below the McConnell Thrust, Ghent & Miller (1973) estimate the temperature to have been between a high of 250–280°C and a low of 150–180°C. Based on the lack of lawsonite, P_{load} is less than 3 kb; using structural and stratigraphic reconstructions, P_{load} is probably in the range of 1–2 kb. Jamison & Spang (1976, p. 872) describe a method which uses twin lamellae in naturally deformed calcite and dolomite in order to estimate the differential stress. For two different localities within the McConnell Thrust Plate, their results imply that the differential stress may have been as high as 1.25 kb.

Geology of the study area

The study area is in the McConnell Thrust Plate, 7 km W of the eastern margin of the Front Ranges and 7 km NW of Exshaw, Alberta (Fig. 1). The macroscopic deformation

mechanisms active in the structural development of the area were thrusting and flexural slip folding. Fig. 2 represents a generalized cross section showing the termination of a minor splay thrust in the hanging-wall of the Lac des Arcs Thrust. The Lac des Arcs Thrust dips 45–50° SW, paralleling bedding in the footwall and climbing up section in the hanging-wall (Fig. 3). A detailed map and cross section of the area are given by Brown & Spang (1978). The actual geological map of the area is very similar to the generalized cross section, because the structures plunge to the NW. The surface of both the splay and the Lac des Arcs Thrusts are both concave upward and both flatten at depth in such a manner that, at any elevation, the dip of the splay is slightly steeper than the Lac des Arcs Thrust. The splay thrust terminates vertically within the study area (Fig. 4), with the last few metres of the thrust actually dipping NE. Additional thrust

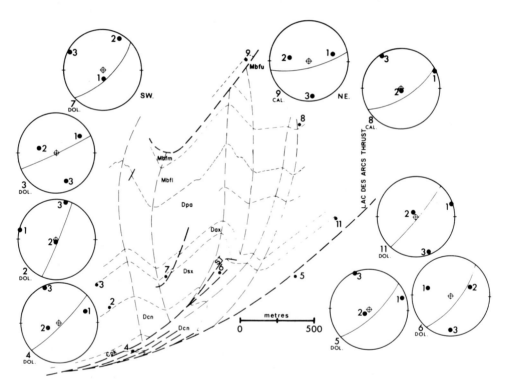

FIG. 2. Generalized cross section showing the termination of a splay thrust (ST) in the hanging-wall of the Lac des Arcs Thrust. The stratigraphy is summarized in Table 1. Principal axes from numerical dynamic analysis of calcite or dolomite twin lamellae are plotted on lower hemisphere equal area projections. The primitive circle is oriented in a vertical plane bearing N55E corresponding to the orientation of the generalized section. The solid great circle is the local bedding plane and the dashes on the primitive circle are horizontal. Numbers refer to the principal axes: maximum principal compression (1), intermediate principal axis (2) and maximum principal extension (3).

TABLE 1. *Stratigraphy of the study area*

ERA	PERIOD	FORMATION AND THICKNESS (METRES)	DESCRIPTION
P A L E O Z O I C	Mississippian	Livingstone Fm. (Mlv) 285	c. crystalline, light grey Ls; skeletal in parts
	Lower Mississippian	Banff Fm. Upper Part (Mbfu) 125	cherty, skeletal, c. crystalline, light grey Ls; flaggy, greyish brown, f. crystalline Ls; greyish brown, dolomitic Ls
		Middle Part (Mbfm) 60	cherty, very skeletal in parts, f. to c. crystalline, light to dark grey Ls
		Lower Part (Mbfl) 190	very flaggy, medium grey, calc. Sh; weathering brown to light orange brown
		Exshaw Fm. 10	(grouped with Mbfl) calc., black fissile Sh; weathers ochre
	Upper Devonian	Palliser Fm. (Dpa) 320	f. to c. crystalline, light grey Ls and Dol; weathers blue-grey
		Alexo Fm. (Dax) 60	m. to f. crystalline, flaggy Ls and Dol; minor calcite filled vugs
		Southesk Fm. (Dsx) 190	m. to c. crystalline, grey to white Dol; minor Ls; minor calcite filled vugs
		Cairn Fm. (Dcn) 220	m. to f. crystalline, grey to dark grey Dol and dolomitic Ls; minor flat pebble Cong; extensive calcite filled vugs; minor chert
	Middle Cambrian	Pika Fm. (Є pk) 70	very f. to m. crystalline, grey to dark grey Ls

faults include a group of imbricate thrust faults between the splay and the Lac des Arcs Thrust. Below sample 7, a small thrust is observed to cut the overturned common limb of a fold pair with a visible offset of less than 70 m. The thrust at the base of sample 9 appears to have formed as an 'out of syncline thrust'.

The folds in the study area may be characterized as macroscopic kink bands with narrow hinge zones, planar limbs and tectonically thickened hinges (Fig. 4). For any one kink band, the kink boundaries are nearly parallel, slightly curved and intersect upward (Brown & Spang 1978). Common centres of curvature can be defined only for packages of layers approximately 25 m thick or less. Across the study area, from SE to NW, the trend of the kink axes rotates counterclockwise, possibly by more than 25°, with an accompanying increase of plunge (Brown & Spang 1978). Three kink bands have been mapped in the study area. The W kink band is in the hanging wall of the splay thrust. The central kink band is located above leading edge of the splay thrust, and the E kink band extends from the

footwall of the splay thrust to a higher level than the splay's leading edge.

Although the traces of the axial surfaces terminate to the NW the folds continue in the subsurface to the NW. The termination of the traces is a function of intersecting kink boundaries and NW structural plunge. The folds are presumed to terminate down-plunge when the line of intersection between the kink boundaries intersects the Lac des Arcs Thrust (Brown & Spang 1978). It is emphasized that these folds clearly do not represent concentric folds as envisaged by Dahlstrom (1970) in his 'Foothills family' of structures. Unlike concentric folds, kink bands do not require upper and lower detachments, since there does not have to be a room problem associated with the continuance of a kink band.

Mesoscopic deformation mechanisms include fractures and minor amounts of small scale thrusting and folding. Locally penetrative, axial planar cleavage is developed in the shales of the lower Banff Formation. In this unit, the cleavage is so well developed in the W kink band and E boundary of the central

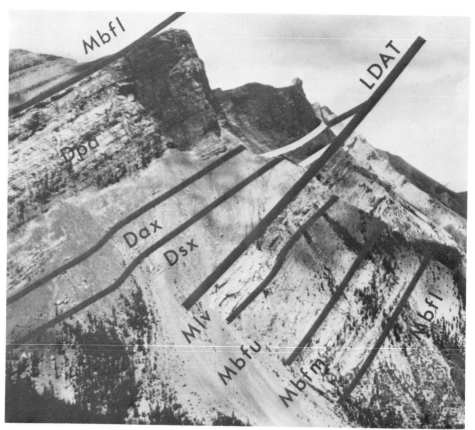

FIG. 3. The study area is in the hangingwall of the Lac des Arcs Thrust (LDAT). View is looking NW from the most NE portion of the study area.

kink band, that determination of bedding is nearly impossible. Elsewhere in the McConnell Thrust, Spang et al. (1979) have attributed the formation of cleavage in the Banff Formation mainly to the dissolution of calcite. Although fractures not belonging to an obvious set are locally numerous, two dominant fracture sets appear throughout the entire study area. The two sets are nearly orthogonal and roughly normal to bedding. The poles to one set and the lineation formed by the intersection of the other set with bedding are approximately parallel to the fold hinges within small subdomains.

Microscopic deformation mechanisms include pressure solution (stylolites), filled fractures, and intragranular strain. In the carbonates, the dominant intragranular deformation mechanism is twinning, with bent twins being uncommon.

Dynamic analysis of samples

The method of numerical dynamic analysis was originally proposed by Spang (1972). Both cal-

cite and dolomite possess known twin gliding systems with restricted glide planes, glide directions and fixed senses of shear (Turner, et al. 1954). In both minerals, the twinning strain can be regarded as simple shear in the glide direction. The geometry is such that the c-axis, pole to twin lamellae, and glide direction are all coplanar (Fig. 5). Assuming that the twin lamellae represent planes of high resolved shear, then the principal axes of dynamic analysis lie in the same plane as the c-axis and twin plane pole, making angles of 45 and 135° to the twin plane. Using the second order tensor transformation formula, the principal axes for each twin set are rotated into the thin section coordinates forming the numerical dynamic analysis tensor. Principal axes and their orientations can be calculated by means of taking the eigenvalues and eigenvectors of the numerical dynamic analysis tensor (Spang 1972). If each sample is deformed in a single irrotational stress field, then the accuracy of the calculated principal axes is approximately $10° \pm 10°$ (Spang & van der Lee 1975, p. 1271). These principal axes for the naturally

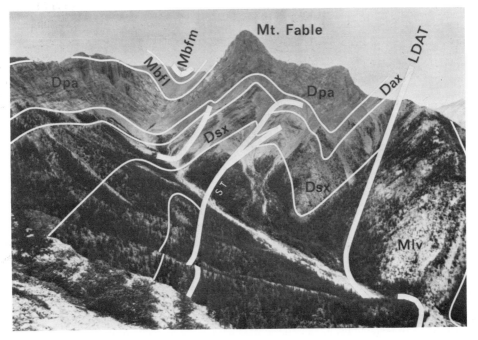

FIG. 4. View of SE slopes of Mt. Fable showing the trace of the Lac des Arcs Thrust (LDAT), splay thrust (ST) and three minor thrusts (thrusts are heavy white lines and are also shown in Fig. 2). Also shown are the three kink bands.

deformed calcite and dolomite analysed in this study are shown in Fig. 2.

In all the samples, the magnitude of the intermediate principal axis is small (i.e. ≈ 0) indicating a planar deformation. Samples 3, 4, 5, 8 and 11 show a maximum principal compression in the transport direction either nearly layer parallel or slightly in the up-dip direction. In these same samples, the maximum principal extension is also in the transport plane and at a high angle to bedding. With the exception of sample 4, which is from a group of imbricate thrusts between the splay thrust

and the Lac des Arcs thrust, all these samples come from relatively simple southwesterly dipping, homoclinal sequences.

Samples 2, 6, 7 and 9 have dramatically different principal axis orientations, and with the exception of sample 2, are structurally related to minor thrusts. Sample 2 represents a planar deformation in the transport plane with compression at a high angle to bedding and near layer parallel extension. These orientations may be the result of late stage stresses caused by locking of the limbs of the adjacent kink band (fold) at high limb dips. Sample 6

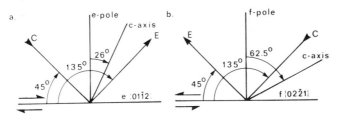

FIG. 5. Dynamic interpretation of twin lamellae in calcite (a) and dolomite (b) showing the angular relationships among the c-axis, pole to twin lamellae, glide direction, extension axis (E) and compression axis (C).

represents compression at a high angle to bedding and extension at a low angle ($\approx 30°$) to bedding in the dip direction. The orientation of the faults is not shown on the stereonet, but the principal axes bear approximately the same relationships to the fault as they do to bedding. Samples 7 and 9 are from the hanging-walls of a forelimb thrust and an out of syncline thrust, respectively. In sample 9 the maximum principal compression is layer parallel, at a high angle to the local transport direction and nearly parallel to the local kink axes. To some extent, sample 9 is similar to sample 7, showing a layer normal extension with the maximum compression being layer parallel and at a high angle to both the local transport direction and the local kink axis.

Discussion of results

In general, the calculated principal axes show a planar deformation in a vertical plane parallel to the transport direction. The maximum principal compression is either layer parallel or slightly up-dip from bedding in the transport direction. These results agree closely with data reported elsewhere for other samples in the McConnell Thrust Plate which are not related to local small scale structures (Spang *et al.* 1975) and in the Foothills structurally beneath the McConnell Thrust (Spang & van der Lee 1975, fig. 6a). These results are compatible with a regional compression in the transport direction without fanning of the thrust plate which would have resulted in a maximum principal extension parallel to bedding and perpendicular to the transport direction. Extension fractures in this orientation must have formed under a differential stress which was not large enough to initiate twinning.

Local reorientation of the principal axes is observed in four of the samples, three of which are near minor thrusts. Spang *et al.* (1975) noted similar reorientations near minor structures elsewhere in the McConnell Thrust Plate. In the Idaho–Wyoming Thrust belt, Allmendinger (1978) notes a compression at a high angle to bedding and at 60° to thrust faults on the overturned limbs of folds, with the maximum principal extension often bedding parallel in the dip direction, which is similar to sample 6 in this study. The orientation of the maximum compression may represent a very high layer parallel shear strain related to the thrust faults above and below sample 6.

Although our samples from the more complex areas show some compression and extension axes in the same orientation as the areas away from minor structures, there is no strong tendency for these samples to show multiple deformation events. Allmendinger (1978) apparently also finds only a few samples showing probably older maxima of compression axes. Based on these observations, it may be inferred that most of the twinning in these samples, and perhaps in all the samples, occurs during the formation of the thrusts and related folding. However, the evidence for this inference is certainly not conclusive.

Sample 9 in the hanging-wall of an out of syncline thrust and sample 7 in the hanging-wall of a forelimb thrust both show a maximum extension at a very high angle to the layering. The out of syncline thrust is interesting in that the displacement goes to zero at both ends of the fault. In sample 7, the compression at a high angle to the transport direction may represent lateral constraint which could cause the maximum and intermediate principal stresses to be interchanged. Similarly, Venter & Spang (1973) interpreted minor folds in the McConnell Thrust Plate with hinges parallel to the transport direction to be the result of compression perpendicular to the transport direction.

In sample 2, the maximum compression is at a very high angle to bedding. This may be caused by a locking of the kink band at high limb dips. In this case, the maximum compression direction, which is nearly horizontal, may represent the regional horizontal compression. However, sample 3, stratigraphically higher and in the same structural position as sample 2, does not show the same reorientation.

Conclusions

Based on our data, the following conclusions can be drawn:

A. In general, the rocks were subjected to a compression in the transport direction either layer parallel or slightly in the up-dip direction with extension perpendicular to layering in the transport direction.

B. Local reorientation of the principal axes is related to minor structures.

C. Most of the twinning appears to have formed during internal deformation of the thrust plate rather than as a function of the early initiation of thrusting.

ACKNOWLEDGMENTS. Support for field and laboratory work was provided by a grant to J. H. Spang from the Natural Sciences and Engineering Research Council of Canada.

References

ALLMENDINGER, R. W. 1978. Dynamic analysis of thrust plates with overturned folds in the Idaho-Wyoming thrust belt. *Geol. Assoc. Can., Abs. with Progs.* **3,** 358.

BALLY, A. W., GORDY, P. L. & STEWART, G. A. 1966. Structure, seismic data, and orogenic evolution of southern Canadian Rocky Mountains. *Bull. Can. Pet. Geol.* **14,** 337–81.

BROWN, S. P. & SPANG, J. H. 1978. Geometry and mechanical relationship of folds to thrust fault propagation using a minor thrust in the Front Ranges of the Canadian Rocky Mountains. *Bull. Can. Pet. Geol.* **26,** 551–571.

DAHLSTROM, C. D. A. 1970. Structural Geology of the eastern margin of the Canadian Rocky Mountains. *Bull. Can. Pet. Geol.* **18,** 332–406.

GHENT, E. D. & MILLER, B. E. 1973. Authigenic minerals from the Blairmore Group (Cretaceous), southwestern Alberta, Canada. *Bull. geol. Soc. Am., Abs with Progs.* **6,** 481–82.

JAMISON, W. R. & SPANG, J. H. 1976. Use of calcite twin lamellae to infer differential stress. *Bull. geol. Soc. Am.* **87,** 868–72.

PRICE, R. A. & MOUNTJOY, E. W. 1970. Geologic structure of the Canadian Rocky Mountains between Bow and Athabasca Rivers, a progress report. *Spec. Pap. geol. Assoc. Can.* **6,** 7–26.

SPANG, J. H. 1972. Numerical method for dynamic analysis of calcite twin lamellae. *Bull. geol. Soc. Am.* **83,** 467–72.

—— & VAN DER LEE, J. A. 1975. Numerical dynamic analysis of quartz deformation lamellae and calcite and dolomite twin lamellae. *Bull. geol. Soc. Am.* **86,** 1266–72.

——, JAMISON, W. R. & SMITH, J. A. 1975. Dynamic analysis of the McConnell thrust plate and associated structures. *EOS,* **56,** 1062.

——, OLDERSHAW, A. E. & STOUT, M. Z. 1979. Development of cleavage at Pigeon Mountain, Front Ranges, Canadian Rocky Mountains. *Can. J. Earth Sci.* **16,** 1108–15.

TURNER, F. J., GRIGGS, D. T. & HEARD, H. C. 1954. Experimental deformation of calcite crystals. *Bull. geol. Soc. Am.* **65,** 883–934.

VENTER, R. H. & SPANG, J. H. 1973. Deformation of the plates bounding the McConnell Thrust Fault at Mt. Yamnuska, Alberta. *EOS,* **54,** 146.

WHEELER, J. O., CHARLESWORTH, H. A. K., MONGER, J. W. H., MULLER, J. E., PRICE, R. A., REESOR, J. E., RODDICK, J. A. & SIMONY, P. S. 1974. Western Canada. *In:* SPENCER, A. M. (ed). *Mesozoic-Cenozoic Orogenic Belts-Data for Orogenic Studies.* Spec. Publ. Geol. Soc. London, **4,** 809 p.

J. H. SPANG, Department of Geology, University of Calgary, Alberta, T2N IN4 Canada.

S. P. BROWN, Mobil Oil Canada Ltd., Box 800, Calgary, Alberta, T2P 2J7 Canada.

The microfabric of calcite tectonites from the Helvetic Nappes (Swiss Alps)

S. M. Schmid, M. Casey & J. Starkey

SUMMARY: The crystallographic orientations of calcite in tectonites from the Morcles Nappe and the Glarus Overthrust have been measured by X-ray texture goniometry. The orientation data are represented by pole figures, inverse pole figures and as orientation distribution functions.

The patterns of preferred orientation observed in the specimens from the Morcles Nappe are correlated with intracrystalline slip mechanisms. The patterns exhibit quasi-axial symmetry and in some cases the axis of symmetry is oblique to the symmetry of the macroscopic fabric. This obliquity is interpreted as the result of a rotational strain path and may be used to infer direction and sense of shear.

Some specimens of the Lochseiten mylonite from the Glarus Thrust show no strong preferred crystallographic orientation. This suggests that grain boundary sliding was the major deformation mechanism.

The crystallographic orientation (texture) of experimentally deformed limestones has been measured by X-ray methods for specimens deformed within a wide range of experimental conditions (Wenk *et al.* 1973; Casey *et al.* 1978). It is tempting, therefore, to compare the observed textures with those from naturally deformed limestones. The limestones of the Helvetic Nappes, deformed at temperatures estimated to be not higher than 400°C offer such an opportunity because they have not been annealed after deformation and are therefore likely to have preserved a syntectonic microfabric.

Samples were collected from (1) the area of the Morcles Nappe in W Switzerland and (2) along the Glarus Overthrust in E Switzerland (Table 1). The Morcles Nappe has an inverted limb where the stratigraphic sequence is preserved in spite of a drastic thickness reduction of as much as 1:100 (Badoux 1972). Along the Glarus Overthrust an extremely thin mylonitic layer (1 m thick, Schmid 1974), has been completely detached from its original substratum and sandwiched between two thrust blocks.

X-ray texture goniometry

Apparatus and data analysis

The specimens were analysed with the combined reflection and transmission scan method (Siddans 1976) using Co K_α radiation. A computer controlled texture goniometer built by Seiffert-Scintag was used for the analysis. For the specimens presented in Fig. 1, eight reflections of calcite were measured (see Casey

TABLE 1. *Localities of analysed specimens*

Specimen No.	Lithology	Locality
7816	fine-grained limestone (Dogger)	Inverted limb Morcles Nappe, near Saillon
7822	white, fine-grained marble (Urgonian)	Inverted limb Morcles Nappe, near Saillon
71	limestone conglomerate (Tertiary)	Inverted limb Morcles Nappe, SE Dents de Morcles
63	Lochseiten mylonite	Foostock
6	Lochseiten mylonite	Lochseite
115	Lochseiten mylonite	Ringelspitz

The dip azimuth of both lineations and foliations is SSE–ESE in the Morcles area. For the Lochseiten mylonites with a subhorizontal foliation the transport direction was assumed to be towards the N, based on field geological evidence.

Thrust and Nappe Tectonics. 1981. The Geological Society of London

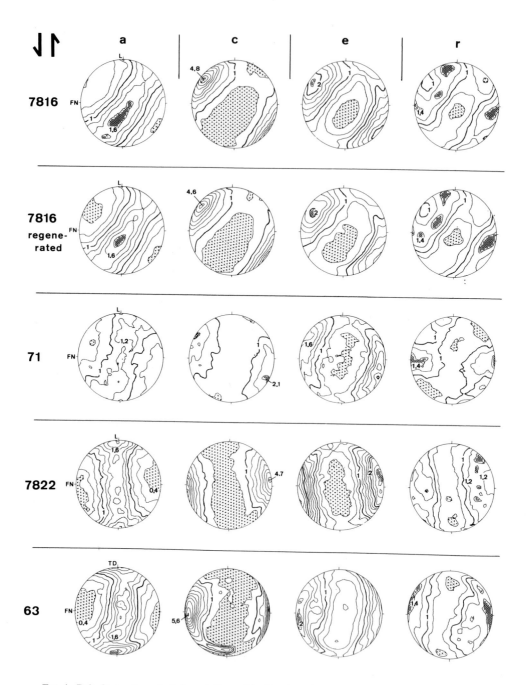

FIG. 1. Pole figures for selected crystallographic directions for some of the specimens studied. The regenerated pole figures for specimen 7816 (degree of expansion 16) are included for comparison with the measured data. Contour intervals for the *a*, *e* and *r* patterns are 0.2 times uniform, contour intervals for *c* are 0.5. FN indicates the position of the foliation normal, L the lineation and TD the transport direction.

et al. 1978, table 1). The counting time was 50 s. for each 5° step in the azimuth and tilt and 100 s on two background positions after every increment in tilt (for the weak *c*-reflection counting times were doubled). The defocussing correction in reflection mode is based on calibrations using a limestone with no preferred orientation kindly provided by H. Siemes, Aachen.

For the calculations of the orientation distribution function (O.D.F.) the digital data were transferred to a CDC-computer. The programs used are based on the methods of Bunge (1969) and Bunge & Wenk (1977). The orientation distribution function is represented as a series of generalized spherical harmonic functions and the pole figures and inverse pole figures are represented as series of spherical surface harmonics. Linear relationships exist between the coefficients of the pole figure and the orientation distribution series expansions. Once sufficient pole figures have been measured and expressed as spherical harmonic expansions, the orientation distribution function coefficients may be calculated. From these coefficients it is possible to calculate serial sections through the O.D.F., to calculate inverse pole figures and to calculate pole figures for any diffracting plane. In Fig. 1 a set of pole

figures recalculated from the O.D.F. gives an indication of the consistency of the input data. The programs used are general and handle triclinic specimen symmetry (Casey, unpubl. manuscript 1979).

Graphical representation of texture data

The three representations of texture data used in Figs 1–3 are briefly introduced here, for further discussion see Bunge (1969) and Bunge & Wenk (1977).

Pole figures (Fig. 1)

The preferred orientation of a particular crystal direction is represented in an upper hemisphere equal area projection with respect to specimen coordinates. The specimen X axis (X_s) was chosen parallel to the lineation or supposed transport direction (labelled L and TD respectively in Fig. 1), Y_s is parallel to the foliation normal (labelled FN) and Z_s is in the centre of the pole figure. All pole figures in Fig. 1 are oriented such that the sense of shear as inferred from field geological evidence is sinistral. The orientation patterns are contoured in multiples of a uniform distribution.

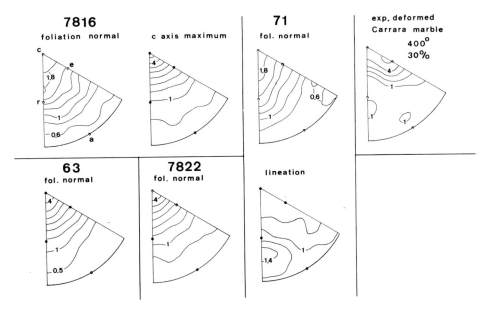

FIG. 2. Inverse pole figures for selected specimen directions (degree of expansion 16). Contour intervals are 0.2 for specimens 7816 (foliation normal) and specimen 71; 0.5 for specimens 63, 7822 and the *c*-axis maximum of 7816; 1.0 for the experimentally deformed marble (from Casey *et al.* 1978).

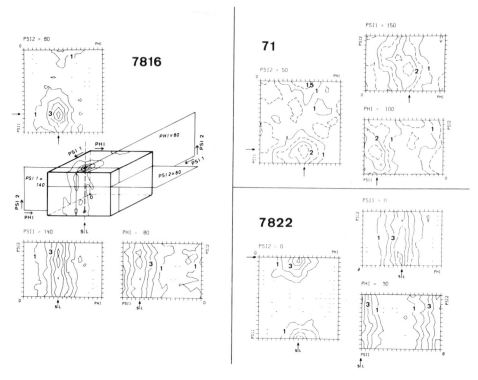

FIG. 3. Three mutually perpendicular sections through the orientation distribution function of selected specimens (degree of expansion 12 for specimens 71 and 7822, degree 16 for specimen 7816). The positions of the sections for specimen 7816 are indicated by the block diagram. Arrows indicate the positions of the sections for the other specimens, SL indicates the skeleton line. Contour intervals are 1.0 for specimens 7816 and 7822; 0.5 for specimen 71. Negative values are indicated by - .

Inverse pole figures (Fig. 2)

These represent the preferred orientation of a particular specimen axis in crystal coordinates (X_c parallel to $[m_1]$ or $[10\bar{1}0]$, Y_c parallel to $[a_2]$ or $[\bar{1}2\bar{1}0]$ and Z_c parallel to the c-axis, using Miller-Bravais indices). Contours are in multiples of a uniform distribution.

The orientation distribution function (O.D.F., Fig. 3)

A given orientation of three crystal axes in a specimen coordinate system can be described by a set of three Eulerian angles (Psi 1, Phi and Psi 2) specifying the rotations necessary to bring the crystal axes away from coincidence with the specimen axes and into their actual position. This orientation can be represented by a point in a block diagram, Fig. 3. The convention of Bunge (1969, fig. 2.5) is used

here. That is, all rotations are anticlockwise as viewed towards the origin of the coordinate system and are performed in the sequence Psi 1 around Z_c, Phi around the new X_c and finally Psi 2 around the new position of Z_c. The block diagram is cut in three mutually perpendicular planes. The contours indicate the volume fraction of grains with a particular orientation in terms of multiples of a uniform distribution.

Results

All pole figures in Fig. 1, with the exception of those for specimen 71, show a strong tendency towards axial symmetry around the position of the c-axis maximum. The axial symmetry is not perfect because the e-poles form a point maximum rather than a 26° small circle as expected for perfect symmetry. This departure from axial symmetry may be seen in the inverse pole figure for the direction of the c-axis maximum of specimen 7816 (Fig. 2): the contours deviate from ideal circles and a very weak ridge towards e is developed. Specimen 7822 shows the closest approach to axial symmetry (Fig. 2).

The c-axis maxima of specimens 63 and 7822 (Fig. 1) coincide approximately with the foliation normal but in specimens 71 and 7816 the maxima are displaced from the foliation normal by 30°, in the case of specimen 71 and 40° for specimen 7816. In both cases the displacement is clockwise from the foliation normal, that is to say in a sense opposite to the sense of shear. The contours for c and e in specimen 63 (to a smaller extent also in 7816 and 71) in Fig. 1 depart from small circles around the point maximum and the high concentration areas are elongated in the plane of projection (X–Z plane of the finite strain ellipsoid).

A more complex set of pole figures was obtained from specimen 71. There is a relatively strong r-maximum near the foliation normal and a secondary maximum near the lineation (compare the well developed r-shoulder in the inverse pole figure for the foliation normal of this specimen in Fig. 2). The inverse pole figure for the lineation in 71 shows a maximum near $\langle r_2 : r_3 \rangle$ (Fig. 2).

The orientation distribution functions for both specimens 7816 and 7822 (Fig. 3) are characterized by a cylindrical zone of higher concentration (skeleton line, Bunge 1969) parallel to the Psi 2 axis. This reflects the high degree of axial symmetry around the c-axis maximum (no preference for a particular rotation angle Psi 2 around the final position of the c-axis). Note that the position of the skeleton line in the Pse 1–phi plane is different for specimens 7816 and 7822. This is an expression of the different position of the c-axis maximum relative to specimen coordinates in these two specimens.

Specimen 71 shows a more complex O.D.F. with a less clearly developed skeleton line and a preference for Psi 2 to lie between 40° and 90°. This corresponds to at least 2 out of the 3 r-poles lying nearly at 90° to the lineation and near the foliation normal, the third r-pole is parallel to the secondary maximum of the r-pole figure (compare Fig. 1).

Two additional specimens of Lochseitenkalk were measured (specimens 6 & 115, Table 1). Their orientation patterns were indistinct and weak relative to those already described, for instance the maximum concentration of the e orientation pattern for specimen 6 is less

than 1.6 times uniform, the maximum for 115 is less than 1.4.

Microstructure

Morcles area

In specimens 7816 and 71 the matrix grains are elongated, with axial ratios up to 1:1.5, in a plane which is oblique to the foliation by 50° in 7816, and variable up to 25° in 71, Fig. 4. The shorter axes of the grains are therefore nearly parallel to the c-axis maximum in these specimens rather than perpendicular to the foliation. It should be mentioned at this point that foliation is macroscopically well developed as a good rock cleavage in all the specimens. In the case of specimen 71 conglomerate pebble shapes with an estimated axial ratio of 50:10:1 (pers. comm. J. Barber) indicate that the macroscopic foliation is apparently parallel to the principal plane of flattening in the finite strain ellipsoid.

Specimens 7816 and 71 have grain sizes between 5 and 30 μm, while specimen 7822, the marble, is only slightly coarser grained (10–50 μm). Specimen 7816 is free of larger calcite intraclasts; specimens 71 and 7822 contain a few isolated intraclasts up to 0.5 mm diameter (Fig. 4b), making up less than 10% of the rock volume. In specimens 7816 and 7822 e-twins are abundant and broad, undulose extinction and bent twins indicate that dislocation glide systems were active. In specimen 71 however, only a few twins are visible in the intraclasts and the matrix grains are free from twinning. The intraclasts of this latter specimen contain deformation bands in the grain interior and equiaxial subgrains near the grain boundary (Fig. 4b). These subgrains have the same diameter as the matrix grains, suggesting that syntectonic recrystallization by subgrain rotation may have lead to the fine-grained mosaic of matrix grains with straight and well equilibrated grain boundaries, which are typical for both specimens 71 and 7822. Specimen 7816, however, exhibits very serrated grain boundaries indicative of grain boundary migration.

Glarus area

Specimen 63 of Lochseiten mylonite shows no macroscopically visible lineation. The microstructure is different from that observed in the rocks from Morcles (Fig. 4d): large, twinned and extremely intensely strained intraclasts occur in a very much finer grained matrix (less than a few μm). The matrix grains are

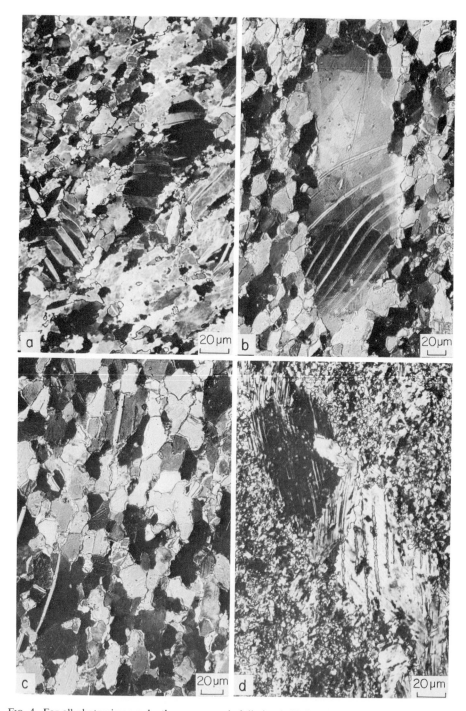

FIG. 4. For all photomicrographs the macroscopic foliation is N–S and perpendicular to the plane of section, the supposed sense of shear is sinistral. The orientation of the photomicrographs therefore corresponds to that of the pole figures of Fig. 1. (a) Specimen 7816; note broad deformation twins and serrated grain boundaries; the plane of mean grain elongation is oblique to the foliation. (b) Specimen 71; note deformation bands and subgrains in the larger intraclast which are flattened in the plane of foliation. Note however that the matrix grains are flattened in a plane oblique to the foliation. (c) Specimen 7822; mosaic of grains with equilibrated grain boundaries. (d) Specimen 63; large intraclasts with deformation twins preferentially oriented parallel to the foliation in a very fine-grained recrystallized matrix.

equiaxial. U-stage measurements on intraclasts indicate a very strong preferred orientation of the c-axes perpendicular to foliation. This, together with the observation that specimens 6 and 115 with their weak textures contain no such intraclasts, suggests that the strong texture of specimen 63 may be attributed solely to the intraclasts which make up about one third of the rock volume.

Discussion and conclusions

The well established slip systems for calcite are e-twinning, r-glide and f-glide (see review by Carter 1976). Experimental deformation of polycrystalline calcite, usually coaxial and with $\sigma_1 > \sigma_2 = \sigma_3$, leads to an axially symmetric texture which can be completely characterized by one inverse pole figure for the shortening direction (Fig. 2). Within the range of experimental conditions where twinning is of major importance (low T, high stress) the axis of shortening rapidly rotates towards the c- and e axis directions in an inverse pole figure representation (Wenk *et al.* 1973; Casey *et al.* 1978, Spiers 1979). Wenk *et al.* (1973) attribute this texture to the combined effect of e-twinning and r-glide. Lister (1978), by computer simulation of texture development in calcite, found that a maximum near r develops if f-glide is as equally easy as r-glide, combined with a lower resolved shear stress for e-slip. This texture was found by Wenk *et al.* (1973) at higher temperatures and confining pressures.

At this point, it is important to stress the difficulties of comparing experimental data with our naturally deformed rocks which surely followed a rotational strain path (a strong component of simple shear is certainly indicated from field geological evidence). We know from experiments with $\sigma_1 \neq \sigma_2 \neq \sigma_3$ (Kern 1971) and from experiments simulating a rotational strain path (Rutter & Rusbridge 1977) that both the ratio of the magnitudes of the principal stresses and the strain path influence the resulting texture. Lister *et al.* (1978) came to the same conclusion based on texture simulation work.

Obliquity of textures

An attempt to interpret the oblique textures in specimens 7816 and 71 may be made with reference to the experiments of Rutter & Rusbridge (1977). By redeforming coaxially shortened marble which developed a strong c-axis maximum near the compression axis such that the previous shortening direction was oblique to the new σ_1 direction they found that the c-axis maximum rotates rapidly towards the new σ_1 direction. This results in the final c-axis maximum being oblique to the finite shortening axis. Their experiment may be qualitatively compared with a simple shear situation, where the short axis of the finite strain ellipsoid continuously rotates away from σ_1. It might then be expected that the c-axis would rotate away from the foliation normal (assumed to be essentially parallel to the Z-axis of the strain ellipsoid) towards σ_1, a situation compatible with our observations and known sense of shear found in specimens 7816 and 71. Rutter & Rusbridge (1977) suggested that this obliquity arises because the texture rapidly "forgets" its earlier deformation history (after only 35% shortening). The obliquity between grain elongation and finite strain observed in our specimen, as well as the discrepancy between the amount of flattening in pebbles and matrix grains (specimen 71) suggest that grain shape as well as texture may only record the last strain increments. These features are probably due to grain boundary migration and/or syntectonic recrystallization.

As a consequence of this interpretation, flattening perpendicular to the foliation during the last increments of strain must be postulated for specimen 7822, although positive field evidence for this is missing. Calcite c-axis maxima oriented oblique to the foliation normal have been observed in other naturally occurring deformed rocks (Wenk *et al.* 1968; Wenk & Shore 1975). The sense of obliquity may eventually be used as a useful criterion to infer unknown transport direction and sense of shear if more data should confirm the interpretation offered here.

Comparison with experiments

A direct comparison between inverse pole figures from experimentally, coaxially deformed specimens and the inverse pole figures of Fig. 2 must be restricted to inverse pole figures derived for those specimen directions which were parallel to σ_1 during the last strain increments. The high degree of symmetry around the direction of the c-axis maximum, combined with the observation from experiments that texture may only record the final increments of strain (Rutter & Rusbridge 1977), suggests that it is probably the c-axis maximum that coincides with the direction of σ_1 during the last strain increments. Parallelism between the c-axis maximum and σ_1, would then indicate, by analogy with experimental data, that e-twinning and r-glide were the major deformation mechanisms leading to the texture development.

Deformation mechanisms in the Lochseiten mylonite

The weak texture in the Lochseiten mylonite samples 6 and 115 suggests superplastic flow with grain boundary sliding as the dominant deformation mechanism (Schmid et al. 1977), a mechanism which would have been favoured by the extremely small grain size found in both these specimens and in the matrix of specimen 63. The microstructure of specimen 63 (Fig. 4d) suggests that this small grain size is the product of syntectonic recrystallization of the larger intraclasts deforming by e-twinning and glide possibly on r and f. Such a recrystallization-

induced change in deformation mechanism in the Lochseiten mylonite would have dramatically weakened this lubricating layer (Schmid et al. 1977) and could explain the observation that shear was confined to this extremely thin mylonite horizon in the Glarus region.

ACKNOWLEDGMENTS. We are grateful to H. J. Möck from Scintag for providing the control software on the texture goniometer. F. Pirovino and E. Schärli prepared the samples and thin sections. J. Barber, Leeds, kindly provided specimen 71. The advice of A. Siddans, Leeds, in designing the texture goniometer used in this study was very helpful. J. S. would like to thank J. G. Ramsay for an invitation to spend a sabbatical leave in his department and to thank the ETH to make the visit possible. We thank O. A. Pfiffner for critically reading the manuscript. Field work was supported by the Swiss National Science Foundation (grant 2.859–0.77).

References

BADOUX, H. 1972. Tectonique de la nappe de Morcles entre Rhone et Lizerne. *Beitr. geol. Karte Schweiz*, **143**, 1–78.

BUNGE, H. J. 1969. *Mathematische Methoden der Texturanalyse*. Akademie Verlag, Berlin, 330 p.

—— & WENK, H. R. 1977. Three dimensional analysis of three quartzites (trigonal crystal and triclinic specimen symmetry). *Tectonophysics* **40**, 357–85.

CARTER, N. L. 1976. Steady state flow of rocks. *Rev. Geophys. Space Phys.* **14**, 301–60.

CASEY, M., RUTTER, E. H., SCHMID, S. M., SIDDANS, A. W. B. & WHALLEY, J. S. 1978. Texture development in experimentally deformed calcite rocks. *Proc. 5th Int. Conf. on Textures of Materials*, Springer Verlag, Berlin, 231–40.

KERN, H. 1971. Dreiaxiale Verformungen an Solnhofen Kalkstein im Temperaturbereich von 20°C–650°C. *Contrib. Mineral. Petrol.* **31**, 39–66.

LISTER, G. S. 1978. Texture transitions in plastically deformed calcite rocks. *Proc. 5th Int. Conf. on Textures of Materials*, Springer Verlag, Berlin, 199–210.

——, PATERSON, M. S. & HOBBS, B. E. 1978. The simulation of fabric development in plastic deformation and its application to Quartzite: The model. *Tectonophysics*, **45**, 107–58.

RUTTER, E. H. & RUSBRIDGE, M. 1977. The effect of non-coaxial strain paths on crystallographic preferred orientation development in the experimental deformation of a marble. *Tectonophysics*, **39**, 73–86.

SCHMID, S. M. 1974. The Glarus overthrust: Field evidence and mechanical model. *Eclog. geol. Helv.* **68**, 247–80.

——, BOLAND, J. N. & PATERSON, M. S. 1977. Super-plastic flow in fine-grained limestone. *Tectonophysics*, **43**, 257–91.

SIDDANS, A. W. B. 1976. Deformed rocks and their textures. *Philos. Trans. R. Soc. London.* **A. 283**, 43–54.

SPIERS, C. J. 1979. Fabric development in calcite polycrystals deformed at 400°C. *Bull. Minéral.* **102**, 282–89.

WENK, H. R. & SHORE, J. 1975. Preferred orientation in experimentally deformed dolomite. *Contrib. Mineral. Petrol.* **50**, 115–26.

——, TROMMSDORFF, V. & BAKER, D. W. 1968. Inverse pole figures of two carbonate fabrics. *Schweiz. mineral. petrogr. Mitt.* **48**, 467–70.

——, VENKITASUBRAMANYAN, C. S. & BAKER, D. W. 1975. Preferred orientation in experimentally deformed limestone. *Contrib. Mineral. Petrol.* **38**, 81–114.

S. M. SCHMID, Geologisches Institut der ETH, Zürich, Switzerland.
M. CASEY, Department of Earth Sciences, The University, Leeds, England.
J. STARKEY, Geology Department, University of Western Ontario, London, Ontario, Canada.

Very low grade metamorphism with a reverse gradient induced by an overthrust in Haute-Savoie (France)

J. Aprahamian & J.-L. Pairis

SUMMARY: The observed distribution of metamorphic transformations, using: (1) the metamorphic facies of Taveyanne Sandstones, (2) the mineralogical composition of the argillaceous fraction (which shows index minerals like paragonite, corrensite and allevardite), (3) the crystallinity indices of the illites, enables us to show that a reverse gradient (the maximum of which must be located in the thrust plane) is superimposed on the already known gradient which decreases both towards the top of the series and towards the external part of the chain.

To account for the observed relationships, we propose that heat was produced by friction along the thrust plane; the theoretical implications of such a model are discussed.

It is pointed out that such a reversed metamorphic gradient will only be observed following favourable circumstances of nappe thickness, rate of motion, thermal properties of the rocks and rate of erosion.

Although metamorphism has long been studied in the Alps, it is only recently that the problem of low or very low grade metamorphism has received much attention. The latter occurs in the neighbourhood of the external crystalline massifs of the Alpine chain in the subalpine domain. Our investigation point, the Platé massif, (Fig. 1f) is in the northern part of this zone. It is the southern extension of the Mesozoic and Cenozoic series which, in Switzerland, are thrust to make up the Nappe of Morcles. Here they are separated by a major contact from the external crystalline massifs (Aiguilles Rouges massif). The rocks range in age from Liassic to Oligocene, with an important stratigraphic break between Upper Cretaceous and Lutetian. They have a total thickness up to 2500 m, and are mostly calcareo-argillaceous with, at times, sandy intercalations. The uppermost part of the series comprises a thick detrital formation (sometimes up to 750 m). This latter formation, the Taveyanne Sandstones of uppermost Eocene-lower Oligocene age, has a flysch-like character (greywacke beds containing basaltic andesitic fragments alternating with shales) and was deposited between the ultrahelvetic flysch and the more external Val d'Illiez Sandstones. The prealpine nappes, which have the ultrahelvetic flysch at their base are thrust over the Taveyanne Sandstones.

A very low grade metamorphism affects the overthrust series. This paper deals with the intensity and distribution of the transformations in connection with the tectonics of the massif and more particularly with the thrust plane of the prealpine nappes.

Metamorphism in the Taveyanne Sandstones

These metamorphosed greywackes (Martini & Vuagnat 1965) exhibit three different facies (Martini 1968).

A. The green facies (with albite, chlorite, calcite and sometimes phengite) differs from other facies by the absence of lime-silicates and by its preferential occurrence in the neighbourhood of thrust units. In the more internal parts of the massif it occurs transformed by the addition of prehnite into a microspeckled green facies.

B. The laumontite facies is a speckled facies with laumontite, albite, chlorite, sphene and corrensite. It is typically represented in the Taveyanne Sandstones of the external part of the massif.

C. The pumpellyite-prehnite facies is also a speckled facies but is characterized by pumpellyite, prehnite, albite and sphene. It develops at the expense of laumontite facies (Martini ascribes this to a later metamorphic event; this point will be discussed later). At times, one can also observe laumontite with these minerals which gives a transitional mixed facies, but also epidote, anticipating the greenschist facies which one finds to the E of Platé.

The conditions of formation are the following:

The green facies (A) appeared first at $T < 200°C$, and under a load pressure of $P > 1.6$ kb supplemented by a tectonic shear pressure. Recent hypotheses suggest that there was a flow of fluids which helps to explain the ap-

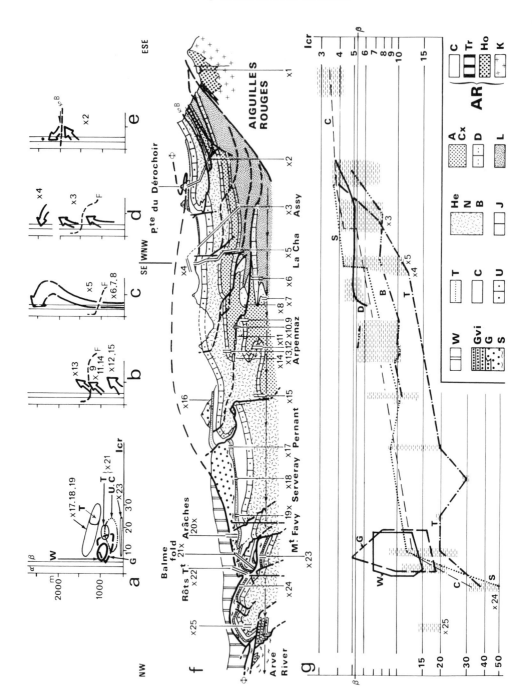

pearance of this facies (Sawatzki 1975; Kubler *et al.* 1974).

The laumontite facies (B), according to Martini, would have developed at $T > 200°C$ and $P > 1.6$ kb. However, Sawatzki suggests T-P conditions: $100°C < T < 200°C$ and $0.7 < P < 1.5$ kb with a 'normal' gradient of 30°C/km.

The pumpellyite-prehnite facies (C), according to Martini, was formed in the same temperature and burial ranges as those responsible for the laumontite facies but with an increased pressure due to tectonic effects. An increase in temperature can also result in the same effects. Thus, for Rusinov (1965), according to Liou (1971), the transformation of laumontite to prehnite is thought to take place slightly above 200°C.

To conclude, the distribution of different facies with pumpellyite-prehnite in the internal parts of the massif and only laumontite in the external regions [this latter even disappears to the SW of the studied region, i.e. SW of Thônes Synclinal (Sawatzki 1975)] means that there is a metamorphic gradient decreasing towards the external parts of the chain.

Metamorphism in the formations below the Taveyanne Sandstones

We shall refer to previous studies (Aprahamian *et al.* 1975), which are a part of a wider study of the Platé massif (Pairis 1975). To appreciate the degree of metamorphic transformations, we have used the mineralogical composition of the argillaceous fraction (<2 μm) and the crystallinity indices of the illites of this fraction (Icr).

The mineralogical compositions depend on the original composition, and hence on the sedimentation conditions. Some unusual compositions give rise to particular minerals, such as index minerals of transformation, like corrensite and paragonite. The absence of these minerals does not necessarily indicate a different degree of transformation, but may correspond simply to an unfavourable original composition. These two minerals, which are good transformation indicators, unfortunately produce a widening of the illite peak at 10 Å, thus modifying the crystallinity index. Moreover, this index, frequently used to establish the recrystallization stages may simply correspond to a crystallization state inherited from a detrital material, which would therefore seem to have an apparently 'advanced' state of crystallization in its present context.

Composition of the group of argillaceous minerals

The distribution of argillaceous minerals confirms the existence of a transformation gradient decreasing towards the external part of the chain. Paragonite, corrensite (with an exceptionally good degree of crystallization), and

FIG. 1. General section across the Platé Massif (f) and crystallinity index (Icr) variations. X 1-X 25: sections sampled (157 samples). L: Liassic; D: Dogger; Cx: Callovo–Oxfordian; A: 'Argovian'; J: Tithonian; B: Berriasian; N: Neocomian shales; He: Hauterivian; U: Urgonian; C: Upper Cretaceous; T: Tertiary limestones; S: Tertiary shales; G: Taveyanne Sandstones; Gvi: Val d'Illiez Sandstones; W: prealpine nappes; AR: Aiguilles Rouges massif; K: crystalline basement; Ho: Upper Carboniferous; Tr: Triassic; C: Upper Cretaceous. Heavy lines: tectonic contacts; ϕ: thrust plane of the prealpine nappes; τ_B: Barmus shearing. a–e: Scattering of Icr as a function of altitude; anchizone lies between straight lines α (Icr = 2.8) and β (Icr = 5.3); Icr<2.8: epizone (i.e. the lower the Icr, the better the crystallization). For a–d, the corresponding detailed plots are available: they have not been included due to lack of space; an example of such a plot is given for e: see Fig. 2. a: X 17–18–19 for T and S of Serveray sector; X 21 for U, C and T of the Balme fold; X 23 for U, C, T and S under the Balme fold thrust; G and W for Taveyanne Sandstones & ultrahelvetic flysch of X 20 and X 22. For explanation see text. b–e: The tips of the arrows indicate vertical trends of Icr variations; the area of the arrows represents the dispersion area of the data. Note that τ_B and overturned faults F or folds (b) yield recurrent Icr. f: Position of sampled sections in the massif; X 4 for T, S, G of the Grandes Platières (SE of Flaine) eastward from the general section. g: Lateral Icr variations (length scale same as f above, logarithmic vertical scale for Icr). Dashed areas: scattering of Icr in corresponding X-sections; for G and W see a; curves with capital letters are for the corresponding stratigraphic levels. Note: (1) Icr absolute values & dispersion increase northwesterly towards the outer part of the massif; (2) overlapping of G and W shows identical transformations at symmetrical distances from the thrust plane; (3) to the E, intersections of curves result from the reverse gradient; (4) no detectable transformation for X 24 and 25: excessive closeness to the nappe front entails insufficient amplitude of motion.

allevardite are essentially localized in the internal sector of the massif. Moving towards the external part, one notes variations of mineralogical compositions that marks the different classical stages of the diagenesis-anchizone passage, going from the exclusive illite-chlorite mixture to the more diversified mixtures with the various irregularly interstratified clays, montmorillonite and kaolinite.

For the most external sections, the extremely variable compositions can be attributed to their sedimentary origins. In the external sections, the transformations had been more or less negligible.

The illite crystallinities

In the different sections illite crystallinities

vary both vertically and horizontally (Fig. 1), and confirm the transformation gradient decreasing towards the external part of the massif (Fig. 1g). A more detailed examination, however, permits us to see a parallel vertical evolution of the different sections (Fig. 1b-e and Fig. 2), with an increase in the index values in the lower part, which corresponds to a normal gradient of transformation, apart from perturbations of tectonic origin. However, in the upper part of the sections (Fig. 1c, d, e and Fig. 2) there is clearly an inverse gradient which always occurs near the thrust plane of the nappe.

In the external sector, no transformation appears at once. However, if one refers to Fig. 1a, one can see that if this is the case for the Tertiary beds far from the nappe (Serveray

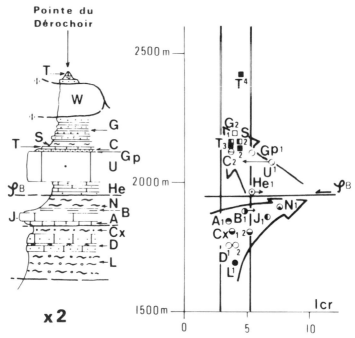

FIG. 2. Derochoir section (x 2): scatter plot of crystallinity indices (Icr) as function of altitude (detail of Fig. 1e). Height scale gives the altitude for both lithological section and Icr plot. Note the improvement of Icr above 2000 m, in the neighbourhood of Φ (the big arrows indicate vertical trends of Icr variations in the series). τ_B: Barmus shearing; Φ: thrust plane of the prealpine nappes; α (Icr = 2.8) and β (Icr = 5.3): anchizone boundaries; L: Liassic (shales); D: Dogger (sandy limestones and shales); Cx: Callovo-Oxfordian (shales); A: 'Argovian' (sandy limestones & argillaceous limestones); J: Tithonian (limestones); B: Berriasian (argillaceous limestones & shales); N: Neocomian (shales); He: Hauterivian (sandy limestones and shales); U: Urgonian (limestones); Gp: 'Gault' (glauconitic sandstones); C: Upper Cretaceous (limestones); T: Tertiary limestones; S: Tertiary shales; G: Taveyanne Sandstones; W: Prealpine nappes (wildflysch). For U1 the argillaceous fraction exhibits 20% paragonite (index mineral for epizone or anchizone): its great amount widens the 10 Å peak, and gives an unreliable Icr value; for B1 and He1, Icr values are improved by inherited material (pointed out by the amount of quartz & feldspars in the argillaceous fraction); for these 3 data small arrows are directed according to the suitable correction.

sector, X 17–18–19, T) it is certainly not so near the thrust plane (Balme fold, X 21, T) where a transformation is quite evident. This phenomenon is confirmed by the fact that, immediately over these beds, one finds the laumontite facies in the Taveyanne Sandstones that are in stratigraphic continuation with them. Thus, one finds everywhere, in the uppermost part of the overthrust series a reverse gradient which appears to develop from the nappe contact and is marked by a bordering of the green facies. One must therefore conclude that the different facies of the greywackes and the reverse gradient of crystallinity have been brought about by the emplacement of the nappe.

Conditions of appearance and detection of inverse gradient

Here we will consider only the inverse gradients of metamorphism of slight or very slight intensity which are of lower grade than the greenschist facies or the epizone, according to the index minerals and/or the crystallinity indices.

In the geological literature, the models considered and the cases of inverse metamorphic gradients, which have been described, are usually concerned with deeper domains (thickness and temperatures, equal to or greater than 20 km and 500°C). These studies are often based on numerous physical data and mathematical computations. We have not investigated the numerical aspects of the problem, but we are using such numerical studies as a basis, and we propose a simplified explanatory model based on field observations in the Platé Massif.

The studies consulted consider the possibilities for the realization of an inverse gradient, principally through the effect of the hot mass of the upper parts and the release of heat by friction as the additional heat factor (Toksöz & Bird 1977; Graham & England 1976; England 1978).

In any case, (to prevent a regularization of the gradient) the movement of the upper mass should be rapid compared with the heat loss through conduction. A rapid movement is necessary also so that the release of heat by friction be noticeable. It is also necessary that the movement continued for a long time and affected a sufficient thickness of terrane. Typical values considered for the different factors were: displacement rate, 0.1–10 cm/yr; thickness, 20 km or more; duration, millions of years; displacement, the amplitudes being

many tens of kilometres.

In our case, it seems that the principal parameters to modify are thickness and temperature. The different studies in the region have led the authors to suggest a thickness of 5–6 km for the nappe. It has been seen above that the temperature attained must be situated around 200°C. Though the duration of displacement is not known exactly, we can state that the movement is at least 15 km along the thrust plane.

With a normal geothermal gradient it is difficult to obtain conditions of pumpellyite-prehnite facies at the depth noted above. To explain the presence of these minerals, Martini (1968) invoked a supplementary pressure (shear stress). However, the observations made in the massif do not permit us to consider that there had been an increase in the thickness of the nappe or an extent of movement sufficient to permit the necessary increase in the pressure. Even if one could find a sufficient increase in pressure to explain the pumpellyite-prehnite facies, that would not allow an explanation of the parallel improvement of the crystallinity indices of illites which are produced by an increase in the temperature (Kubler 1967). We therefore conclude that an increase in temperature is necessary in order to explain this phenomenon.

The flow of the necessary supplementary heat cannot be provided from depth by an increase in the geothermal gradient. An examination of all the figures indicating the evolutionary stages of the gradient shows that, even after the halt of the movement of the nappe, until equilibrium, the mean gradient remains less than normal. It is difficult to see how it could be higher during the emplacement without invoking another source of heat. This heat source must be located in the transformed zones, and more particularly at the thrust plane, to have caused the observed distribution of transformations in relation to this surface.

Figs 1a & 1g (curves G & W) show that at comparable distances, symmetrical about the thrust plane, the Taveyanne Sandstones and the ultrahelvetic flysch are transformed in an identical manner. The transformation mechanism by thermal effects due to emplacement of a hot mass cannot be retained here as the only explanation of the observed facts (it would be necessary for the ultrahelvetic flysch to be more transformed than its relative autochton).

Whereas in the models cited in the literature, the introduction of heat by friction constitutes only a complementary addition, influencing principally the distribution of trans-

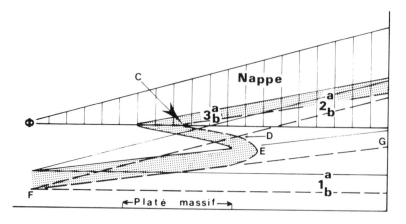

F<small>IG</small>. 3. Schematic explanatory model of metamorphism in the Platé Massif. Idealized cross section with approximately identical horizontal and vertical scales (horizontally the segment 'Platé Massif' is about 15 km long). ϕ, thrust plane; a, approximate limit of laumontite appearance (Icr 10–12); b, approximate limit of the appearance of pumpellyite-prehnite association (Icr $\simeq 5$); 1, position of a & b in the autochton before the arrival of the nappe; 2, regularization profile after the movement stopped, given a gradient identical to 1; the portions of 2a and 2b above ϕ correspond to their position before the movement started; 3, position of a and b towards the end of movement; diffusion of frictional heat from ϕ places these curves above 2 in the nappe. C: turning point of curve 3b on the thrust plane due to heat production on ϕ; CE: reverse part of the gradient; EF: portion of curve 3b corresponding to a shift of curve 1: effect of burial which, alone, would have caused curve FG; DE: portion of the inverse gradient deleted by gradient regularization (curve 2b).

formations (pushing them down), in this instance, the frictional heat determines both the production and distribution of the transformations.

In order to illustrate this phenomenon, we have constructed a diagram (Fig. 3). For the central part (Platé Massif), we have used the data already mentioned from the field studies. A certain number of simplifications were necessary: we have neglected the tectonic factors other than the simple movement of sliding all along the thrust plane (arbitrarily made to horizontal); we have not tried to take into account any possible effects due to erosion during displacement, but have simply assumed that since its departure the nappe decreased in thickness towards its front, which permits us to extend the diagram laterally in a theoretical manner.

In the relative autochton, one sees an inverse gradient, the portion CE of the curve obtained by the diffusion of heat towards the base. A part of this heat evidently comes from the thrust mass, but it is supplemented by the heat produced at the surface of friction. It is this heat production which permits point C of the curve to be on the thrust plane. It is in the reverse part of the gradient that the metamorphic greywackes are located. The

pumpellyite-prehnite facies development, at the cost of laumontite facies, can be explained by the model: the two curves have moved forward together during the nappe displacement. Curve 3b represents, therefore, an earlier stage of curve 2a. The portion EF of curve 3 corresponds to a shift of curve 1 produced by the heat coming from depth, which was the starting of the regularization of the gradient by the effect of burial. This effect alone would have caused curve FG.

One can note that the evolution towards complete regularization (curve 2) would restrict the horizontal and vertical extension of the inverse gradient by deleting the entire portion DE. Given other geometrical conditions, it would be possible to have a regularization gradient that would totally obliterate this inverse gradient. This underlines the problematic character of the preservation of such a metamorphic zonation, the production of which requires very particular conditions. The proposed model permits such conditions but they would, not necessarily arise at all nappe contacts.

In order for the phenomenon to be preserved, one concludes that the relative autochton should have undergone practically no earlier transformation. This is necessary so that the transformation may be recognized in the strip of land nearest the thrust, and so that there still exists underneath an even less transformed part of the sequence. It is also necessary that the phenomenon not be destroyed by any subsequent events, such as a well advanced regularization or a new metamorphic episode.

However, in order that the phenomenon could be observed in the field, one must have, in an overthrust region, many exposed vertical sections of the relative autochton (1500–2000 m), starting from the thrust plane, in order to be able to permit such variations to be well defined vertically as well as horizontally. A zone which has been highly and rapidly uplifted and exposed to active erosion could present the desired conditions of preservation and observation, for such events would permit a rapid cooling and also allow the possibility of creating long vertical sections. In order to have all these necessary concomitant conditions it is necessary to search in the external domain of the Alps, far from the crystalline massifs without, however, approaching the maximum advanced limit of the nappe. We already have indications of the conditions met in some of these sectors. In the case of the Digne-Remollon Nappe, it appears that the amplitude of the movement had been slight, and the thickness of the thrust material (about 2000 m) insufficient: no inverse gradient has been detected here. The movement is also insufficient in the most exposed frontal part of the Embrunais-Ubaye Nappes. However, the presence of the zeolite facies in proximity to a nappe contact in the Champsaur (S of Pelvoux) and in other septentrional subalpine massifs between the transverse valley of Annecy and the Swiss border leads us to hope that we can find the same exceptional conditions already found in the Platé Massif.

ACKNOWLEDGMENTS. We are grateful to Dr. N. J. Price and Dr. E. H. Rutter for their careful reviews of the manuscript and suggestions for its improvement.

We are also grateful to J. Girault, S. McCarty and A. K. Tangri who have been a help to us for the English translation of this paper.

References

APRAHAMIAN, J., PAIRIS, B. & PAIRIS, J.-L. 1975. Nature des minéraux argileux et cristallinité des illites dans le massif de Platé et le revers occidental des Aiguilles Rouges; implications possibles d'un point de vue sédimentaire, structural et métamorphique. *Ann. Centre Univ. Savoie* **2**, 95–119.

ENGLAND, P. C. 1978. Some thermal considerations of the Alpine metamorphism -past, present & future. *Tectonophysics*, **46**, 21–40.

GRAHAM, C. M. & ENGLAND, P. C. 1976. Thermal regimes and regional metamorphism in the vicinity of overthrust faults: an example of shear heating and inverted metamorphic zonation from southern California. *Earth planet. Sci. Lett.* **31**, 142–52.

KUBLER, B. 1967. Anchimétamorphisme et schistosité. *Bull. Centre Rech. Pau-S. N. P. A.* **1**, 259–78.

——, MARTINI, J. & VUAGNAT, M. 1974. Very low grade metamorphism in the Western Alps. *Schweiz. mineral. petrogr. Mitt.* **54**, 461–9.

LIOU, J. G. 1971. Synthesis and stability relations of prehnite, $Ca_2Al_2Si_3O_{10}(OH)_2$. *Am. Mineral.* **56**, 507–31.

MARTINI, J. 1968. Etude pétrographique des Grès de Taveyanne entre Arve et Giffre (Haute-Savoie, France). *Schweiz. mineral. petrogr. Mitt.* **48**, 539–654.

—— & VUAGNAT, M. 1965. Présence du facies à zéolites dans la formation des 'grès' de Taveyanne (Alpes franco-suisses). *Schweiz. mineral. petrogr. Mitt.* **45**, 281–93.

PAIRIS, B. 1975. *Contributions à l'étude stratigraphique, tectonique et métamorphique du massif de Platé (Haute-Savoie)*. Thesis, 3rd. Cycle D., Univ. of Grenoble, 151.

RUSINOV, V. L. 1965. On prehnite finds and the clastic nature of epidote in rocks of some areas of contemporary hydrothermal metamorphism. *Izvestiya. Akad. Nauk. U.S.S.R.* **2**, 33–43.

SAWATZKI, G. 1975. Etude géologique et minéralogique des flyschs à grauwackes volcaniques du synclinal de Thônes (Haute-Savoie, France). *Grès de Taveyanne et grès du Val d'Illiez. Arch. Sc. Genève*, **28**, 265–368.

TOKSÖZ, M. N. & BIRD, P. 1977. Modelling of temperatures in continental convergences zones. *Tectonophysics*, **5**, 181–93.

J. APRAHAMIAN, J.-L. PAIRIS, Institut Dolomieu. Laboratoire associé au C.N.R.S. n° 69. Rue Maurice-Gignoux, 38031 Grenoble Cedex–France.

Saline horizons acting as thrust planes along the southern margin of the Damara Orogen (Namibia/SW-Africa)

H. J. Behr, H. Ahrendt, A. Schmidt & K. Weber

SUMMARY: At the S margin and at the base of the Naukluft Nappes of the late Proterozoic-early Palaeozoic Damara Orogen in Namibia so-called 'Unconformity Dolomites' are developed along thrust planes of nappes and within imbricate structures. Micro-probe analyses, phase-petrological relationships of the unusual mineral composition of the 'Dolomite', the salinity and composition of fluid inclusions as well as other geochemical data prove a saline origin of the 'Unconformity Dolomite'. These data combined with observations on the relationship of deformation and mineral growth, calculated geothermal gradients and radiometric datings lead to the conception that the 'Unconformity Dolomite' is a hot saline intrusion which has already intruded a pre-existing nappe pile. After intrusion and rapid crystallization, the rocks directly below the rigid dolomite plate acted as a thrust plane for last nappe movements which brought the Naukluft Nappes into their present position.

The 'Sonderforschungsbereich 48, University of Göttingen' is studying the geosynclinal and orogenic development of the intracratonic branch of the Damara mobile belt which forms part of the late Precambrian–early Palaeozoic Pan-African belt system. This paper deals with a rock type, known as 'Unconformity Dolomite' which, strata-like, forms the basal parts of the Naukluft Nappes and occurs widespread within thrusts and faults of the Damara Orogen. Therefore, this rock type seems to be of great importance from a tectonic point of view for a geodynamic interpretation of the Damara Orogen.

Geological setting

The extent of the area investigated is marked in Fig. 1 by black lines. The area includes the platform sediments of the Nama basin, the sedimentary rocks of the Naukluft Nappes overlying Nama beds in the N part of the Nama basin and the orthogeosynclinal sediments of the S Damara belt, including the sediments of the Kamtsas and Duruchaus Formation of the Nosib Group. In addition, to illustrate the geological position of the Naukluft nappes, the isolines of illite-crystallinity in the Nama Group (after Ahrendt et al. 1977) and the regional distribution of isograds in the Damara Orogen (after Hoffer unpubl.) are drawn on Fig. 1 (illite-crystallinity increases with decreasing values).

The 'Unconformity Dolomite'

Korn & Martin (1959) first mentioned a strata-like dolomite underlying the Naukluft Nappes and named it 'Unconformity Dolomite' (abbr. 'Udol') because of its unconformity with respect to the over and underlying series. They ascribed the dolomite to be sedimentary in origin, whereas Münch (1978) believed it to be a blastomylonite representing the lubrication layer of the Naukluft Nappes. As shown in Fig. 2, Münch took the view that the 'Udol' is built up in a bilaterally symmetrical manner with increasing cataclasis and recrystallization towards the centre. Before recrystallization, the core, therefore should have been composed of a very mobile suspension of ground dolomite saturated with liquid and gas phases, containing all mechanically reworked products of the series overridden by the nappe movement. Recent investigations on the mineral content, on fluid inclusions and on tectonic deformation, however, lead to a completely different interpretation of the genesis of the 'Udol'. The main results are summarized below. Detailed analytical data will be presented in another special publication.

Petrography

The main components of the 'Unconformity Dolomite' are stoichiometric dolomite, calcite and up to 35% of authigenic albite with a content of 0–5% anorthite. Therefore, petrographically, the 'Udol' can be best described as a siliceous albite-dolomite. In addition, more than 30 different minerals have been identified so far from inclusions of rock fragments and from the 'Udol', among which the high content of talc is striking. The prevailing part of all clastic inclusions in the dolomite matrix are cherts and albitites, not basement or nappe

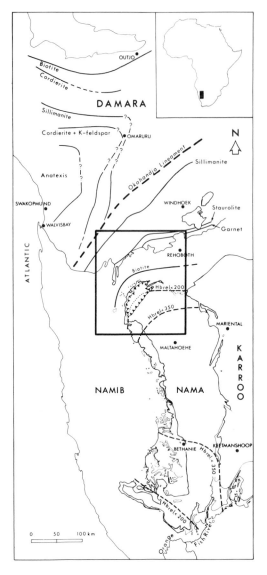

FIG. 1. Sketch map of the investigated area (heavy black line). Isolines of illite crystallinity in the Naukluft Nappes and in the Nama Group after Ahrendt *et al.* (1977), isograds in the Damara Orogen after Hoffer (unpubl.).

cherts', which originated diagenetically from Na-silicates such as magadiite or kenyaite. For the albitites, one can assume Na-carbonates and analcime-rich sediments as original material. The widespread distribution of Mg-riebeckite, which is found especially in the cherts, boron-silicates and crystalline rock inclusions is characteristic of the 'Udol'. The high Ti contents of tourmaline and Mg-riebeckite are unusual. Besides rutile, brookite was formed contemporaneously with Mg-riebeckite.

Fluid inclusions

In order to estimate the temperature of formation of the 'Udol' measurements on fluid inclusions were carried out. Tourmaline, Mg-riebeckite and, above all, albite and dolomite are extremely rich in 3- and 4-phase fluid inclusions of primary origin. The results of the measurements are shown in Figs 3 & 4. In all inclusions, there are halite crystals; the final melting-points of which indicate a salinity of the included solution of about 40% NaCl equivalents. The final melting-points of the ice lie in the positive range with a maximum between +5 and 10°C (see Fig. 3). That means that a small amount of CO_2 leads to formation of clathrates; CO_2-phases by themselves were not noticed. As shown in Fig. 3, the composition of the solutions and the homogenization temperatures change continuously from N to S. Beside NaCl in the N area, there are very often $CaCl_2$ crystals included which dissolve at between 450 and 480°C. In the S area, KCl crystals, which are dissolved at about 100°C before the homogenization of the gas phase, occur as second solid phase. As shown in Fig. 4, the minimum temperatures of formation of the 'Udol' decrease from 480–400°C to 320–280°C from N to S. The lithostatic pressure, at the time of mineralization, was determined in the N and in the S at about 700 bar; that means an overburden of about 2–3 km.

Discussion of the data

For a regional interpretation, the temperatures of formation were put into a figure of Ahrendt *et al.* (1977) showing values and isolines of illite crystallinity in the Naukluft area (Fig. 4) (NB: illite crystallinity increases with decreasing values). Temperatures and illite crystallinity decrease in the same way from N to S, but recrystallization in the 'Udol' and synkinematic recrystallization in the Naukluft Nappes and the underlying and adjoining Nama cannot be

material. The content of boron-silicates, which mainly occur in cherts and albitites, is extraordinarily high; so far, tourmaline, dumortierite and danburite have been identified. Beside boron-silicates, the percentage of albite in these cherts can be so high, that one can find all transitions to pure albitites, which are exclusively built up of idiomorphic albites. The composition and structure point to 'Magadi-

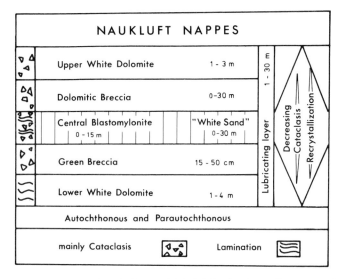

FIG. 2. Idealized standard profile of the Naukluft lubricating layer. In nature all five units are never present in a single profile (after Münch 1978).

of the same origin. While recrystallization in the Naukluft Nappes and in the Name beds caused by regional metamorphism shows a temperature of about 300–350°C and requires a depth of about 4–5 km, the recrystallization temperature of the 'Udol' is about 100–150°C higher (see Fig. 3) and it is recrystallized at a depth of only 2–3 km, as mentioned above. The higher temperatures for the formation of the 'Udol' would have required, if caused by regional metamorphism, a geothermal gradient of about 120–180°C/km. This is

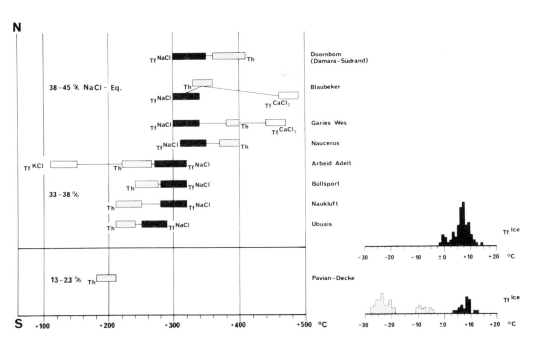

FIG. 3. Fluid inclusion measurements in the 'Unconformity Dolomite' and in the Naukluft Nappes. (Th: Temperature of homogenization; Tf: Temperature of crystal disappearance; Tf ice: Final melting point of ice).

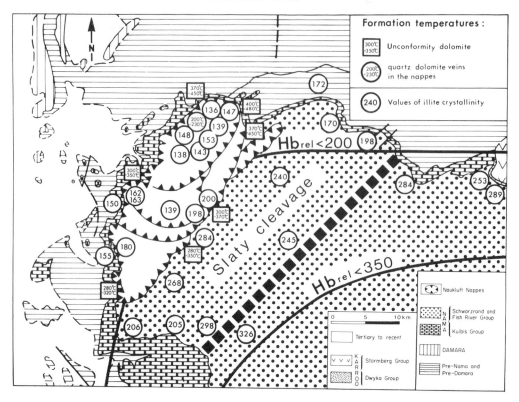

Fig. 4. Temperatures of formation of the 'Unconformity Dolomite'. Isolines and values of illite crystallinity after Ahrendt *et al.* (1977).

unlikely. An explanation of these high temperatures by friction heat can also be excluded if one postulates a highly mobile suspension (Münch 1978) for the 'Udol'. The geological situation of the 'Udol' becomes clearer if one additionally takes into consideration the temperatures of formation together with the K/Ar age determinations done in this region (Ahendt *et al.* 1977) shown in Fig. 5.

The synkinematic metamorphism in the Nama has a radiometric age of about 530 Ma. The same ages were found in parts of the southern Damara and in the Naukluft Nappes. In both units there are younger ages of about 495 Ma which may be interpreted as cooling ages or as dating a rejuvenation during post-crystalline deformation. The same age of 495 Ma was found in the 'Udol' representing the time of recrystallization. That is to say, at this time of recrystallization the overlying nappes and underlying series were already cooled down after their peak of metamorphism, so that the difference of temperature between the 'Udol' and the surrounding series was most probably in the range of 200–300°C. This difference of temperature together with the exotic mineral content of the 'Udol' can be best explained by a hot saline intrusion (see Fig. 6). After recrystallization, further tectonic shortening led to the formation of a thrust plane below the rigid dolomite plate. This overthrusting has mylonitizised the underlying series to a depth several metres without recrystallization so that the tectonic movements did not take place in the 'Udol' but below, in the underlying series. This can be proved by textural analyses which show a preferred mineral orientation resulting from tectonic movements in the underlying series, while the 'Udol' itself shows no preferred orientation. These last movements took place after regional metamorphism, because the isolines of illite crystallinity were cut off discordantly by the Naukluft Nappes (see Figs 4 & 5).

Conclusions

Cyclical, playa lake sediments with dolomite, sodium carbonates, sodium silicates and borates were the original material of the 'Udol' underlying the Naukluft Nappes. The basin of sedimentation was situated in the S graben zone of the Damara Trough (see also Martin &

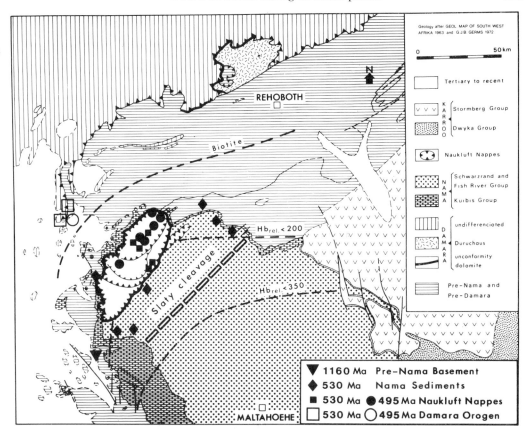

FIG. 5. K/Ar age determinations in the Naukluft area. In addition: Biotite isograd, isolines of illite crystallinity and southern boundary of slaty cleavage after Ahrendt *et al.* (1977).

Porada 1977). During a subfluence or an A-subduction, in the course of which the basement was transported to the N, parts of the saline sequence subjected to abnormally high pore pressure were squeezed out. The evaporite pulp intruded in nappe piles, thrust planes, fault zones and pocket-like, pipe-like and dyke-like into the over-and underlying series. The temperature of formation of the 'Udol' can be proved to be in the range of 380–480°C. Consequently, the temperature was 100–200°C higher than in the overlying nappes and the underlying autochthonous series during nappe movement. This is one of the main reasons why the 'Udol' is not regarded any longer as a lubricating layer but as a hot saline intrusion (For different interpretations of the 'Udol' compare Figs 2 & 6). Before crystallization took place, Mg-riebeckite was formed abundantly in connection with a Mg-Fe metasomatism. After intrusion and rapid crystallization, the rocks directly below the rigid dolomite plate acted as a thrust plane. During

this time of post-crystalline deformation, the nappes of the Naukluft with their higher metamorphic grade were being pushed onto the lower metamorphic rocks of the Nama beds in the SE, discordantly cutting the isolines of synkinematic recrystallization in the underlying series, as shown in Figs 1, 4 & 5. The position of the biotite isograd of Damara metamorphism is important in determining the distance of transportation (see Figs 1 & 5) because we also find biotite in the higher metamorphic parts of the Naukluft Nappes, where the biotite has grown before nappe movement. Therefore, we can derive a minimum distance of transportation of about 50 km for the biotite-bearing parts of the nappes.

Rocks, similar petrologically to the 'Unconformity Dolomite' are to be found in similarly tectonic positions widespread at the S margin of the Damara Orogen (see the Duruchaus Formation on Fig. 5) and in the N of the orogen. These evaporitic sequences, which

172   *H. J. Behr* et al.

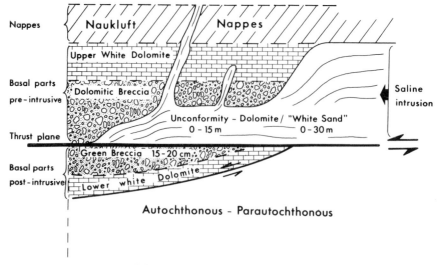

FIG. 6. Development of the basal parts of the Naukluft Nappes (Schematic section).

have not been noticed until now, must have covered large parts of the graben zones not only of the Damara but also of the other parts of the Pan-African belt.

ACKNOWLEDGMENTS. This work forms part of the research programme of the Sonderforschungsbereich 48 'Entwicklung, Bestand und Eigenschaften der Erdkruste, insbesondere der Geosynclinalräume', University of Göttingen (Federal Republic of Germany). Funds for this work were provided by the Deutsche Forschungsgemeinschaft (German Research Society). Thanks are due to Dr H.-G. Münch for some samples from the Naukluft area.

References

AHRENDT, H., HUNZIKER, J. C. & WEBER, K. 1977. Age and degree of metamorphism and time of nappe emplacement along the southern margin of the Damara Orogen/Namibia (SW-Africa). *Geol. Rdsch.* **67**, 719–42.

KORN, H. & MARTIN, H. 1959. Gravity tectonics in the Naukluft Mountains of South West Africa. *Bull. geol. Soc. Am.* **70**, 1047–78.

MARTIN, H. & PORADA, H. 1977. The intracratonic branch of the Damara Orogen in South West Africa. I. Discussion of geodynamic models. *Precambrian Res.* **5**, 311–38.

MÜNCH, H.-G. 1978. Das Schmiermittel an der Basis der Naukluft-Decke, Südwestafrika. *Z. dt. geol. Ges.* **129**, 7–31.

H.-J. BEHR, H. AHRENDT, A. SCHMIDT & K. WEBER, Geologisches Institut der Universität, Goldschmidt-str. 3, D-34 Göttingen, West Germany.

Sliding and other deformation mechanisms in a glacier of salt, S Iran

C. J. Talbot

SUMMARY: One of the salt glaciers in S Iran is interpreted here as an analogue of a gravity-driven, thrust nappe complex which has overridden its own debris. Fabrics from different parts of the body are interpreted in terms of grain boundary diffusion and dynamic recrystallization, together with tensional separation and sliding along the cubic cleavages of porphyroclasts of clear halite.

Slides generate within the salt as ramps, where the salt glacier slows and thickens to surmount the bedrock obstructions to its general downslope flow. Zones of plastic flow-folds and smaller zones of large-scale crenulation cleavage form upstream of the obstructions and the slides emerge from the downstream end of such zones. Few, if any, ramp directly to the surface and most turn to flats within the salt sheet where they may heal as a result of stress-drop annealing.

The competence of the salt mass is assumed to decrease down its length in response to a decrease in grain size and a relative increase in insoluble grains. Such a decrease in competence accounts for the change in character of the internal deformation of the salt sheet when traced downstream. First the slides and then the crenulation cleavage fail to develop upstream of successive obstructions and eventually all internal folding ceases. Instead, the salt glacier moves over the last few bedrock ridges as accommodation folds and another type of slide appears to form by layer parallel slip.

All the slides in the salt glacier originate near irregularities in its bedrock channel. The slide propagation zones remain stationary and the salt tears as it passes through, and beyond them. Instead of eroding its bedrock, the salt glacier effectively smooths irregularities in its channel by shearing over the infilling bodies of static salt.

Approximately 60 diapirs of Hormuz (Infra-Cambrian) salt emerge at the surface in the Zagros mountains of southern Iran (Harrison 1931; O'Brien 1957; Kent 1970; Ala 1974; Colman-Sadd 1978). Many of these emergent diapirs are now degraded at the surface, but others are still mountains of salt which reach heights over 1000 m above the surrounding plains (Ala 1974). Several of these salt mountains have, associated with them, extrusive sheets of salt which extend over the surrounding country rocks. Such extrusive sheets have been known as salt glaciers since Lees (1927) first described them.

This work is based on a study of the larger of the two salt glaciers in the salt mass at Kuh-e-Namak (Dashti) which lies about 170 km SE of Bushehr on the Gulf Coast of S Iran. On the advice of Sir Peter Kent, this particular salt body was chosen as a well-exposed example, being relatively accessible and known to be one of those most likely to be still moving. The salt glacier is considered here as an analogue of a gravity nappe still attached to its root zone. It is debatable whether the salt glacier studied is sufficiently large to be labelled a nappe. However, it consists of Infra-Cambrian rock salt with a gneissose texture which has moved over a rigid basement of younger rocks.

It displays many of the characteristics of a nappe complex—but on a smaller scale than in most other rocks. Model theory suggests that this small-scale morphological similarity is the result of the extra mobility of the salt in relation to most other rocks.

This work concentrates on field and laboratory observations relevant to the deformation mechanisms and structures within the salt, with particular reference to the sliding surfaces. The slides in the salt glacier will be shown to differ in several ways from the interpretation of the situation in other nappe complexes.

Kuh-e-Namak (Dashti)

Kuh-e-Namak (Dashti) is a mountain of Hormuz salt which reaches 1500 m above sea level in Dashti Province in Iran near 28°15′N, 51°41′E. It consists of a topographic dome with an elliptical 5600 × 2000 m plan with its long axis aligned NE–SW. This dome overlies a diapir intruded along a steep NE–SW normal fault where it breaks a NW–SE trending rounded anticlinal ridge of the Zagros fold belt (Fig. 1). On its long flanks, the salt mass is limited at the surface by country rocks of anhydrites, limestones and dolomites which range in age from the Triassic to the Eocene–

Thrust and Nappe Tectonics. 1981. The Geological Society of London

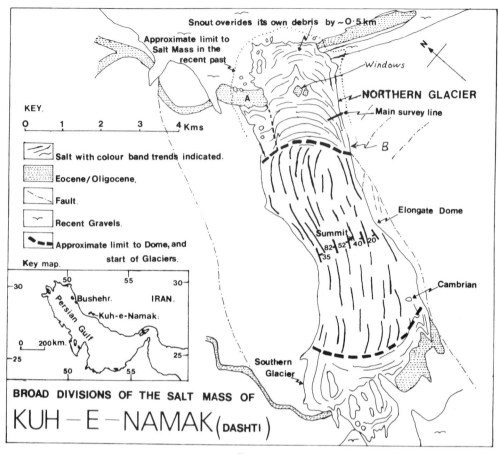

FIG. 1.

Oligocene. Two extrusive sheets of halite extend downhill to the NW and SE over a former land surface eroded in the flanks of the anticline (Fig. 2). The observations reported here were made in the larger of these two salt glaciers, that in the NE. This approaches 3000 m in length, 2600 m in width and varies in thickness from perhaps 100 m to a few tens of metres. At its snout the base of the glacier is approximately 90 m above sea level.

Wherever it is exposed, the salt mass displays a banding defined by different grain sizes and, in particular, by different proportions of insoluble Hormuz materials of various colours (black, magenta, pale green, honey, pink and white). The salt also displays a gneissose flow foliation defined to a greater or lesser extent by the shapes and orientations of one or more of its three components: halite porphyroclasts, a fine-grained groundmass of halite and spicules of insoluble components (usually specularite or $CaSO_4$). The attitudes of the

rigid boundaries imposed by the country rocks control the orientations of the deformation fabric within the salt mass and both these

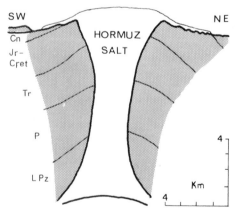

FIG. 2. An interpretive NE–SW cross section through the salt mass at Kuh-e-Namak (Dashti) showing both salt glaciers.

aspects allow the salt glacier to be subdivided into various structural regimes. New deformation structures and fabrics generate in the salt where the rigid boundaries change in orientation over short distances. Where the bed-rock boundaries to the dome, diapir and glacier are essentially straight planes extending over significant distances, the flow foliation and banding are parallel to each other and to their rigid boundaries. Maturing structures and fabrics in such regimes may be inherited from upstream but no new deformation structures develop in them.

The steep NE–SW trending banding and foliation in the dome is consistent with the salt having been extruded to the surface up a steep pipe (elongated in its NE–SW dimension) from a deep source layer. Lees (1931) and Gera (1972) have published simple analyses of how an 8 km thick sequence of dense country rocks can support a column of salt reaching 1500 m above sea level. Thick residual soils blanket those parts of the dome in which dirty salt reaches the surface and demonstrate that some salt must be lost from the surface of the dome by solution. However, significant volumes of salt have flowed downhill to feed the glaciers and, in the precipitous flanks of the dome, the steep banding and foliation curl to parallel the dip slopes of the country rocks over which the glacier has been extruded. The gently dipping banding and foliation in most of the salt glacier is consistent with lateral flow in a body spreading under its own weight (Ramberg 1977).

The zones in the salt glacier, in which new deformation structures and fabrics generate, appear to be where longitudinal shortening forces are fed back through its body from the obstructions it surmounts in its general downhill movement. Despite dissection by solution, the top surface of the glacier slopes generally down to the snout; thereby demonstrating that slow-moving, gravity-driven materials move in the direction of their surface slope even if this involves local upward movement along their base (Elliott 1976*a*).

Seasonal streams flowing off the snout of the glacier have excavated gorges up to 14 m deep in the unconsolidated sandy gravels of an alluvial fan which is still forming downstream of the snout of the salt glacier. Clasts of black limestone, gypsum and native sulphur derived from the Hormuz salt mass are recognizable at most exposed levels in this fan. Some of the gorges extend a few hundred metres behind the extremities of the salt glacier and in these it is obvious that, like many other nappe complexes elsewhere, the salt glacier has overridden its own (fluvially reworked) debris. However, mounds of unsorted Hormuz debris around the front and sides of the salt sheet indicate that it is currently wasting, at least in its lower reaches.

The general character of the salt sequence first exposed in the dome undergoes several changes as it moves generally downslope to the snout of the salt glacier. The average grain size decreases from perhaps 4 cm in the dome to closer to 1 mm in the snout. The relatively few, thick (1–50 m?) colour bands in the dome have been repeated many tens of times and dramatically thinned (to millimetres up to a few metres) by the time they reach the snout. The colours intensify downstream as the large discrete joint blocks of limestone etc. (e.g. 3 m^3) which emerge embedded in the otherwise clean salt of the dome are milled to sand-and silt-sized particles and are mixed more or less uniformly within each layer in the salt. Although some of these changes occur throughout the glacier, most are thought to occur in the zones of longitudinal shortening associated with obstructions across the glacial channel.

Evidence will now be presented for a variety of mechanisms by which ductile strains develop in the salt. The slides will then be described, before an attempt is made to integrate the deformation structures and mechanisms into an overall picture.

Mechanisms of ductile strain

Granulation

Where the steep colour bands and foliation of the dome curl to the gentle inclinations typical of the glacier, the transparent, coarse grains of halite begin to granulate around their margins (Fig. 3a). Down the length of the glacier, a decreasing proportion of the halite gneisses consist of porphyroclasts (<20 cm) of the clear halite which progressively separate in an ever increasing proportion of opaque, fine-grained (< a few mm) halite $\mp$ insoluble grains. In the snout, a few isolated porphyroclasts survive surrounded by large areas of fine-grained, dirty salt.

Granulation appears to occur by the dynamic recrystallization of small sub-grains around the margins of the porphyroclasts. Any cubic cleavages visible in the sub-grains have been rotated several degrees from their orientation in the larger parent grain (see Fig. 3b).

(a)

(b)

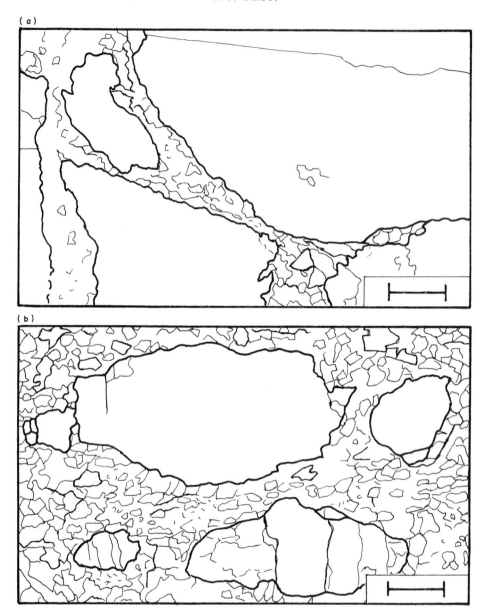

FIG. 3. Grain boundaries traced from ground surfaces of hand specimens. Scale bars = 1 mm. a) The beginning of granulation at the end of the dome. b) Such 'elliptical' sections through porphyroclasts of halite are thought to result by grain boundary diffusion of sub-circular sections (+ granulation). These grains exhibit various stages of tensional separation to newer, smaller, porphyroclasts of sub-circular section. c) A halite porphyroclast which has suffered simple shear by cleavage slip (upper 2/3 of figure). The surrounding smaller grains show a ribbon fabric typical of glacier salt characterized by cleavage slip. d) Serrated margins in white halite (top) and dirty magenta halite (bottom). Dotted areas represent ultra fine-grained halite and unresolvable insoluble material.

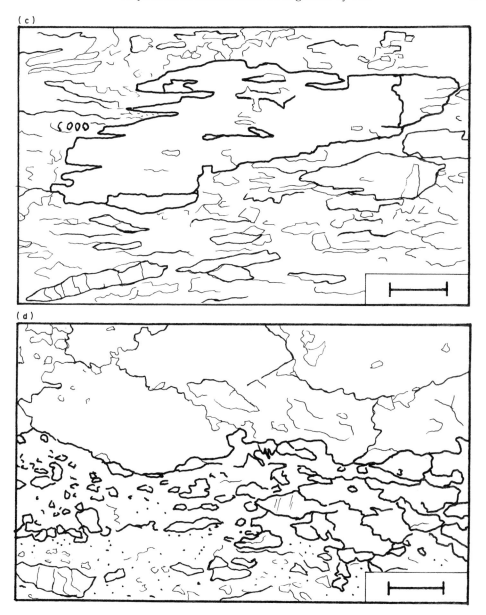

FIG. 3.

Grain boundary diffusion

Throughout the dome, and in many of the higher reaches of the glacier, sub-spherical grains of clear halite appear to have deformed to generally ellipsoidal shapes without any noticeable decrease in volume. Such strains are not discernable for any one particular grain but are inferred from the grain-size of equidimensional, clear grains round about or just upstream. It seems reasonable to assume that grain boundary diffusion has occurred in such cases. In the dome, such strains occur without granulation but in the salt glacier they appear to occur in granulating salt (Fig. 3b).

Tensional failure on the cleavage

The sub-spherical porphyroclasts of clear halite common in many parts of the glacier are presumed to rotate as they are carried downstream. This would account for the majority of them having their cubic cleavage planes in the principal planes of the strain fabric when they strain to ellipsoids in zones of particularly high strain. As they become increasingly ellipsoidal, the longer axes of the halite grains must reach their tensional strength, for few exceed a principal axial ratio of 3 or 4 : 1 in any section. As they exceed this limit, they separate at more or less regular distances along one or both the cleavages perpendicular to the foliation (see Fig. 3b). Many of the porphyroclasts strain to triaxially oblate ellipsoids and their separation occurs first along the cleavage which results in smaller, new grains which are prolate with their long axes lying in the foliation but perpendicular to the direction of flow (i.e. parallel to any fold axes generating nearby). These new grains, in turn, tend to separate along their long axes and form still smaller grains which are only slightly ellipsoidal, and have their longest axes perpendicular to the foliation which is also a general plane of flattening. Still more strain results in these grains passing through sub-spherical shapes prior to repeating the whole process on a smaller scale.

Such pulling apart of halite grains occurs repeatedly in salt which passes through zones of high strain. Each separation results in an abrupt decrease in the long axes of grains and the formation of new grains which pass through sub-spherical ('undeformed') shapes. In effect, the flow foliation is continually regenerating in zones of high strain. Where lateral spreading by gravity is dominant, the regenerated foliation parallels the colour banding and no obvious deformation structures develop. Where longitudinal shortening forces predominant, near obstructions to flow, the foliation regenerates obliquely to the colour banding and folding develops (Talbot 1979).

In the dome, tensional failure develops new grain boundaries without granulation. In the glacier, however, the new grain boundaries are very soon granulated and the new, smaller porphyroclasts separate widely in their fine-grain groundmass as they are carried downstream (Fig. 3b).

Cleavage slip

In zones apparently localized along the base of the salt glacier and along the internal slides, porphyroclasts with suitable orientations which were originally subspherical have strained by simple shear slippage along the cleavage planes parallel to the direction of movement. Granulation along some of the slipped cleavage planes can occur (Fig. 3c). Nearby, porphyroclasts with cleavages in other orientations appear relatively undeformed apart from marginal granulation. Close to the internal slides in the salt glacier, black or magenta salt layers display a ribbon-like fabric which is attributed to so much slippage and associated granulation along cleavage planes that few other types of grain boundaries are obvious. (Fig. 3c).

Recrystallization

Halite grains of all sizes exhibit serrated margins (Fig. 3d) in parts of the salt glacier. Such post-kinematic recrystallization appears to have developed in salt fabrics showing evidence of straining by all the other mechanisms of ductile strain. Serrated grain margins are most obvious in the glacier where the foliation parallels the colour bands between the zones of longitudinal strain. It seems likely that they record the results of stress-drop annealing in parts of the glacier being passively carried along by other strain mechanisms in deeper parts of the glacier.

Pressure solution

Veins of white, re-precipitated salt develop close to locations where slides generate within the glacier. They consist of clean, fine-grained halite which is white in the surrounding dirty salt. None are noticeably fibrous, although the salt in them was presumably mobilized by pressure solution associated with the ductile strains close to the propagation zones of the slides. Kent (1970) has suggested that solution of the salt increases the proportion of insoluble components down the length of the glacier. While this process may well occur, it cannot easily be studied in the field.

Pinnacles (∓ capping blocks of limestone) left by solution on the surface of the glacier, curl from their vertical axes in apparently random directions and such deformations may be caused by differential solution.

Slides

The sole thrust

The channel down which the glacier extends appears to have been a land surface which includes a fault-controlled river valley. The contact between the salt and the country rocks is exposed at several locations around the margins of the glacier and around two windows of bed rock in its interior (Fig. 1). In all locations, the colour bands and foliation parallel the base of the glacier. Nowhere along the basal contact is a particularly dirty layer of salt obvious as in the case of many temperate ice glaciers. Dirt bands at, or near, the base appear to consist of entrained Hormuz material rather than of debris eroded from the bedrock. Limestone and dolomite surfaces exposed by recent wastage of the salt are free of soil and generally smooth, but are neither polished nor slickensided. Some shallow grooves, 2 m wide and approximately 30 cm deep have been eroded on the upstream face of a limestone ridge, now damming part of the N margin of the salt glacier (ridge A in Fig. 1). These grooves were the only indication recognized that the salt glacier might erode its bedrock channel.

Although the sole thrust is a boundary along which old halite has moved over younger rock, the evidence of true slip along the contact is ambiguous over most of its length. No fibres of halite were seen along the contact, but a cleavage slip fabric is common in a basal zone of a few metres thick.

Listric normal shear zones

On part of its SE margin the salt glacier just downstream of the dome can be seen to have flowed down over a cliff in the bedrock about 60 m high (location B on Fig. 1). This exposure was inaccessible but, from a distance, the colour bands appear to parallel the gentle slopes of the bedrock and change in height over a shear zone approximately 10 m wide. This shear zone is partially obscured by surface efflorescence, but is steep in its upper portions and curves to parallel the shape of the buried cliff face. It has the general effect of a listric, normal-shear zone. (Fig. 5).

In parts of the precipitous NE slopes of the salt dome, the salt appears to be involved in other listric normal shear zones as it enters the higher reaches of the glacier. Such zones are represented on the top surface by what looks like a crude fracture cleavage in which the opaque cleavage planes are rarely closer than a centimetre apart in the otherwise clear halite. Granulation and cleavage slip probably occur in such zones; and a stream flowing over one of them showed no sign of draining into it and the 'fractures' are tightly closed.

Ramp generation zones

The most obvious slides in the salt glacier are those generated within the salt immediately upstream of obstructions to its general downstream flow. Most such obstructions are scarp faces of bedrock ridges across the channel, but some appear to consist of stationary or slow-moving salt.

I have described elsewhere (Talbot 1979) how the upper reaches of the glacier slow and thicken to surmount such obstructions by developing trains of internal asymmetric, plastic-flow folds of sub-similar style. Individual folds tighten and increase in amplitude as they pass down each train (Fig. 4). Near the downstream end of particularly long fold trains, an extra component enters the story— the colour bands exhibit flexural slip by developing a large scale crenulation cleavage. A new, shorter wavelength folding develops on the limbs of the maturing anticlines turning them into anticlinoria. These minor folds tighten up in a short distance of downstream travel and become a crenulation cleavage. When the macrolithons are only 50–70 cm wide, each can be seen to have overridden the underlying macrolithon by 200–300 cm. However, individual colour bands can still be traced without interruption from one macrolithon to the next, even at this stage. Downstream of perhaps four or five of such cleavage zones, angular disconformities between the colour bands indicate that discrete slide zones have developed (Fig. 4).

Slide generation zones are visible in several deeply dissected examples. No slides were seen to root in the sole thrust; all the slide generation zones actually inspected were generated by internal strain well within the salt. Most of the thrusts originated as comparatively steep ramps ranging in upstream dip from *c.* 10 to 38° on the steep overturned limbs of

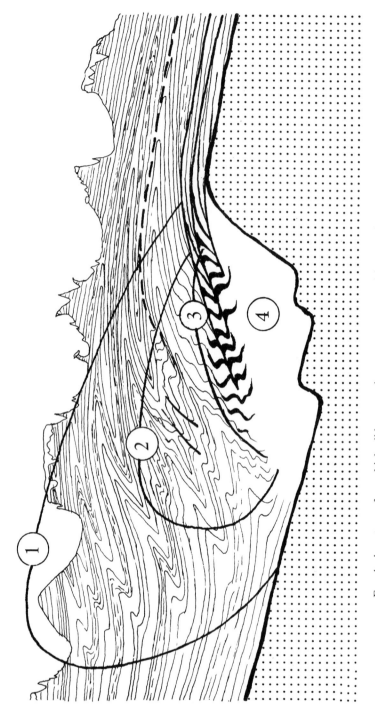

FIG. 4. A cartoon of a multiple slide generation zone reconstructed from sections through several such zones and parts of zones exposed at different levels in the upper reaches of the salt glacier (flow left to right over dotted bed rock). Boundary 1 encloses an area of obvious flow folds, boundary 2 an area of crenulation, boundary 3 an area of reprecipitated salt veins (shown in black) in which thrusts generate and 4 is in static salt. Thrusts are indicated by heavy unbroken lines and a lag as a heavy dashed line.

anticlinoria. Lag slides formed, with upstream dips of 23–34°, on the long limbs of anticlinoria. A few sheared, short, overturned limbs with upstream dips of about 55° were seen in the long limb of one anticlinorium and appeared to be incipient thrusts. These are included in the cartoon summarizing my interpretation of how the slides generate (Fig. 4).

The ends of multiple slides were usually associated with swarms of *en-echelon* veins developed between the colour bands in the macrolithons (Fig. 4). Such veins consist of white, recrystallized salt and are not developed far from the slide-generation zones. In longitudinal section, successive slides in any one set originate at shallower levels downstream, so that their ends (or beginnings) define a body of static salt immediately upstream of the obstruction. Such a static mass of salt lessens the effect of the obstruction considerably, by smoothing off the topography over which the deepest salt moves as a series of thrust slices. In some locations, a single zone of tectonic melange consisting of pods of white, recrystallized halite, in sheared mass of dirty salt a few metres thick, seems to fulfil the function of spaced slides elsewhere.

Sets of multiple slides are common in the upper reaches of the glacier but become increasingly rare downstream. In the last 500 m of the glacier, only single slides may generate as ramps at the downstream end of comparatively minor fold trains. Still nearer the snout, first the slides and eventually even the internal folds die out.

Slide flats

As in all rocks, the slides in the salt glacier are only obvious where they result in angular disconformities, intense strain gradients or stratigraphic disruptions. No attempt was made to establish stratigraphic sequences in the gneissic salt in sufficient detail to substantiate the existence of slides parallel to the colour banding. Despite this limitation, it was usually possible to trace slides from where they were reasonably obvious (as ramps with upstream dips) up and over the obstruction which appeared to be responsible for their generation. Above and downstream of this obstruction, they usually seemed to continue as flats with gentle downstream inclinations within the glacier but the lowest often became the sole thrust (Fig. 4). Thrust and lag slides could not be distinguished from each other at a distance from the place where they generated.

In areas of deep dissection, it is possible that some slides ramp directly to what is now the top of the glacier. However, most appear to turn to flats either within the glacier or at its base and do not reach the top surface of the glacier for considerable distances downstream. Within those distances such inconspicuous slides may be joined by others generated at further obstructions downstream. However, such a picture supposes that the slides remain active beyond the place where they are folded in the next fold train (i.e. the next potential slide generation zone) and this seems unlikely. It is also possible that stress-drop annealing below the zones of obvious ductile strain anneal the slides. My field observations have been insufficient to resolve such questions.

One line of reasoning strongly suggests that numerous slides do exist parallel to the colour banding just behind the snout. Steep, straight-planar fractures extend upwards through the salt from the crests of many of the bedrock ridges over which the salt sheet flows. Very few such long, straight-planar fractures exist. However, downstream of most, are similar fractures which curl downstream on a large scale when traced upwards; the same fractures are segmented into short, steep lengths which are offset along the foliation on a small scale. Downstream of these examples, are still further curled and segmented fractures which merge into the general brick-wall pattern of joints (see snout region in Fig. 5). The long, straight-planar fractures are interpreted as annual dry season structures formed by thermal stresses. The ductile flow thought to occur in the annual two-month rainy season accounts for the general rarity of such straight fractures as each would be deformed as it is carried downstream when the salt is sufficiently wet to flow. The general curl of the preceding dry season fractures demonstrates that the glacier movement during each wet season involves some simple shear and that the upper layers generally move faster than the lower layers. Such a situation is in accord with Ramberg's (1977) findings that, in gravitational flattening bodies of large length to thickness ratios, the greatest displacement is near the top surface. If these various inferences are correct then the segmentation of the fractures indicates that discrete slides exist in the salt glacier even in the snout. Certainly some of the levels along which the segmentation has occurred have small-scale, ribbon-like fabrics indicating slip on the cleavage of halite grains. Others are dirt bands and might represent concentrations of insoluble components along zones of halite solution.

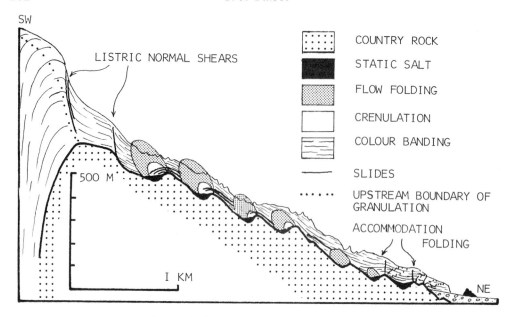

FIG. 5. An interpretive longitudinal profile of the NE salt glacier at Kuh-e-Namk (Dashti) illustrating the structural regimes and how they change in character down its length.

However, even if such layer-parallel slides do exist there can be no certainty that they are in continuity with slides generated far up-stream. It is perhaps more probable that any such slides arise as surfaces of internal slip, as the colour bands of the glacier flex over the last few obstructions which the salt glacier encounters just short of the snout. Here, the bedrock topography tends to be smoothed somewhat by bodies of static salt ∓ fluvial debris (Talbot 1979). At this stage, instead of developing asymmetric internal flow-folds as it did further upstream, the whole glacier de-velops accommodation-folds over irregularities in its bed.

Summary

The relative decrease in grain size and the relative increase in the proportion of insoluble grains down the length of the salt glacier is thought to result in the decrease in compet-ence of the body of the salt sheet down its length. Such a downstream decrease in com-petence would account for the diminishing size of successive regimes affected by longitudinal shortening forces fed back through the glacier from obstructions of equivalent size. It would also account for the changes in relative impor-tance of the various mechanisms of defor-mation exhibited by the salt glacier down its length.

In longitudinal profiles of most parts of the salt glacier, asymmetric folds develop in vag-uely ovoid areas within the salt immediately upstream of obstructions over which the glacier flows (see Fig. 5). Plastic flow folding starts at the lower upstream boundaries of these areas and, if flexural slip develops, multi-ple slides originate as ramps at their down-stream boundaries. Downstream of the obstruction, the folding becomes isoclinal and the colour banding, foliation and any slides still active become parallel to each other and dip downstream (Fig. 5).

Traced downstream in longitudinal profiles, such ovoid areas decrease in size while the ob-structions show no such systematic decrease. As the areas of obvious folding decrease, so first the slides cease to generate and then the crenulation fails to develop. Eventually, near the snout, even the internal folds do not de-velop and, instead, the whole salt glacier bends over the underlying topography. Any slides at this stage are likely to be the result of layer-parallel slippage induced by such accom-modation folds.

Elliott (1976b p. 299) has described how the thrusts exposed in the Canadian Rockies die out along strike into groups of asymmetric, non-cylindrical folds. He interpreted such folds as defining a zone in which damage by flexural slip-folding accumulates and leads to a ductile fracture, a process very similar to that observed in the salt glacier. However, Elliott describes the fractures as having propagated behind the zone of folding as though the folds and fracture tips moved through stationary rock. In the salt glacier, the folds and slides generate in locations fixed relative to stationary obstructions of bedrock. The slide propagation zones are therefore stationary and the salt folds and tears as it flows through and beyond them.

How many of these observations and interpretations concerning the salt glacier relate to slide complexes in other rocks is for the reader to judge. It is interesting to speculate on the degree of success that the method of balancing sections of the salt glacier might have in reconstructing the salt dome, the diapir and its source layer.

ACKNOWLEDGMENTS. My first visit to the salt glacier was considerably aided by the very welcome co-operation and logistic support of the Iranian Geological Survey. Air photographs were kindly supplied by the Iranian Oil Participants Limited. Travel funding by the University of Dundee and the Carnegie Trust is gratefully acknowledged. I would also like to thank R. B. Stoneley, F. H. Hubbard and R. Templeton for useful discussions and Eric Rogers for his company in the field and for the discussion we started in 1976.

References

ALA, M. A. 1974 Salt diapirism in southern Iran, *Bull. Am. Assoc. Petrol. Geol.* **58,** 1758–70.

COLMAN-SADD, S. P. 1978. Fold development in Zagros Simply Folded Belt, southwest Iran. *Bull. Am. Assoc. Petrol. Geol.* **62,** 984–1003.

ELLIOTT, D. 1976a. The motion of thrust sheets. *J. geophys. Res.* **81,** 949–63.

—— 1976b. The energy balance and deformation mechanisms of thrust sheets. *Phil. Trans. R. Soc. Lond.* **A283,** 289–312.

GERA, F. 1972. Review of salt tectonics in relation to the disposal of radioactive wastes in salt formation. *Bull. geol. Soc. Am.* **83,** 3551–74.

HARRISON, J. V. 1931. Salt domes in Persia. *J. Inst. Pet. Tech.* **17,** 300–20.

KENT, P. E. 1970. The salt plugs of the Persian Gulf region. *Trans. Leicester lit. phil. Soc.* **44,** 56–88.

LEES, G. M. 1927. Salzgletscher in Persien. *Mitt. geol. Ges. Wien,* **22,** 29–34.

—— 1931. Salt—some depositional and deformation problems. *J. Inst. Pet. Tech.* **17,** 259–80.

O'BRIEN, C. A. E. 1957. Salt diapirism in South Persia. *Geologie Mijnbouw* **19,** 357–76.

RAMBERG, H. 1977. Some remarks on the mechanism of nappe movement. *Geologiska Foreningen i Stockholm Forhandlingar,* **99,** 110–7.

TALBOT, C. J. 1979. Fold trains in a glacier of salt in southern Iran. *J. struct. Geol.* **1,** 5–18.

C. J. TALBOT, Department of Geology, The University Dundee, Scotland, DD1 4HN.

The Caledonides of northern Norway: relation between preferred orientation of quartz lattice, strain and translation of the nappes

A.-M. Boullier & J.-M. Quenardel

SUMMARY: In the area of Birtavarre (eastern Troms) evidence of nappe tectonics exist at all scales. The preferred orientation of the c-axis of quartz shows a monoclinic symmetry and consists of a girdle containing Y and oblique to Z. The obliquity of the girdle–angle θ between the c-axis girdle and the YZ plane–is interpreted in terms of simple shear, and the strain is calculated from these data. The results from this study are: (1) almost all the quartz-bearing samples give a consistent sense of simple shear (movement towards the SE) except for some gneisses supposed to be allochthonous Precambrian. (2) the calculated strain is too low to explain the displacement of the nappes (more than 40 km for a 2 km thick unit): X/Z ratio is less than 10 on the average. Possible reasons for this are discussed.

The allochthonous character of the Caledonian Nappes of eastern Troms (N Norway) is now widely accepted (Gayer & Roberts 1973; Gayer 1973; Quenardel 1977; Sturt & Roberts 1978; Gustavson 1978; Binns 1978). A pile of thin nappes, the Kalak Nappe complex, is found in the Birtavarre and Skibotn valleys. The regional foliation is nearly horizontal and the associated stretching lineation has a relatively constant NW–SE trend (Fig. 1). The regional foliation is penetrative and is found throughout the entire thickness of the metamorphic rocks in the nappe pile. In Laksefjord (Finnmark), Gayer et al. (1978) and Williams (1978) concluded that the L–S tectonite fabric is essentially due to simple shear deformation in the Kalak and Laksefjord Nappes. Thus, a model involving progressive, homogeneous simple shear deformation (Escher & Watterson 1974) could be applied for the formation of the L–S fabric in the same nappe sequence in eastern Troms. By using the crystallographic preferred orientations of quartz grains we attempt to determine the strain and the shear sense on the Caledonian nappes of the Birtavarre area. This has been done to determine the mechanism of nappe emplacement, in an area where the tectonic evolution of the structural features appears to be relatively simple, but where no strain markers are known to exist.

Geological setting

The tectonostratigraphic sequence

The tectonostratigraphic sequence recognized by Quenardel (1978) on a section across the eastern Troms segment (Kåfjord meridian) is summarized in Table 1. Upper internal units occur only in southern Troms. They wedge out between Narvik and the Birtavarre region. Detailed mapping has revealed that major tectonic discontinuities separate the units (Quenardel & Boullier, 1979). Within the units both upper and basal truncations of layering may occur. One of the most important features of the nappe succession is the increase of Caledonian metamorphic grade by successive jumps from lower units to upper ones (Table 1). This pattern supports the assumption of different metamorphic conditions in the nappes before their tectonic superposition. The metamorphism has been dated at 417 ± 5 m.y. in the middle internal units (Trollvik Nappe) by Dangla et al. (1978).

It is widely accepted that the translation direction of the nappes is from NW to SE (e.g. Gustavson 1972). The amplitude of this translation is at least 40 km for the middle external unit and 200 km for the rootless internal units in view of the Alta-Kvenangen basement window (Fig. 1).

Mesoscopic scale deformation

It is possible to distinguish several tectonic units which have experienced different tectonic and metamorphic histories (see Fig. 1 & Table 1).

(1) The lower and middle internal units in which four phases of Caledonian deformation are recorded (Quenardel 1978; Dangla 1979). During the first phase (D_1) rare isoclinal to tight folds occur contemporaneously with the S_1 foliation. The second phase of deformation

TABLE 1. *Schematic tectonostratigraphic sequence recognized by Quenardel (1977) on a section across the eastern Troms segment (see Fig. 1).*

	Lithologic composition	Climax of Caledonian metamorphism	Presumed age
Upper internal units		Absent in the studied area	
Middle internal units	Metasedimentary rocks (micaschists, quartzites, marbles), Amphibolites. Granitic sheet and dykes in the Tyrollvik Nappe	Medium to high grade with local migmatization (Dangla 1979) (kyanite-sillimanite)	Cambrian Ordovician? Silurian?
Lower internal unit (Birtavarre Nappe)	Metasedimentary rocks (schists, quartzites, marbles) Metagraywackes Amphibolites	Medium grade (andalusite-staurolite)	Eocambrian? Cambrian Ordovician? Silurian?
Upper external unit ("basement" slab)	Infracrustal and supracrustal rocks	Medium retrograde metamorphism (muscovite, epidote, garnet, biotite) from Precambrian medium to high grade rocks	Precambrian sedimentary cover (or Eocambrian?) Precambrian basement
Middle external unit (Saana Nappe)	Meta-arkoses Quartzites and schists	Low to medium grade (muscovite, epidote ±garnet±biotite)	Eocambrian +Cambrian?
Lower external unit (Jerta Nappe)	Quartzites Shales	Very low to low grade (chlorite, sericite)	Eocambrian Cambrian
Autochthonous baltic shield	Hyolithus schists on Precambrian gneisses	None	Cambrian on Precambrian basement

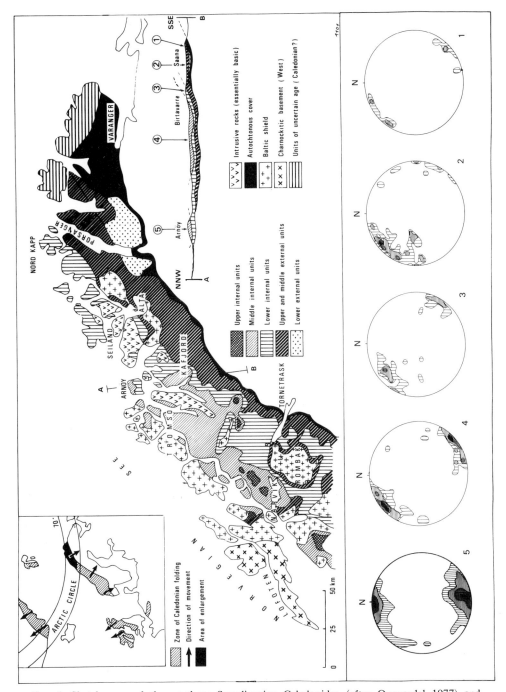

FIG. 1. Sketch map of the northern Scandinavian Caledonides (after Quenardel 1977) and stereograms of the stretching lineation. Equal area projection on the lower hemisphere. 1. middle external unit. 2. upper external unit. 3. lower internal unit. 4. middle internal units. 5. middle internal unit in Arnöy and Sauköy (after Bechennec & Hervé 1973).

(D_2) also corresponds to isoclinal folds and to the development of a nearly horizontal S_2 foliation which is very widespread; S_2 appears as the regional foliation and bears a NW–SE stretching lineation defined by quartz and feldspar ribbons or by a mineral alignment. D_3 is characterized by the development of drag-folds, often verging to SSE, and of boudinage-like structures: both structures are interpreted as the result of bulk differential displacement (Quenardel & Boullier 1979). The last phase of deformation (D_4) produces chevron folds and flexures of the thrust planes.

(2) The upper external unit, in which the tectonic and metamorphic evolution of the basement slab is more complicated. The three last phases recognized in the internal units are usually seen in the basement slab; but, boudinage-like structures and a mylonitic foliation predate the development of the regional S_2 foliation. These pre-S_2 structures are thought to be Precambrian (Quenardel 1976).

(3) The middle external unit, in which the sequence of deformation phases is difficult to establish due to the lack of marker units. A blastomylonitic foliation is observed in the feldspathic meta-quartzites and this foliation, which exhibits a strong NW–SE trending stretching lineation, is probably the equivalent of the S_2 regional foliation. At the front of this unit (Saana, Finland) a continuous reduction of the grain size of the rocks can be followed downwards, from low to medium grade blas-tomylonites to mylonites and ultramylonites. These are, in turn, folded and crushed under very low grade metamorphic conditions at the sole of the thrust.

Microscopic deformation

Our observations are principally on thin sections cut parallel to the XZ plane of the strain ellipsoid (XY plane assumed parallel to the S_2 foliation and the X direction assumed parallel to the l_2 stretching lineation). We concentrated our work on the quartzofeldspathic samples and on the simple cases where the S_2 foliation was not visibly reworked by later deformation. The regional S_2 foliation is blastomylonitic as defined by Higgins (1971) and Sibson (1977) and corresponds to different metamorphic conditions in different structural units. Apart from the different nature of the porphyroblasts, the same characteristics are present within the different structural units: the S_2 foliation is defined by mica layers and quartz ribbons. The latter are polycrystalline and composed of large irregular grains and subhedral smaller

ones (II-4 type of Boullier & Bouchez 1978). The larger quartz crystals have undulatory extinction and show prismatic subgrain boundaries which are oblique to the XY plane. The examination of XZ thin sections with an inserted gypsum plate shows that the quartz grains have a strong preferred lattice orientation. The porphyroblasts, which are epidote, feldspar or garnet in the external units, or feldspar, garnet or kyanite in the internal units, are slightly deformed (bent twins or bent cleavage planes). The porphyroblasts deflect the mica- and quartz-layers. Their inclusion pattern and the asymmetry of the deflected layers often indicate a rotation sense which is generally consistent with thrusting to the SE. This indicates that the blastomylonites have suffered a plastic deformation (strained porphyroblasts, substructure and lattice preferred orientation of quartz grains) which is contemporaneous with and slightly follows the thermal peak of metamorphism. The metamorphic grade varies from one unit to the other, with the result that the temperature conditions during the deformation were lower in the external unit than in the internal ones.

Preferred lattice orientation of quartz

Description

Measurements of quartz c-axis orientations were made with a U-stage on three typical blastomylonites from the upper external unit (Fig. 2). The data have been plotted on the lower hemisphere using the counting programme of Bouchez & Mercier (1974). The diagrams show a large pole-free area around X and that the quartz c-axes define a girdle passing through Y and oblique to the Z direction (monoclinic symmetry). The monoclinic symmetry of quartz c-axis preferred orientation is also revealed by examination of XZ thin sections on an ordinary stage. The intersection of (0001) basal plane with the surface of thin section is determined inserting a gypsum plate. The data from this method are plotted on rose-diagrams (Fig. 3). This technique is not as informative as the U-stage measurements, since it does not take into account the dip of the (0001) plane; but it is quicker and more convenient for determining the angular relationships between the (0001) basal plane of quartz and the foliation plane. In this study, it appears that there is a well-defined asymmetry of the (0001) plane relative to the XY plane (S_2 foliation) and that the sense of the obliquity angle is almost homogeneous.

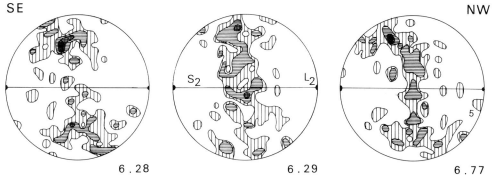

SE   NW

6 . 28   6 . 29   6 . 77

FIG. 2. Preferred orientation of quartz c-axis in blastomylonites of upper external unit. Equal area projection on the lower hemisphere. Contours: 1, 2, 4, 6%. S_2 foliation plane and l_2 stretching lineation are represented respectively by the line and the half-dots—100 measurements for each stereogram.

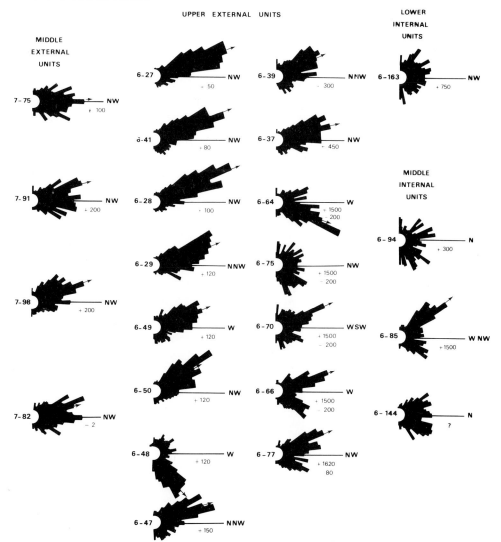

FIG. 3. Rose diagrams or weighted projections of the (0001) plane traces of quartz in blastomylonites. 300 measurements for each diagram in thin section normal to S_2 foliation and parallel to l_2 stretching lineation.

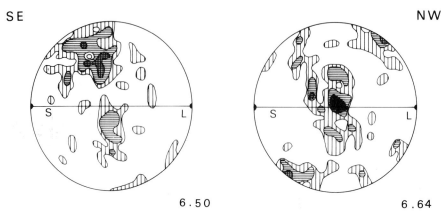

SE   NW

6.50   6.64

FIG. 4. Preferred orientation of quartz *c*-axis in two gneiss samples of the upper external unit (see discussion in text). 100 measurements. Equal area projection on the lower hemisphere. Contours: 1, 2, 4 and 6%.

Additional measurements have also been made on two groups of samples which have peculiar (0001) weighted projections. The first group (6.50 and 6.48) shows a well-defined (0001) trace peak at high angle from the foliation plane (30 and 55° respectively) corresponding to a high angle between the prismatic subgrain boundaries and the *S* foliation plane in a *XZ* section S_2-l_2. In a *YZ* section sporadic minor folds superimposed on the mylonitic foliation can be observed. An analysis of the *c*-axis preferred orientation of sample 6.50 (Fig. 4) shows a strong maximum at 30–60° from *Z* in an outline of oblique girdle similar to the girdles presented in Fig. 2. The second group of samples (6.75, 6.70 and 6.64) are orthogneisses in the same area, where the stretching lineation has an irregular direction but where no post foliation deformation could be observed. The rocks are characterized by a low grade Caledonian metamorphism superimposed on the orthogneissic foliation which corresponds to a higher grade metamorphism. The 6.75 sample does not show any well-defined (0001) trace concentration (Fig. 3) but 6.70 and 6.64 have an inverse sense of obliquity with reference to the dominant sense. The *c*-axis preferred orientation of 6.64 (Fig. 4) shows a strong *Y* maximum scattered in one girdle oblique on the *XY* plane, and a secondary maximum which lies in the *XZ* plane and defines the (0001) trace peak in the rose diagram.

Interpretation of the lattice preferred orientation of quartz

We have seen that, in the samples studied here, the quartz grains show evidence of plastic deformation which has produced a lattice preferred orientation by intracrystalline gliding. The pattern of preferred orientation can be interpreted in terms of slip systems (Tullis *et al.* 1973; Lister *et al.* 1978) and of geometric characteristics of the deformation (Nicolas *et al.* 1971, 1973). In the present case, that is *c*-axis girdle oblique to the *XY* plane and assuming that the stretching lineation is close to the flow direction we conclude that:

(1) the dominant slip direction should be a direction at high angle to the [0001] because of the large [0001] free area around the flow direction *X* (Fig. 2) and of the prismatic subgrain boundaries in quartz grains. Bouchez (1978) has shown that the pole maxima of the prismatic subgrain boundaries which have been optically determined, are close to the flow direction (*X*). These pole maxima also coincide with the ⟨*a*⟩ axis maxima determined with a X-ray goniometer (Bouchez, op cit.). Thus the optically visible subgrain boundaries are tilt walls normal to the slip direction which is an ⟨*a*⟩ axis, the easiest slip direction in quartz (Christie *et al.* 1964). The glide plane cannot be uniquely determined from the fabric diagrams, but gliding on any plane containing ⟨*a*⟩ could explain the fabric patterns described here. The most commonly reported glide planes in quartz are (0001), {10$\bar{1}$0} and {01$\bar{1}$1} (Carter *et al.* 1964; Tullis *et al.* 1973; Blacic 1975) and we infer that these were the active slip planes during deformation of these rocks.

(2) the deformation is mainly rotational (simple shear): this assumption can explain the monoclinic symmetry of the *c*-axis preferred orientation on the *XY* plane. The pole of the *c*-axis girdle does not correspond to *X*, but should represent the ⟨*a*⟩ maximum, i.e. the

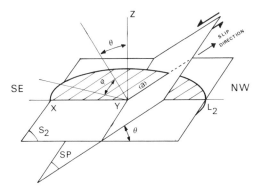

FIG. 5. Deformation of a previously roundshape quartz grain by intracrystalline gliding in the $\langle a \rangle$ direction (after Laurent & Etchecopar 1976). θ is the angle between the slip plane (SP) and the foliation S_2 (XY plane of the strain ellipsoïd). ϕ is the shear angle.

average slip direction (see Bouchez 1978; Bouchez *et al.* 1979). The angle between X and the $\langle a \rangle$ maximum defines the asymmetry of the crystallographic preferred orientation and is sensitive to the data which plot near the ZX plane, i.e. by the grains in which basal slip is probably dominant.

Many authors have recently deduced the shear sense from the lattice preferred orientation of quartz (Bouchez & Pecher 1976; Laurent & Etchecopar 1976; Brunel & Geyssant 1978; Bossière & Vauchez 1978; Berthé *et al.* 1979). Burg & Laurent (1978) and Van Roermund *et al.* (1979) have clearly shown the relation between the asymmetry of the c-axis girdle and the shear sense in a small-scale shear zone. Following these authors, we interpret the c-axis girdle as due to a rotational deformation (simple shear) which corresponds to a thrust movement in the SE direction (see Fig. 5). This sense is consistent with the large-scale observations (Quenardel & Boullier, 1979).

The two peculiar groups of samples (Fig 4) warrant further discussion. We interpret the c-axis preferred orientation of the first one (6.50) as due to the effect of the minor fold phase on the pre-existent D_2 preferred orientation (probably an oblique girdle with a Y maximum) because the substructure in quartz (prismatic subgrain boundaries) seems to be related to that latter deformation. Thus, in such cases, the S_2-l_2 reference strain ellipsoid is probably not appropriate, and further detailed studies should take into account the late deformation as proposed by Brunel (1980). In the second group of samples (6.64), the

c-axis preferred orientation, and particularly the strong Y maximum, is attributed to the high grade orthogneissic foliation. This kind of c-axis pattern has previously been described in high temperature mylonites (Wilson 1975; Boullier & Bouchez 1978). These particular samples belong to an unusual unit of mylonitic gneisses, gneisses and metasediments, thought by Quenardel (1976) to be Precambrian. We think that, in this case, the D_2 simple shear deformation accompanied by a low grade metamorphism, was not strong enough to rotate the pre-existing orthogneissic foliation completely and to bring the associated stretching lineation in the flow direction, nor strong enough to reorganize the c-axis pattern.

We have studied only a few samples on the internal units (Fig 3). Except for 7.85, they do not show any (0001) trace maximum on the weighted projections and quartz grains are black when observed between crossed Nicols in a XZ section (c-axis pattern tending towards Y maximum). We know that the deformation temperature was higher in this sample (higher metamorphic grade, see Table 1). Hence we infer that gliding on prismatic planes was predominant in these samples, as observed in high temperature experiments. In this case, no statement can be made about the geometric characteristics of the deformation by looking solely at thin sections.

Strain measurements

The method

Ramsay & Graham (1970) have calculated strain profiles across shear zones by using the relationship between the shear angle (ϕ) and the angle θ defined by the foliation (XY plane) and the shear plane. Burg & Laurent (1978) have applied this method of strain calculation to a small-scale shear zone in a granodiorite, demonstrating that a good correlation exists between the θ angle defined by the c-axis girdle and the θ angle deduced from strain measurements and calculations. Therefore, assuming that the foliation is the XY plane of finite strain and that the pole of the c-axis girdle is the shear direction (see Fig. 5), we have applied this method of strain calculation to our samples. θ is determined on the rose diagrams as the angle between the arithmetic average of the main (0001) trace peak (arrows in Fig. 3) and foliation plane. The data are presented in Table 2. θ is known with an accuracy of $\pm 2°5$. When two peaks exist, the dominant one is chosen; the secondary peak is

TABLE 2. *Values of the shear angle ϕ, the shear strain γ and the X/Z ratio of strain ellipsoid, calculated from the obliquity angle between the (0001) plane trace maximum and the S_2 foliation plane (see Fig. 3).*

Sample	Distance to thrust plane (m)	θ	ϕ	γ	X/Z	
7.75	+100	<1°				
7.91	+200	17.5°	70.1°	2.9	10.1	Middle external
7.98	+200	20°	67.2°	2.4	7.5	unit (Saana
7.82	(−2)	13.5°	75.7°	3.9	17.4	Nappe)
6.27	+50	20°	67.2°	2.4	7.5	
6.41	+80	21.5°	65°	2.1	6.4	
6.28	+100	23.5°	61.8°	1.9	5.3	
6.29	+120	17.5°	70.7°	2.9	10.1	
6.49	+120	20°	67.2°	2.4	7.5	
6.50	+120	30°	49.1°	1.1	3.0	
6.48	+120°	55°	"negative strain"			Upper external
6.47	+150	19.5°	68.0°	2.5	8.0	unit
6.39	+300	24°	61.0°	1.8	5.0	(basement slab)
6.37	+450	14.25°	74.8°	3.7	15.5	
6.64	+1500 (−200)	22.5°	63.4°	2.0	4.8	
6.75	+1500 (−200)		no peak defined			
6.70	+1500 (−200)	23.5°	61.8°	1.9	5.3	
6.66	+1500 (−200)	18.5°	69.3°	2.6	8.9	
6.67	+1620 (−80)	22.5°	63.4°	2.0	4.8	
6.163	+750		no peak defined			Lower internal unit (Birta-varre Nappe)
6.94	+300		no peak defined			middle internal
7.85	+1500	37.5°	28.2°	0.5	1.7	units
7.144	? Arnöy		no peak defined			

interpreted as due to crystals showing a reverse shear sense (i.e. referring to the general shear sense). This choice is justified by the results obtained by Etchecopar (1977) with a two dimensional simulation model.

Interpretation of the results

In the middle external unit, sample no 7.75 has a very low θ angle and hence a very high strain which is coherent with the strong mylonitic foliation and the very fine-grain size of the rock. In the same unit, the shear strain seems to increase towards the base (7.75) and the roof (7.82) of the nappe, but more data are needed to verify such an interpretation. This seems not to be the case in the first section of the upper external unit (samples 6.27–6.37, except 6.50 and 6.48): the strain is heterogeneous inside this unit and would indicate that there are at least three slices in this section. Thus, no clear relationship between shear strain and the limits of the nappes can be established as Chapman *et al.* (1979) have done for the Laksefjord Nappe (N Norway).

On average, the X/Z ratio does not exceed 10. This is a maximum value of finite strain recorded by intracrystalline gliding in quartz since a small component of pure shear would rotate the XY plane towards the shear plane and then lower the θ angle (Burg & Laurent 1978). Assuming the thickness of the upper external unit to be approximately 2 km, this ratio would give a value of 20 km for X. Consequently, even if we neglect the thrust front erosion, the simple shear due to S_2 and recorded by the lattice preferred orientation of quartz, is not sufficient to explain the emplacement of the nappes (at least 40 km horizontal movement for the upper external units).

Discussion

The discrepancy between the shear strain deduced from preferred orientation and the minimum horizontal movement of the nappes could be explained in three ways.

(i) The *c*-axis preferred orientation and θ could have been stablized during simple shear. In this case, the γ determination by preferred orientation would have only limited value for large strain deformations. Carreras *et al.* (1977) describe a stable microstructure and a stable microfabric relative to the axis of finite strain in quartzites for shear strain greater than 2. The stabilization of the microstructure can be due to a continuous cyclic recrystallization (White 1977) but this phenomenon does not explain the stable *c*-axis pattern. In our case we do not observe stable microstructure in quartz ribbons since large grains coexist with small ones. Moreover, other authors have recently demonstrated that quartz fabric is controlled in orientation by kinematic framework (Burg & Laurent 1978; Van Roermund *et al.* 1979), as predicted by the simulation model of Lister (1977).

(ii) The simple shear by plastic flow in quartz does not represent the total strain undergone by the rocks during the D_2 deformation phase and some other mechanisms could have been operating, e.g. pressure solution, discontinuous sliding on mica rich layers as described by Berthé *et al.* (1979), grain boundary sliding. However we have no evidence of the existence of such mechanisms in the rocks studied here, except may be for the grain boundary sliding, but its effect cannot be quantified.

(iii) The simple shear by plastic flow in quartz is representative of almost all the strain associated with the S_2 regional foliation. In this case S_2 represents the early stage of nappe development and probably of initiation of the pile formation, by a similar mechanism of simple shear to that proposed by Escher & Watterson (1974). The translation of the pile is almost entirely accommodated by deformation in a thin layer of mylonites, ultramylonites and cataclasites at the base of the lower unit (the middle external unit in the Birtavarre cross-section). This schematic evolution has been proposed by Gee (1978), Guézou (1977) and Prost *et al.* (1977) for the central Caledonides and by Olesen (1971) for the Langedalen area (Troms). But the Birtavarre area differs from the Langedalen by the following characteristics: The D_2 associated stretching lineation has a constant direction throughout the entire pile (see Fig. 1) and the stretching lineation has the same SE trend in the ultramylonitic layer at the base of the pile. Moreover, the D_3 folds also indicate a south-eastwards thrusting. This continuity of direction indicates that there is no significant kinematic change in the flow direction during the deformation in the nappes; the formation of the nappe pile and its translation. Hence, the stress direction seems to have been more or less constant during this tectonic evolution.

Conclusions

In this work we have shown that a good correlation exists between the shear sense as deduced from the *c*-axis preferred orientation and that observed in the field on map to mesoscopic scales. The exceptions can be reasonably explained by particular aspects of their deformation history. The quantitive results obtained by this method must be used very carefully but provide the approximate strain undergone by the rocks. More detailed investigations on the strain measurements together with *c*-axis preferred orientation analysis are required in order to improve the method. We have demonstrated, however, that the flow direction and probably the stress direction seem to have been constant during the major tectonic evolution of the nappes in the Lyngenfjord area.

ACKNOWLEDGMENTS. We are grateful to R. Caby, A. Etchecopar, M. Brunel, J. L. Bouchez and A. Nicolas for positive criticisms and suggestions. We thank A. Goodwin who revised the English text.

References

BECHENNEC, F. & HERVE, A. 1973. *Etude des bâtis cristallophylliens des îles d'Arnöy et de Lauköy (Troms, Norvege septentrionale). Analyse structurale et petrographique*. Thèse 3e cycle, Orsay, (Unpubl.).

BERTHE, D., CHOUKROUNE, P. & GAPAIS, D. 1979. Orientations préférentielles du quartz et orthogneissification progressive en régime cisaillant: l'exemple du cisaillement sud-armoricain. *Bull Minéralogie,* **102,** 265–272.

BINNS, R. E. 1978. Caledonian nappe correlation and orogenic history in Scandinavia North of Lat. 67° N. *Bull. geol. Soc. Am.* **89,** 1475–90.

BLACIC, J. D. 1975. Plastic deformation mechanisms in quartz: the effect of water. *Tectonophysics,* **27,** 271–94.

BOSSIERE, G. & VAUCHEZ, A. 1978. Déformation naturelle par cisaillement ductile d'un granite de Grande Kabylie occidentale (Algérie). *Tectonophysics,* **51,** 57–81.

BOUCHEZ, J. L. 1978. Preferred orientations of quartz $\langle a \rangle$ axes in some tectonites: kinetic inferences. *Tectonophysics,* **49,** T25–T30.

—— & MERCIER, J. C. 1974. Construction automatique des diagrammes de densité d'orientation. Présentation d'un réseau de comptage. *Sci. Terre* **XIX,** 57–64.

—— & PECHER, A. 1976. Plasticite du quartz et sens de cisaillement dans les quartzites du grand chevauchement central himalayen. *Bull. Soc. géol. Fr.* **XVIII,** 1377–85.

——, DERVIN, P., MARDON, J. P. & ENGLANDER, M. 1979. La diffraction neutronique appliquée à l'étude de l'orientation préférentielle de réseau dans les quartzites. *Bull. Minéralogie,* **102,** 225–31.

BOULLIER, A. M. & BOUCHEZ, J. L. 1978. Le quartz en rubans dans les mylonites. *Bull. Soc. géol. Fr.* **XX,** 253–262.

BRUNEL, M. Quartz fabrics in shear-zone mylonites: evidence for a major imprint due to late strain increments. *Tectonophysics,* **64,** 33–44.

—— & GEYSSANT, J. 1978. Mise en évidence d'une déformation rotationelle Est-Ouest par l'orientation optique du quartz dans la Fenêtre des Tauern (Alpes orientales). Implications géodynamiques. *Rev. Géogr. phys. Géol. dyn.* **XX,** 335–46.

BURG, J. P. & LAURENT, Ph. 1978. Strain analysis of a shear zone in a granodiorite. *Tectonophysics,* **47,** 15–42.

CARRERAS, J., ESTRADA, A. & WHITE, S. 1977. The effect of folding on the *c*-axis fabrics of a quartz mylonite. *Tectonophysics,* **39,** 3–24.

CARTER, N. L., CHRISTIE, J. M. & GRIGGS, D. T. 1964. Experimental deformation and recrystallization of quartz. *J. Geol. Chicago,* **72,** 687–733.

CHAPMAN, T. J., MILTON, N. J. & WILLIAMS, G. D. 1979. Shape fabric variations in deformed conglomerates at the base of the Laksefjord, Norway. *J. geol. Soc. London,* **136,** 683–91.

CHRISTIE, J. M., GRIGGS, D. T. & CARTER, N. L. 1964. Experimental evidence of basal slip in quartz. *J. Geol. Chicago,* **72,** 734–56.

DANGLA, P. 1979. *Géologie de la rive orientale du Kåfjord (Troms, Calédonides de Norvège du Nord). Etude de la migmatisation caledonienne.* Thèse 3e cycle, Orsay, 259 p. (Unpubl.).

——, DEMANGE, J. C., PLOQUIN, A., QUENARDEL, J. M. & SONET, J. 1978. Données géochronologiques sur les Calédonides scandinaves septentrionales (Troms, Norvège du Nord). *C.r. Acad. Sci. Paris,* **286D,** 1653–6.

ESCHER, A. & WATTERSON, J. 1974. Stretching fabrics, folds and crustal shortening. *Tectonophysics,* **22,** 223–31.

ETCHECOPAR, A. 1977. A plane kinematic model of progressive deformation in a crystalline aggregate. *Tectonophysics,* **39,** 121–39.

GAYER, R. A. 1973. Caledonian geology of Arctic Norway. *In: Arctic Geology.* Mem. Am. Assoc. Petrol. Geol. **19,** 453–68.

——, ROBERTS, J. D. 1973. Stratigraphic review of the Finnmark Caledonides, with possible tectonic implications. *Proc. Geol. Assoc. London,* **84,** 405–41.

——, POWELL, D. B. & RHODES, S. 1978. Deformation against metadolerite dykes in the Caledonides of Finnmark, Norway. *Tectonophysics,* **46,** 99–115.

GEE, D. 1978. Nappe displacement in the scandinavian Caledonides. *Tectonophysics,* **47,** 393–419.

GUEZOU, J. C. 1977. Histoire paléozoïque d'un segment central des Calédonides scandinaves internes. *Rev. Géogr. phys. Géol. dyn.* **XIX,** 453–70.

GUSTAVSON, M. 1972. The Caledonian mountain chain of the southern Troms and Ofoten areas. Part III. Structures and structural history. *Nor. geol. Unders.* **283,** 1–56.

—— 1978. Caledonides of north-central Norway. *In: Caledonian Appalachian Orogen of the North Atlantic Region,* Pap. geol. Surv. Can. **78–13,** 25–30.

HIGGINS, M. W. 1971. Cataclastic rocks. *Prof. Pap. U.S. geol. Surv.* **687,** 97 p.

LAURENT, P. & ETCHECOPAR, A. 1976. Mise en évidence à l'aide de la fabrique du quartz d'un cisaillement simple à déversement ouest dans le massif de Dora Maïra (Alpes occidentales). *Bull. Soc. géol. Fr.* **XVIII,** 1387–93.

LISTER, G. S. 1977. Discussion: crossed-girdle *c*-axis fabrics in quartzites plastically deformed by plane strain and progressive simple shear. *Tectonophysics,* **39,** 51–4.

——, PATERSON, M. S. & HOBBS, B. E. 1978. The simulation of fabric development in plastic deformation and its application to quartzite: the model. *Tectonophysics,* **45,** 107–58.

NICOLAS, A., BOUCHEZ, J. L., BOUDIER, F. & MERCIER, J. C. 1971. Textures, structures, and fabrics due to solid state flow in some European lherzolites. *Tectonophysics,* **12,** 55–86.

——, BOUDIER, F. & BOULLIER, A. M. 1973. Mechanisms of flow in naturally and experimentally deformed peridotites. *Am. J. Sci.* **273,** 853–76.

OLESEN, N. Ø. 1971. The relative chronology of fold phases, metamorphism and thrust movements in the Caledonides of Troms, North Norway. *Nor. geol. Tidsskr.* **51,** 355–77.

PROST, A. E., GUEZOU, J. C., POINT, R., QUENARDEL, J. M., SANTARELLI, N., HENRY, A. & ELLENBERGER, F. 1977. Une transversale dans les Caledonides scandinaves centrales: du socle baltique à la côte atlantique. *Rev. Géol. phys. Géol. dyn.* **XIX,** 481–502.

QUENARDEL, J. M. 1976. Geology of the Manndalen region. A section across the Caledonides of northern Norway. *Abstract, XIIth Geol. Wintermötet, Göteborg.*

—— 1977. Les grands traits structuraux des Caledonides scandinaves septentrionales. *Rev. Géogr. phys. Géol. dyn.* **5,** 471–80.

—— 1978. Géologie de la rive orientale du LyngenFjord (Calédonides de Norvège du Nord). *Comm. 103e congr. nation. des Soc. Savantes, Nancy-Metz,* 11 p.

—— & BOULLIER, A. M. 1979. La tectonique tangentielle dans le Troms oriental (Calédonides de Laponie): ses manifestations méga-, méso et microsopiques. *Bull. Soc. géol. Fr.* **XXI,** 457–66.

RAMSAY, J. G. & GRAHAM, R. H. 1970. Strain variations in shear belts. *Can. J. Earth. Sci.* **7**, 786–813.

SIBSON, R. H. 1977. Fault rocks and fault mechanisms. *J. geol. Soc. London,* **133**, 191–214.

STURT, B. & ROBERTS, J. D. 1978. Caledonides of northernmost Norway (Finmark). *In: Caledonian-Appalachian orogen of the north Atlantic region.* Pap. geol. Surv. Canada, **78–13**, 17–24.

TULLIS, J. A., CHRISTIE, J. M. & GRIGGS, D. T. 1973. Microstructures and preferred orientations of experimentally deformed quartzites. *Bull. geol. Soc. Am.* **84**, 297–314.

VAN ROERMUND, H., LISTER, G. S. & WILLIAMS, P.
F. 1979. Progressive development of quartz fabrics in a shear zone from Monte Mucrone, Sesia-Lanzo Zone, Italina Alps. *J. struct. Geol.* **1**, 43–52.

WHITE, S. 1977. Geological significance of recovery and recrystallization processes in quartz. *Tectonophysics,* **39**, 143–70.

WILLIAMS, G. D. 1978. Rotation of contemporary folds into the X-direction during overthrust processes in Laksefjord, Finnmark. *Tectonophysics,* **48**, 29–40.

WILSON, C. J. L. 1975. Preferred orientation in quartz ribbon mylonites. *Bull. geol. Soc. Am.* **86**, 968–74.

A.-M. BOULLIER, Centre Geologique et Geophysique, U.S.T.L., 34060 Montpellier Cedex, France.

j.-M. QUENARDEL, Laboratoire de Géologie Structurale, Univ. Paris Sud, 91405 Orsay, France.

Structure and distribution of fault rocks in the Alpine Fault Zone, New Zealand

R. H. Sibson, S. H. White & B. K. Atkinson

SUMMARY: The Alpine Fault Zone, which is the dominant strand in a dextral system of transform faults along the boundary between the Indo-Australian and Pacific plates, forms a pronounced lineament about 1 km in width. Within the fault zone, the cross-strike passage from cataclasite through augen mylonite (both derived from largely granitoid basement to the NW) to mylonites derived from the high-grade Alpine Schists on the upthrown south-eastern side, is thought to reflect the original distribution of fault rocks with depth below near-surface gouge zones. Structural data suggest that the fault rocks had their fabrics impressed during the late Cenozoic phase of oblique compression when the Southern Alps were 'ploughed-up' along the fault. Mylonitic foliation indicates a dip approaching 50°SE for the fault zone at depth, while penetrative stretching lineations plunge in a direction sub-parallel to the present-day interplate slip vector, consistent with dextral-reverse-oblique shear across the fault zone. Pseudotachylyte friction-melt is fairly widely distributed and can be found cutting all other fault rock types apart from gouge. Models for the evolution of the fault zone are considered.

The Alpine Fault Zone (Kupfer 1964) strikes NE–SW across the South Island of New Zealand, forming a sharp north-western boundary to the Southern Alps. It is apparently the main strand in an active dextral system of continental transform faults linking Benioff zones of opposing thrust-sense along the boundary between the Indo-Australian and Pacific plates. Although the precise timing of the strike-slip movements remains uncertain, a total post-Jurassic dextral displacement of 480 km is well established, as is the change in late Miocene times from a transcurrent regime to one involving a component of reverse slip (Wellman 1956; Suggate 1963). In the late Cenozoic this led to the formation of the Southern Alps by uplift of as much as 20 km across the fault.

For much of its length the fault zone forms a pronounced lineament, about 1 km in width, separating markedly different terrains. To the NW, a cover series of Upper Cretaceous–Tertiary sediments and extensive Quaternary gravels overlies a basement of mainly Lower Palaeozoic sediments, variably metamorphosed and invaded by granitoid intrusions which range up to early Cretaceous in age. The upthrown Southern Alps to the SE are largely composed of deformed metasediments from the Carboniferous–Jurassic New Zealand Geosyncline, and for some 400 km along the strike the hanging-wall rocks are fairly uniform quartzo-feldspathic schists of garnet-oligoclase grade (Fig. 1).

In this paper we report some preliminary findings on the structure and distribution of fault rocks within the Alpine Fault Zone, and

their bearing on the structural evolution of the Southern Alps. Our results are based on two seasons of sampling along the fault zone at the localities shown in Fig. 1. The project has been undertaken in the belief that microstructural studies of fault rocks in a major dislocation zone, across which there has been a large component of reverse dip-slip, can be expected to yield information on macroscopic fault mechanisms and associated processes of mineral deformation at different crustal levels. Detailed textural studies by optical and transmission electron microscopy are still under way. Consequently, this preliminary discussion is founded largely on field observations and deals only with the gross structure of the fault zone.

Throughout this paper the fault rock nomenclature generally follows that of Sibson (1977), though some particularly descriptive local terms (e.g. 'curly schist-mylonite') are retained because of widespread usage. The fullest previous account of the Alpine Fault rocks has been given by Reed (1964). On the basis of detailed petrographic studies, he recognized three broad textural groups: (a) incoherent fault pug, fault breccia and shattered rocks; (b) coherent cataclasite, mortared and brecciated rocks; and (c) mylonite, augen mylonite, ultramylonite and blastomylonite. He argued that these three groups could be correlated chronologically with periods of fault displacement occurring respectively in the Quaternary and in the late Tertiary phases of the Kaikoura Orogeny, and in the late Jurassic to early Cretaceous Rangitata Orogeny. In contrast, our structural data indicate that all

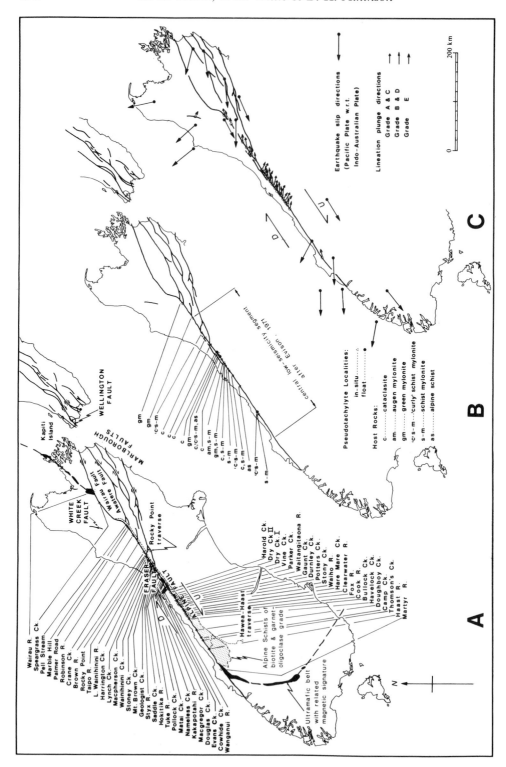

rock fabrics within the Alpine Fault Zone proper have been impressed during the late Cenozoic phase of dextral-reverse-oblique slip.

Alternative movement histories for the Alpine Fault

Clearly, the age of the fault rocks is of key relevance to the dispute over the timing of the Alpine Fault movements. Two main schemes for the displacement history have been put forward:

(1) Displacement along the Alpine Fault has taken place in two distinct phases with about 350 km of dextral strike-slip occurring in the Rangitata Orogeny, the remaining 130 km of strike-slip, accompanied by as much as 20 km of vertical displacement with the SE side up-thrown, taking place in the Kaikoura Orogeny (Grindley 1963, 1974; Suggate 1963; Fleming 1970; Wellman & Cooper 1971).

(2) Displacement along the fault has occurred entirely during the Cenozoic with dextral transcurrent movements beginning in latest Eocene times (*c.* 38 Ma ago) at the earliest, as indicated by the sea-floor spreading data which place constraints on the evolution of the Alpine Fault as a transform boundary between the Indo-Australian and Pacific plates (Molnar *et al.* 1975; Walcott 1978). Wellman (1964) suggested that Alpine Fault displacements were restricted to the Kaikoura Orogeny, beginning in the Miocene, while Carter & Norris

(1976) have argued that in accord with the sea-floor data, transcurrent movements began in the mid-Oligocene (*c.* 30 Ma ago) and continued through to the late Miocene (*c.* 10 Ma ago), when a change in the orientation of the interplate slip-vector led to oblique compression along the boundary and the uplift of the Southern Alps which continues today.

The most direct evidence for two separate phases of fault movement comes from a NNE–SSW trending swarm of mid-Cretaceous lamprophyre dykes which is apparently dextrally offset by some 120–130 km (Wellman & Cooper 1971). Dykes from this swarm cut high-grade mylonites and flaser gneisses associated with the Fraser Fault which lies just NW of, and subparallel to, the Alpine Fault (Young 1968) (Fig. 1). However, they have not so far been found within the Alpine Fault Zone proper. Also, the validity of the dyke swarm as a displaced reference line may be questioned as its boundaries are ill-defined (see Hunt & Nathan 1976).

Composite section through the Alpine Fault Zone

Owing to the thick cover of rain-forest and the extensive Quaternary fanglomerates and glacial outwash gravels along the front of the Southern Alps, *in situ* rock exposure is generally far from continuous in stream sections cutting across the fault zone. However, by

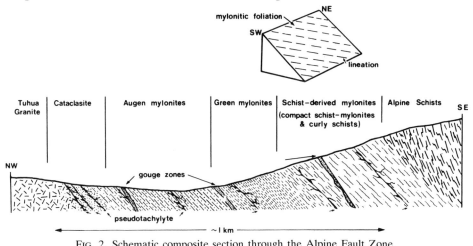

FIG. 2. Schematic composite section through the Alpine Fault Zone.

FIG. 1. (a) Sampling localities along the Alpine Fault. (b) Established pseudotachylyte localities. (c) Lineation plunge directions and earthquake slip-vectors (after Walcott 1978) in the Alpine Fault System. (Note—all lineations are penetrative stretching lineations in ductile mylonites, apart from that associated with the White Creek Fault, which is a fault surface striation.)

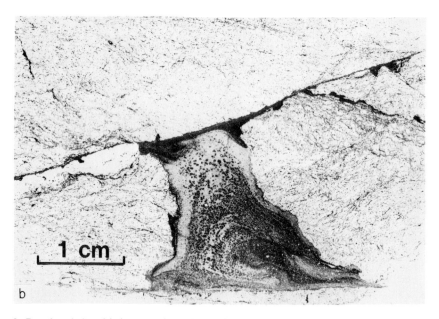

FIG. 3. Pseudotachylyte friction-melt from the Alpine Fault Zone: (a) Pseudotachylyte fault with injection veins cutting 'curly' schist mylonite, Dry Creek I; (b) Photomicrograph of pseudotachylyte fault/injection vein complex, Dry Creek I, showing flowbanding and spherulitic devitrification texture.

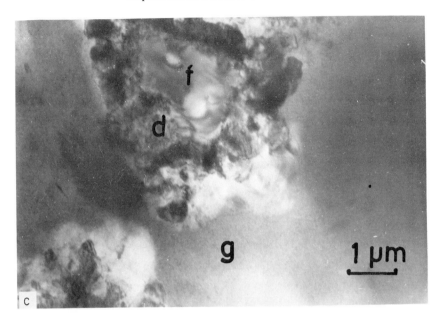

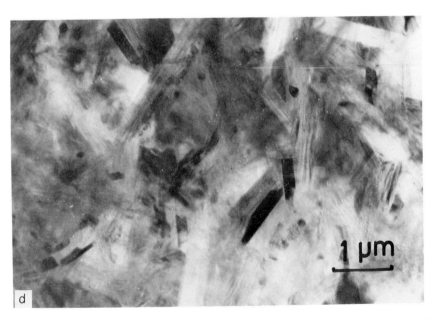

FIG. 3. (c) partial devitrification, d, around quartz/feldspar fragments, f, in a glassy pseudotachylyte groundmass, g, Thomson's Creek, and (d) pseudotachylyte groundmass devitrified largely to phyllosilicates, Wanganui River. Transmission electron micrographs showing.

making many traverses we have been able to piece together a composite, 'hard-rock' section from the granitoid basement NW of the fault to the Alpine Schists of the Haast Schist Group on the upthrown, SE side (Fig. 2). In this we have been aided by the near-constant lithology of the hanging-wall. Note that in any particular river traverse, this composite section may be truncated at any place within the fault zone by the most recent fault break, with the SE portion of the section thrust over Quaternary gravels along a gouge zone. As a result, the upper part of the section only is exposed in most traverses. Other gouge zones locally disrupt the sequence and may cause repetition of lithologies. Typically the total width of the fault zone is about 1–1.5 km (cf. Kuper 1964), but the relative proportions of the different fault rocks vary from one traverse to the next, particular textural types being completely absent in some sections. The proportions, as shown in Fig. 2, are broadly characteristic of the central Alpine Fault region, being based on the near-continuous Saddle Creek and Harold Creek sections.

Passing into the fault zone from the downthrown side, we follow Reed (1964) in believing that the bulk of the quartzo-feldspathic cataclasites and augen mylonites are derived from the Tuhua Group granitoid assemblage outcropping NW of the Alpine Fault, though cataclasites are also locally developed in indurated Palaeozoic and older sediments. However, in the region between MacPherson Creek and Douglas Creek, the situation immediately W of the Alpine Fault Zone is complicated by the presence of high-grade gneissic granites, mylonitic gneisses and coarse augen mylonites belonging to the Fraser Formation (Young 1968). Rocks of this formation have evidently been raised from deeper crustal levels by reverse slip on the Fraser Fault which bounds them to the W (Fig. 1). Mylonitic foliation associated with the Fraser Formation veers around considerably and locally appears to be truncated by the Alpine Fault Zone, within which the mylonites tend to be consistently oriented. It is also apparent that some cataclasites at the base of the Alpine Fault Zone have developed by disruption of Fraser formation fabrics. Thus, we would argue that fabrics within the Alpine Fault Zone post-date those of the Fraser Formation.

The origin of the green mylonites in our composite section remains a problem at this stage (Reed categorises them as blastomylonites), but in the upper part of the sequence the fault rocks contain quartz-plagioclase-

biotite-garnet assemblages and are clearly derived from the Alpine Schists. They include fine-grained, compact schist-mylonites interfingered to some extent with the rather coarser 'curly' schist-mylonites. Progressing up through the schist-mylonites, recognizable enclaves of Alpine Schist appear, containing prolific 'fish-hook', minor fold hinges probably related to the Alpine F_2 structures of Rangitata age described by Grindley (1963) and Cooper (1974). In the higher-strain regions, hinge-lines of these structures have been swung round from their general NE–SW trend, as seen in the valleys of the Franz Josef and Fox Glaciers, to be smeared out along the direction of finite elongation within the mylonites (see below). The proportion of these Alpine Schist enclaves increases progressively through a distance of a hundred metres or so until the transition is complete. Good exposures of this transition zone can be found in the headwaters of Harold Creek, Hare Mare Creek and, especially, the Clearwater River.

Retrograde metamorphism within the fault zone is variable and may be controlled by the local availability of aqueous hydrothermal fluids (see also Reed 1964). However, crossing the fault zone from NW to SE, the change from truly cataclastic, discontinuous deformation in the cataclasites, accompanied by some chloritization of mafics and saussuritization of feldspars, to progressively more ductile mylonites formed by quasi-plastic processes (Sibson 1977) is accompanied by an increase from sub-greenschist to high greenschist grades of metamorphism.

Distribution of pseudotachylyte

Pseudotachylyte friction-melt was first recorded at a single locality in the Alpine Fault Zone by Wallace (1976), who referred to it as 'hyalomylonite'. However, the dark flinty 'ultramylonite' described by Reed (1964) and Young (1968—see especially fig. 6) from both the Alpine and Fraser Faults, possesses the characteristic fault/injection vein habit of pseudotachylyte (Sibson 1975). Microscopic examination of material from Reed's type ultramylonite locality at Dry Creek I yields clear evidence of a chilled melt phase (Fig. 3), confirming it as pseudotachylyte friction-melt, the product of seismic slip on discrete planes (Sibson 1975).

In fact, pseudotachylyte in various stages of devitrification seems to be fairly widely distributed in the Alpine Fault Zone; we have now recorded it at 19 localities spread over 270 km along the fault trace (Fig. 1). Interestingly, most of these localities are in the central Alpine Fault region, currently noted for its low seismicity (Evison 1971). Though most extensively developed in association with cataclasites, for example at Douglas Creek, it can be found at one place or another cutting all other fault rock types apart from gouge and, rarely, the Alpine Schists themselves. In rocks of the mylonite series, most of the pseudotachylyte has been generated by slip along SE-dipping fractures coincident with the mylonitic foliation, which has clearly acted as a preferential plane of brittle failure.

Structural data from the fault zone

Ductile shear zones develop by heterogeneous simple shear under plane strain conditions, and may be expected to contain penetrative L–S fabrics (Ramsay & Graham 1970). For high values of shear strain, mylonitic foliation should lie sub-parallel to the walls, with a stretching lineation in the foliation indicating the transport direction across the shear zone. Pre-existing structures in the host rocks may be deformed as passive markers with linear features, such as fold hinges, rotated and smeared out into near-parallelism with the transport direction (Escher & Watterson 1974).

Structural data from the Alpine Fault Zone, comprising 'best-fit' orientations for mylonitic foliation and stretching lineations at different localities, are listed in Table 1. The quality of the data varies considerably and is graded on the following basis: grade A—>5 lineation measurements, well clustered; Grade B—>5 lineations, poorly clustered; Grade C—2–5 lineations, well clustered; Grade D—2–5 lineations, poorly clustered; Grade E—1 lineation measurement only. Examples of the different grades of structural data are given in Fig. 4.

TABLE 1. *Structural data*

Location	Mylonitic Foliation	Stretching Lineation	H/V	Grade
Pell Strm.	019/56SE	52–079	0.7	A
Palmer Rd.	045/47SE	30–076	1.6	D
Robinson R.	047/60SE	35–070	1.4	E
Brown R.	040/35SE	25–081	1.9	E
L. Wainihinihini R.	049/67SE	—	—	
Lynch Ck.	042/45SE	32–080	1.5	C
MacPherson Ck.	053/28SE	17–088	2.7	C
Mt. Brown Ck.	045/44SE	19–075	2.7	B
Saddle Ck.	050/40SE	25–084	1.9	B
Matai Ck.	055/65SE	57–102	0.4	C
Pollock Ck.	052/40SE	36–110	0.8	D
L. Waitaha R.	039/30SE	—	—	
Macgregor Ck.	050/34SE	25–093	1.7	B
Douglas Ck.	055/56SE	—	—	
Cowhide Ck.	056/42SE	27–092	1.6	D
Harold Ck.	058/42SE	28–103	1.3	B
Dry Ck. II	057/54SE	40–094	0.9	D
Dry Ck. I	039/32SE	26–088	1.7	B
Vine Ck.	046/24SE	21–104	1.7	C
Parker Ck.	037/40SE	38–105	0.8	C
Gaunt Ck.	058/61SE	33–079	1.4	D
Darnley Ck.	055/59SE	34–079	1.4	B
Potters Ck.	040/38SE	37–115	0.7	C
Stony Ck.	051/34SE	24–092	1.8	D
Hare Mare Ck.	040/36SE	34–118	0.7	B
Clearwater R.	053/42SE	40–120	0.5	A
Fox R.	040/52SE	51–122	0.3	E
Cook R.	046/48SE	31–079	1.5	E
Havelock Ck.	045/24SE	21–102	1.8	D
Bullock Ck.	052/40SE	—	—	
Doughboy Ck.	047/36SE	—	—	
Thomson's Ck.	045/35SE	—	—	
Martyr R.	058/60SE	22–071	2.4	E

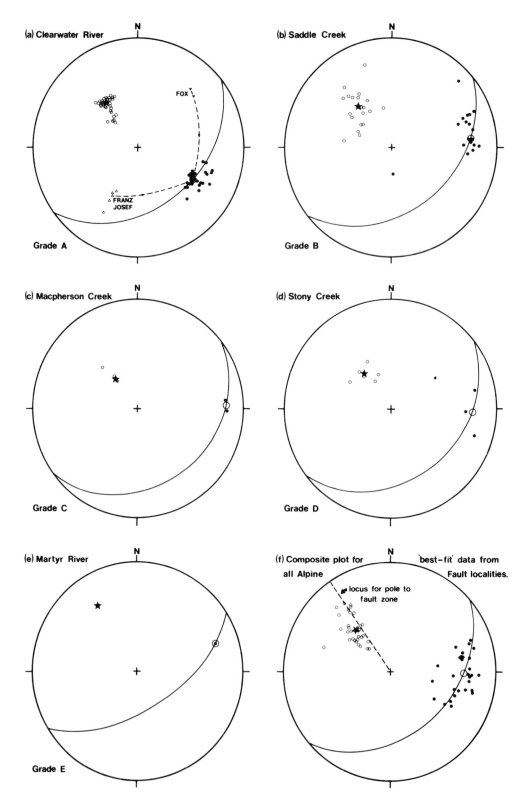

FIG. 4. Examples of structural data from the Alpine Fault Zone (lower hemisphere, equal-area projections). Small open circles—poles to mylonitic foliation; closed circles—stretching lineations; triangles—F_2 hinge-line lineations from the Alpine Schists; stars—best-fit poles to mylonitic foliation; large open circles—best-fit stretching lineation.

Dip of the fault zone

From the preceding discussion, it follows that the attitude of the mylonitic foliation should give some indication of the dip of the fault zone at depth. A composite plot for the fault zone (Fig. 4f) yields an overall, 'best-fit' orientation of 049/41 SE for the foliation. However, Wellman (1955), followed by Suggate (1963), demonstrated the widespread occurrence of gravity collapse 'nappelets' along the steeper parts of the alpine front, and suggested that the dip of the fault steepens to near-vertical values at depth (Fig. 5a). In our experience, though, these superficial nappes are well developed only in shattered, intensely jointed rock whose behaviour resembles that of a cohesionless aggregate. Our measurements, on the other hand, have been largely restricted to stream sections in comparatively intact, 'hard-rock', mylonites. Moreover, we find similar dip values in localities such as Saddle Creek where the mountain front is not particularly steep. It is also difficult to see how such major vertical displacements as have occurred in the late Cenozoic could have been effected by compression across a vertical fault.

Thus, allowing for some biasing of the dip measurements on the low side as a result of superficial collapse, a value of perhaps 50° is indicated for the dip of the fault zone at depth, which is compatible with current gravity models for the Southern Alps (Woodward 1979). Another point worth noting is that the regional strike of the central Alpine Fault can be accurately determined as 055°; the pole to the fault zone must, therefore, lie somewhere along the dashed line in Fig. 4f. Though the scatter is considerable, poles to mylonitic foliation cluster slightly to one side of this line, indicating a consistently more northerly strike for the foliation than for the fault zone. This is in accord with the mylonites having developed by dextral-reverse-oblique shear across the fault zone, as suggested by the stretching lineations (see below).

Stretching lineations and slip-vectors

Penetrative stretching lineations are variably developed in all mylonitic rocks within the fault zone. In the augen and green mylonites, the dominant linear fabric element is quartz, streaked out within the foliation into elongate ribbons or trails of fine equant recrystallized grains, and sometimes paralleled by alignments of other acicular minerals such as hornblende, when they are present. Within the schist-derived mylonites the lineation is most prominent in quartz-rich layers, apparently developed by the intensive flattening and smearing-out of the mainly detached hinges of minor alpine F_2 folds, as can be demonstrated in the transition passage to the Alpine Schists. The realignment of hinge-lines towards the direction of maximum finite elongation in the mylonites, in the manner described by Escher & Watterson (1974), is well displayed in the headwaters of the Clearwater River (Fig. 4a). Hinge-line lineations in the Alpine Schists, plunging respectively SW and NE in the valleys of the Franz Josef and Fox Glaciers, have apparently been strained along great-circle paths (Ramsay 1967, p. 470) into near coincidence with the stretching lineation.

In some traverses there is considerable scatter in lineation orientation; this may arise from strain inhomogeneities within the shear zone, the superficial collapse described previously, or the rotation of large slivers of the mylonite belts on high-level discontinuities during uplift.

Best-fit plunge directions for different locations are plotted in Fig. 1; all are consistent with the L–S mylonitic fabric having developed

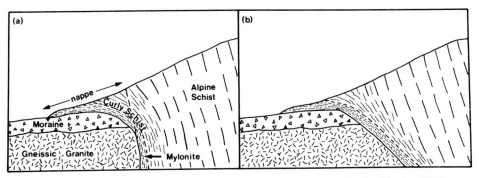

FIG. 5. Alternative models for the dip of the Alpine Fault Zone at depth; (a) after Wellman (1955), (b) this study.

by dextral-reverse-oblique shear across the fault zone. In the NE, the lineation plunge directions are aligned along the general strike of the Marlborough Faults which trend sub-parallel to the present-day slip vector between the Pacific and Indo-Australian plates, as evinced by horizontal slip directions derived from earthquake fault plane solutions (Rynn & Scholz 1978; Walcott 1978). Further to the SW, in the region of greatest alpine uplift, the lineations plunge in a direction suggesting compression more nearly perpendicular to the fault strike. Similar conclusions were previously reached from a study of joints and other structural features in this region (Gunn 1960).

Ratios of horizontal to vertical displacement

For high shear strains, stretching lineations should lie very close to the 3-D slip vector across ductile shear zones (Escher & Watterson 1974). Assuming also that the lineation attitude has stayed unchanged during uplift, the ratio of horizontal to vertical displacement across the fault zone at the time of fabric development can be estimated, using:

$$\frac{H}{V} = \cos \alpha \cdot \cot \beta \qquad (1)$$

where α is the angle between the direction of plunge and the strike of the fault zone, and β is the plunge magnitude. Values of H/V for Alpine Fault mylonites have been calculated taking the regional strike of the fault zone as 055° (apart from the Pell Stream locality where the strike has swung N to 048°), and are listed in Table 1.

Horizontal movement at the time of mylonitization generally exceeds vertical movement, except at Pell Stream which lies at the foot of the major bend in the Alpine Fault, and in the region immediately adjacent to the area of greatest alpine uplift. The Pell Stream value is of particular interest because the greater width of schists exposed in the Spenser Mountains sandwiched between the Awatere and Wairau Faults (Bowen 1964) also indicates that this is a region of anomalously high uplift, presumably as a result of the increased misalignment of the interplate slip vector in the vicinity of the bend. Broadly speaking, the regional variation in H/V ratios follows that inferred for the late Quaternary from displaced geomorphic features (Wellman 1953; Suggate 1963), but direct correlation, for example at Maruia River between the Pell Stream and Palmer's Road localities (Suggate 1960), is not possible.

Minor structures affecting the mylonites

The mylonitic foliation is generally fairly planar, but is locally affected by:

(1) Kink bands of varying attitudes, which are often associated with minor faults and gouge zones.

(2) Macroscopic folds: apart from rather open structures these tend to be rare, but in the lower reaches of Saddle Creek, augen mylonites have been ductilely deformed into reclined, macroscopic folds which plunge due E, sub-parallel to the stretching lineation (cf. the structures described by Carreras et al. 1977).

(3) Crenulations of varying amplitude and attitude, the most common having hinge-lines coincident with the stretching lineation. In the schist-derived mylonites, generally symmetrical, wavy crenulations are responsible for the appearance of the 'curly' schists, and may have developed by instabilities arising from layer-normal compression in the manner described by Cosgrove (1976).

Age of fault rocks in the Alpine Fault Zone

There is a clear inference from the structural data that the fabrics of the Alpine Fault mylonites developed during the late Cenozoic phase of oblique compression; they could not have arisen from purely transcurrent movements. As the cataclasites, pseudotachylytes and gouge zones are of similar age to, or post-date the mylonites, it appears that all fabrics within the fault zone developed during this period of movement.

Carter & Norris (1976) suggested, on stratigraphic grounds, that reverse slip on the Alpine Fault began in the late Miocene (c. 10 Ma ago), continuing spasmodically through the Plio-Pleistocene to the present-day. The average H/V ratio for the Alpine Fault mylonites has a value of about 1.4. From this one can also infer that the dextral-reverse-oblique shear accompanying mylonitization was comparatively short-lived; otherwise the vertical displacement across the fault zone becomes impossibly large. Using this average ratio and, for the sake of argument, adopting Suggate & Lensen's (1973) estimate of 1.3 cm/yr for the average rate of Holocene strike-slip, a vertical displacement of 20 km across the fault zone could be accomplished in 2.2 m.y. Isotope studies of the Alpine Schists adjacent to the fault (and of the schist-derived mylonites—C. J. Adams pers. comm.) suggest

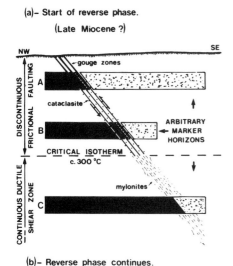

(a)- Start of reverse phase.

(Late Miocene ?)

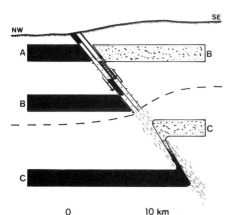

(b)- Reverse phase continues.

0   10 km

(c)- Present-day situation.

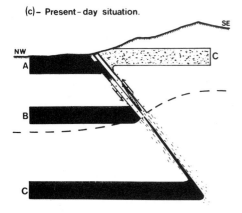

FIG. 6. Interpretative model for the Alpine Fault Zone in the late Cenozoic (highly schematic and only approximately to scale).

that major argon outgassing took place 4–5 Ma ago (Gabites & Adams 1978; Sheppard *et al.* 1975). By late Pliocene–early Pleistocene times (*c.* 2–3 Ma ago), the Alpine Schists were exposed to erosion. It is worth pointing out that particularly intense mylonitization probably occurred at the time of transition from purely transcurrent to dextral-reverse-oblique slip, because initial misorientation of the fault zone would have led to increased frictional constraints against movement and high stresses (Sibson 1974). Consequently, we tentatively associate the development of the mylonitic fabrics in the Alpine Fault Zone with the major isotopic event 4–5 Ma ago.

By itself, this structural evidence that the present fabrics in the Alpine Fault rocks are no older than late Miocene does not discriminate between the alternative movement histories, but it does rule out Reed's (1964) three-fold subdivision of fault rock types on a chronological basis. Nor is the interpretation contradicted by the known distribution of Cretaceous lamprophyre dykes which intrude the mylonites of the Fraser Formation (Young 1968), but have not been recorded from the Alpine Fault Zone itself. It may be that mylonitic fabrics in the Fraser Formation result from an earlier phase of Alpine Fault activity.

Interpretative model for the late Cenozoic evolution of the fault zone

Reed's (1964) threefold division of fault rocks can be largely explained by the development of the various textural types at different depths within the fault zone during the late Cenozoic compressive phase, rather than at widely separate times.

We interpret the NW–SE passage across the fault zone from cataclasite through augen mylonite to schist-derived mylonite as reflecting the original distribution of fault rock types with increasing depth below gouge zones which accommodate most of the near-surface displacement. A simple model for the evolution of the fault zone which can account for the observed distribution of different fault rock types is given in Fig. 6. At the start of the late Cenozoic phase of reverse slip across the Alpine Fault, one may reasonably expect a zone of discontinuous frictional deformation in the upper crust to give way below the greenschist transition to continuous deformation in mylonitic shear belts (Sibson 1977). The effect of continuing reverse slip is to juxtapose fault rocks initially formed in radically different environments. Of course, our representation of the upper zone of discontinuous deformation is grossly oversimplified; a more realistic model would incorporate a complex anastomosing mesh of discontinuities and crush zones, but the overall effects of reverse shear should be similar. Moreover, it is clear that fault rock textures originally formed at depth may be modified during their passage to the surface. Mylonites are likely to suffer some cataclastic deformation during upwards transport and as a result of pressure relief, originally cohesive rocks may tend to disaggregate and undergo near-surface hydrothermal alteration.

The pseudotachylytes are interpreted as having developed by seismic slip on discrete planes within the frictional regime, mainly in association with the cataclasites, but also in the mylonites as they were raised from their originally ductile environment to levels where brittle failure along the foliation became dominant (cf. Grocott 1977; Sibson 1979).

Further elaboration of this model requires better knowledge of the deformation environments associated with the different fault rock types; this we hope to gain from our continuing microstructural and petrographic studies. Also, in the simple model the transition between discontinuous and continuous deformation is considered to be sharp, the interface being displaced as a passive marker. In reality, the transition will be gradational and its position may be partly governed by the effect of uplift and erosion on isotherm patterns. Another possibility, considered below, is that shear heating within the fault zone may progressively raise the transition to higher crustal levels. It should also be borne in mind that the larger earthquake fault ruptures may be expected to propagate down through the mylonitic shear belts, causing transient loss of continuity from time to time.

Possible shear heating

One puzzling aspect of the mylonitic rocks within the fault zone is the variable, but rather slight, extent to which even the highest grade (biotite-garnet) assemblages have been retrogressed. In part this may result from a lack of the aqueous fluids needed to promote exothermal, retrograde reactions, as indicated by the general scarcity of hydrothermal veining within the fault zone. A further factor may be the extreme rapidity of uplift, which would maintain high temperatures on the upthrown side of the fault. However, Sheppard et al. (1975)

suggested qualitatively that shear heating as a result of the displacement across the Alpine Fault Zone could account, at least in part, for the argon outgassing of the neighbouring Alpine Schists in the late Cenozoic. Such a process would help to explain the general lack of retrogression, and could also have affected the transition between frictional and quasi-plastic deformation in the fault zone, as it evolved.

It seems probable that shear heating, if it has occurred, would have been especially intense following the changeover from purely transcurrent movements to oblique compression, because of the higher stresses needed to induce and maintain reverse slip across an unsuitably oriented fault zone. Further, from a dimensional viewpoint, the observed effects are consistent with the time periods of 5–10 Ma envisaged for this compressive phase. Gabites & Adams (1978) have shown that in the Haast region, isotopic disturbance of the Alpine Schists extends some 20 km horizontally from the fault trace, or about 14 km perpendicularly from the fault zone, accepting a sheet-dip of 45° to the SE. A rough estimate of the time needed to conduct a significant amount of heat to this distance is given by the thermal relaxation time for an infinite slab,

$$t_r = \frac{l^2}{\kappa} = 6.2 \times 10^6 \text{ yrs} \qquad (2)$$

where the thermal diffusivity $\kappa = 10^{-2} \text{ cm}^2 \cdot \text{s}^{-1}$ and the slab thickness, $l = 14$ km. From more detailed analyses (Scholz et al. in press, Sibson et al. 1979) it is clear that shear heating for several Ma could have induced significant temperature increases of tens of degrees at approximately 20 km from the fault, provided shear stress levels within the fault zone were of the order of 1–1.5 kbar. For the same conditions, temperatures at depth within the fault zone would have been raised by a hundred degrees or so, the most pronounced effect being towards the base of the frictional regime where the shear resistance is likely to have been greatest (Sibson 1977). As a result, the transition to quasi-plastic behaviour is likely to have migrated upwards with time.

Conclusions

Field studies of fault rocks and their distribution within the Alpine Fault Zone indicate:

(1) The NW–SE passage across the fault zone from granite-derived cataclasite to schist-derived mylonite on the upthrown side, though discontinuous, largely reflects the original distribution of fault rocks with depth.

(2) Within the fault zone, mylonitic foliation generally dips a little over 40° to the SE; it seems likely that a similar or slightly greater dip characterizes the fault zone as a whole at depth.

(3) Penetrative stretching lineations within the mylonites plunge in a direction sub-parallel to the present-day slip-vector between the Indo-Australian and Pacific plates, and cannot be related to a phase of purely transcurrent fault displacement.

(4) The fault rocks therefore had their fabrics impressed during the late Cenozoic phase of oblique compression across the fault zone. Mylonites of the Fraser Formation to the NW may result from an earlier phase of Alpine Fault activity.

(5) Pseudotachylyte friction-melt in varying stages of devitrification is fairly widely distributed along the fault zone. Though best developed in association with the cataclasites, it can be found cutting all other fault rock types apart from gouge.

(6) Significant shear heating may have accompanied the late Cenozoic phase of oblique compression and could help to account for the lack of pervasive retrogression in the fault zone, though another contributing factor may be a general lack of circulating hydrothermal fluids.

ACKNOWLEDGMENTS. We acknowledge with thanks the help and advice readily afforded us by the NZ Geological Survey and Geophysics Division, DSIR. This work forms part of a project funded by the US Geological Survey under the National Earthquake Hazards Reduction Programme, Contract Nos. 14-08-0001-17662, 14-08-0001-G-377, 14-08-0001-G-466. S. H. White acknowledges financial support from The Royal Society. B. K. Atkinson was assisted by a Royal Society Travel Grant. Figs 2. 3 and 5 reproduced by kind permission of the Royal Society of New Zealand.

References

BOWEN, F. E. 1964. Sheet 15 Buller. Geologic Map of New Zealand 1 : 250,000 *N.Z. Department of Scientific and Industrial Research*, Wellington, New Zealand.

CARRERAS, J., ESTRADA, A. & WHITE, S. 1977. The effects of folding on the c-axis fabrics of a quartz mylonite. *Tectonophysics*, **39**, 3–24.

CARTER, R. M. & NORRIS, R. J. 1976. Cainozoic history of southern New Zealand: an accord between geological observations and plate-tectonic predictions. *Earth planet. Sci. Lett.* **31**, 85–94.

COOPER, A. F. 1974. Multiphase deformation and its relationship to metamorphic crystallisation at Haast River, South Westland, New Zealand. *N.Z. J. Geol. Geophys.* **17**, 855–80.

COSGROVE, J. W. 1976. The formation of crenulation cleavage. *J. geol. Soc. London*, **132**, 155–78.

ESCHER, A. & WATTERSON, J. 1974. Stretching fabrics, folds and crustal shortening. *Tectonophysics*, **22**, 223–31.

EVISON, F. F. 1971. Seismicity of the Alpine Fault, New Zealand. *In*: COLLINS, B. W. & FRASER, R. (eds), *Recent Crustal Movements* R. Soc. N.Z Bull. **9**, 161–5.

FLEMING, C. A. 1970. The Mesozoic of New Zealand: chapters in the history of the circum-Pacific mobile belt. *Q. J. geol. Soc. London*, **125**, 125–70.

GABITES, J. E. & ADAMS, C. J. D. 1978. Excess radiogenic argon and age of metamorphism and uplift in the Haast Schists, Haast Pass, Lakes Wanaka and Hawea, South Island, New Zealand. *Proc. Int. Conf. Geochron. Cosmochron. Isotope Geol.* Aug. 1978 Snowmass Colorado U.S.A.

GRINDLEY, G. W. 1963. Structure of the Alpine schists of South Westland, Southern Alps, New Zealand. *N.Z. J. Geol. Geophys.* **6**, 872–930.

—— 1974. 'New Zealand' *In*: SPENCER, A. (ed.), *Data for Orogenic Studies: Mesozoic-Cenozoic Belts.* Spec. Publ. geol. Soc. London, **3**, 387–416.

GROCOTT, J. 1977. The relationship between Precambrian shear belts and modern fault systems. *J. geol. Soc. London*, **133**, 257–262.

GUNN, B. M. 1960. Structural features of the Alpine Schists of the Franz Josef-Fox Glacier region. *N.Z. J. Geol. Geophys.* **3**, 287–308.

HUNT, T. & NATHAN, S. 1976. Inangahua Magnetic Anomaly, New Zealand. *N.Z. J. Geol. Geophys.* **19**, 395–406.

KUPFER, D. H. 1960. Width of the Alpine Fault Zone, New Zealand. *N.Z. J.Geol. Geophys.* **7**, 685–701.

MOLNAR, P., ATWATER, T., MAMMERICKX, J. & SMITH, S. M. 1975. Magnetic anomalies, bathymetry and the tectonic evolution of the South Pacific since the Late Cretaceous. *Geophys. J. R. astron. Soc.* **40**, 383–420.

RAMSAY, J. G. 1967. *'Folding and Fracturing of Rocks'*. McGraw-Hill, New York, 568 pp.

—— & GRAHAM, R. H. 1970. Strain variation in shear belts. *Can. J. Earth Sci.* **7**, 786–813.

REED, J. J. 1964. Mylonites, cataclasites, and associated rocks along the Alpine Fault, South Island, New Zealand. *N.Z. J. Geol. Geophys.* **7**, 654–84.

RYNN, J. M. W. & SCHOLZ, C. H. 1978. Seismotectonics of the Arthur's Pass region, South Island, New Zealand. *Bull. geol. Soc. Am.* **89**, 1373–88.

SCHOLZ, C. H., BEAVAN, J. & HANKS, T. C. in press. Metamorphism, argon depletion, heat flow and stress on the Alpine fault *J. geophys. Res.*

SHEPPARD, D. S., ADAMS, C. J. D. & BIRD, G. W. 1975. Age of metamorphism and uplift in the Alpine Schist Belt, New Zealand. *Bull. geol. Soc. Am.* **86,** 1147–53.

SIBSON, R. H. 1974. Frictional constraints on thrust, wrench and normal faults. *Nature (phys. sci.),* **249,** 542–3.

—— 1975. Generation of pseudotachylyte by ancient seismic faulting. *Geophys. J. R. astron. Soc.* **43,** 775–94.

—— 1977. Fault rocks and fault mechanisms. *J. geol. Soc. London,* **133,** 191–213.

—— 1979. A comment on 'Frictional heating on a fault zone with finite thickness' by R. K. Cardwell, D. S. Chinn, G. F. Moore and D. L. Turcotte. *Geophys. J.R. astron. Soc.* **56,** 237–8.

——, WHITE, S. H. & ATKINSON, B. K. 1979. Fault rock distribution and structure within the Alpine Fault Zone: a preliminary account. *In:* WALCOTT, R. I. & CRESSWELL, M. M. (eds), *The Origin of the Southern Alps* R. Soc. N.Z. Bull. **18,** 55–65.

SUGGATE, R. P. 1960. The interpretation of progressive fault displacement of flights of terraces. *N.Z. J. Geol. Geophys.* **3,** 364–74.

—— 1963. The Alpine Fault. *Trans. R. Soc. N.Z. Geol.* **2,** 105–29.

—— & LENSEN, G. J. 1973. Rate of horizontal fault displacement in New Zealand. *Nature,* **242,** 518.

WALCOTT, R. I. 1978. Present tectonics and Late Cenozoic evolution of New Zealand. *Geophys. J.R. astron. Soc.* **52,** 137–64.

WALLACE, R. C. 1976. Partial fusion along the Alpine Fault Zone, New Zealand. *Bull. geol. Soc. Am.* **87,** 1225–8.

WELLMAN, H. W. 1953. Data for the study of Recent and Late Pleistocene faulting in the South Island of New Zealand. *N.Z. J. Sci. Tech* **B34,** 270–88.

—— 1955. The geology between Bruce Bay and Haast River, South Westland. *Bull. N.Z. Geol. Surv. n.s.* **48.**

—— 1956. Structural Outline of New Zealand. *N.Z. Dept. Sci. Indust. Res. Bull.* **121.**

—— 1964. Age of the Alpine Fault, New Zealand. *In:* SUNDARAM, R. K. (ed.). *Proc. Section IV, Rock Deformation and Tectonics,* 22nd Int. geol. Congr. New Delhi, 148–62.

WELLMAN, P. & COOPER, A. 1971. Potassium-argon age of some New Zealand lamprophyre dykes near the Alpine Fault. *N.Z. J. Geol. Geophys.* **14,** 341–50.

WOODWARD, D. J. 1979. The crustal structure of the Southern Alps, New Zealand, as determined by gravity. *In:* WALCOTT, R. I. & CRESSWELL, M. M. (eds), *The Origin of the Southern Alps* R. Soc. N.Z. Bull. **18,** 95–8.

YOUNG, D. J. 1968. The Fraser Fault in Central Westland, New Zealand, and its associated rocks. *N.Z. J. Geol. Geophys.* **11,** 291–311.

R. H. SIBSON, S. H. WHITE & B. K. ATKINSON, Department of Geology, Royal School of Mines, Imperial College, London SW7 2BP.

Uplift rates and thermal structure in the Alpine Fault Zone and Alpine Schists, Southern Alps, New Zealand

C. J. Adams

SUMMARY: Rates of vertical and horizontal movement at the Alpine Fault Zone and within the adjacent Alpine Schists (Haast Schist Group) are deduced from K-Ar age data of metamorphic and mylonitic rocks. The relative contributions of Jurassic–Cretaceous (Rangitata) and Miocene–Recent (Kaikoura) orogenic phases are also estimated.

After Jurassic regional metamorphism, the Haast Schists were uplifted regionally 18–20 km at rates 0.3–0.4 mm/yr until mid-Cretaceous times. No differential vertical movements occurred on the Alpine Fault at this time. During the Miocene–Recent orogeny, a maximum of 10 km uplift, produced mylonitic rocks at the Alpine Fault and brought Alpine Schists (Haast Schist Group) to the surface. Ages of mylonite, blastomylonite and pseudotachylyte indicate intense fault movement was occurring 5–10 Ma ago. Ages as young as 0.7 Ma occur in the adjacent Alpine Schists. From these data, uplift rates at the Alpine Fault for the period late Miocene–Pliocene are in the range 2.5–5 mm/yr and late Pleistocene–Recent, 7–14 mm/yr.

The estimation of horizontal displacements at the Alpine Fault in the Jurassic–Cretaceous and Miocene–Recent orogenic phases depends critically on the reality of a Cretaceous (?) lamprophyre dyke swarm cut by the Alpine Fault. If this is accepted, then about 360 km horizontal movement is pre-Upper Cretaceous and 120 km is younger. If the dyke swarm evidence is dismissed, then a total 480 km displacement on the Alpine Fault is entirely post-Cretaceous and may have occurred during the Miocene–Recent orogenic phase. This is, then, broadly associated with large-scale motions of the Indian and Pacific plates in the late Cenozoic and Quaternary.

Analysis of the age patterns within the Alpine Fault mylonites and the adjacent Alpine Schists support the possibility that a 15 km wide thermal aureole, about the Alpine Fault or at zones of intense shearing within the Alpine Schists, has been created by frictional generation of heat during relatively rapid aseismic shear sustained over the last 5 Ma. This thermal effect has been sufficient to cause complete argon loss from rocks over a 10 km wide zone immediately E of the Alpine Fault.

Introduction

Although thrusts and nappes are frequently observed in orogenic belts, their rates of formation and associated thermal effects can rarely be measured. This is because they often occur in older orogens where the uncertainties in the dating of displacements are large compared to the timespan of the events themselves. Apart from the surface expressions of faulting, very young examples of thrusts associated with regionally and dynamically metamorphosed rocks are rare. However, an exception occurs in the South Island, New Zealand, where late Miocene–Recent movement at the Alpine Fault has exposed mylonites and cataclasites formed by dextral-reverse-oblique slip.

A discussion is presented here of K-Ar ages of rocks in this fault zone and an adjacent metamorphic terrane and from these data

some limits may be placed upon the time and rate of fault movement. A general summary of the geological history is given in Table 1.

The Alpine Fault

The Alpine Fault (Wellman & Willett 1942, see also Suggate 1963) of the South Island, New Zealand, forms an active plate boundary between the Indian and Pacific plates. It crosses the South Island obliquely (Fig. 1) from Milford Sound in Fiordland to the Maruia valley in the NE (Fig. 2) where it breaks into subsidiary faults. On a regional scale the Alpine Fault is very straight, but in detail there may be several active fault traces within a 1 km zone. In several places over-thrusting to the NW can be seen, where small nappes of Alpine Schists are thrust up to 1 km over Palaeozoic granites, metasediments and,

TABLE 1. *Geological history in the region of the Alpine Fault Zone and Alpine Schists, Southern Alps, New Zealand*

Period	
0–2 Ma	Alpine Schists appear as detritus in Pleistocene glacial gravels.
0–10 Ma	Acceleration of plate motion of Pacific plate normal to the Alpine Fault, with continued dextral strike slip movement. Rapid increase in differential uplift rates at the Alpine Fault to form the Southern Alps. Probable shear heating of the Alpine Schists causes complete argon loss from rocks within 10 km of fault. Late deformation, low grade metamorphism of Kaikoura Orogeny in the Alpine Schists.
10–25 Ma	Initiation of Kaikoura Orogeny. Rapid dextral strike slip movement at the Alpine Fault (see below).
0–25 Ma	*Either*: 120 km dextral displacement at Alpine Fault as recorded by possible Cretaceous linear lamprophyre dyke swarm, during the period Miocene–Recent. *Or*: Full, 480 km dextral displacement at Alpine Fault as indicated by plate tectonic data for late Cenozoic motions of Pacific (wrt. Indian) Plate, for the period Miocene–Recent.
80–25 Ma	Cretaceous–Cenozoic basinal sedimentation. Marine transgression commences in mid-late Cretaceous, culminates in Oligocene.
~ 80(–120) Ma	Intrusion of at least some lamprophyre dykes in late Cretaceous (perhaps others earlier), in both the Foreland Belt and the Haast Schist terrane. *Either*: 360 km dextral displacement on Alpine Fault as recorded by possible Cretaceous linear lamprophyre dyke swarm. *Or*: No dextral displacement at Alpine Fault, as indicated by plate tectonic data (see above). No differential vertical movements at the Alpine Fault.
80–120 Ma	Major uplift phase (~ 20 km) of plutonic and metamorphic complexes, in particular, in the Foreland Belt. Deposition of mid-Cretaceous terrestrial sediments on uplifted orogen.
~ 110–140 Ma	Calc-alkaline granite-granodiorite plutonic phase of the Rangitata Orogeny in Foreland Belt only. Rare associated volcanism. Possible associated regional metamorphism.
~ 120–190 Ma	Possible continued local Torlesse Group sedimentation and late tectonism and low grade metamorphism. Major phase of uplift (~ 20 km) of earlier, Permo-Triassic metasediments of the NZ Geosyncline. No differential vertical movements at Alpine Fault during this uplift phase.
~ 190 Ma	Major tectonism and regional metamorphism of sediments of the NZ Geosyncline during the early phases of Rangitata Orogeny, to form the metamorphic rocks of the Haast Schist Group (Alpine Schists, Otago Schists and Marlborough Schists as sub-units). Little or no equivalent in Foreland Belt.
~ 200–300 Ma	Deposition of Permo-Triassic sediments in the NZ Geosyncline, forming the Torlesse and Hokinui Facies.
300-380 Ma	Granite-granodiorite plutonic phase of Tuhua Orogeny. Final formation of Foreland Belt.
~ 440 Ma	Tectonic and metamorphic phase of Tuhua Orogeny; low grade regional metamorphism of Greenland Group.
~ 480–500 Ma	Deposition of Cambro-Ordovician Greenland Group, only in the Foreland Belt.

more importantly, Plio-Pleistocene gravels (Suggate 1963). On a large scale at depth, the fault plane probably dips at 40–45° to the SE (Sibson *et al.* this volume).

Horizontal displacements

The maximum dextral displacement (480 km) at the Alpine Fault (Wellmann 1955) affects pre-Upper Cretaceous rocks. For example, Palaeozoic rocks forming a Foreland belt and Carboniferous–Jurassic sediments of the adjacent NZ Geosyncline can be matched on either side of the fault (Fig. 1). The youngest rocks affected by this displacement are mid-

Cretaceous granites and their associated K-Ar mineral age patterns, which record the time of later uplift in the mid-late Cretaceous (80–110 Ma). These granites were intruded into the Foreland Belt during the Rangitata (Jurassic–Cretaceous) Orogeny. During this same orogeny, rocks of the adjacent NZ Geosyncline (Fig. 1) were folded and regionally metamorphosed; those of medium–high rank are collectively termed the Haast Schists.

Of the total 480 km displacement, the relative components of Cretaceous movement during the Rangitata Orogeny and more recent movement during the Kaikoura (Miocene–Recent) Orogeny are difficult to assess. A

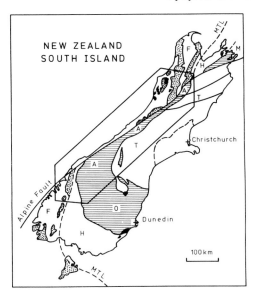

FIG. 1. Main elements of the Jurassic–Cretaceous, Rangitata Orogenic Belt in New Zealand. Precambrian–Palaeozoic Foreland Belt (F) is separated by the Median Tectonic Line (MTL) from sediments of the NZ Geosyncline to the E. These latter include Carboniferous–Jurassic low-grade metasediments of the Hokinui (H) and Torlesse (T) facies and possible higher-grade metamorphic equivalents of the Haast Schist Group (ruled). The last-named is subdivided in the Otago Schists (O), Marlborough Schists (M) and the Alpine Schists (A-A-A) which are coincident with the Southern Alps mountain chain. Regional metamorphism of the Haast Schists and granite-granodiorite plutonism in the Foreland Belt (stipple) occurred during the Rangitata Orogeny and both are overlain by post-orogenic mid-Cretaceous terrestrial sediments (solid). Box delineates area of Fig. 2.

smaller post-Cretaceous horizontal displacement of about 120 km, appears to be recorded by a suggested linear dyke swarm of lamprophyres which cut Cretaceous granites to the NW of the Alpine Fault and Haast Schists to the SE (Wellman & Cooper 1971). On the basis of Cretaceous K-Ar ages of these dykes, Wellman & Cooper (1971) suggested that about 360 km dextral displacement occurred during the Rangitata Orogeny and the remaining 120 km dextral movement took place in the late Cenozoic, Kaikoura Orogeny. However, the concept of a single dyke swarm has been doubted (Hunt & Nathan 1976) and

whilst the lamprophyres of the northern part of the 'swarm' are reliably dated as Cretaceous (Adams & Nathan 1978), the ages of those in the southern section, in the Haast Schists, may be too old owing to the possible presence of excess argon in adjacent country rocks (Gabites & Adams 1978).

The evidence of Cretaceous and Cenozoic plate movements in the SW Pacific region (Molnar *et al.* 1975; Walcott 1979) suggests strongly that all the dextral movement on the Alpine Fault has occurred since the Miocene.

Very much smaller displacements (10–100 m) are seen in Quaternary river valley features and glacial deposits.

Vertical displacements

Recent vertical movements at the Alpine Fault, and in the Southern Alps immediately to the E, can be assessed from displacements of various geomorphic features (e.g. Suggate 1968), tilted lake strandlines, river sediment loads and offshore sedimentation rates (Adams, J. 1979). These data suggest Holocene and late Pleistocene uplift rates of 10–15 mm/yr at the Alpine Fault and a maximum of 20–24 mm/yr in the Southern Alps. (Adams, J. 1979). Uplift rates, integrated over a much longer period, have been obtained by interpreting very young K-Ar mineral ages (4–8 Ma), in Alpine Schists close to the Alpine Fault, as the time when substantial vertical movements were occurring on the fault (Mason 1961) during Miocene and Pliocene times. The *amount* of inferred vertical movement ranges from 2.8 km (Hurley *et al.* 1962), through 11–14 km (Mason 1961) to 18 km (Suggate 1963). These various interpretations are discussed later.

The Alpine Schists

Within the Haast Schist Group, the Alpine Schists form a 25 km wide belt of greenschist-amphibolite facies metasediments, immediately to the E of the Alpine Fault. They grade eastwards into prehnite-pumpellyite facies metasediments of the Torlesse Group (Carboniferous–Jurassic) (Fig. 1, T) and south-eastwards into the Otago schists, greenschist facies metasediments, forming another sub-unit of the Haast Schist Group (Fig. 1, O). The Alpine Schists are dominantly quartzo-feldspathic schists but basic/ultramafic metavolcanic(?) horizons also occur (Mason 1962). The rank of the schists increases rapidly westwards from prehnite-pumpellyite facies at

C. J. Adams

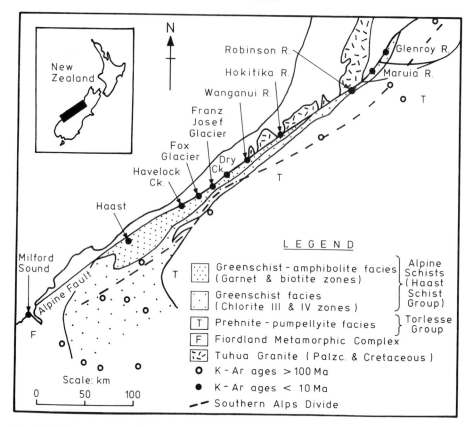

FIG. 2. K-Ar age patterns in the Alpine Fault Zone, the Alpine Schists (stipple) (Haast Schist Group), and adjacent rocks, showing distribution of age data reflecting a regional Jurassic–Cretaceous, Rangitata orogenic event (>100 Ma) and a younger (<10 Ma), more localized Miocene–Recent, Kaikoura orogenic event (after Adams, C. 1979).

the Southern Alps divide to mid-amphibolite facies (oligoclase zone ≡ staurolite-kyanite zone) at the Alpine Fault (Mason 1962) (Fig. 2).

The earliest structures (Rangitata orogenic phase) in the Haast Schist Group are large recumbent folds which are best preserved in the Otago Schists. Although the Alpine Schists show similar early recumbent folds, their overall structural style is dominated by later wrench-fault tectonics during shearing associated with initiation of the Alpine Fault (Grindley 1973). At the Southern Alps divide, the adjacent Torlesse greywackes form steeply plunging north-facing folds bounded by strike-slip and reverse faults but closer to the Alpine Fault, the Alpine Schists form a separate belt of SW plunging folds (Lillie *et al.* 1957; Gunn 1960; Mason 1962; Grindley 1963; Findlay 1979). Findlay (1979, fig. 4) has suggested that

the several structural sections of the above-named authors in the central Southern Alps region represent, from S to N, increasing depths in the structural pile. From mesoscopic fold-styles he interprets the larger structures as a series of disharmonic steplike folds which result from movement along localized, near-vertical zones of intense transposition (1–5 km wide) which anastomose laterally and vertically between enclaves of only mild plication. Although the metamorphic isograds were essentially developed during the earlier fold phases, there is recrystallization of biotite associated with the intense development of the latest foliation in the above-mentioned zones of transposition. There is no evidence of the age of these zones in this area but to the S at Haast, the lamprophyre dykes post-date the main metamorphism and earlier structures and parallel the axes of late folds associated with final uplift. *If* the Cretaceous age for these dykes is accepted, then clearly the latest fold phase is of Rangitata age. However, if the lamprophyre ages are considered unreliable, then the last fold phase might be associated with the Kaikoura Orogeny.

Mylonites and cataclasites at the Alpine Fault

Mylonites and cataclasites occur at numerous localities on the central section of the Alpine Fault, generally in a zone 100 m–1 km wide (Reed 1964; Sibson *et al.* this volume). Mylonitic rocks, mostly derived from the Alpine Schists, include fine-grained mylonite, ultramylonite, green phyllonite and muscovite- and biotite-blastomylonite (Reed 1964). Sibson *et al.* (ibid) record many occurrences of pseudotachylyte (occasionally glassy) in veins cutting all mylonite types but in particular, the granite-derived types.

Cataclastic rocks such as crushed and mortared granite are more common on the NW side of the fault. In the Wanganui-Hokitika River section on the NW side of the Alpine Fault, gneissic augen mylonites occur, forming the Fraser Formation (Young 1968).

Incoherent fault rocks, such as fault pug and gouge, are commonly found in narrow zones (1–10 m) at active fault traces (Reed 1964).

Age data for the Alpine Schists

Poles and angles of rotation for the Pacific plate, with respect to the Indian plate, from the Oligocene to the present have been determined by Chase (1978). Assuming that no accommodation is occurring within the Pacific plate, then these data can be used to estimate motions of the Pacific plate, with respect to the Indian plate, at the central section of the Alpine Fault, both parallel and perpendicular to the fault plane (Walcott 1979). For the period 0–4 Ma, these are 40 ± 1 and 22 ± 1 mm/yr; for 0–10 Ma, 34 ± 3 mm/yr, and 3 ± 4 mm/yr; and for 10–21 Ma, 24 ± 7 mm/yr and -4 ± 8 mm/yr. Thus, whilst lateral movement has been continuous and substantial over the last 20 Ma, crustal shortening, normal to the fault has, essentially, occurred only in the last 10 Ma and provides a *maximum* for late Cenozoic uplift rate in the Southern Alps. This can be checked by consideration of K-Ar age data

of the Alpine Schists, which record stages in the uplift history of the Southern Alps and oblique-strike-slip-reverse movement at the Alpine Fault.

Estimation of vertical movements

Adams, C. (1979) has reviewed published age data for the Alpine Schists (Hurley *et al.* 1961; Mason 1961; Harper & Landis 1967; Sheppard *et al.* 1975; Gabites & Adams 1978), and estimated the amounts of uplift during the Rangitata (Jurassic–Cretaceous) and Kaikoura (Miocene–Recent) orogenic episodes. Rocks of the Haast Schist Group, metamorphosed up to amphibolite facies and representing conditions of 600°C, and 6 kbar were probably formed at depths of 20–30 km, assuming a geothermal gradient in the range 20–30°C/km. Thus, the highest rank rocks of the Alpine Schists must have been uplifted about 25 ± 5 km in the Rangitata and Kaikoura post-orogenic uplifts. In the Otago Schist sector of the Haast Schists, lower grade metamorphic rocks yield K-Ar ages in the range 125–195 Ma (Adams 1978; C. J. Adams, D. G. Bishop, J. E. Gabites & P. Robinson, in prep.), which imply that the metamorphism is at least early Jurassic and that the subsequent post-metamorphic uplift and cooling has continued for at least 70 Ma. Within this metamorphic sequence, an 8–10 km thickness of pumpellyite-actinolite facies rocks took 25 Ma (190–165 Ma) to pass through the argon retention isotherm (about 250–300°C for these rock types (Damon 1968)), i.e. an uplift rate of 0.3–0.4 mm/yr. Continued uplift brought these rocks to the surface before the mid-Cretaceous, since Cretaceous terrestrial sediments overlie the schists. If the argon retention isotherm is estimated to be at a depth of about 10 km (i.e. geothermal gradient 25–30°C/km), then the total component of Rangitata orogenic uplift is 18–20 km. Similar age patterns can be recognized elsewhere in the Haast Schist terrane, and to a lesser extent in the plutonic rocks of the Foreland Belt to the W (Sheppard *et al.* 1975). In both cases, the inferred Rangitata orogenic uplift appears to be substantial and sufficient to bring deep-seated metamorphic and igneous rocks to the surface before the mid-Cretaceous. Thus, within the intervening Alpine Schist sector, where a *total* uplift of 20–30 km has occurred, about 20 km could have been associated with the Rangitata orogenic phase. The vertical movements associated with the Kaikoura Orogeny are thus limited to less than 10 km. The age data also

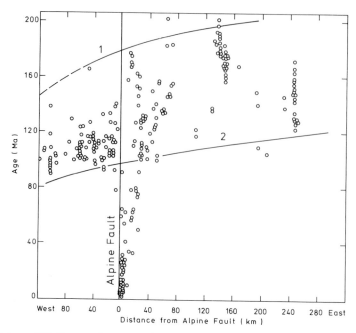

FIG. 3. K-Ar and Rb-Sr ages of metamorphic and plutonic rocks of the Rangitata Orogenic Belt in the South Island, New Zealand, shown in relation to the Alpine Fault. These include principally biotite and muscovite ages of granites and granodiorites W of the fault, and biotite and muscovite ages of schists and gneisses in the Alpine Schists immediately E of the fault. More than 30 km E of the fault the data are principally K-Ar total-rock ages of slates, phyllites and schists (essentially finely crystalline assemblages of quartz±chlorite±muscovite±biotite). Line 1 defines a minimum age for regional metamorphism and line 2 a minimum age for post-orogenic uplift (from Gabites & Adams 1978, with additions).

permit one to infer that the Jurassic–Cretaceous (Rangitata) uplift was *regional* in character and no *differential* vertical movement occurred at the Alpine Fault at that time.

Within a narrow zone E of the Alpine Fault, about 25 km wide, the Rangitata uplift age pattern described above, is abruptly modified and K-Ar ages decrease rapidly north-westwards from 100 to 120 Ma close to the Southern Alps divide (Fig. 3), to less than 10 Ma within 10 km of the Alpine Fault. As discussed above, the Alpine Schists in this zone would have been sufficiently uplifted during the Rangitata phase, to cool below the argon retention isotherm and hence begin to accumulate radiogenic argon. It can be argued, there-fore, (Sheppard *et al.* 1975) that the young ages, <10 Ma, imply the *superimposition* of a separate late Cenozoic thermal metamorphism discussed in more detail below. In some areas the young age pattern is complicated by the presence of excess argon in these rocks (Ga-bites & Adams 1978), and mineral isochron ages are a little younger, 5±1 Ma, than indi-vidual mineral ages. In general, at all points within the schists, close to the Alpine Fault, the minimum ages are less than 10 Ma and the majority are in the range 4–6 Ma. The youngest ages, 0.7 Ma, occur in the central section of the Alpine Schists (see section 6). High grade schists occur as pebbles in Plio-Pleistocene gravels (~ 2 Ma) W of the South-ern Alps and hence the schists had been up-lifted to the surface by then, a maximum of 10 km, since their time of cooling through the argon retention isotherm about 5±1 Ma ago. Therefore, for the period 2–5(±1) Ma ago, late Miocene–Pleistocene, the schists were up-lifted at a maximum rate 2.5–5 mm/yr. For the recent period 0–0.7 Ma ago (late Pleistocene), rocks in the central section of the Alpine Schists have been uplifted from the 250–300°C argon retention isotherm in about 0.7 Ma. If the depth to this isotherm was 5–10 km (cor-responding to a geothermal gradient at that time, in the range 25–50°C/km, see section 6), then uplift has occurred at rates 7–14 mm/yr). These uplift rates for the Mio-Pliocene and

Pleistocene are thus less than, but broadly similar to, the Holocene–Pleistocene rates derived from geomorphic data and the maximum rates derived from Pleistocene to late Pliocene plate tectonic data. They also confirm the acceleration of uplift during the period late Miocene–Recent. Thus, strong differential movements at the Alpine Fault have occurred in the late Miocene–Recent, at rates an order of magnitude faster than those of the earlier Rangitata (Jurassic–Cretaceous) phase.

Estimation of horizontal movements

The amount and rate of Jurassic–Cretaceous and/or Miocene–Recent transcurrent movement at the Alpine Fault depends critically on the reality of the lamprophyre dykes as a single swarm cut by the Alpine Fault, and the reliability of their measured Cretaceous ages. In either case, at least 120 km of transcurrent movement is post-Cretaceous and most probably occurred in the interval Miocene–Recent. If, as is argued below that the oldest ages within the young Alpine Schist age pattern, 5–10 Ma, are related to early movements on the Alpine Fault, then horizontal fault rates averaged over the last 5–10 Ma are 12–24 mm/yr. If the lamprophyre dyke evidence is dismissed, and all the transcurrent movement has occurred in the Miocene–Recent interval, then movements rates are correspondingly larger (at least 50 mm/yr).

Age data for Alpine Fault mylonites and adjacent schists

K-Ar dating of mylonites is, in prinicple, uncertain because the mylonitization process does not necessarily involve high temperatures sufficient to expel pre-existing radiogenic argon completely from the original rocks. However, the Alpine Fault mylonites are intimately developed with blastomylonites which *do* show crystallization of new muscovite on slip-planes and pseudotachylyte veins occur. Thus, the temperatures developed during either muscovite crystallization or local rock fusion should have been sufficient to de-gas the fine-grained mylonites. Dating of pseudotachylyte glass is also inherently uncertain since the rapid formation and chilling (as shown by glassy textures) could inhibit complete argon loss during formation, especially under high confining pressure. Thus, it seems prudent to reverse the normal 'rule' of K-Ar age interpretation and regard the minimum pseudotachylyte and mylonite total-rock ages as the closest estimate of the time of faulting.

New ages for mylonite, blastomylonite and pseudotachylyte from the Alpine Fault mylonites and adjacent Alpine Schists, in the Fox and Franz Josef Glacier regions, are listed in Table 2 and shown on a geological sketch map (Fig. 4). Analytical methods have been described elsewhere (Adams 1975).

A whole-rock age of a low-potassium phyllonite from Dry Creek (6399) is anomalously old, 125 Ma, which is evidence of incomplete degassing during formation and the presence of inherited radiogenic argon. The other mylonite total rock ages, 7.0, 11.9 and 15.2 Ma, might also show a similar (but lesser) effect and, as mentioned above, the youngest value is probably the most reliable. Significantly, it is closest to muscovite ages from blastomylonites at Dry Creek and Cook River (4.6, 4.8 and 5.1 Ma). A whole-rock age of a partly-devitrified pseudotachylyte at Harold Creek, 9.8 Ma, is also most safely regarded as a maximum age for faulting.

The blastomylonite ages are in accord with a muscovite age (5.7 Ma) from adjacent Alpine Schists at Fox Glacier and, in general, fall within the range of other mica ages in the garnet-oligoclase zone schists at the Lewis Pass (Sheppard *et al.* 1975), Hokitika and Wanganui Rivers (Mason 1961), Havelock Creek (J. E. Gabites, pers. comm.) and Haast River (Gabites & Adams 1978). Surprisingly, however, new biotite ages from the Alpine Schists at Fox and Franz Josef Glaciers and Dry Creek are even younger, in the range 0.7–3.4 Ma, which must reflect the lower argon retentivity of finely crystalline biotite compared with coarse muscovite and more specifically the ubiquitously developed *new* biotite on the late schistosity. A compilation as made in Fig. 5, of all mineral ages (and one pseudotachylyte whole-rock age) on a simplified oblique geological sketch of the central Alpine Schists (after Findlay 1979) has been compiled from several horizontal sections. This can also, in effect, be viewed as a sub-vertical section of the structural pile of the schists. The highest level is represented by the Jacobs River area and the lowest is near Dry Creek. The vertical thickness implied is difficult to assess, but probably does not exceed 10 km. The young ages lie within a zone of intense transposition close to the Alpine Fault and the ages occurring at the 'top' of the section are generally older than those at the 'bottom'. At each 'level', the ages are youngest, not at the Alpine Fault or within the associated mylonites, but 2–5 km to the E.

Table 2. *K-Ar determinations, Alpine Fault mylonites and Alpine Schists*

Sample no.*		K wt%	$^{40}Ar(radiogenic)/$ nl/g	% total	Age Ma[†]
HAROLD CREEK, Wanganui River (S64/200005)[‡]					
6785TR	pseudotachylite	0.96	0.350	32	9.3±0.5 ⎱ 9.8
			0.378	28	10.2±0.5 ⎰
DRY CREEK, nr Whataroa (S63/077913)					
6391bi	biotite-schist	6.76	1.30	30	4.95±0.4
6392bi	"	6.62	0.414	31	1.61±0.5 ⎱ 1.6
			0.416	24	1.61±0.5 ⎰
6393bi	"	6.61	0.349	12	1.32±0.5 ⎱ 1.1
			0.252	13	0.98±0.5 ⎰
6394mu	blastomylonite	7.37	1.33	29	4.62±0.4
6396TR	mylonite	0.26	0.121	7	11.9±0.9
6398TR	"	2.196	0.598	33	7.0±0.5
6399TR	"	0.128	0.646	44	125±3
6400TR	"	2.06	1.22	69	15.2±0.5
FRANZ JOSEF GLACIER (S71/825663)					
6690bi	biotite-schist	5.71	0.371	27	1.67±0.5
6692bi	"	6.61	0.465	33	1.81±0.5
6696bi	"	5.49	0.300	5	1.41±0.7
FOX GLACIER (S79/725594)					
6679bi	biotite-schist	5.97	0.263	13	1.13±0.5 ⎱ 1.2
			0.331	19	1.42±0.5 ⎰
6680mu	muscovite-schist	2.51	0.555	36	5.7±0.4
6682bi	biotite-schist	6.41	0.165	7	0.66±0.4 ⎱ 0.7
				8	0.77±0.4 ⎰
6684bi	"	5.13	0.674	19	3.38±0.4 ⎱ 3.4
			0.689	12	3.45±0.4 ⎰
COOK RIVER, nr Fox Glacier (S78/644593)					
6389mu	blastomylonite	5.74	1.08	41	4.84±0.4
6390mu	"	7.13	1.41	35	5.09±0.4

* TR = total rock (200–400 μ), bi = biotite, mu = muscovite.
† Decay constants ^{40}K, $\lambda_\beta = 0.496 \times 10^{-9} yr^{-1}$.
     $\lambda_e = 0.581 \times 10^{-10} yr^{-1}$.
Abundance $^{40}K/K = 0.01167$ at.%
‡ Grid reference, NZ map series NZMS 1,1:63600.

A similar pattern is seen 50 km to the S at Haast River, where the youngest isochron ages, 5±1 Ma, are found 5–10 km E of the fault (Gabites & Adams 1978). The pattern of ages seen in this inferred vertical section may be correlated with the known pattern of uplift rates, both along the Southern Alps and perpendicular to the mountain divide (Adams, J. 1979), with the youngest ages occurring in the area of highest relief and uplift rate. Uplift has clearly been sufficiently rapid for it to outstrip erosion, thus raising the isotherms and increasing the geothermal gradient. Uplift rates based on K-Ar cooling age data and depth estimates of argon retention isotherms during the late Cenozoic, must thus take into account the possibility of much higher geothermal gradients (say, 50°C/km) than normal (20–30°C/km).

Thermal effects of faulting

From the young ages in the Alpine Schists, Sheppard *et al.* (1975) concluded that they resulted from a separate, late Cenozoic thermal event, originating either (1) faulting and associated frictional heating at the Alpine Fault, or (2) shearing within the schists themselves. In Fig. 3 it can be seen that the young age pattern is asymmetric about the Alpine Fault and no young ages occur to the W.

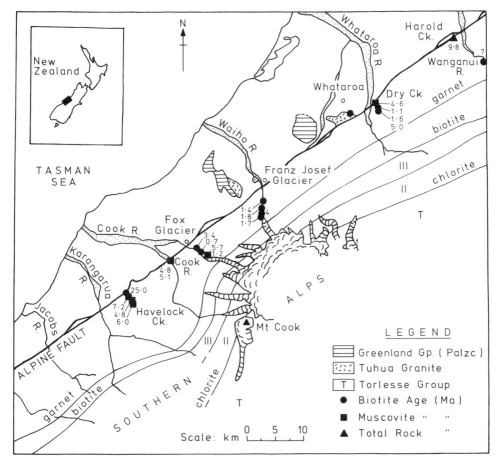

FIG. 4. K-Ar biotite and muscovite ages of blastomylonite (Alpine Fault Zone) and schists immediately adjacent to the east (Alpine Schists, Haast Schist Group). Ages are shown in relation to metamorphic facies of the Alpine Schists; Garnet(-Oligoclase), Biotite and Chlorite zones of the greenschist facies. (II and III refer to textural subdivisions of the chlorite zone.) Age data of Mason (1961) and J. E. Gabites (pers. comm.) are included. A single whole-rock age of a pseudotachylite from Harold Creek is also shown.

However, downthrow on the W side, to accommodate Tertiary–Quaternary sedimentation, could have buried any fault rocks and their associated thermal aureole. However, Young (1968) showed that *uplift* W of the fault has also been substantial, >5 km, to bring the thick Tertiary sequence to the surface. On balance, one would expect to see, in the western age pattern, some thermal effects mirroring those of the E.

To assess thermal effects of mylonitization at the Alpine Fault, Sibson *et al.* (this volume) calculated thermal profiles produced by frictional generation of heat during aseismic shear, about a fault zone 1 km wide, at fault rates 10–50 mm/yr, for 1–5 Ma, and against shear resistances of 0.1 and 1 kbar (Fig. 6). To apply to the Alpine Fault situation, such a model must indicate a thermal aureole consistent with (1) crystallization of micas in blastomylonite and adjacent schists, i.e. lower greenschist facies, and (2) a K-Ar age effect extending at least 15 km perpendicular to the fault plane. From the thermal profiles of Sibson *et al.* (ibid) the following points can be made: (1) a purely vertical fault movement, even at rates of 10 mm/yr for 5 Ma (cf. Alpine Fault) is insufficient to create a wide thermal aureole; (2) shear resistances of ~1 kbar are required to generate a large thermal increment sufficient to induce a metamorphic effect; (3) if the horizontal component of oblique strike slip reverse

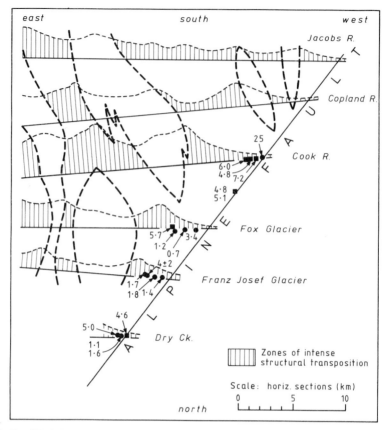

FIG. 5. Simplified E–W structural sections of the Alpine Schists in the central Southern Alps (taken from Findlay 1979, fig, 4), displayed to form an oblique aerial view of the western slopes of the Alps looking S over the Alpine Fault. Zones of intense structural transposition in the schists (vertical ruling) and intervening enclaves of only mild plication (from Findlay 1979) are extrapolated between the sections (heavy dashed lines). The diagram may also be visualized as a vertical section of the Alpine Schist structural pile, looking S, with E to the left of the diagram, the Alpine Fault dipping about 45° to the SE. On the structural sections are projected or interpolated the K-Ar age data of Fig. 4 using the same symbols.

fault movement has been at least 12–24 mm/yr for 5 Ma against a shear resistance of 1 kbar, then a wide thermal aureole could be created with sufficient thermal increment (100–200°C) close to the fault to initiate argon degassing of the Alpine Schists. The thermal increment must be added to the temperature commensurate with the depth of burial (5–10 km) at the onset of faulting and the total temperature induced would have to be in excess of 250°C. To create a thermal aureole sufficient to de-gas rocks 15 km from the fault (as seen at Haast), the models tend to impose temperatures that are rather too high at the fault itself. However, they could be modified to allow frictional heating, not only at the Alpine Fault, but more widely distributed within the zones of intense structural transposition in the schists themselves. In this way, the thermal profile would be broadened slightly and flattened. The Alpine Fault itself must be regarded as a transitional zone from dominantly plastic to brittle fault processes and products, across which there is, consequently, a steep thermal gradient. This is accentuated to some extent by the chilling effect of the cold downthrown rocks on the W side. Frictional drag must occur at the fault itself (Adams, J. 1979) and thus the maximum rate of shearing (and hence temperature rise) occurs immediately E of the fault and within the Alpine Schists. This accounts for the ages of mylonitic rocks at the

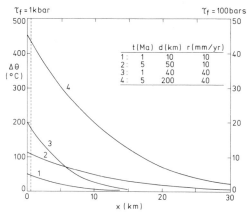

FIG. 6. Temperature profiles about a fault zone during steady aseismic shear (from Sibson *et al.* 1979, simplified), showing induced thermal increment $\Delta\theta$ (°C) due to frictional heating, at distance x (km), from a 1 km fault zone undergoing displacements d (km), for t (Ma), i.e., at rates r (mm/yr). Shear resistances $\tau_f = 0.1$ and 1.0 kbar. Thermal diffusivity $\kappa = 10^{-1}\,\mathrm{m^{-2}\,s^{-1}}$ and conductivity $K = 2\cdot10^{-2}\,\mathrm{erg.cm^{-1}.°C^{-1}.s^{-1}}$.

fault being slightly older than the minimum ages that occur 2–5 km to the E, where the argon retention isotherm is sustained at a higher level in the structural pile.

From the models of Sibson *et al.* (ibid) it seems possible that the rate and duration of movement at the Alpine Fault, could be sufficient to induce the required large thermal metamorphic effects in the adjacent rocks. The K-Ar age pattern seen in the mylonites and Alpine Schists seems consistent with such a thermal metamorphism and allows an indepen-

dent check on the thermal history of the country rocks close to a major fault zone.

Conclusions

1. Regional uplift of 18–20 km occurred in the Alpine Schists (Haast Schist Group) in the Jurassic and early Cretaceous at rates of 0.3–0.4 mm/yr. No differential vertical movement occurred at the Alpine Fault at this time.

2. Dependent upon the critical evidence of a Cretaceous(?) lamprophyre dyke swarm, the total transcurrent movement (480 km) on the Alpine Fault may be divided between a mid-late Cretaceous phase of 360 km, and a Miocene–Recent phase, 120 km.

3. Miocene–Recent uplift in the Southern Alps, adjacent to the Alpine Fault is 5–10 km. From an analysis of K-Ar age patterns in the Alpine Schists, the vertical fault rates at the Alpine Fault are, at maximum, 2.5–5.0 mm/yr for the period 2–5($\pm$1) Ma and 7–14 mm/yr for the period 0–0.7 Ma (assuming geothermal gradients in the range 25–50°C/km).

4. Late-Cenozoic and Quaternary oblique strike-slip reverse faulting at the Alpine Fault may have been sufficiently rapid and sustained to induce a thermal aureole by frictional heating of the Alpine Schists, extending up to 15 km E of the fault plane. This could explain the zone of young K-Ar ages seen in the Alpine Schists adjacent to the Alpine Fault.

ACKNOWLEDGMENTS. I thank G. W. Bird for his help and judgement in the field, and J. E. Gabites for her assistance with potassium and argon analyses. She also kindly provided unpublished K-Ar age data on the Alpine Schists. Don Nicholson is thanked for some particularly difficult mineral separations.

References

ADAMS, C. J. 1975. New Zealand potassium-argon age list-2. *N.Z. J Geol. Geophys.* **18**, 443–67.
—— 1978. Age of metamorphism and plutonism in the Jurassic-Cretaceous Rangitata Orogenic Belt, South Island, New Zealand. *In:* ZARTMAN, R. E. (ed.), *Short papers of the Fourth International Conference, Geochronology, Cosmochronology, Isotope Geology,* U.S. Geol. Surv. Open-file Report 78–701, 1–3.
—— 1979. Age and origin of the Southern Alps. *In:* WALCOTT, R. I. & CRESSWELL, M. M. (eds.), *The Origin of the Southern Alps.* Bull. R. Soc. N.Z. **18**, 73–8.
—— & NATHAN, S. 1978. Cretaceous chronology of the Lower Buller Valley, South Island, New Zealand. *N.Z. J Geol. Geophys.* **21**, 455–62.
ADAMS, J. 1979. Vertical drag on the Alpine Fault,

New Zealand. *In:* WALCOTT, R. I. & CRESSWELL, M. M. (eds.), *The Origin of the Southern Alps.* Bull. R. Soc. N.Z. **18**, 47–54.
CHASE, C. G. 1978. Plate kinematics: The Americas, East Africa and the rest of the world. *Earth planet. Sci. Lett.* **37**, 353–68.
DAMON, P. E. 1968. Potassium-argon dating of igneous and metamorphic rocks with applications to the Basin ranges of Arizona and Sonora. *In:* HAMILTON, E. I. & FARQUHAR, R. M. (eds), *Radiometric Dating for Geologists.* Interscience, London, 1–71.
FINDLAY, R. H. 1979. Summary of structural geology of Haast Schist terrain, central Southern Alps, New Zealand: Implication of structure for uplift of and deformation within Southern Alps. *In:* WALLCOTT, R. I. & CRESSWELL, M. M. (eds,

The Origin of the Southern Alps. Bull R. Soc. N.Z. **18,** 113–20.

GABITES, J. E. & ADAMS, C. J. 1978. Excess radiogenic argon and age of metamorphism and uplift in the Haast Schists, Haast Pass, Lakes Wanaka and Hawea, South Island, New Zealand. *In*: ZARTMAN, R. E. (ed.), *Short Papers of the Fourth International Conference, Geochronology, Cosmochronology, Isotope Geology,* U.S. Geol. Surv. Open-file rep. 78–701, 126–8.

GRINDLEY, G. W. 1963. Structure of the Alpine Schists of South Westland, Southern Alps, New Zealand. *N.Z. J Geol. Geophys.* **6,** 872–930.

—— 1974. New Zealand. *In*: SPENCER, A. M. (ed.), *Mesozoic-Cenozoic Orogenic Belts; Data for Orogenic Studies.* Spec. Pub. Geol. Soc. London, **4,** 387–416.

GUNN, B. M. 1960. Structural features of the Alpine Schists of the Franz Josef-Fox Glacier region. *N.Z. J Geol. Geophys.* **3,** 287–308.

HARPER, C. T. & LANDIS, C. A. 1967. K-Ar ages from regionally metamorphosed rocks, South Island, New Zealand, and some tectonic implications. *Earth planet. Sci. Lett.* **2,** 419–29.

HUNT, T. & NATHAN, S. 1976. Inangahua magnetic anomaly, New Zealand. *N. Z. J Geol. Geophys.* 19, 395–406.

HURLEY, P. M., HUGHES, H., PINSON JR, W. H. & FAIRBAIRN, H. W. 1962. Radiogenic argon and strontium diffusion parameters in biotite at low temperature obtained from Alpine Fault uplift in New Zealand. *Geochim. cosmochim. Acta* **26,** 67–80.

LILLIE, A. R., GUNN, B. M. & ROBINSON, P. 1957. Structural observations in the central Alpine region of New Zealand. *Trans. R. Soc. N.Z.* **85,** 113–29.

MASON, B. H. 1961. Potassium-argon ages of metamorphic rocks and granites from Westland, New Zealand. *N.Z. J Geol. Geophys.* **4,** 352–6.

—— 1962. Metamorphism in the Southern Alps of New Zealand. *Bull. Am. Mus. nat. Hist.* **123,** 217–48.

MOLNAR, P., ATWATER, T., MAMMERICKX, J. & SMITH, S. M. 1975. Magnetic anomalies, bathymetry and the tectonic evolution of the South Pacific since the Late Cretaceous. *Geophys. J. R. astron. Soc.* **40,** 383–420.

REED, J. J. 1964. Mylonites cataclasites and associated rocks along the Alpine Fault, South Island, New Zealand. *N.Z. J Geol. Geophys.* **7,** 645–84.

SHEPPARD, D. S., ADAMS, C. J. & BIRD, G. W. 1975. Age of metamorphism and uplift in the Alpine Schist belt, New Zealand. *Bull. geol. Soc. Am.* **86,** 1147–53.

SIBSON, R. H., WHITE, S. & ATKINSON, B. H. 1979. Fault rock distribution and structure within the Alpine Fault zone: A preliminary account. *In*: WALCOTT, R. I. & CRESSWELL, M. M. (eds.), *The Origin of the Southern Alps.* Bull. R. Soc. N.Z. **18,** 55–66.

SUGGATE, R. P. 1963. The Alpine Fault. *Trans. R. Soc. N.Z.* **2,** 105–29.

—— 1968. The Paringa Formation, Westland, New Zealand. *N.Z. J Geol. Geophys.* **11,** 345–55.

WALCOTT, R. I. 1979. Plate motion and shear strain rates in the vicinity of the Southern Alps. *In*: WALCOTT, R. I. & CRESSWELL, M. M. (eds.), *The Origin of the Southern Alps.* Bull. R. Soc. N. Z. **18,** 5–12.

WELLMAN, H. W. 1955. New Zealand Quaternary tectonics. *Geol. Rdsch.* **43,** 248–57.

—— & WILLETT, R. W. 1942. The geology of the West Coast from Abut Head to Milford Sound – Part 1. *Trans. R. Soc. N. Z.* **71,** 282–306.

WELLMAN, P. & COOPER, A. 1971. Potassium-argon ages of some New Zealand lamprophyre dykes near the Alpine Fault. *N. Z. J Geol. Geophys.* **14,** 341–50.

YOUNG, D. J. 1968. The Fraser Fault in central Westland, New Zealand and its associated rocks. *N. Z. J Geol. Geophys.* **11,** 291–311.

C. J. ADAMS. Institute of Nuclear Sciences, DSIR, Lower Hutt, New Zealand.

III.
THRUST AND NAPPE REGIMES
A. 'THE OLD WORLD'

Caledonides
Alpine
Eurasia

The internal geometry of nappes: criteria for models of emplacement

M. A. Cooper

SUMMARY: The geometric and stratigraphic properties of thrust sheets and fold nappes are controlled by the mechanisms by which they were initiated and emplaced. Thrust sheets that have developed by gravity gliding have their internal stratigraphies truncated by the basal thrusts which cut up-section at the trailing edges. In contrast thrust sheets that have developed by gravitational spreading have their internal stratigraphies truncated by the overlying thrust sheets, and their basal thrusts cut up-section at the leading edges. Fold-nappes have complicated geometries and correlation of stratigraphy between successive nappes is difficult. The basic geometric and stratigraphic properties of thrust sheets and fold-nappes developed by different mechanisms may be used as criteria for testing the applicability of these mechanisms to particular areas of orogenic belts. The Valley and Ridge Province of the Appalachians has geometric and stratigraphic properties consistent with thrust sheet development by gravitational spreading. The western nappes of the Central Scandinavian Caledonides are more complex but have properties suggesting development by buoyant upwelling of the orogen infrastructure. There is, however, a lack of detailed cross-sections of orogenic belts based on geophysical and/or borehole data in addition to the geological data. The interpretation of geological data in isolation is often too dependent on subjective information coloured by the mechanism preferred by the individual concerned.

Since the classic work of Heim (1921) in the Alps, the problems of the causes of initiation and the mechanics of emplacement of nappes have received much attention. The approaches vary from elegant theoretical treatments (Hubbert & Rubey 1959; Elliott 1976a,b; Chapple 1978), to experimental models (Bucher 1956; Ramberg 1966) and to empirical conceptual models developed to account for the geology of areas which have been mapped in detail (Van Bemmelen 1966; Price & Mountjoy 1970; Scholten 1973; Milici 1975; Gee 1978). In this paper, I shall attempt to demonstrate how the different geometric and stratigraphic properties of thrust sheets and fold-nappes result from the mechanisms by which they developed. I intend to use the term nappe in its broadest sense to include both thrust sheets and fold-nappes, defining a nappe as any large volume of rock underlain by a zone of tectonic discontinuity on which movement has occurred.

Thrust sheets

Thrust sheets are defined here as bodies of rock underlain by thrust surfaces and within which no *significant* stratigraphic repetition

due to large scale folding occurs. Two major theories of gravity emplacement have been proposed (Fig. 1) both of which result in the loss of gravitational potential; (1) gravity gliding (Lugeon & Gagnebin 1941; Hubbert & Rubey 1959) involving a thrust sheet moving down a low angle slope on a décollement horizon and (2) gravitational spreading (Bucher 1956; Price & Mountjoy 1970) where thrust sheets develop (serially) towards the foreland due to loading by earlier and structurally higher thrust sheets.

Gravity gliding

Early workers in alpine geology considered that the large thrust sheets characteristic of the Alps were emplaced by compressive forces. This is mechanically difficult because the compressive forces necessary to accomplish thrust sheet motion (Smoluchowski 1909; Hubbert & Rubey 1959) cannot be transmitted for great distances through the sheets. The compressive forces thus tend to produce local internal deformation of the thrust sheet instead of movement (Hubbert 1937, 1951; Ramberg 1977). These mechanical problems were appreciated by some of the early alpine geologists e.g.

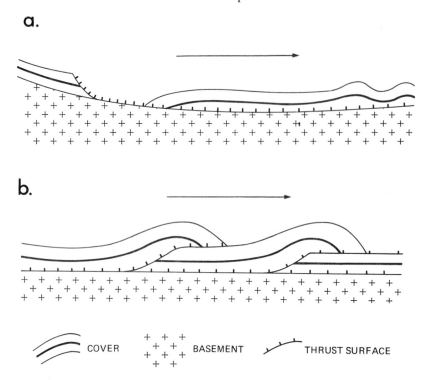

FIG 1. Diagram to show the essential differences between thrust sheets developed by gravity gliding and those developed by gravitational spreading. (a) Gravity gliding, note how the internal stratigraphy is truncated by the basal thrust and the sole thrust slopes in the direction of transport. (b) Gravitational spreading, note how the internal stratigraphy is truncated by the overlying thrust sheet and that the sole thrust slopes in the opposite direction to the transport direction.

Schardt (1898) and led to the development of the gravity gliding mechanism for emplacement. However, the problem of overcoming resistance to motion remained for subsequent resolution by a variety of theoretical models. These include reduction of sliding friction by high pore fluid pressures (Hubbert & Rubey 1959) and thrust sheet motion on 'weak' horizons (décollement zones) either on narrow zones of discrete shear (Van Bemmelen 1966), or on wider zones of distributed shear (Kehle 1970).

The Ultrahelvetic Nappes of the Alps illustrate the important geometric properties of thrust sheets emplaced by gravity gliding (Lugeon & Gagnebin 1941; Badoux 1963; Lemoine 1973). There appear to be no detailed restored balanced sections of the Ultrahelvetic Nappes and so I have used the schematic reconstruction of Badoux (1963) to illustrate the geometric properties (Fig. 2). The geometric consequences of gravity gliding that have been diagrammatically illustrated in Fig. 3, are: (1) the basal thrust surfaces are listric

and cut up-section at the trailing edge. (2) As a result the internal stratigraphy of individual thrust sheets is truncated by the basal thrust at the trailing edge. (3) The potential amount of relative displacement between thrust sheets can greatly exceed the section length of individual thrust sheets. (4) There is not necessarily any lateral stratigraphic continuity between successive thrust sheets. (5) The transport paths of thrust sheets may cross. (6) The thrust sheet composed of the structurally highest rocks usually moves first and has the potential to move the furthest.

Consider a sequence of undeformed rocks in a situation suitable for gravity gliding to occur due to orogenic uplift (Fig. 3). The youngest elements of the sequence detach first and move down-slope followed by other thrust sheets of successively deeper and, therefore, older parts of the sequence. This may produce an inverted bulk stratigraphy, although the internal stratigraphy of each thrust sheet is still the right way up; this process is termed divérticulation (Lugeon 1943). Debelmas & Kerckhove (1973)

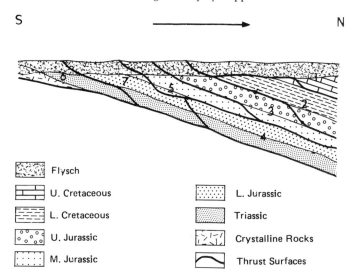

S ⟶ N

Flysch

U. Cretaceous

L. Cretaceous

U. Jurassic

M. Jurassic

L. Jurassic

Triassic

Crystalline Rocks

Thrust Surfaces

FIG. 2. Schematic reconstruction of the Ultrahelvetic Nappes in the Zone de Cols (after Badoux 1963). 1. Plaine Morte Nappe, 2. Anzeinde Nappe, 3. Sex Morte Nappe, 4. Bex Nappe, 5. Arveyes Nappe, 6. Meillert Nappe, 7. Chamossaire Nappe. The arrow indicates the direction of movement of the nappes during emplacement. The Plaine Morte Nappe composed of the youngest rocks was emplaced first and is now structurally the lowest nappe of the sequence.

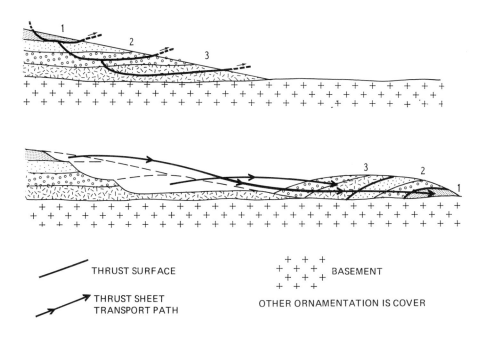

THRUST SURFACE

THRUST SHEET TRANSPORT PATH

BASEMENT

OTHER ORNAMENTATION IS COVER

FIG. 3. Development of the divérticulation phenomenon by gravity gliding.

concluded that the divérticulation pheno-menon can only be produced by gravity gliding. Hence, gravity gliding may produce large lateral differential displacements between thrust sheets, cause lack of lateral stratigraphic contin-uity and result in crossing transport paths.

Gravity gliding mechanisms have been prop-osed in many orogenic belts, where thrust sheets have developed with similar geometric properties to those of the Ultrahelvetic Nap-pes. Scholten (1973) has described gravity glid-ing in the Rocky Mountains S of the Lewis & Clark Line based on regional tectonic and stratigraphic arguments. Roberts & Crittenden (1973) came to a conclusion similar to Schol-ten's, further S in the Nevada/Utah seg-ment, where gravity gliding in the hinterland suprastructure has produced a sequence of younger on older thrusts. In both of the above examples divérticulation has not been recog-nized.

Gravitational spreading

The concept of gravitational spreading was introduced by Bucher (1956). It has subse-quently been developed by geologists working in the foreland of the Canadian Rocky Moun-tains (Dahlstrom 1970; Price & Mountjoy 1970; Price 1973). The gravitational spreading model proposes upwelling and lateral spread-ing of a hot, mobile infrastructure in the core of the orogen. In the foreland the lateral spreading is manifested by motion on an array of listric thrust surfaces which develop serially towards the foreland margin. The motions of thrust sheets in the foreland have been de-scribed by Burchfiel & Davis (1975). They proposed that the initial thrust sheet moves towards the foreland margin to overlie younger rocks; as the motion continues, the underlying rocks eventually attain their critical shear stress for failure. When this occurs a new thrust surface develops beneath the first thrust and hence further away from the orogen core. Repetition of this process causes the serial development of thrusts towards the foreland margin. The process is, however, self-limiting (Burchfiel & Davis 1975). The proposed serial development of structurally lower and more distal thrusts has been demonstrated on geological grounds. An elegant stratigraphic argument was developed by Bally et al. (1966) for serial thrust development in the foreland of the Canadian Rocky Mountains. They showed that the depocentres of the foredeeps, which formed in front of the moving thrust sheets, were migrating eastwards towards the fore-land margin with time. The rocks of each foredeep became involved in eastward direc-ted thrusting, exposed to erosion and subse-quently redeposited in the next (more easterly) foredeep.

The classic sections of the foreland of the Canadian Rocky Mountains (Bally et al. 1966; Price & Mountjoy 1970) illustrate the impor-tant geometric and stratigraphic properties of thrust sheets developed by gravitational spreading (Fig. 4). These are as follows: (1) The basal thrust surfaces are listric and always cut up-section in the direction of transport i.e. at the leading edge. (2) At the trailing edge of each individual thrust sheet the internal stratigraphy is truncated by the overlying thrust sheet and *not* by the basal thrust sur-face. (3) The amount of relative displacement between thrust sheets rarely exceeds the cross-strike length of the underlying thrust sheet; I have estimated that in Fig. 4 it is 20% of the thrust sheet cross-strike length. (4) There is lateral stratigraphic continuity between succes-sive thrust sheets. (5) Transport paths never cross. (6) The basal thrust sheet at the foreland is the last to move.

The last three properties are apparent from a mechanistic view of gravitational spreading (Fig. 5). Thrust sheet complex ABCD moves onto the underlying sequence, loading it and eventually causing it to fail on a lower, and more distal, thrust surface DEF. To attain the critical shear stress for failure on DEF sliding friction on DE and the shear strength of the rock along EF must be overcome. When these conditions are satisfied, further significant dis-placement on ADC is inhibited and movement of the thrust sheet complex on DEF begins. This imposes limitations on relative displace-ments between thrust sheets, rendering major stratigraphic juxtapositions unlikely. The geometric properties of secondary structures e.g. folded thrust planes, associated with gravi-tational spreading mechanisms are described by Dahlstrom (1970).

Fold-nappes

The concept of fold-nappes was developed by early workers in the Alps, notably Heim (1921), whose sections of the Lower and Mid-dle Penninic Nappes provided the type exam-ples. The structural style of these nappes (Wunderlich 1963; Milnes 1974) indicates that they formed in a predominantly ductile envi-ronment, thus complicating stratigraphic rela-tionships between nappes and making correla-tion difficult. Rigorous theoretical and

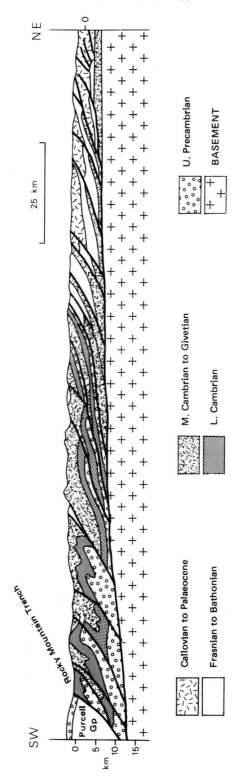

FIG. 4. Cross-section of the foreland belt of the Canadian Rocky Mountains (after Price & Mountjoy 1970).

1. γ DEF < γCrit

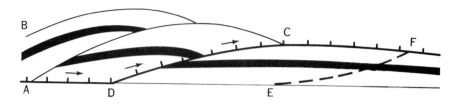

2. γ DEF $\approx$ γCrit

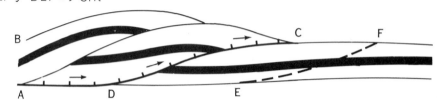

3. γ DEF > γCrit

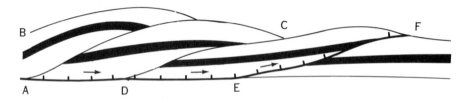

└──┴──┴──┴──┘ Dominant active thrust surface with sense of movement

FIG. 5. Three stage model illustrating the initiation of a structurally lower and more distal thrust surface DEF, due to loading by thrust sheet complex ABCD. τ_{DEF} shear stress on DEF, τ_{crit}, critical shear stress for failure on DEF.

mechanistic models have not as yet been developed for fold-nappes, but some of the results of the centrifuged models of Ramberg (1966) and Talbot (1974) are similar to cross-sections of the Alps. The driving force in these models is gravitational instability caused by density inversions. The process of fold-nappe formation can thus be interpreted as a manifestation of lateral spreading resulting from the ductile upwelling of the hot bouyant, metamorphic infra-structure of the orogen.

Price & Mountjoy (1970) suggest that such a process operating in the Shuswap complex in the core of the North American Cordillera provided the gravitational potential for the horizontal movements of the foreland thrust and fold belt. There is, however, no detailed discussion on the evolution of the Shuswap complex during the upwelling process. This is symptomatic of the general lack in the literature of theoretical models for the development of nappes in the central regions of orogenic belts. The majority of models for nappe development are concerned with foreland tectonics and touch only superficially on the tectonics of the orogen core. The imprecise nature of the ideas on fold-nappe development thus makes it difficult to erect characteristic geometric criteria. However, it can be said that such structures have complicated and unpredictable geometries and that stratigraphic intercorrelation is difficult.

Application of the criteria

The Valley and Ridge Province of the Appalachians

This segment of the Appalachian Orogen is a region for which there is sufficient geophysical and borehole data to allow the construction of detailed cross-sections (Gwinn 1970 fig. 3, Roeder & Witherspoon 1978 figs 1 and 2). It can be seen on a typical cross-section of the Valley and Ridge Province (Fig. 6) that the nappes of this region fall into the category of thrust sheets. This cross-section exhibits none of the geometric properties typical of gravity gliding (cf. Fig. 3). The geometric characteristics of the Valley and Ridge Province are, therefore, not consistent with the development of the thrust sheets by the mechanism of gravity gliding. In contrast, the geometric criteria of gravitational spreading as illustrated in Fig. 5. (cf. Fig. 6) are satisfied. The evidence for the sequential development of thrust surfaces from the interior to the foreland is discussed by Perry (1978) and is explained in terms of gravitational spreading by Bearce (1978) and Roeder *et al.* (1978). I conclude that the sequence of development of the thrust surfaces and the internal geometry of the thrust sheets indicate that the Valley and Ridge Province developed by a gravitational spreading mechanism.

The Central Scandinavian Caledonides

The Central Scandinavian Caledonides have been intensively studied since the 1960s (Nicholson & Rutland 1969; Nicholson 1974; Gee 1975a,b, 1978). The Precambrian Baltic basement is overlain by a thin sedimentary autochthon above which is a stack of allochthonous, wedge-shaped nappes. The eastern and structurally lower nappes are, in part, stratigraphically related to the autochthonous foreland sequence, whilst the western structurally higher nappes were derived from some distance W of the present Norwegian coast. Gee (1975a,b) summarized the internal stratigraphy of the individual nappe units in a broad W–E traverse from Trondheim to Östersund, which revealed little stratigraphic continuity between the nappes. He used the wedge geometry of the nappes as evidence for their emplacement by gravitational spreading (Gee 1975a p. 509–510). The model has subsequently been modified (Gee 1978) because of the recognition of mega-boudin structures involving several of the nappes (Gee 1977). The mechanism of nappe emplacement remains unchanged (Gee 1978, figs 10 & 11) but the development of the mega-boudins is regarded as being due to the gravitational collapse of the dense pile of nappes overlying the relatively lighter granitic basement. This is thought to have maintained the eastward motion of the nappes causing displacements 'which nearly double the estimates of translation distance' (Gee 1978 p. 413).

The development of gravity tectonics after emplacement has been described elsewhere in the Central Scandinavian Caledonides (Ramberg 1966; Cooper & Bradshaw 1980). The mechanism by which the pile of nappes accumulated is however open to discussion. Zachrisson (1969, 1973) has shown that many of the western nappes thin westwards partly because the internal stratigraphies are truncated by the basal thrusts. Although such relationships are noted by Gee, he uses the overall wedge-shaped geometry to support the gravitational spreading model (Fig. 7). This detailed internal geometry of the western nappes is,

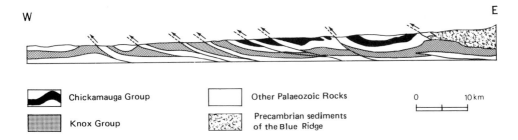

W   E

▬ Chickamauga Group		☐ Other Palaeozoic Rocks	0 10 km
▦ Knox Group		▦ Precambrian sediments of the Blue Ridge	

FIG. 6. Portion of a cross-section of the Valley and Ridge belt of the Appalachians (based on section T8, Roeder & Witherspoon 1978).

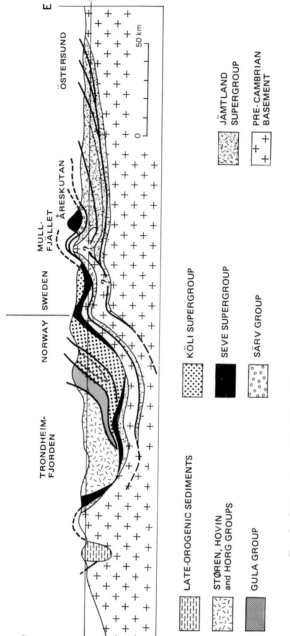

Fig. 7. Cross-section of the Central Scandinavian Caledonides along the line of the Trondheim–Östersund traverse (after Gee 1978).

however, incompatible with the geometric criteria for gravitational spreading erected above, for, as pointed out by Zachrisson (op. cit.), such stratigraphic geometry will not allow basal thrusts to cut down-section at the trailing edges. The other objection is the lack of lateral stratigraphic continuity between successive nappes, thus requiring large relative displacements. The eastern nappes, in contrast, have geometric properties compatible with thrust sheet development by gravitational spreading (Gee *et al.* 1978, plate 1). The geometric properties of the western nappes appear to support a gravity gliding mechanism for nappe emplacement, but the medium grade metamorphism of the western nappes coeval with emplacement (Gee 1975*b*) seems to preclude such a relatively high level process. Many of the western nappes throughout the Scandinavian orogen are characterized by large folds temporally and spatially related to nappe emplacement (e.g. Nicholson & Rutland 1969). They are thus fold-nappes rather than thrust sheets and are more difficult to deal with geometrically. The western nappes have complex geometric properties and stratigraphic correlations between nappes are very difficult.

The spatial relationship of the western nappes to the belt of characteristic foreland tectonics comprising the eastern nappes is analogous to the relationship of the Shuswap complex to the foreland trust and fold belt of the Canadian Rocky Mountains (Price & Mountjoy 1970). I therefore conclude that the western nappes of the Central Scandinavian Caledonides were emplaced as a result of lateral spreading, following upwelling, of the hot, buoyant, metamorphic infrastructure of the orogen. A more rigorous description of the mechanism of nappe emplacement awaits the development of theoretical models of fold-nappe evolution and the appreciation of their geometric consequences. The process of lateral spreading was manifested at the foreland as the emplacement by gravitational spreading of the eastern nappes.

Conclusions

The gravitational spreading and gravity gliding mechanisms both produce thrust sheets with geometric properties that are consequent upon their distinctive mechanisms. The mechanisms by which fold-nappes develop are less rigorously defined, but can be regarded as a result of the buoyant upwelling of an orogen infrastructure. Gravitational spreading produces basal thrusts cutting up-section at leading edges whereas gravity gliding produces basal thrusts that cut up-section at trailing edges. The geometric properties of fold-nappes are generally complicated.

The geometric properties established as being consequent upon the various mechanisms may be used as criteria for rejecting or accepting the application of such mechanisms to areas of other orogenic belts. However, before the criteria can be applied it is necessary to have detailed cross sections of the area of the orogenic belt under consideration. These should not be based solely on surface geological data but should have additional control provided either by geophysical or borehole data. In the absence of such independent controls it is difficult for the geologists to construct an objective cross-section that is not influenced by his pre-conceived ideas on thrust sheet and fold-nappe geometry and on the mechanism of their emplacement.

ACKNOWLEDGMENTS. I wish to thank the following: Dr J. Hossack for many hours of fruitful discussions on thrust and nappes: Drs R. Standley and J. Diggens and Messrs M. Garton and D. Watson for constructive criticisms of early drafts of the manuscript; Mr A. Sutton and Mr W. Ralph for producing the figures and the City of London Polytechnic Typing Centre for typing the manuscript.

References

BADOUX, H. 1963. Les unités ultrahelvetiques de la zone des cols. *Eclog. geol. Helv.* **56**, 1–13.

BALLY, A. W., GORDY, P. L. & STEWART, G. A. 1966. Structure, seismic data and orogenic evolution of Southern Canadian Rocky Mountains. *Bull. Can. Pet. Geol.* **14**, 337–81.

BEARCE, D. N. 1978. Structure of the eastern Coosa Valley, Alabama. *Am. J. Sci.* **278**, 461–76.

BUCHER, W. H. 1956. The role of gravity in orogenesis. *Bull. geol. Soc. Am.* **67**, 1295–318.

BURCHFIEL, B. C. & DAVIS, G. A. 1975. Nature and controls of Cordilleran orogenesis, Western United States: Extensions of an earlier synthesis. *Am. J. Sci.* **275-A**, 363–96.

CHAPPLE, W. M. 1978. Mechanics of thin-skinned fold-and-thrust belts. *Bull. geol. Soc. Am.* **89**, 1189–98.

COOPER, M. A. & BRADSHAW, R. 1980. The significance of basement/cover relationships in the tectonic evolution of the Salta region, Norway. *J. geol. Soc. London*, **137**, 231–40.

DAHLSTROM, C. D. A. 1970. Structural geology in the eastern margin of the Canadian Rocky Mountains. *Bull. Can. Pet. Geol.* **18**, 332–406.

DEBELMAS, J. & KERCKHOVE, C. 1973. Large gravity nappes in the French-Italian and French-Swiss Alps. *In*: DE JONG, K. A. & SCHOLTEN, R. (eds). *Gravity and Tectonics*, Wiley, New York, 189–200.

ELLIOTT, D. 1976a. The energy balance and deformation mechanisms of thrust sheets. *Philos. Trans. R. Soc. London*, **A283**, 289–312.

—— 1976b. The motion of thrust sheets. *J. geophys. Res.* **81**, 949–63.

GEE, D. G. 1975a. A tectonic model for the central part of the Scandinavian Caledonides. *Am. J. Sci.* **275-A**, 468–515.

—— 1975b. A geotraverse through the Scandinavian Caledonides–Østersund to Trondheim. *Sver. geol. Unders.* **C717**, 66p.

—— 1977. Extension of the Offerdal and Särv Nappes and Seve Supergroup into Northern Trondelag. *Nor. geol. Tidsskr.* **57**, 163–70.

—— 1978. Nappe displacement in the Scandinavian Caledonides. *Tectonophysics*, **47**, 393–419.

——, KUMPULAINEN, R. & THELANDER, T. 1978. The Tasjön décollement, Central Swedish Caledonides. *Sver. geol. Unders.* **C.742**, 35p.

GWINN, V. E. 1970. Kinematic patterns and estimates of lateral shortening, Valley and Ridge and Great Valley Provinces, central Appalachians, south-central Pennsylvania. *In*: FISHER, G. W. *Studies of Appalachian Geology: Central and Southern*. Wiley, New York, 127–46.

HEIM, A. 1921. *Geologie der Schweiz*. 11. *Die Schweizer Alpen*. Tauchnitz, Leipzig.

HUBBERT, M. K. 1937. Theory of scale models as applied to the study of geologic structures. *Bull. geol. Soc. Am.* **48**, 1459–520.

—— 1951. Mechanical basis for certain familiar geologic structures. *Bull. geol. Soc. Am.* **62**, 355–72.

—— & RUBEY, W. W. 1959. Role of fluid pressure in mechanics of overthrust faultings. *Bull. geol. Soc. Am.* **70**, 115-206.

KEHLE, R. O. 1970. Analysis of gravity sliding and orogenic translation. *Bull. geol. Soc. Am.* **81**, 1641–64.

LEMOINE, M. 1973. About gravity gliding tectonics in the Western Alps. *In*: DE JONG, K. A. & SCHOLTEN, R. (eds.), *Gravity and Tectonics*, Wiley, New York, 201–16.

LUGEON, M. 1943. Une nouvelle hypothese tectonique: la diverticulation. *Bull. Soc. vaud. Sci. nat.* **62**, 301–3.

—— & GAGNEBIN, E. 1941. Observations et vues nouvelles sur la géologie des Prealpes Romande. *Mem. Soc. vaud. Sci. nat.* **47**, 1–90.

MILNES, A. G. 1974. Structure of the Pennine Zone (Central Alps): A new working hypothesis. *Bull. geol. Soc. Am.* **85**, 1727–32.

MILICI, R. C. 1975. Structural patterns in the southern Appalachians: Evidence for a gravity slide mechanism for Alleghanian deformation. *Bull. geol. Soc. Am.* **86**, 1316–20.

NICHOLSON, R. 1974. The Scandinavian Caledonides. *In*: NAIRN, A. E. M. & STEHLI, F. G. (eds). *The Ocean Basins and Margins*, 2. *The North Atlantic*, Plenum Press, London, 161–203.

—— & RUTLAND, R. W. R. 1969. A section across the Norwegian Caledonides; Bodø to Sulitjelma. *Nor. geol. Unders.* **260**, 86p.

PERRY, W. J. Jr. 1978. Sequential deformation in the Central Appalachians. *Am. J. Sci.* **278**, 518–42.

PRICE, R. A. 1973. Large-scale gravational flow of supracrustal rocks, Southern Canadian Rockies. *In*: DE JONG, K. A. & SCHOLTEN, R. (eds). *Gravity and Tectonics*, Wiley, New York, 491–502.

—— & MOUNTJOY, E. W. 1970. Geological structure of the Canadian Rocky Mountains between Bow and Athabasca rivers—a progress report. *Spec. Pap. geol. Assoc. Can.* **1**, 7–25.

RAMBERG, H. 1966. The Scandinavian Caledonides as studied by centrifuged dynamic models. *Bull. geol. Instn. Univ. Uppsala*, **43**, 72p.

—— 1977. Some remarks on the mechanism of nappe movement. *Forh. geol. Foren. Stockholm*. **99**, 110–7.

ROBERTS, R. J. & CRITTENDEN, M. D. Jr. 1973. Orogenic mechanisms, Sevier Orogenic Belt, Nevada and Utah. *In*: DE JONG, K. A. & SCHOLTEN, R. (eds). *Gravity and Tectonics*, Wiley, New York, 409–28.

ROEDER, D. & WITHERSPOON, W. D. 1978. Palinspastic map of east Tennessee. *Am. J. Sci.* **278**, 543–50.

——, YUST, W. W. & LITTLE, R. L. 1978. Folding in the Valley and Ridge province of Tennessee. *Am. J. Sci.* **278**, 477–96.

SCHARDT, H. 1898. Les régions exotiques du versant nord des Alpes Suisses. *Bull. Soc. vaud. Sci. nat.* **34**, 114–219.

SCHOLTEN, R. 1973. Gravitational mechanisms in the Northern Rocky Mountains of the United States. *In*: DE JONG, K. A. & SCHOLTEN, R. (eds). *Gravity and Tectonics*, Wiley, New York, 473–90.

SMOLUCHOWSKI, M. S. 1909. Mechanics of overthrusts. *Geol. Mag.* **6**, 204–5.

TALBOT, C. J. 1974. Fold nappes as asymmetric mantled gneiss domes and ensialic orogeny. *Tectonophysics*, **24**, 259–76.

VAN BEMMELEN, R. W. 1966. The structural evolution of the Southern Alps. *Geol. Mijnbouw.* **45**, 405–44.

WUNDERLICH, H. G. 1963. Ablauf and Altersverhältnis der post-varistischen Tektonik und Metamorphose im Westalpenbogen. *Geol. Minjbouw.* **42**, 155–69.

ZACHRISSON, E. 1969. Caledonian Geology of Northern Jämtland—Southern Vasterbotten. *Sver. Geol. Unders.* **C644**, 33p.

—— 1973. The westerly extension of Seve rocks within the Seve-Koli Nappe Complex in the Scandinavian Caledonides. *Forh. geol. Foren. Stockholm*, **95**, 243–51.

M. A. COOPER, Department of Geology, City of London Polytechnic, Walburgh House, Bigland Street, London E1.

The strain profile above a major thrust fault, Finnmark, N Norway

N. J. Milton & G. D. Williams

SUMMARY: The base of the Laksefjord Nappe, Finnmark, N Norway consists of a strained conglomerate. Field studies of the deformation suggest a simple strain profile, with strain depending on height above the basal thrust within the Nappe. A combination of simple shear deformation, related to movement on, or initiation of, the basal thrust, with a relatively constant flattening component is proposed. A mathematical model based on down surface slope stress and the steady state flow law is suggested for the simple shear component of the strain.

The Laksefjord Nappe lies within the Caledonides of Finnmark, N Norway. It is composed of a series of thrust slices of meta-conglomerate, quartzite and phyllite, metamorphosed to lower greenschist facies. It is thrust over parautochthonous, late Precambrian–Ordovician sediments of the Gaissa Nappe, and is itself overthrust by the amphibolite facies Kalak Nappe (see Fig. 1). The lowest stratigraphic and structural unit in the Laksefjord Nappe is the conglomerate of the Ifjord Formation. This is a thick metacong-lomerate with clasts of quartzite and granite-gneiss (with subsidiary epidosite, carbonate, jasper etc.) set in a schistose to quartzitic matrix. The clast size ranges from pebbles to cobbles and boulders, and clasts are deformed, so that, in general, they lie within the cleavage with their long axes parallel to a stretching lineation. The deformation of the clasts is seen to increase as the basal thrust is approached, and this inspired the authors and T. J. Chapman to undertake a study of strain patterns within the conglomerate.

Methods

A full account of the methods used in analysis of strain in the conglomerate and the results obtained is provided by Chapman *et al.* (1979). This will be briefly summarized below.

At each locality two joint faces were chosen perpendicular to the cleavage and, where possible, parallel and perpendicular to the lineation. The distribution of the localities was controlled by the availability of suitable joint faces. The axial ratios of 30 pebbles were measured on each joint face, and the harmonic mean of the ratios calculated as an estimate of the two-dimensional strain ellipse (Lisle 1977). The two strain ellipses thus measured (both of which, being perpendicular to the cleavage, contain the Z axis of strain) were combined to

give the overall strain ellipsoid. This was adjusted using the method of Gay (1968a,b), to allow for the clast/matrix ductility contrast. From the $X:Y:Z$ ratio of the ellipsoid, two parameters were calculated to describe the state of strain. Lodes parameter γ is defined as $\gamma = (2\bar{\varepsilon}_2 - \bar{\varepsilon}_1 - \bar{\varepsilon}_3)/(\bar{\varepsilon}_1 - \bar{\varepsilon}_3)$ and $\bar{\varepsilon}_s$ as

$$\bar{\varepsilon}_s = \frac{1}{\sqrt{3}}\sqrt{(\bar{\varepsilon}_1 - \bar{\varepsilon}_3)^2 + (\bar{\varepsilon}_2 - \bar{\varepsilon}_3)^2 + (\bar{\varepsilon}_3 - \bar{\varepsilon}_1)^2}$$

where $\bar{\varepsilon}_1 = \ln X$ etc.

Results

The contour map of $\bar{\varepsilon}_s$ shows the following features (Fig. 2):
1. Contours of $\bar{\varepsilon}_s$ run NE–SW, roughly parallel to the basal thrust.
2. Strain magnitudes are greatest near the thrust and decrease with distance from it.
3. In the SW of the area, two belts of higher $\bar{\varepsilon}_s$ are seen above minor internal thrust faults.
4. The $\bar{\varepsilon}_s$ contours 'V' down the major valleys.
5. In places, the basal thrust is seen to cross-cut the $\bar{\varepsilon}_s$ contours.

The contoured Flinn plot (ln X/Y against ln Y/Z) where the contouring is arbitrary and is used to show the main grouping of points, shows that the strains lie mostly in the flattening field. The middle-range contours outline elongate areas parallel to, and below, the plane strain line (Fig. 3).

Interpretation

The $\bar{\varepsilon}_s$ contours are subplanar. They dip to the NW and are sub-parallel to the basal thrust. It is proposed that the strain pattern is essentially one-dimensional, and that strain depends only on height within the nappe. The basal thrust and internal thrusts post-date the pebble deformation, which may be related to a sole thrust, not exposed at Ifjord or Langfjord,

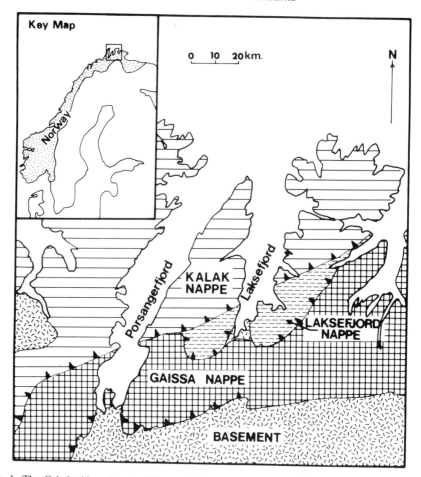

Fig. 1. The Caledonides of central Finnmark showing the position of the Laksefjord Nappe.

to which the observed thrusts are imbricate. The strain is probably a combination of simple shear strain, related to movement on, or initiation of, the sole thrust and varying with height within the Nappe, and a flattening component. This combination would result in a strain profile which, on a Flinn plot, would lie parallel to the plane strain line, but displaced into the flattening field (Sanderson 1976). Varying simple shear, increasing with proximity to basal thrusts, has already been proposed for the Kalak and Laksefjord Nappes (Williams 1978) on the evidence of rotated folds. Fig. 4 shows a graph of the simple shear component of strain calculated for individual localities and expressed as $(\gamma = R - 1/\sqrt{R}$, where $R = (X/Y)^2)$, against height of the locality above the basal thrust, which is thought to be a close approximation to height above the sole thrust. The shear strain can be seen to increase

rapidly, perhaps exponentially, as the thrust is approached.

The Model

The relative simplicity of the strain profile encouraged the authors to attempt to erect a mathematical model for the deformation of the Nappe.

A slab of rock with surface slope α and uniform composition (density ρ) lies on an interface above an undeforming basement. The downslope shear stress τ within the slab varies with depth h as:

$$\tau = \rho g h \alpha \qquad (1)$$

where g is the acceleration due to gravity (Elliott 1976).

Because of the very large strains recorded from the base of the Laksefjord Nappe accompanied by extensive plastic deformation of

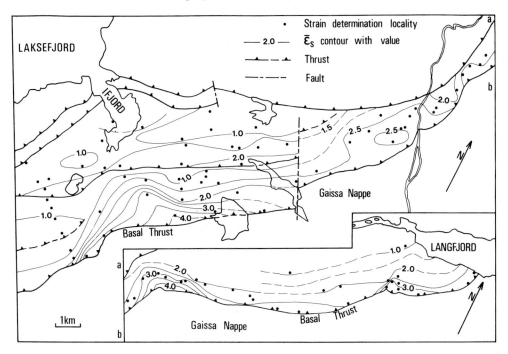

Fig. 2. Contour map showing the amount of strain ($\bar{\varepsilon}_s$) in the deformed basal conglomerate of the Laksefjord Nappe.

quartz, it is believed that deformation took place by steady state flow of the rocks by intracrystalline processes. Such steady state flow of rocks may be expected to obey the relationship

$$\dot{\varepsilon} \propto \frac{1}{T} \exp - \left(\frac{Q}{RT}\right) \tau^{\eta} \qquad (2)$$

where $\dot{\varepsilon}$ is the strain rate, Q and η depend on the properties of the rock, R is the gas constant and T is the temperature. This is only one of several possible relationships defining creep of rocks at crustal levels, but all contain the exponential term. Equations (1) and (2) have already been combined by Nye (1959) to explain the strain rate profile in glaciers. In crustal rocks, the situation may be further complicated by the temperature variation with depth.

$$T = 273 + Gh \qquad (3)$$

where G is the geothermal gradient.

The combination of equations (1), (2) and (3) gives a relationship between strain rate ($\dot{\varepsilon}$) and depth (h) of the form shown in Fig. 4-inset; an exponential rise in $\dot{\varepsilon}$ similar to the rise in γ observed in the field.

Although there appears to be a broad simi-larity between observed shear strain and strain rate of the mathematical model, it is felt that this model is by no means the whole answer, as shear stress and temperature, and therefore deformation, would continue to increase with depth below the thrust surface, unless shear stresses were unable to cross the interface. It is more likely that deformation around the in-itiating thrust fault takes the form of a sub-horizontal shear zone, and only the upper por-tion of the shear zone is preserved in the base of the nappe; the lower portion being left in the nappe 'root zone' as nappe translation is continued.

The shear deformation within the conglom-erate is insufficient to account for the total translation of the nappe. Integration of the shear in the nappe profile suggests that the relative movement across the deformed con-glomerate is in the order of 7 km, while a minimum displacement of 70 km has been suggested by Gayer & Roberts (1973). It is suggested that translation of the Nappe has occurred mainly by sliding on a thrust plane, and that the deformation observed in the basal conglomerate is related to the initiation of the thrust zone as a major sub-horizontal shear zone.

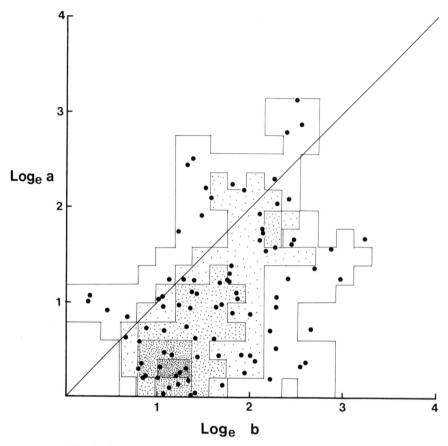

FIG. 3. Contoured Flinn plot showing strains from all the localities.

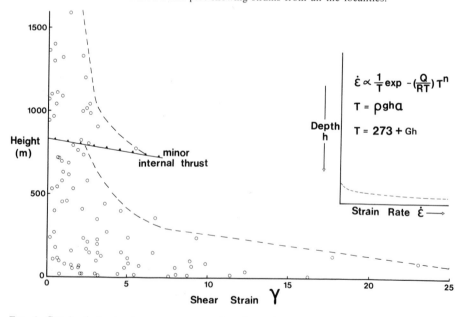

FIG. 4. Graph of simple shear component of strain against heights above the basal thrust for individual localities. Inset; Curve showing the relationship between strain rate and depth in the thrust sheet model.

References

CHAPMAN, T. J., MILTON, N. J. & WILLIAMS, G. D. 1979. Shape fabric variations in deformed conglomerates at the base of the Laksefjord Nappe, N Norway. *J. geol. Soc. London,* **136,** 683–91.

ELLIOTT, D. 1976. The motion of thrust sheets. *J. geophys. Res.* **81,** 949–63.

GAY, N. C. 1968a. Pure shear and simple shear deformation of inhomogeneous viscous fluids. 1. Theory. *Tectonophysics,* **5,** 211–34.

—— 1968b. Pure shear and simple shear deformation of inhomogeneous viscous fluids. 2. The determination of strain in a rock from objects such as deformed pebbles. *Tectonophysics,* **5,** 295–302.

GAYER, R. A. & ROBERTS, J. D. 1973. Stratigraphic review of the Finnmark Caledonides with possible tectonic implications. *Proc. Geol. Assoc.* **84,** 405–28.

LISLE, R. J. 1977. Estimation of the tectonic strain ratio from the mean shape of deformed elliptical markers. *Geol. Mijnbouw.* **56,** 140–4.

NYE, J. F. 1959. The motion of ice sheets and glaciers. *J. Glaciol. London,* **3,** 493–507.

WILLIAMS, G. D. 1978. Rotation of contemporary folds into the X direction during overthrust processes in Laksefjord, Finnmark. *Tectonophysics,* **48,** 29–40.

N. J. MILTON, G. D. WILLIAMS. Department of Geology, University College, P.O. Box 78, Cardiff, U.K.

The Moine Thrust Zone: an overview

K. R. McClay & M. P. Coward

SUMMARY. The geometry of structures within the Moine Thrust Zone are similar to those found in classic thin-skinned tectonic regimes such as the southern Canadian Rocky Mountains. The deformation style and strain patterns along the strike of the Moine Thrust Zone are controlled by the position of the floor (or Sole) thrust. The stacking sequence of thrust nappes is from E to W in the direction of transport. Reactivation of some thrusts has caused reversals in the stacking sequence. The mylonites associated with the Moine Thrust have undergone a long and complex history of progressive deformation.

Detailed descriptions of the Moine Thrust Zone at Loch Eriboll are given and the relationships of the Moine Thrust Zone to other major Caledonian tectonic features of the NW Highlands are discussed.

The NW boundary of the Caledonian Orogeny in Britain is marked by a belt of foreland thrusting—the Moine Thrust Zone (Fig. 1). The first comprehensive account of the thrust zone was given by Peach et al. (1907) in the classic NW Highlands memoir of the Geological Survey. Many subsequent accounts have described detailed portions of the thrust belt (Ramsay 1969; Soper & Brown 1971; Soper & Wilkinson 1975; Christie 1960; Phemister 1960 and Johnson 1960, 1961). In particular, considerable attention has been paid to problems of Moine stratigraphy, metamorphism and deformation (Johnson 1975; Johnstone 1975; Powell 1974; Harris et al. 1978). The purpose of this review is to emphasize current studies and interpretations (Elliot & Johnson in press) of the thrust belt itself. This paper was initially prepared as a guide for the post-conference field trip (Coward & McClay 1979) and has since benefited greatly from discussions with field trip participants.

In this overview, analogies are drawn between structures found in the Moine Thrust Zone and those observed in the Canadian Rocky Mountains and the Appalachians. The Moine Thrust Zone extends from Eriboll in the N to Sleat on Skye in the S, a distance of over 190 km (Fig. 1). Proterozoic meta-sediments (the Moine schists) which were last deformed in the Caledonian Orogeny (500–400 Ma) were thrust over a foreland of early Proterozoic Lewisian gneiss, unmetamorphosed late Proterozoic 'Torridonian' and Cambro-Ordovician sediments (Peach et al. 1907).

The Moine Thrust Zone, termed the 'belt of complication' by the Geological Survey, varies from 0 to 11 km wide. Within the thrust belt there are several thrust bounded nappes stacked on top of each other. The lowermost thrust sequence contains an imbricated sequence of Cambro-Ordovician rocks and the basal thrust is termed the Sole Thrust.

The Sole Thrust climbs down the stratigraphy from NW to SE; in the NW it lies in the Cambro-Ordovician sediments but to the E it must lie within the Lewisian complex as these gneisses are involved in the imbricate sequence. Above this imbricate zone are several large thrust nappes of Lewisian and Cambrian rocks. The thrusts which bound these nappes are not parallel but converge and diverge and the nappes are lens shaped in plan. Wrench-fault bounded and fold core terminated thrust faults are found.

The most easterly thrust in the belt of complication (the Moine Thrust) carries mylonites and the Moine schists over the foreland. This is structurally the highest thrust, though locally small faults thrust underlying quartzites over the Moines. The transport direction is WNW, as seen from slickensides and listric faults (Ramsay 1969). The sequence of faults is presumably from E to W, towards the foreland, as the eastern faults are folded above steps in the underlying thrusts. The eastern thrusts, however, were reactivated and were also the last to move, slicing through intrusions in the underlying nappes.

Displacements on individual thrusts and thrust sheets vary from 3.5 to 25–30 km (Coward et al. in press; Elliot & Johnson in press). Total Moine displacement across the thrust belt has been estimated as at least 40–50 km (Ramsay 1969; Coward & Kim this volume). This paper briefly summarizes the stratigraphy of the NW Highlands and the structure of the

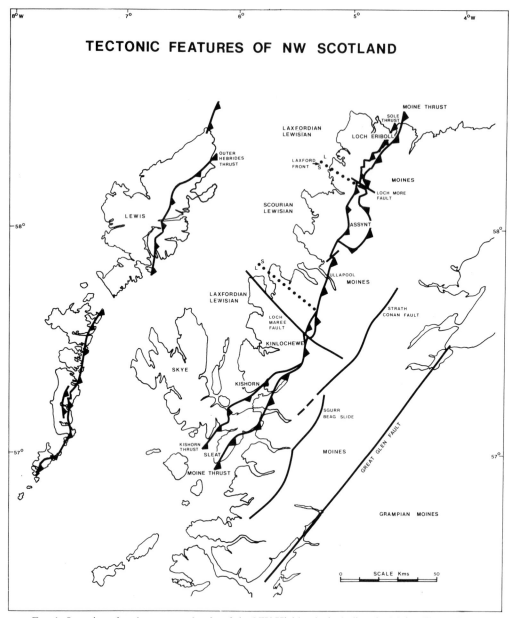

FIG. 1. Location of major structural units of the NW Highlands, including the Moine Thrust Zone and the Outer Hebrides Thrust. Subdivisions in the Lewisian foreland are designated S: Scourian, L: Laxfordian.

thrust zone (from N to S) is reviewed. In particular, the Loch Eriboll section is described in detail.

Stratigraphy

The stratigraphic and inferred time relationships of the Moine Thrust Zone are summarized in Fig. 2.

The Lewisian gneiss

The Lewisian rocks of the NW Highlands (Fig. 1) were first described in detail by Peach *et al.* (1907). On the mainland, the Lewisian is divided into several units, a central block between Laxford and Loch Broom (Fig. 1), and units both N and S of the central block (Fig. 1). At Scourie and southwards the grey Lewisian

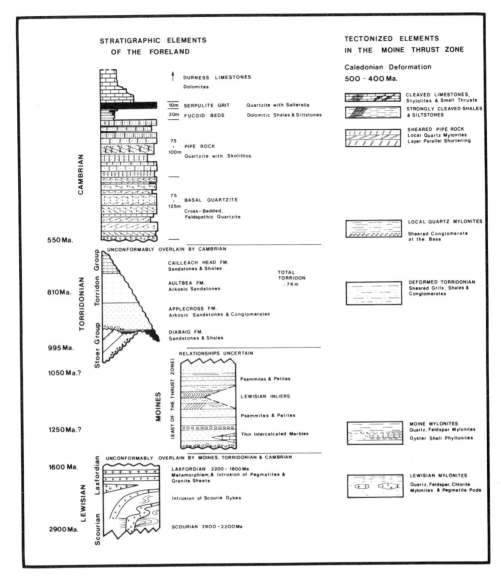

FIG. 2. Summary of the stratigraphy and inferred time relationships of the NW Highlands. Thicknesses are given for the Cambrian succession but the other units are not drawn to scale.

gneisses and amphibolites are cut by a series of discordant NW trending metamorphosed basic dykes. N of Laxford, there are no such discordant dykes and the gneisses and amphibolites are cut by large volumes of granites and pegmatites. A similar feature is found S of Loch Broom (Fig. 1). The chronology of the Lewisian complex was defined by Sutton & Watson (1951). They considered that the gneisses N of Laxford are the reworked equivalents of the gneisses and dykes to the S. This

period of reworking was termed the Laxfordian and dated at between 1850 and 1575 Ma (Giletti *et al.* 1961; Lambert & Holland 1972). The early period of gneiss formation was termed the Scourian (Sutton & Watson 1951) and dated at 2900–2600 Ma (Giletti *et al.* 1961; Moorbath *et al.* 1969). Further subdivision of the Lewisian has been made by Park (1970) and the Lewisian history summarized by Watson (1975) and Bowes (1969).

The Scourian history can be divided into at

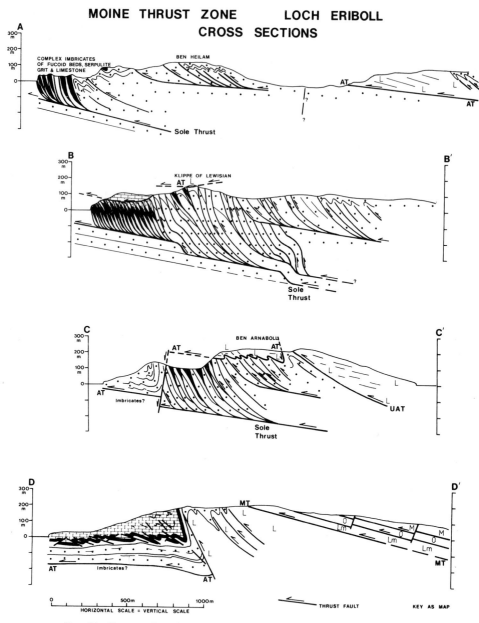

FIG. 3*b*. Cross sections A–D across the Moine Thrust Zone at Loch Eriboll.

least four deformation events (Coward *et al.* in press; Beach *et al.* 1974), accompanied by phases of granulite and amphibolite facies metamorphism. The NW–SE trending amphibolite dykes cut across the f4 folds. Across the Laxford front, these dykes become deformed into E–W trends. The gneisses become swamped with granite and pegmatite sheets. A locally intense fabric with a gently SE plunging lineation is developed. The Laxfordian fabric with concordant granites and pegmatites is folded around second phase Laxfordian folds (Coward *et al.* in press).

The Moines

The Moines comprise an ill-defined assemblage of Proterozoic metamorphic rocks of largely sedimentary origin. In the main, they are a monotonous sequence of metamorphosed sandstones and shales of uncertain age which overlie the Moine Thrust. The Moine rocks 'sensu stricto' are bounded to the NW by the Moine Thrust and by the Great Glen Fault to the SE (Harris *et al.* 1975, Harris *et al.* 1978). The psammitic Central Highland Granulites are commonly accepted as equivalents of the Moines s.s. (Harris *et al.* 1978).

The lithological characteristics of the Moines are described in detail by Johnstone (1975) and Johnstone *et al.* (1969). These authors have divided the Moines (s.s.) into three tectonostratigraphic divisions—the Morar, Glenfinnan and Locheil. The relationships between these divisions, which are separated by major tectonic discontinuities are, however, uncertain.

The Moines (s.s.) in places lie unconformably upon Lewisian gneisses (Peach *et al.* 1907) which appear to be of Scourian type (Watson 1975). The Moine (s.s.) is overlain by Middle Old Red Sandstone and is intruded by the Carn Chuinneag Granite (Rb-Sr isochron 560 ± 10 Ma). Radiometric ages from the Moines range from 1100 to 320 Ma (Harris *et al.* 1978) reflecting a long and complex history.

As a whole, the Moines of Scotland had been considered as an older part of the Dalradian (late Proterozoic–early Phanerozoic) sedimentary succession because the Central Highland Moine passes up without a break into the younger supergroup, and no unconformity has been recognized within the Moine (Harris *et al.* 1978).

Recently Brook *et al.* (1977) reported Rb/Sr whole rock ages of about 1100 Ma from gneisses and meta-pelites in the Moines of the NW Highlands. This 1100 Ma event may be correlated with the Grenville in Canada. In addition

there are also whole rock ages of 550–600 Ma (Morarian) obtained from granites and pegmatites throughout the Moines (Pidgeon & Johnson 1974; van Breeman *et al.* 1974). Thus it appears likely that at least part of the Moine (s.s.) belongs to an older sedimentary sequence than the Central Highland Granulites (Harris *et al.* 1974; Powell 1974) since it is unlikely that these latter rocks are older than about 668 ± 23 Ma (Johnstone 1975). Similarly, earlier correlations of the Moines with the 'Torridonian' are not justified. Suggested ages for sedimentation of the Moine (s.s.) are 1250–1050 Ma (Brook *et al.* 1977).

In the tectonic history of the Moines, Powell (1974) records several deformation phases, probably of Grenville age. Basement gneisses form the cores of large fold nappes in the Moines which were originally eastward verging since modified slightly by NW verging Caledonian structures.

There is no evidence of Grenville or Morarian events to the W of the Moine Thrust. The Lewisian rocks give only pre-'Torridonian' mineral ages and the 'Torridonian' rocks were only gently warped during the Precambrian. As the Precambrian structures in the Moines verge eastwards, the Lewisian rocks may have formed the hinterland to any Grenville Orogeny. The basement gneisses to the Moines have been correlated with the Lewisian gneiss and if this correlation is correct then the present line of the Moine Thrust would not represent a suture line between two Grenville age plates. However, the westernmost outcrops of basement gneiss in the Moine Nappe contain high pressure granulite to eclogite facies minerals and must represent lower gneissic crust uplifted during the Precambrian, presumably during the Grenville Orogeny.

The 'Torridonian'

The 'Torridonian' is the name long given to the thick sequence of arkosic red-beds which rest unconformably on the Lewisian gneisses of the foreland and thrust zone.

Detailed field-mapping, palaeomagnetic studies and radiometric dating has revealed the 'Torridonian' of Peach *et al.* (1907) comprises two quite distinct successions. The Stoer Group and Torridon Group are separated by a 25° angular unconformity, a 50° change in palaeomagnetic pole position and approximately 180 Ma as determined by Rb/Sr whole rock isochrons. As Stewart (1969, 1975) has indicated, the term 'Torridonian' has historical but little stratigraphical significance.

The older Stoer Group (995 ± 24 Ma) comprises 2.3 km of red arkosic sandstones and siltstones with locally derived breccias. These sediments were deposited on a hilly Lewisian land surface as bajada and playa deposits which are overlain by fluvial sands which are often pebbly. Local lake cycles and a volcanic mudflow occur. The Stoer Group crops out in a narrow belt between Stoer and Loch Maree.

The more extensive and younger Torridon Group (810 ± 17 Ma) oversteps the Stoer Group onto a rugged Lewisian topography. Red and purple arkosic sandstones, often pebbly, predominate but red and grey shales occur throughout the 7 km thick succession. Four formations are recognized. Sedimentological analysis indicates that the bulk of the Torridon Group was deposited by rivers on large alluvial pans draining an upland region which lay to the NW (Williams 1969a & b.). The thicker grey shale units in the Diabaig and Cailleach Head Formations of the Torridon Group probably were associated with a marine influence although some of the shales elsewhere in the sequence may represent local lakes.

The Diabaig Formation the lowermost formation of the Torridon Group, is considerably thicker in the S and absent in the N of the region. Such facies variations may have influenced the style of structures in the thrust zone (Barton 1978). Following the deposition of the Torridon Group and prior to the deposition of overlying Lower Cambrian quartzites the 'Torridonian' was gently folded about fold axes trending approximately N–S with a fold wavelength of approximately 50 km. There is a large syncline in the W, while in the E near the thrust zone, Torridon sediments and the underlying gneisses form a large Precambrian anticline. Peneplanation of these structures preceded the deposition of the Cambro-Ordovician sequence which oversteps from the Torridon Group onto the Lewisian (Soper & Barber 1979).

The Cambro-Ordovician sediments

The Cambro-Ordovician sediments were deposited on an almost plane erosion surface, in marked contrast to the older irregularly dissected surface beneath the 'Torridonian'. The Cambrian base rests sometimes on 'Torridonian', sometimes on Lewisian. The lowermost Cambrian rocks are quartz-rich sandstones and grits (the Basal Quartzite) sometimes with a conglomerate at the base. In places trough cross-laminations are well developed. These pass up into well bedded quartz-sandstones with vertical bioturbation structures (the 'Pipe

Rock'). The burrows are of the genus Skolithus (Hallam & Swett 1966). In undeformed rock, the pipes are normal to bedding and circular on the bedding plane and thus make ideal strain markers for estimating layer parallel strain ratios and layer parallel shear. The quartz sandstones are overlain by rusty weathering shales with hard dolomitic beds (the Fucoid Beds). Abundant flattened worm casts on the bedding planes were originally mistaken for the remains of fucoids and so give the rock its name. These beds contain the earliest shelly fossils in this sequence and are characterized by the tribolite Olenellus. The Fucoid Beds are followed by a 10 m thick grit (the 'Serpulite Grit') which takes its name from small conical fossil shells, originally named Serpulites, but now known as Salterella. There are vertical worm burrows in the Fucoid Beds and Serpulite Grit as well as Pipe Rock. The highest Cambro-Ordovician sediments are a thick sequence of limestones and dolomites (the Durness Limestone, Fig. 2).

Post-Cambrian intrusives

These include a suite of felsite, porphyrite and lamprophyre sills in the Assynt area and also large alkaline intrusives and syenites in SE Assynt. The large intrusives form the Loch Borrolan and Loch Ailsh complexes, both generally of laccolithic shape. They intruded Cambrian sediments during the thrusting and so could date the main thrust episode (Sabine 1953; Woolley 1970).

Regional structure and orogenesis

The Moine Thrust Zone is one of a number of NNE trending structures in the NW Highlands (Fig. 1). Further to the W, the Outer Hebrides Thrust, of probable Caledonian age (Francis & Sibson 1973) occurs solely within Lewisian gneisses. To the E, major tectonic discontinuities occur within the Moine series; these are tectonic slides such as the Sgurr Beag slide (Tanner 1971). It appears likely that the Moine Thrust Zone is one of a number of related major thrust-nappe structures that evolved during the Caledonian Orogeny. Movement on the Moine Thrust has been dated close to 430 Ma (Van Bremen et al. 1979) from syntectonic igneous intrusions in Assynt.

Recent isotopic studies (summarized by Harris et al. 1978) permit one to infer that, at least in part, the Moines have undergone a Grenville age metamorphic event and as such must be older than the 'Torridonian' sediments.

Dewey (1969) postulated that the Moine Thrust is one of a series of related thrust nappes which started in the Grampian region of NE Scotland in early Ordovician times (the Grampian Orogeny of Lambert & McKerrow 1977) and moved westwards towards the foreland in late Ordovician/Silurian times. Recent geochronology by Van Breeman *et al.* (1979) support this diachroneity of thrust movements.

The driving mechanism for these thrust-nappes is uncertain. If we use the criteria outlined by Bally (this volume) and the involvement of basement together with the thick mylonite development (i.e. initially deep levels of thrusting), this seems to rule out significant gravity sliding as an emplacement mechanism. The Grampian Orogeny at 500 Ma may have been associated with plate collision and closing of an early Atlantic Ocean, though the relationship of this to the classic Iapetus model of Dewey (1969) is unclear. The Grampian metamorphism was associated with thermal re-equilibration after crustal thickening (Richardson & Powell 1976). It is unlikely that the Moine Thrust formed as a result of a collision event some 50–70 Ma earlier in SE Scotland, but it may have formed as a result of isostatic uplift and equilibration after collision and thickening.

Post-Caledonian sediments in the form of Devonian conglomerates and sandstones form a molasse along the eastern part of the Scottish Highlands. Apart from a few conglomerate outcrops near Tongue, no molassic sediments have been preserved near the Moine Thrust Zone.

There are several major NE trending normal faults in the NW Highlands, presumably related to the opening of the Atlantic Ocean. One such important fault occurs at Durness and drops down an outlier of Moine Mylonites and schists some 15 km NW of the main thrust zone outcrop.

In the southern part of the Moine Thrust Zone, the rocks are intruded by granites and basaltic dykes emanating from the Tertiary volcanic centres.

Structures of the Moine Thrust Zone

Major thrust units

Between the foreland and the Moine Thrust itself, 'the belt of complication' varies from 0 to 11 km in width and consists of several thick thrust nappes and numerous thrust faults. The thrust nappes contain Lewisian as well as Cambro-Ordovician and 'Torridonian' sediments. In the northern part of the thrust zone Lewisian, Moine and Cambro-Ordovician rocks are involved in the thrust slices whereas S of Ullapool deformed 'Torridonian' appears in the thrust structures. Detailed maps of selected parts of the Moine Thrust Zone are given in Figs 3–6. From N to S the major thrust units are:

The Arnaboll Nappe

The Arnaboll Thrust (Fig. 3) carries Lewisian gneiss and its Cambrian cover over a wide imbricated sequence of Cambrian rocks on the eastern side of Loch Eriboll. To the S, the Moine Thrust cuts across the Arnaboll Thrust to rest directly on the imbricated Cambrian.

The Glencoul Nappe

The Glencoul Thrust carries a thick slice of Lewisian gneiss (at least 500 m thick at Glencoul), with its Cambrian cover (Fig. 4). It can be traced from N of Glen Dhu to near Inchnadamph where it dies out in the overturned limb of a recumbent fold in Cambrian quartzites (Bailey 1934).

The Ben More Nappe

The Lewisian gneiss in the Ben More Thrust carries 'Torridonian' cover as well as Cambrian. It can be traced from S of the stack of Glencoul (Fig. 4), where it is displaced by a strike-slip fault within the Glencoul Nappe (Fig. 4) to the W side of Ben More Assynt. Klippes of the Ben More Thrust occur to the W of Ben More Assynt, and carry Lewisian, 'Torridonian' and Cambrian onto the imbricated Cambrian. In the southern part of Assynt the Moine Thrust overrides the Ben More Thrust to rest directly on the foreland.

The Kinlochewe Nappe–Kishorn Nappe

The Kinlochewe Thrust carries Lewisian rocks with a folded cover of 'Torridonian' and Cambrian sediments over Lower Cambrian sediments (Fig. 5). The Moine Thrust overlaps onto the foreland to the S, but a similar thrust, the Kishorn Thrust emerges from beneath the Moine Thrust near Loch Carron. Imbricated Cambrian rocks occur beneath the Kinlochewe

Thrust at Kinlochewe (Fig. 5) and at Ord on Skye.

The Tarskavaig Nappe

The Tarskavaig Thrust (Fig. 6) carries a group of intensely deformed sediments (the Tarskavaig Moines) over the folded 'Torridonian' of the Kishorn Nappe. The Tarskavaig Nappe outcrops as klippen in southern Skye (Fig. 6).

The Moine Nappe

The Moine Thrust is the easternmost thrust plane in the 'belt of complication' and this carries Moine mylonites and Moine psammites over the thrust zone. Within the Moine Nappe there are highly tectonized slices of Lewisian which are probably both the result of earlier (pre Caledonian) deformation of the Moines and Lewisian and also Caledonian thrust slices

bounded by tectonic slides. In the following sections, detailed descriptions are given of several areas of the Moine Thrust Zone:

Loch Eriboll

On the eastern shore of Loch Eriboll (Fig. 3a) a number of features of the thrust zone are relatively well-exposed. Hence this area is treated in some detail, and even though the scale may be smaller than that in the Canadian Rocky Mountains or the Appalachians, a number of analogous features are developed. A detailed map and cross sections are presented in Figs 3a & b. The broad structure of this area can be divided into five distinct subareas. From N to S these are (Fig. 3a):

I *The Lower Imbricate* sequence comprising folded and imbricated Pipe Rock (upper zones), the Fucoid Beds and the Serpulite Grit.

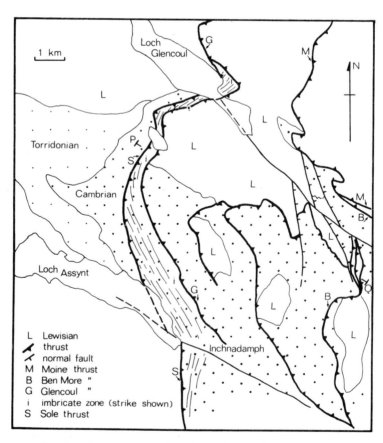

FIG. 4a. Map of N Assynt (see Fig. 1) showing the major thrusts.

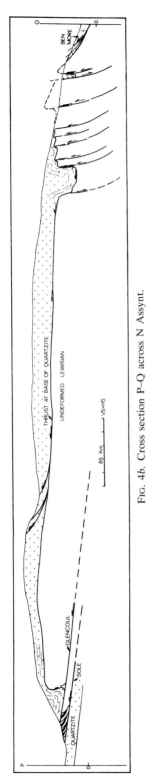

FIG. 4b. Cross section P–Q across N Assynt.

II *The Upper Imbricate* sequence consisting of closely spaced steep imbricate faults involving the Fucoid Beds, the Serpulite Grit, and the lower part of the Durness Limestone.

III *The Arnaboll Nappe* which consists of two thrust masses of Lewisian gneisses with their cover of basal Cambrian quartzite. This nappe rides over the imbricate sequences (Fig. 3).

IV *The Folded Cover of the Arnaboll Nappe.* This is the Cambrian sedimentary sequence carried by the Arnaboll Nappe and includes part of the Durness Limestone Group. These sediments are folded into a tight overturned syncline—the Kempie syncline (Fig. 3).

V *The Moine Nappe* with the Moine Thrust at the base and carrying Moine and Lewisian mylonites, and the Moine psammites over both the Arnaboll Nappe and the imbricate sequences.

I The Lower Imbricate Sequence

This duplex contains imbricated and folded slices of Pipe-Rock, Fucoid Beds and Serpulite Grit in the N and also Limestone in the S (Fig. 3*a* & *b*), below the Arnaboll thrust plane.

At Ben Hielam (Fig. 3*a*) the leading edge of this imbricate sequence is folded. On the eastern slopes of Ben Hielam the exposure is dominantly folded Pipe Rock. There are probable repetitions of stratigraphy within this part of the area but the uniform Pipe Rock lithology makes the recognition of thrust faults difficult.

Strain analysis of the Pipe Rock by Beckett (1980): similar to that of Coward & Kim (this volume), shows that there appears to be a fairly uniform layer parallel shortening (strain ratios ∼1.6–2.0 : 1) upon which is superimposed variable layer-parallel shear strains ($\gamma = 0.03$–9.5). High shear strains are particularly developed in the more silty units of the upper Pipe Rock. Local mylonite zones associated with imbricate faults are found within the Pipe Rock at Ben Hielam (White 1979*a*).

In the S, the Lower Imbricate sequence is bounded by a roof thrust lying within the Durness Limestone (as slices of limestone are found in the imbricates) but below Ben Arnaboll, the Arnaboll Thrust slices through the imbricate sequence. The floor thrust to this imbricate sequence is presumably the Sole Thrust lying within the quartzites.

II The Upper Imbricate Sequence

The Upper Imbricate Sequence consists of evenly spaced listric thrust faults which cause

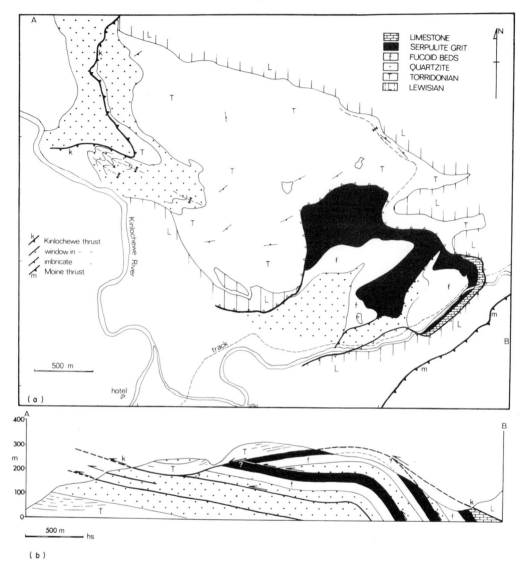

FIG. 5a. Map of Kinochewe (see Fig. 1).
FIG. 5b. Cross section A–B across Kinlochewe.

rapid repetitions of stratigraphy—Fucoid Beds, Serpulite grit and limestone. These imbricates are well exposed along the E coast of Loch Eriboll (Fig. 3a). Folding is not observed in this sequence of imbricates though it may be present at the leading edge of the sequence and also along strike, presumably where the thrusts die out. The imbricate faults are steeply dipping (Fig. 3b) and often only a few metres apart. Curved imbricate fault planes are well exposed along the coastal cliffs N of Ard Neackie (Fig. 3a). A 'pressure solution' type cleavage is developed in the Fucoid Beds but large

'trumpet pipes' show no layer parallel shortening. The Upper Imbricate sequence is bounded by a 'roof thrust' bringing over a large mass of limestone (Fig. 3b) and a 'floor thrust' which is presumed to be the Sole Thrust lying within the Fucoid Beds.

III & IV The rocks above the Arnaboll Thrust

At the base of the Arnaboll Nappe, a thin green-black phyllonite-mylonite marks the Arnaboll Thrust. Above this, allochthonous 'Laxfordian' type Lewisian carries a cover of

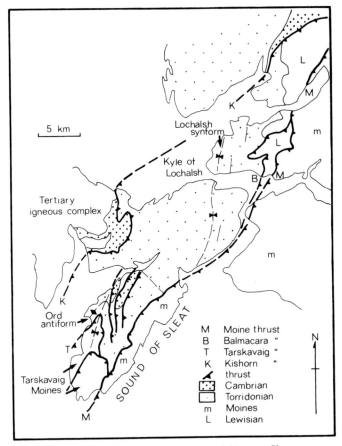

FIG. 6. Simplified geological map of Sleat on Skye.

Cambrian rocks. Within the Arnaboll Nappe there are other significant thrusts—the Upper Arnaboll Thrust and Thrust 'with no name' (Coward 1980 in press), which thrust Lewisian on top of Lewisian.

At Kempie, the Cambrian rocks of the cover of the Arnaboll Nappe (Fig. 3*a*) are folded into a tight inclined syncline. The steep overturned limb of this syncline has a pronounced Caledonian cleavage. Adjacent to the steeply dipping Cambrian, the Lewisian rocks also have an intense fabric shown by shattered quartz and feldspar grains and new growth of chlorite and epidote. This fabric strikes NNE and carries a down dip mineral lineation. Elsewhere these zones of Caledonian deformation can be identified by their trend and low grade mineral assemblages. These shear zones give rise to folds in the Cambrian quartzite. In other areas, the Lewisian shows little or no Caledonian deformation.

S of Kempie Bay, the core of the Kempie syncline is imbricated (Figs. 3*a* & *b*) producing

a complex outcrop pattern of limestone, Serpulite Grit and Fucoid Beds. The imbrication is presumably due to space problems within the core of this tight fold. To the E between Ben Arnaboll and Loch Hope the Arnaboll Thrust is itself faulted. One such thrust occurs on Ben Arnaboll and brings the underlying quartzite back on top of the Lewisian (Fig. 3*a*). Similar thrusts are found around the northern part of Ben Arnaboll (Fig. 3*a*). In these localities the Cambrian and Lewisian rocks are intensely deformed and locally mylonitized. Other intensely deformed 'pinched-in' folds of basal Cambrian quartzite can be recognized S of Ben Arnaboll and also on the hill E of Hope (Fig. 3*a*).

V The Moine Nappe

The Moine Thrust (Fig. 3*a*) brings Moine and Lewisian mylonites together with deformed Moine psammites over both the Arnaboll Nappe and the Imbricate sequences.

within the sequence of mylonites above the Moine Thrust, other thrusts (Fig. 3a) most likely mark the junction between different mylonite zones. Madgwick (1980) noted that different minor structures—e.g. folded veins were found at these thrust boundaries. A more detailed description of the mylonites is given in subsequent sections.

The irregular outcrop pattern of the Moine Thrust plane and the higher thrust planes may in part be caused by later Tertiary faulting breaking up the outcrop and may in part reflect initial spoon or scoop shaped fault planes. Such fault plane shapes would give rise to differential movement of the thrust nappe and this is also indicated by the minor structures in the mylonites (discussed in a subsequent section).

Faulting

A number of NNE trending faults are found on the E side of Loch Eriboll (Fig. 3a). Loch Hope appears to be centred on such a structure. Where observed these faults appear to be normal faults though they often terminate in associated strike-slip faults. These faults are likely to be associated with the opening of the Atlantic and the formation of the Minch.

The Mylonite zones

The mylonites of the Moine Thrust Zone were first described by Lapworth (1885) from the Eriboll district, and later by Peach et al. (1907), Peach & Horne (1930) and more recently by Christie (1960) and White (1979a).

The term mylonite was originally proposed by Lapworth (1885) for a microscopic breccia with a fluxion structure in which the interstitial grains have only partly recrystallized. Subsequently, other authors have applied the term to a variety of rocks along the thrust zone. Here the term is applied to rocks in which the grains show evidence of intense strain by plastic deformation leading to a change in grain shape as well as a grain size reduction by dynamic recrystallization.

In a study of the mylonites developed in the Assynt area, Christie (1960) recognized two kinds of mylonites—primary crystalloblastic mylonites and secondary mylonites characterized by cataclastic breakdown of the minerals. Some similar features are found in the Loch Eriboll mylonites.

Distribution of the mylonites at Loch Eriboll are shown in Fig. 3a. The bulk of the mylonites are associated with the Moine Thrust plane but local mylonites are developed on the Arnaboll

thrust plane and in the imbricate faulted area on Ben Hielam. Three basic types of mylonites—phyllonites are found: quartzite mylonites, Lewisian mylonite—phyllonites and Moine mylonites.

The quartzite mylonites

The quartz rich mylonites are developed in local shear zones within the Pipe Rock in the Ben Hielem imbricate zone (I Fig. 3a); within thin slices of Pipe Rock at the base of the Arnaboll and Moine Thrust planes; or associated with shear zones and tight infolds of basal quartzite into the Lewisian of the Arnaboll Thrust sheet.

The quartzite mylonites show original detrital quartz grains (500–1000 μm) which have been highly deformed and broken into ribbon grains (elongations 10–20 : 1) with recrystallization (principally at grain margins) to give a fine-grained ground mass (5–15 μm). Both oblate and prolate grain shapes are found. The most intense strains within the quartz grains appear to be associated with layer parallel extensional strains in the quartzites (Beckett 1980). The basal quartzites contain significant detrital feldspar (both orthoclase and plagioclase). The feldspar grains in the shear zones, deformed principally by cataclasis giving rise to fractured feldspar augen in a finely recrystallized quartz matrix. Strong crystallographic preferred orientations are found in some of the quartz mylonites and these are the subject of further research. White (1979a) used recrystallized grain size, in a quartz mylonite at Hielam as a palaeopiezometer and estimated differential stress of 0.37–1.28 kbar for the mylonite formation. There are, however, problems in using grain-size as a palaeopiezometer as discussed by White (1979b).

Weak to moderate WNW–ESE stretching and rodding lineations are found in the quartzite mylonites. The foliation planes in the mylonites are generally sub-parallel to bedding and also to the fault surfaces with which they are associated.

The Lewisian mylonites

A thin zone of platy Lewisian mylonite 0.5–1.3 m thick is found locally along the Arnaboll Thrust plane at Ben Arnaboll. This is a dark grey-black, fine-grained platy rock with a weak WNW–ESE stretching lineation developed on the foliation planes. A similar dark platy mylonite is found at Allt on Teampuill (NE of Loch Hope) where it is associated with infolds of basal Cambrian quartzite and shear zones in the Lewisian of the Arnaboll Thrust slice.

Other Lewisian mylonites-phyllonites occur above the Moine Thrust plane itself, ranging in thickness from a few metres to 50 m or more. Mineral assemblages are quartz-feldspar-chlorite-sericite and secondary carbonate. These slices above the Moine Thrust plane exhibit a strong WNW–ESE stretching lineation. The enveloping foliation generally dips gently ESE, sub-parallel to the bounding faults. These mylonites-phyllonites exhibit several phases of folding which are discussed in a subsequent section.

The Moine mylonites

Beneath the Moine schists and psammites but above the Moine Thrust plane, there is a variable thickness of fine-grained siliceous, grey, banded mylonites (V Fig. 3a) and at least 600 m thick as seen on the northern coast. Intercalcated with these siliceous mylonites, there is a distinctive unit, 50–80 m thick, of strongly foliated chloritic 'quartz eye' rock named the 'Oyster Shell' rock (Peach *et al.* 1907). The upper parts of this rock contain thin bands of granular marble. Of uncertain origin (Peach *et al.* 1907; Soper & Wilkinson 1975; Barton 1978), the 'Oyster Shell' phyllonite forms a distinctive strongly foliated unit near the base of the Moine mylonites.

The siliceous Moine mylonites are very fine-grained (1–20 μm) quartz-sericite-feldspar rocks often with semi translucent light and dark colour banding, a strong platy foliation and in general a WNW–ESE stretching lineation. The feldspar fragments form augen with the foliation defined by quartz grain size variations and thin bands of sericitic micas. The 'Oyster Shell' rock commonly exhibits two low angle conjugate crenulation like foliations which deform the main foliation. These are thought to be a 'shear band' cleavage which results from progressive large strains (White *et al.* 1980). They indicate that the mylonites have suffered layer parallel extension. Crystallographic preferred orientations are found in the siliceous mylonites and are the subject of continuing research.

Folding in the mylonites

Soper (1971) and Soper & Wilkinson (1975) outlined over four main phases of deformation in the Moine nappe beginning with the formation of the mylonites, followed by the development of tight to open asymmetric folds and lastly box folds and kink bands.

Recent studies on the thrust zone at Loch Eriboll have modified the rather simplistic classification of structures (H. Dyan pers. comm. 1980; Madgwick 1980 and studies by the authors). The dominant foliation throughout the area is the S_1 of Soper (1971) which appears to be a distinct episode of mylonite formation, probably at deeper levels in the crust than the later deformation and final emplacement of the mylonites. D_2 and D_3, however, appear to be stages in a sequence of essentially progressive simple shear deformation in which the fold axes initiated normal to the transport direction and then were subsequently rotated into the transport direction.

D_2–D_3 folds with strongly curved hinge lines are commonly found in the mylonite sequence. The D_4 box fold and kink band fold axes generally plunge to the SE. These indicate shortening almost parallel to the strike of the thrust zone, possibly formed by local differential movement of the thrusts.

Deformation mechanisms

Detailed microstructural studies (by the authors) in general confirm the above conclusions. S_1 foliation is characterized by a grain shape and crystallographic preferred orientations. D_2–D_3 structures deform these earlier fabrics and a crenulation cleavage is well developed in the more phyllonitic Lewisian slices. 'Early' mylonite textures are produced by crystal—plastic deformation mechanisms—dislocation creep and possibly diffusional creep, whereas D_2–D_3 and D_4 deformations are additionally associated with pressure shadows and stylolites indicating a component of fluid assisted diffusion deformation ('pressure solution'). The Lewisian phyllonites, in places, have abundant carbonate filled veins and fractures which may attest to high pore fluid pressures during the last stages of nappe emplacement.

The local quartzite mylonites which are developed in the imbricate zones exhibit both crystal-plastic and pressure solution deformation features. High shear strains are particularly common in the upper levels of the Pipe Rock where there is abundant clay/sericite in the interstices. This most likely both enhances pressure solution and facilitates grain boundary sliding.

In summary, the microstructures indicate that the bulk of the mylonites were formed at relatively deep crustal levels involving essentially crystal-plastic deformation mechanisms, whereas latter emplacement occurred at higher structural levels accompanied by pressure solution and probable high pore fluid pressures.

N Assynt

The Caledonian structures of this area are dominated by the Glencoul Nappe which carries Lewisian rocks with the cover of Cambrian quartzite over imbricated Upper Cambrian sediments.

SW of Glencoul the strike of the imbricates varies from N 60° to N 330° near Loch Assynt (Fig. 4). This change is not due to later folding. The underlying 'Torridonian' and Cambrian strata of the foreland are not folded. Hence this difference in strike must be due to the differential movement of the overlying Glencoul Nappe (Coward & Kim, this volume).

Over most of the Glencoul Nappe, the Cambrian rocks are flat lying (Fig. 4) and only gently folded but at the present western limit of the nappe on the slopes of Glas Bhein they are steeply dipping to overturned and are also highly folded and faulted in the east on the slopes of Ben Uidhe (Fig. 4). Adjacent to the steep limbs of these folds in the quartzite, the Lewisian rocks have a pronounced Caledonian fabric. These zones are listric shear zones of both contractional and extensional fault types and they seem to floor on the Glencoul Thrust plane. They have been described by Coward & Kim (this volume).

On Ben Uidhe, a thrust lies parallel to bedding in Lower Cambrian quartzites. There appears to be relatively little displacement along this thrust, indeed it is not detectable on the eastern slopes of Beinn Uidhe where the Cambrian rocks are folded. Several imbricate faults branch off this thrust and on the E slopes of Glas Bheinn, the main thrust climbs down into Lewisian rocks, so that on the hills S of Glas Bheinn, Lewisian rocks are thrust over Cambrian.

Kinlochewe area

Between Assynt and Loch Broom the Moine Thrust Zone is narrow but near Kinlochewe (Fig. 5a) it widens and between the Sole and Moine Thrusts, the Kinloch Thrust carries a slab of Lewisian gneiss, 'Torridonian' Sandstone and basal quartzite over imbricated Cambrian rocks (Figs. 5a & b). The Kinloch Thrust has been folded and eroded to produce a window on the imbricates. This folding may be due to shortening in the direction of transport or to thrusting and hence thickening in the underlying quartzites. This latter alternative is preferred as small scale folds due to layer parallel shortening are absent. This folding of the Kinloch Thrust suggests that movement in the underlying thrusts postdates the Kinloch Thrust. However, the Kinloch Thrust cuts down stratigraphy from E to W and also cuts across the imbricate zone in Upper Cambrian rocks. It is not a roof thrust and must post-date the imbricates. As in the Arnaboll and Glencoul Thrusts, the Kinloch Thrust must have been generated at a lower level than the floor thrust to the imbricates and then have sliced through the earlier faults.

Above the Kinloch Thrust the 'Torridonian' is folded into the Lewisian gneiss to produce a SW facing syncline with a SE plunging hinge. The overlying Cambrian quartzites are also folded to produce SE plunging folds (Fig. 5a). To the S, the 'Torridonian' sandstones are folded to produce a NE facing syncline also with a SE plunging hinge. (fig. 18. Coward & Kim, this volume). Thus the 'Torridonian' rocks trace out a sheath-like fold where hinges plunge to the SE, parallel to the transport directions of the thrust. On the overturned limbs of this sheath like fold, the 'Torridonian' rocks show little to no cleavage and the Lewisian rocks show no Caledonian deformation.

Thus it is unlikely that the fold hinges were rotated into their SE trend by intense deformation; the folds must have formed with SE plunging hinges, possibly due to differential movement on the Kinloch Thrust.

Lochalsh and Skye

Imbricated Cambrian and 'Torridonian' rocks occur between Kinlochewe and Loch Carron and also on the Sleat Peninsula (Fig. 6) on Skye. At least two levels of floor thrust occur, one in the Fucoid Beds, and the other in the Lower 'Torridonian' shales. Reverse faults generated from the lower floor thrust slice through the upper imbricates.

Though the Cambrian rocks are highly faulted they show little penetrative strain. The pipes remain circular on the bedding plane and often there is little evidence of bedding parallel shear as pipes are normal to bedding even where bedding dips are steep.

The structure of Kishorn Nappe has been described by Coward & Whalley (1980). It is floored by a thrust which slices through the underlying imbricated Cambrian and 'Torridonian'. In the thrust nappe, 'Torridonian' Sandstones are folded into a large recumbent syncline, the axial surface of which passes through the village of Kyle of Lochalsh. On Skye (Fig. 6), there is a complementary recumbent anticline (Bailey 1939, 1955). The westernmost outcrops of 'Torridonian' rocks show no cleavage, but near the Kishorn Thrust plane they are locally shattered and broken by quartz veins. Near Kyle, the cleavage is shown by steeply dipping zones of pressure solution but to the E in the overturned beds the cleavage is more intensely developed and penetrative in nature with a visible orientation of phyllosilicates in the fine-grained lithologies. To the E of Kyle the dip of bedding gradually decreases while the cleavage has a dip of 30–40° to the NE, this being consistently a little steeper than bedding. The cleavage must, therefore, postdate the folding and inversion of stratigraphy.

The bedding cleavage intersection lineation plunges to the SE and is often indistinguishable from the mineral lineation in the rock. Coward & Kim (this volume) considered the oblique cleavage to be formed from strains set up by differential movement of the Kishorn Nappe.

Discussion

Geometry

In this paper, in Coward & Kim (this volume) and also in Elliott & Johnson (in press) geometric aspects of the Moine Thrust Zone have been described. Many of these structures such as ramps, duplex structures with floor and roof thrusts, thrusts terminating in folds both along strike and upwards, can be compared with those found in the Southern Canadian Rockies (Bally et al. 1966; Price & Mountjoy 1970; Price this volume) or those in the Appalachians. (Rodgers 1970; Hatcher this volume). In detail, however, the scale of structures developed is somewhat smaller (e.g. Fig. 3a & b) and this is likely to be a result of the relatively thin Cambro-Ordorician sedimentary sequence, particularly the thin lower units (Fig 2). The detailed map and sections across the E side of Loch Eriboll show many of these geometric features which are also found in Assynt (Elliott & Johnson in press) and further S. In particular much of the folding and layer parallel shortening found in the quartzite on the eastern slopes of Ben Hielam (Fig 3a) is

probably the result of 'blind' thrusts in the sub-surface (cf. Thompson this volume). In general, in the Moine Thrust Zone the thrusts climb up stratigraphic sequence although around Ben Arnaboll (Fig. 3a & b) there is rethrusting on imbricate faults to bring quartzite back onto the Lewisian. Similar features are found in the Glencoul Nappe (Coward & Kim this volume). The thrust stacking sequence is discussed in detail in a subsequent section.

Position of the floor thrust

In Assynt and to the N, in the immediate vicinity of the Moine Thrust Zone, Cambrian quartzites rest unconformably on the Lewisian gneiss; the 'Torridonian' sediments had been previously removed by erosion. In this part of the thrust zone, the Fucoid Beds and the Lower Cambrian quartzites acted as the main fault gathering beds and contain the floor thrusts to the principal imbricate zones. To the S of Assynt, where 'Torridonian' rocks rest on the Lewisian, the Fucoid Beds and Lower 'Torridonian' Shales–Diabaig formation acted as the main fault gathering zones. Barton (1978) argued that the change in structural style along the strike of the Moine Thrust Zone is a result of the absence of the Diabaig Shales in the N (the Diabaig formation thins out northwards from Cailleach Head, Stewart 1975). In the N, however, the Sole Thrust climbs from basement (Lewisian) into the Cambrian sediments at a position E of the Torridon Group outcrop. Once established in the Cambrian bedding glide zones the Sole Thrust would be unlikely to climb down stratigraphic section into the 'Torridonian', even if the easy glide horizons of the Diabaig formation were present.

The shales of the Fucoid Beds and the Lower 'Torridonian' appear to have been easy glide horizons, but in the quartzites slip was less easy, causing differential movement and components of layer parallel shortening in the overlying rocks. Hence at Loch Eriboll, the Pipe Rock in the Lower Imbricate zones exhibits layer parallel shortening and simple shear components (Sole Thrust within the quartzites) whereas the Upper Imbricates (Sole Thrust within the Fucoid Beds) show only simple shear components.

Thus the strain history varies along the length of the thrust zone not necessarily due to different deformation events nor to different pressure–temperature conditions but largely arising from the deformation mechanisms along the floor thrusts.

Thrust stacking sequence

If a classic thin-skinned tectonic model (of the Southern Canadian Rockies, or Appalachians) is assumed for the Moine Thrust Zone, then the stacking sequence is presumed to be from E to W, i.e. towards the foreland in the direction of tectonic transport. The stacking sequences in the imbricate zones conform to this model. For the major thrusts, however, the stacking sequence is from W to E, the Arnaboll, Glencoul and Kishorn Thrusts all slice through the imbricate structures. Thus either the classic thin-skinned tectonics stacking sequence does not apply to the Moine Thrust Zone or these thrusts were generated at a lower structural level than the imbricates and then climbed up to slice through the higher level imbricates. Reactivation of thrusts and faults is evidenced by the structures on Ben

EVOLUTION OF THE MOINE THRUST ZONE AT LOCH ERiBOLL

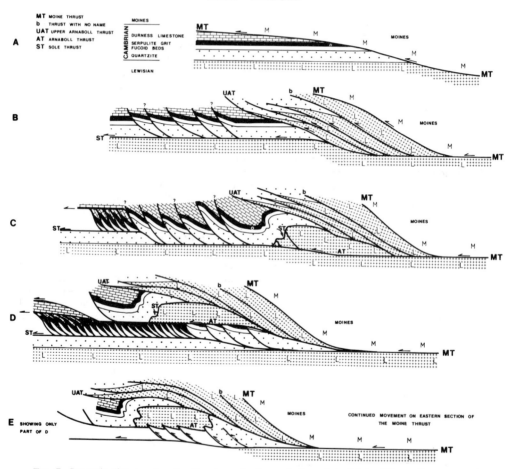

Fig. 7. Synoptic diagram showing the stages in the evolution of the Moine Thrust Zone at Loch Eriboll (not to scale). Part E shows only a segment of the thrust zone. A. Development of the Moine Thrust MT bringing Moines from the E over the Cambro-Ordovician sequence. B. Imbrication of the Lewisian—thrusts b to the Upper Arnaboll thrust and also imbrication of the Cambrian succession (Lower Imbricates Fig. 3). C. Development of the Arnaboll Nappe by generation of the Arnaboll Thrust AT. At the front of the thrust belt, the Sole Thrust ST climbs (ramps) into the Fucoid beds to produce the Upper Imbricates (Fig. 3). D. The Arnaboll thrust climbs section and slices through the Lower Imbricate sequence. E. Continued movement on the eastern portion of the Moine Thrust causes movement on the Sole Thrust and reactivation of imbricate faults.

Arnaboll (Fig. 3*a* & *b*) where quartzite below the Arnaboll Nappe is rethrust on top of Lewisian. A schematic diagram illustrating the sequence of thrust development at Loch Eriboll is given in Fig. 7. Hence an inverted stacking sequence may be generated by late movement of thrusts climbing from a lower structural level. This problem of stacking sequence is discussed by Coward (1980) and in more detail by Barber *et al.* (in prep).

Origin of the mylonites

Although intimately associated with the Moine Thrust plane, the Moine mylonites were formed at relatively deep crustal levels than their present stratigraphic-topographic position. They rest in places, e.g. at Knockan S of Assynt, directly upon little deformed Cambrian sediments. They also override imbricate and thrust structures which are relatively high level brittle features with only thin local mylonitic rocks, whereas the mylonites themselves signify intense ductile deformation. Their present stratigraphic-topographic position is probably due to late movement on the eastern sections of the Moine Thrust (Fig. 7).

Differential movement and transport direction

The general tectonic transport direction is towards WNW approximately 290°. This is parallel to the stretching lineation in the thrust sequence, particularly the mylonites (e.g. Fig. 3*a*) and normal to the general trend of the imbricate faults.

Differential movement of thrust faults is, however, indicated by spoon-shaped fault planes, and some oblique fold axes (cf. Coward & Kim this volume). Differential movement along particular thrust planes may also result in oblique imbricate structures (e.g. Assynt) and may be generated by transverse ramps along the strike of thrust faults.

Major thrusts in the Caledonides

As discussed in the introductory sections of this paper, the Moine Thrust is only one of a series of related thrusts/tectonic slides (Fig. 1) which probably started in the E, in the Grampian region of NE Scotland in late Cambrian times and moved towards the foreland in late Ordovician and Silurian times (Dewey 1969). Application of thin skinned tectonic models with an E–W stacking sequence to the deeper level thrusts of the Caledonian gives rise to the following problems (Coward 1980).

(I) *The Pre-Caledonian structure—the position of the Moines relative to the Lewisian*

According to a thin skinned model, the Moines which have been emplaced on top of the Lewisian should have originally been at a lower structural level. Thus at some stage before the development of the Caledonian Thrusts the stratigraphy was inverted and the Lewisian emplaced on top of the Moines. Large Precambrian eastward verging fold nappes with basement gneiss cores are found within the Moines (Ramsay 1963; Powell 1974). These are modified by later W verging Caledonian structures. Recently Brook *et al.* (1977) reported a 1160 Ma event from the Moines which can be correlated with the Grenville in Canada. The large scale eastward verging fold nappes bringing lower gneissic Lewisian crust on top of Moines may be the result of the Grenvillian Orogeny.

(II) *Position of the floor thrusts to the series of Caledonian Thrusts*

Coward (1980) has discussed the regional significance of the Caledonian Thrust sequence. Watson (1977) considered that the Caledonian Thrusts steepened at depth but Coward argues that the thrusts will flatten out at depth. Using the results of seismic studies (LISPB project Bamford *et al.* 1977, 1978), Coward postulates the existence of a lower crustal detachment horizon (basement shear zone) between crustal layers 2 and 3 (layer 2 seismic velocities 6.1–6.2 km s^{-1}, layer 3 velocity 6.48 km s^{-1}, Bamford *et al.* 1977, 1978). The boundary between layers 2 and 3 is clearly identified beneath the Moines and dips gently to the ESE. The boundary becomes more diffuse southwards and layer 2 thickens to the SE of the Great Glen Fault.

Thus there is evidence for only slightly thickened crust beneath the Moines (Coward 1980) and hence the displacements of the Moine Thrust Zone cannot be taken up by shortening of the whole crust NW of the Great Glen Fault. Coward (1980), therefore, argues that the boundary between layer 2 and 3 represents a sub-horizontal floor thrust to the major Caledonian thrusts and that perhaps it is only to the SE beyond the Great Glen Fault that basement rocks become involved in the Caledonian structures.

Such postulates could possibly be resolved by seismic reflection profiling across the Moine Thrust Zone and south-eastwards in a manner similar to the COCORP Studies of the Appalachians (Brewer *et al.* this volume).

(III) *Driving mechanisms for the thrusts*

The driving mechanism for the Moine Thrust is unknown. Gravity glide mechanisms seem unlikely in view of the deep level of thrusting involved (e.g. Moine mylonites) and because of the lack or paucity of synchronous extensional structures in the major nappe units (see Bally, this volume). The Grampian Orogeny at ~500 Ma in the eastern part of Scotland may have been associated with plate collision and closure of an early Atlantic Ocean (Lambert & McKerrow 1977) but geochronology of igneous rocks involved in the Moine Thrust suggest an age of 430 Ma (Van Breeman *et al.* 1979). Hence it is unlikely that the Moine Thrust resulted from collision some 70 Ma earlier but may have resulted from later isostatic uplift associated with thermal re-equilibration.

Displacements in the thrust zone

Minimum displacements of over 40 km for the Moine Thrust have been estimated by various authors (Ramsay 1969; Soper & Barber 1979; Coward *et al.* in press). Elliot & Johnson (in press) have demonstrated movements of up to 25 km or more on individual thrust surfaces using balanced cross-sections (Dalhstrom 1969). A key factor in reconstructions across the Moine Thrust Zone is the position of the Sole Thrust at depth. In places this will probably only be resolved by seismic reflection profiling and it is likely that significant displacements will be indicated for the Caledonian Thrusts perhaps similar to those obtained recently in the Appalachians (Cook *et al.* 1979).

Conclusions

The geometrical features of structures within the Moine Thrust Zone are similar to those found in classic thin-skinned tectonic regimes of foreland fold and thrust belts (Appalachians and Rocky Mountains). The strain patterns within the thrust zone are controlled by the position of the floor thrust within either the 'Torridonian' shales, Fucoid Beds or within the Cambrian quartzites. Layer parallel shortening is found in the Pipe Rock where the floor or Sole Thrust lies within the quartzites, but not where the Sole Thrust lies in the easy glide horizons of the 'Torridonian' shales and Fucoid Beds.

In general, the stacking sequence is from E to W in the direction of tectonic transport. Some thrusts, however, have been reactivated causing apparent reversals in the stacking sequence. The mylonites have undergone a long and complex history and their present position is probably a result of reactivation of earlier thrusts.

The Moine Thrust Zone is one of a series of Caledonian thrusts. The earliest formed in the E and subsequent thrusts propagated westwards with the Moine Thrust and the Outer Hebrides Thrust being the last to develop Coward (1980) suggests that those thrusts propagated from an originally flat lying or gently inclined shear zone at depth. The driving force for these structures is still uncertain.

ACKNOWLEDGMENTS. The authors wish to thank all the post conference field trip participants for many useful discussions. W. L. Diver, G. Manby, H. Kim, T. Beckett, R. Madgwick and P. Wright are also thanked for critical comments. Mrs D. Norman kindly typed the manuscript.

References

BAILEY, E. B. 1934. The Glencoul nappe and the Assynt culmination. *Geol. Mag.* **72**, 151–65.
—— 1939. Caledonian tectonics and metamorphism in Skye. *Bull. geol. Surv. G.B.* **2**, 46–62.
—— 1955. Moine tectonics and metamorphism in Skye. *Trans. Edinb. geol. Soc.* **16**, 93–166.
——, GORDY, P. L. & STEWART, G. A. 1966. Structure, seismic data, and orogenic evolution of Southern Canadian Rocky Mountains. *Bull. Can. Pet. Geol.* **14**, 337–81.
BAMFORD, D., NUNN, K., PRODEHL, C. & JACOB, B. 1977. LISB–III. Upper crustal structure of Northern Britain. *J. geol. Soc. London*, **133**, 481–8.
——, ——, —— & —— 1978. LISPB–IV Crustal structure of Northern Britain. *Geophys. J. R.*

astron. Soc. **54**, 43–60.
BARBER, A. J., COWARD, M. P. & SOPER, J. (in prep). Models for the evolution of the Moine Thrust Zone.
BARTON, C. M. 1978. An Appalachian View of the Moine Thrust. *Scott. J. Geol.* **14**, 247–57.
BEACH, A., COWARD, M. P. & GRAHAM, R. H. 1974. An interpretation of the structural evolution of the Laxford front. *Scott. J. Geol.* **9**, 294–308.
BECKETT, T. R. 1980. *Strain analysis of the Cambrian Upper Quartzite (Pipe Rock) at Loch Eriboll, NW Highlands.* Hons. Thesis. University of London, Goldsmiths College. (unpubl).
BOWES, D. 1969. The Lewisian of Northwest Highlands of Scotland. *In*: KAY, M. (ed.), *North*

Atlantic Geology and Continental Drift, a Symposium. Mem. Amer. Assoc. Petrol. Geol. **12,** 575–94.

BROOK, M., BREWER, M. & POWELL, D. 1977. Grenville events in Moine rocks of the Northern Highlands, Scotland. *J. geol. Soc. London,* **133,** 489–96.

CHRISTIE, J. M. 1960. Mylonitic rocks of the Moine Thrust Zone in the Assynt region, North-west Scotland. *Trans. Edinb. Geol. Soc.* **18,** 79–93.

COOK, F. A., ALBAUGH, D. S., BROWN, L. D., KAUFMAN, S., OLIVER, J. E. & HATCHER, R. D. JR. 1979. Thin-skinned tectonics in the crystalline Southern Appalachians; COCORP seismic reflection profiling of the Blue Ridge and Piedmont. *Geology,* **7,** 563–7.

COWARD, M. P. 1980. The Caledonian thrusts and shear zones of NW Scotland. *J. Struct. Geol.* (in press).

—— & McCLAY, K. R. 1979. The geology of NW Scotland and the Moine Thrust belt. *Field Guide, Conference on Thrust and Nappe Tectonics,* London.

—— & WHALLEY, J. 1980. Texture and fabric studies across the Kishorn Nappe, near Kyle of Lochalsh, Western Scotland *J. Struct. Geol.* **1,** 259–273.

——, KIM, J. H. & PARKE, J. 1980. The Lewisian structures within the Moine Thrust Zone. *Proc. Geol. Assoc. London.* (in press).

——, FRANCIS, P. W., GRAHAM, R. H., MYERS, J. S. & WATSON, J. 1969. Remnants of an early metasedimentary assemblage in the Lewisian complex of the Outer Hebrides. *Proc. Geol. Assoc. London,* **80,** 387–408.

DAHLSTROM, C. D. A. 1969. Balanced cross sections. *Can. J. Earth Sci.* **6,** 743–58.

DEWEY, J. F. 1969. The evolution of the Appalachian/Caledonian orogeny. *Nature, London,* **222,** 124–9.

ELLIOT, D. & JOHNSON, M. R. W. 1980. Structural evolution in the northern part of the Moine Thrust Zone. *Geol. Trans. R. Soc. Edinb.* (in press).

FRANCIS, P. W. & SIBSON, R. H. 1973. The Outer Hebrides Thrust. *In:* Park & Tarney (eds). *The early Precambrian of Scotland and related rocks of Greenland.* Univ. Keele, 95–104.

GILETTI, B., MOORBATH, S. & LAMBERT, R. ST. J. 1961. A geochronological study of the metamorphic complexes of the Scottish Highlands. *Q. J. geol. Soc. London.* **117,** 233–64.

HALLAM, A. & SWETT, K. 1966. Trace fossils from the Lower Cambrian Pipe Rock of the north-west Highlands. *Scott. J. Geol.* **2,** 101–6.

HARRIS, A. L., SHACKLETON, R. M., WATSON, J., DOWNIE, C., HARLAND, W. B. & MOORBATH, S. 1975. A correlation of the Precambrian rocks in the British Isles. *Spec. Rep. Geol. Soc. London,* **6,** 136pp.

——, JOHNSON, M. R. W. & POWELL, D. 1978. The Orthotectonic Caledonides. (Moines and Dalradians). of Scotland. *Pap. Geol. Surv. Can.* **78,** 79–85.

JOHNSON, M. R. W. 1960. The structural history of the Moine Thrust Zone at Loch Carron, Wester Ross. *Trans. R. Soc. Edinb.* **64,** 139–68.

—— 1961. Polymetamorphism in Movement Zones in the Caledonian Thrust Belt of north-west Scotland. *J. Geol. Chicag.* **69,** 417–32.

—— 1975. Morarian orogeny and Grenville Belt in Britain. *Nature London.* **257,** 301–2.

JOHNSTONE, G. S. 1975. The Moine Succession, *In:* HARRIS, A. L. *et al.* (eds.), *A Correlation of Precambrian rocks in the British Isles.,* Spec. Rep. geol. Soc. London. **6,** 30–42.

——, SMITH, D. I. & HARRIS, A. L. 1969. The Moinian Assemblage of Scotland. *Mem. Am. Assoc. Petrol. Geol.* **12,** 159–80.

LAMBERT, R. ST. J. & HOLLAND, J. G. 1972. A geochronological study of the Lewisian from Loch Laxford to Durness, Sutherland, N. W. Scotland. *Q. J. geol. Soc. London.* **128,** 2–19.

LAMBERT, R. ST. J. & McKERROW, W. S. 1977. The Grampian orogeny. *Scott. J. Geol.* **12,** 271–92.

LAPWORTH, C. 1885. The Highland Controversy in British Geology. *Nature, London,* **32,** 558–9.

MADGWICK, R. 1980. *Analysis of the Moine mylonites at Loch Eriboll, N. W. Scotland.* Hons. thesis, University of London Goldsmiths College, (unpubl).

MOORBATH, S., WELKE, H. & GALE, N. H. 1969. The significance of lead isotope studies in ancient, high grade metamorphic basement complexes, as exemplified by the Lewisian rocks of north-west Scotland. *Earth planet. Sci. Lett.* **6,** 245–56.

PARK, R. G. 1970. Observations on Lewisian chronology. *Scott. J. Geol.* **6,** 379–99.

PEACH, B. N., HORNE, J., GUNN, W., CLOUGH, C. T., HINXMAN, L. W. & TEALL, J. J. H. 1907. The geological structure of the N.W. Highlands of Scotland. *Mem. Geol. Surv. U.K.*

—— & HORNE, J. 1930. *Chapters on the Geology of Scotland.* Oxford University Press, London.

PHEMISTER, J. 1960. *British Regional Geology, Scotland: The Northern Highlands.* H.M.S.O. Edinburgh, 104 p.

PIDGEON, R. T. & JOHNSON, M. R. W. 1974. A comparison of zircon U–Pb and whole rock Rb–Sr systems in three phases of the Carn Chuinneag Granite, W. Scotland. *Earth planet. Sci. Lett.,* **24,** 105–12.

POWELL, D. 1974. Stratigraphy and structure of the western Moine and the problems of Moine orogenesis. *J. geol. Soc. London,* **130,** 575–93.

PRICE, R. A. & MOUNTJOY, E. W. 1970. Geologic structure of the Canadian Rocky mountains between Bow and Athabasca rivers—a progress report. *In:* WHEELER, J. O. (ed.), *Structure of the Southern Canadian Cordillera.* Spec. Pap. Geol. Assoc. Can. **6,** 7–25.

RAMSAY, J. G. 1963. Structures and metamorphism of the Moine and Lewisian rocks of the North-west Caledonides. *In:* JOHNSON, M. R. W. & STEWART, E. H. (Eds.), *The British Caledonides,* Oliver and Boyd, Edinburgh, 143–75.

—— 1969. The measurement of strain and displacement in orogenic belts. *In*: KENT, P. E., SATTERTHWAITE, G. E. & SPENCER, A. M. (eds.), *Time and Place in Orogeny*, Spec. Pub. geol. Soc. London, **3**, 43–79.

RICHARDSON, S. & POWELL, R. 1976. Thermal causes of Dalradian metamorphism in C. Highlands of Scotland. *Scott. J. Geol.* **12**, 237–68.

RODGERS, J. 1970. *The Tectonics of the Appalachians*. Wiley-Interscience New York, 271 p.

SABINE, P. A. 1953. The petrography and geological significance of the post-Cambrian minor intrusions of Assynt and the adjoining districts of N.W. Scotland. *Q. J. geol. Soc. London*, **109**, 137–71.

SOPER, N. J. 1971. The earliest Caledonian structures in the Moine thrust belt. *Scott. J. Geol.* **7**, 241–7.

—— & BARBER, A. J. 1979. Proterozoic folds on the Northwest Caledonian Foreland. *Scott. J. Geol.* **15**, 1–11.

—— & BROWN, P. E. 1971. Relationship between metamorphism and migmatization in the northern part of the Moine Nappe. *Scott. J. Geol.* **7**, 305–325.

—— & WILKINSON, P. 1975. The Moine thrust and Moine Nappe at Loch Eriboll, Sutherland. *Scott. J. Geol.* **11**, 339–59.

STEWART, A. D. 1969. Torridonian rocks of Scotland reviewed. *Mem. Am. Assoc. Petrol. Geol.* **12**, 595–608.

—— 1975. Torridonian rocks of western Scotland, *In*: HARRIS, A. L. *et al.* (eds.), *A Correlation of the PreCambrian rocks in the British Isles*. Spec. Rep. geol. Soc. London, **6**, 43–52.

SUTTON, J. & WATSON, J. V. 1951. The pre-Torridonian metamorphic history of the Loch Torridon and Scourie areas in the north-west Highlands, and its bearing on the chronological classification of the Lewisian. *Q. J. geol. Soc. London*, **106**, 241–307.

TANNER, P. W. G. 1971. The Sgurr Beag Slide—a maga-tectonic break within the Moinian of the Western Highlands of Scotland. *Q. J. geol. Soc. London*, **126**, 425–63.

VAN BREEMAN, O., PIDGEON, R. T. & JOHNSON, M. R. W. 1974. Precambrian and Palaeozoic pegmatites in the Moines of northern Scotland. *J. geol. Soc. London*, **130**, 493–507.

——, AFTALION, M. & JOHNSON, M. R. W. 1979. Age of the Loch Borrolan complex, Assynt and late movements on the Moine thrust. *J. geol. Soc. London*, **136**, 489–96.

WATSON, J. V. 1975. The Lewisian Complex, *In*: HARRIS A. L. *et al.* (eds.), *A Correlation of the Precambrian Rocks in the British Isles*. Spec. Rep. geol. Soc. London, **6**, 15–29.

—— 1977. The Outer Hebrides: a geological perspective. *Proc. Geol. Assoc. London*, **88**, 1–24.

WHITE, S. H. 1979*a*. Grain size and sub-grain size variation across a mylonite zone. *Contrib. Mineral. Petrol.* **70**, 193–202.

—— 1979*b*. Difficulties associated with palaeostress estimates. *Bull. Mineral.* **102**, 210–5.

——, BURROWS, S., CARRERAS, J., SHAW, N. & HUMPHREYS, J. 1980. Mylonite development in ductile shear zones. *J. Struct. Geol.* (in press).

WILLIAMS, G. E. 1969*a*. Characteristics of a Precambrian sediment. *J. Geol. Chicago* **77**, 183–207.

—— 1969*b*. Petrography and origin of pebbles from Torridonian strata (late Precambrian) northwest Scotland. *Mem. Am. Assoc. Petrol. Geol.* **12**, 609–29.

WOOLLEY, A. R. 1970. The structural relationships of the Loch Borrolan complex, Scotland. *Geol. J.* **7**, 171–82.

K. R. McCLAY, Department of Geology, University of London, Goldsmiths College, New Cross, London, SE14 6NW.

M. P. COWARD, Department of Earth Sciences, University of Leeds, Leeds LS2 9JT.

Tectonic slides in the Caledonides

D. H. W. Hutton

SUMMARY: Despite the continuing use of the term 'tectonic slide' in the Caledonian fold belt of Britain and Ireland for the past fifty years, the concept has found few advocates elsewhere. To many geologists outside the British Isles it remains a subject of some confusion.

A review of the literature suggests that slides are a general term for faults which form in close association with syn-metamorphic regional deformation. They are often related to major folds although this is not a diagnostic feature. Neither is any movement sense implied in the term slide; thus, they may be thrusts, lags, oblique slip etc. Classically, these structures lie along and subparallel to the boundaries of major lithological units but transgress the stratigraphy on a larger scale. Structural analogies with the thrusts of the lower grade or non-metamorphic deformed cover sequences can often be seen in slides. However, they are more commonly and possibly fundamentally the result of differing responses to deformation of contrasting, adjacent lithologies in areas of higher strain and metamorphism.

Although recognized in the Caledonides for many years, the fault-like structures known as tectonic slides have rarely been reported from other fold belts. This is probably not because the structure is restricted to one single orogen, but rather that the term is generally misunderstood and, as a source of confusion, is ignored by most orogenic geologists. The purpose of this short paper is therefore three fold: (a) to explain exactly what a slide is; (b) to discuss the need for the term; and (c) to examine the problematic formation of these structures. A more exhaustive treatment of the topic can be found elsewhere (Hutton 1979b).

History of the term

The concept of slides came from E. B. Bailey's work in the complex Dalradian metasediments of the SW Scottish Highlands early this century. Using the then common technique of identifying stratigraphic sequences in reverse order Bailey (1910) identified major recumbent folds in the Ballachullish area of Argyll. In detail, however, the successions on each supposed fold limb would often be different. One or more stratigraphic units would be apparently thinned, intermittently present or absent altogether. Since these effects seemed to occur along easily mappable lines, which usually gently transgressed the stratigraphic sequence (Fig. 1), the idea of faults causally related to the major folds was thus proposed. Bailey (1910) p. 593) identified two main types of 'fold-fault': 'Thrusts' (low angle reverse faults prior to refolding) which replaced the inverted limbs of anticlines; and, 'Lags' (low angle normal faults prior to refolding) which replaced the normal limbs of anticlines. However, since the way-up of the succession was not known, Bailey preferred to use 'fault-fold' as a non-commital general term for all such structures. 'Slide' was adopted as a less clumsy synonym of 'fold-fault' (Bailey 1910, p. 593).

After Vogt (1930) introduced the use of sedimentation structures as way-up evidence in the Dalradian (and the major slides of Ballachulish were identified as 'lags') the term has been used where way-up has been absent or the structure obscure. It has been widely applied throughout the Dalradian outcrop in Scotland and Ireland. Slides have been identified within the Moine of the British Isles and particularly on its margins with the Dalradian (Sutton 1972; Piasecki & Van Breeman 1979) and Lewisian (Peacock 1975). They are also found in the low grade Lower Palaeozoic Caledonides of W Ireland (Dewey & Phillips 1963) in the Fleur de Lys supergroup of Newfoundland (Kennedy 1971), the high grade Caledonian rocks of the Glomfjord region in N Norway (Rutland & Nicholson 1965) and in the southern Appalachians (Hatcher 1972; 1979). The term 'tectonic slide' (Fleuty 1964) has allowed the structure to be distinguished from the more superficial 'gravity slides' and 'mass movement slides'.

Features of slides

Slides are typically difficult structures to detect at outcrop level–a feature which Bailey consistently attributed to their formation in a 'ductile' rather than a 'brittle' tectonic environment. Thus they are rarely associated with

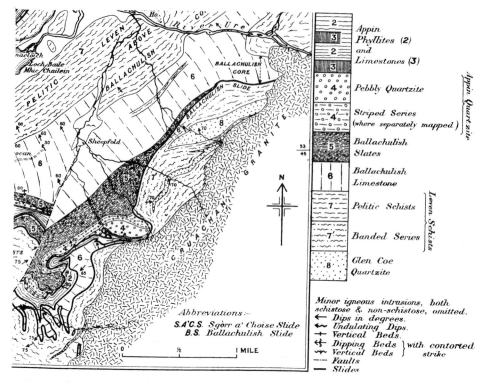

FIG. 1. Part of plate 45 from Bailey (1914) showing the stratigraphic cut-out along the Ballachullish Slide in the Dalradian rocks of Glen Creran, Argyllshire, Scotland. Reproduced by permission.

cataclasis, local bedding or foliation discordance and often (when exposed) they lie along lithological boundaries. Although they may be quite sharp, slide contacts are sometimes gradational, giving the structures, with the features noted above, all the appearance of normal lithological junctions. Their existence classically comes from an appreciation of larger scale stratigraphic relationships. As a result of this, there has been much controversy over the existence of many slides (particularly Bailey's). They have for many critics been objects of faith alone, dependent on a particular view of the stratigraphic succession and often more easily explained, in their view, by non-tectonic sedimentary facies variations. However, with the development of modern structural field techniques and a lessening emphasis on structural analysis based purely on stratigraphic hypothesis, the case for many slides can be more easily examined than in the past. In the Ballachulish area, Bailey's most important slides are accepted as actual structures by current workers, although their significance is a matter of debate (Roberts 1976; Hickman 1978).

A review of literature on slides suggests they have the following features:

(a) They are essentially breaks i.e. discontinuities often observable or inferable at outcrop level and often localized at lithological boundaries.

(b) They lie in planar zones of penetrative cleavage. This cleavage is often an intensification of a more widespread regional deformation fabric that develops close to a metamorphic maximum in orogenic areas.

(c) Slides can have a variety of pre-refolding geometries. Not simply thrusts, or lags (in the sense of Bailey) but also high angle reverse and normal (Dewey & Phillips 1963; Roberts & Treagus 1977) as well as transcurrent or oblique slip faults (Hutton 1977a).

(d) Slides may be associated with folds: (i) They can occur locally in fold limbs where an incompetent horizon has been cut out as a result of high limb strains (Whitten 1957). (ii) Slides and their related zones of deformation

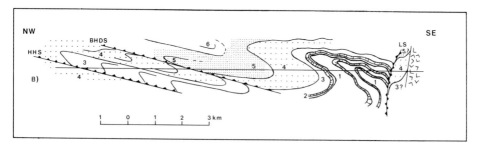

Fig. 2. Diagramatic section of the Dalradian rocks of NW Donegal, Eire showing the principal slides (heavy toothed lines). The Horn Head Slide (HHS) and Breaghy Head-Dunfanaghy Slide (BHDS) are thrusts associated with early (second phase) NW facing recumbent folds. Note that the BHDS is oblique to the axial planes of adjacent folds and superimposes variable younging reversals along its outcrop. The Lackagh Slide (LS) is a later (fourth phase) structure associated with the granite emplacement and an upright synform. This is an oblique/transcurrent fault with a movement direction plunging gently away from the reader. The slides divide the stratigraphy (numbered 1 oldest to 6 youngest) into 'tectonic units'. From Hutton (1977*b*).

can cross-cut folds and either be parallel to their axial planes or, in the more general case, lie oblique to both hinges and axial planes. In the latter situation slide movements can superimpose younging reversals across the slide plane by the excision of intervening hinges and limbs (Fig. 2).

(e) Slides need not be related to major folds (Tanner 1971; Kennedy 1971): a fact that was excluded by the definition of Fleuty (1964). (i) They can occur at simple lithological junctions and form, for example, the typical 'tectonic contact' of high grade terrains. (ii) They may also be found at tectonic fronts where rocks belonging to two different orogenic cycles are interleaved in a series of tectonic slices (bounded by slides) in a regime of high bulk strains and metamorphic overprinting (Peacock 1975; Sutton 1972).

(f) Slides may be characterized by the presence of tectonic schists. These are thought to be formed by the localized mixing and metamorphic convergence of the two adjacent lithologies because of the high syn-metamorphic strains at their interface (Rast 1958).

They are typically thin yet persistent horizons with a coarsely schistose texture often with detached minor fold hinges and boudins of the more competent rock. Tectonic schists share, to some extent, the chemistry of the parent lithologies.

The basic characteristic of slides that is inherent in all the above features is their occurrence in a metamorphic environment. This distinguishes them from the more usual 'brittle' type of fault which is produced by deformation in non-metamorphic or post-metamorphic con-

ditions. This important point has been increasingly recognized in recent years (Tanner 1971; Tanner *et al.* 1970; Rutland & Nicholson 1965) but although briefly discussed by Fleuty (1964) was not specifically incorporated in his definition. An examination of Bailey's occasional references to the nature of slide formation e.g. . . . 'sliding has been associated to an important extent with the phenomena of plastic deformation' (Bailey 1910, p. 610) suggests that he was aware of the metamorphic aspect of these structures. This may be considered, therefore, as the basis of any proposed new definition of the term 'tectonic slide'. One can, however, envisage a situation where a high structural level, 'brittle' fault is subsequently involved in deeper level metamorphic orogenesis. It could then attain many of the features of, and effectively be rejuvenated as, a tectonic slide. However difficult the demonstration of such a history may be for any individual case, we need to include this possibility of reactivated early faults in any new definition (see below).

The need for the term 'tectonic slide'

Do we need this term in the geological literature? Firstly, as products of ductile deformation rather than brittle failure, slides form a distinctive group of faults with their own characteristics (see above) and probably their own distinctive mode of formation (see below). Secondly, as structures of regionally metamorphosed and deformed rocks, they must be much more common in the world's fold belts than hitherto acknowledged. Thirdly, because of the difficulty in detecting these faults on the ground many of them have probably been overlooked in non-Caledonian areas. In rejuvenating the term, attention may be focussed on the possible occurrence of such structures in these areas and it is hoped that structural and stratigraphic knowledge will consequently benefit. This will be made easier by the formulation of a new definition. This is based on the essence of the original meaning and the general evolved usage of the term.

'A tectonic slide is a fault which forms in metamorphic rocks prior to, or during, a metamorphic event. It occurs within a zone of coeval penetrative (i.e. microscopic) deformation that represents an intensification of a more widespread, often regionally developed deformation phase. Within this zone of high strain, slides may lie along and be sub-parallel to (although they will cross-cut on a larger scale) the boundaries of lithological*, tectonic and tectono-metamorphic units'.

'Slide zones' may be considered as zones of intensified deformation (effectively shear zones) in which more than one break (slide) exists.

The formation of slides

Slides form in metamorphic rocks between the lower greenschist facies and upper amphibolite facies. Fault formation by sudden failure in the sense of a developing 'Griffith Crack' is clearly inappropriate in these conditions because of the enormous differential stresses required and the relatively high temperature of the rocks. Overburden stresses could be relieved by high pore pressures generated, for example, by dehydrating evaporites (Hanshaw & Bredehoeft 1968) or rocks rich in such minerals as serpentenite and chloritite (Raleigh & Paterson 1965; Murrell & Ismail 1976). However, rocks of this type do not characterize tectonic slides, nor do the competent 'impermeable' horizons required always overlie slides. Plastic creep instability caused by the longer term application of lower differential stresses (Orowan 1960) can account in a general way for the phenomenon. The typical occurrence of slides along lithological boundaries, however

requires some explanation in such a model. Hutton (1979a, b) has shown that, although tectonic strains increase towards slides, the maximum values achieved may be widely different in contrasting lithologies. This suggests that different rock types may have different creep rates and that, if a lithological junction becomes involved in a zone of intensified strain a discontinuity (slide) will eventually develop. This model tends to be confirmed by the observation that the three-dimensional deformation for both lithologies is dissimilar and not by volume conserving plane strain ($K = 1$): quartzite strains are constrictional ($K > 1$) and pelite strains are of the flattening type ($K < 1$). One may speculate that a progressive syntectonic volume decrease in the pelites generated excess fluid which was transferred across to the quartzites to create the progressive volume increase that the constrictional deformation requires. The excess fluid (H_2O) could be generated during any of the main syntectonic metamorphic dehydration reactions (Fyfe 1976). Clearly, more fluid would be produced in pelites than in quartzites in such reactions and thus a local fluid pressure gradient could be set up across the boundary. Quartz, easily dissolved in H_2O at such temperatures, could be transferred into the adjacent quartzites, themselves quite permeable at the time of such phase changes (Norris & Henley 1976).

In this model, therefore, it is the volume changes, related to the specific metamorphic history of different rock types, imposed on the deforming rocks so as to produce different shapes of strain ellipsoid in them, that leads to the formation of a discontinuity (tectonic slide) at the rock interface. Once initiated as breaks within the shear zones, independent movement on the slides could allow them to propagate along the axis of high strain into less contrasting, or even homogenous, lithologies. In this way slides could climb stratigraphic sections.

Conclusions

Tectonic slides constitute a distinct genetic class of fault noted not for their geometry or structural habits but mainly for the fact that they form in metamorphic conditions. Additionally, they often occur along lithological boundaries and lie within zones of intensified regional cleavage-deformation. One may infer from strain studies that, under conditions of elevated temperature and pressure, faults such as these initiate because of the differing response of contrasting rock types to syn-metamorphic strains.

---

*Lithological units are self-explanatory e.g. associated with e(i) above. Tectonic units are those which are characterized by more than one lithology and by folds or groups of folds e.g. Fig. 2. Tectonometamorphic units are rocks belonging to different orogens e.g. e(ii) above.

Although the term is rarely used outside the British Isles, slides are probably quite common structures. It is considered that because of their distinctive characteristics, problematic formation, non-geometric and rather broad definition, and difficulty in recognition, the term and concept is of some benefit to geologists in metamorphic-orogenic areas.

ACKNOWLEDGMENTS. I would like to thank the Department of Education, Northern Ireland, the Department of Education, Eire and the staff research fund of Queen's University, Belfast for the financial assistance that allowed this work to be done. I also thank Mrs S. Hutton for helpful discussion and Mrs K. Irvine for typing.

References

BAILEY, E. B. 1910. Recumbent folds in the schists of the Scottish Highlands. *Q. J. geol. Soc. London,* **66,** 586–608.

—— 1914. The Ballachulish Fold near the head of Loch Creran. *Q. J. geol. Soc. London,* **70,** 321–7.

DEWEY, J. F. & PHILLIPS, W. E. A. 1963. A tectonic profile across the Caledonides of South Mayo. *Geol. J.* **3,** 237–46.

FLEUTY, M. J. 1964. Tectonic Slides. *Geol. Mag.* **101,** 452–6.

FYFE, W. S. 1976. Chemical aspects of rock deformation, *Philos. Trans. R. Soc. London,* **A283,** 221–3.

HANSHAW, B. B. & BREDEHOEFT, J. D. 1968. On the maintenance of anomalous fluid pressures: II. Source layer at depth. *Bull. geol. Soc. Am.* **79,** 1107–22.

HATCHER, R. D. Jr. 1972. Development model of the southern Appalachians. *Bull. geol. Soc. Am.* **83,** 2735–60.

—— 1980. Thrusts and thrust nappes in the North American Appalachian Orogen. This volume.

HICKMAN, A. H. 1978. Recumbent folds between Glen Roy and Lismore. *Scott. J. Geol.* **14,** 191–212.

HUTTON, D. H. W. 1977*a*. A structural cross-section from the aureole of the Main Donegal Granite. *Geol. J.* **12,** 99–112.

—— 1977*b*. *The structure of the Lower Dalradian rocks of the Cresslough Area, Co. Donegal, Eire, with special reference to tectonic slides.* Thesis, Ph.D., Queen's University, Belfast. (Unpubl.).

—— 1979*a*. The strain history of a Dalradian Slide: using pebbles with low fluctuations in axis orientation. *Tectonophysics,* **55,** 261–73.

—— 1979*b*. Tectonic Slides: a review and reappraisal. *Earth-Science Reviews,* **15,** 151–72.

KENNEDY, M. J. 1971. Structure and stratigraphy of the Fleur De Lys Supergroup in the Fleur De Lys area, Burlington Peninsula, Newfoundland. *Proc. geol. Assoc. Can.* **24,** 59–73.

MURRELL, S. A. F. & ISMAIL, I. A. H. 1976. The effect of decomposition of hydrous minerals on the mechanical properties of rocks at high pressures and temperatures. *Tectonophysics,* **31,** 207–58.

NORRIS, R. J. & HENLEY, R. W. 1976. Dewatering of a metamorphic pile. *Geology,* **4,** 333–6.

OROWAN, E. 1960. Mechanism of seismic faulting. *Mem. geol. Soc. Am.* **79,** 323–45.

PEACOCK, J. S. D. 1975. 'Slide rocks' in the Moine of the Loch Shin Area, Northern Scotland. *Bull. geol. Surv. G.B.* **49,** 23–30.

PIASECKI, M. & VAN BREEMAN, O. 1979. A Morarian age for the 'younger Moines' of central and western Scotland. *Nature,* **278,** 734–6.

RALEIGH, C. B. & PATTERSON, M. S. 1965. Experimental deformation of serpentinite and its tectonic implications. *J. geophys. Res.* **70,** 3965–85.

RAST, N. 1958. The tectonics of the Schiehallion complex. *Q. J. geol. Soc. London,* **114,** 25–43.

ROBERTS, J. L. 1976. The structure of the Dalradian rocks in the North Ballachulish District of Scotland. *J. geol. Soc. London,* **132,** 139–54.

—— & TREAGUS, J. E. 1977. Polyphase generation of nappe structures in the Dalradian rocks of the SW Highlands of Scotland. *Scott. J. Geol.* **13,** 237–54.

RUTLAND, R. W. R. & NICHOLSON, R. 1965. Tectonics of the Caledonides of part of Nordland, Norway. *Q. J. geol. Soc. London,* **121,** 73–109.

SUTTON, J. S. 1972. The pre-Caledonian rocks of the Mullet peninsula. Co. Mayo, Ireland. *Sci. Proc. R. Dubl. Soc.* **A4,** 121–134.

TANNER, P. W. G. 1971. The Sgurr Beag Slide-a major tectonic break within the Moine of the Western Highlands of Scotland. *Q. J. geol. Soc. London,* **126,** 435–63.

—— JOHNSTONE, G. S., SMITH, D. I. & HARRIS, A. L. 1970. Moinian stratigraphy and the problem of the central Ross-shire inliers. *Bull. geol. Soc. Am.* **81,** 299–306.

VOGT, T. 1930. On the chronological order of deposition of the Highland Schists. *Geol. Mag.* **67,** 68–73.

WHITTEN, E. H. T. 1957. A study of two directions of folding: the structural geology of Monadhliath and Mid-Strathspey. *J. Geol. Chicago,* **67,** 14–47.

D. H. W. HUTTON, Department of Geology, Trinity College, Dublin 2, Ireland.

Estimation of the rate and amount of absolute lateral shortening in an orogen using diachronism and strike slipped segments

W. E. A. Phillips

SUMMARY: By reference to the Caledonide Orogen, a method is illustrated by which quantitive estimates may be obtained of lateral movements between opposing forelands of a collision orogen. The procedure involves: 1: Identification of a rigid foreland frame (2 plates) bounding the collision orogen and establishing the orientation of the main movement direction between forelands, 2: Measurement along strike of diachroneity in the ending of arc volcanism and of cooling ages for granites; relating this to a rate of migration of collision along strike of the collision suture, and calculation of the rate of plate convergence from this, knowing the angle between the collision suture and the plate movement direction, 3: Recognition of swings in strike which predate collision, and 4: Measurement of lateral offset of dated collision points in the strike slip sector of the curved orogen and calculation from this of the components of lateral shortening around the curve. Application of these methods to the Caledonide Orogen of the British Isles, Scandinavia and E Greenland, gives values for foreland convergence on a trend of 115–295° of 0.88 cm/year between the Lower Caradoc (430 Ma) and Lower Ludlow (c. 400 Ma). Convergence slowed to 0.75 cm/year on this trend during the Caledonian orogenesis between Lower Ludlow (c. 400 Ma) and the end of the Middle Devonian (c. 365 Ma), giving lateral convergences of about 267 km in the E Greenland W Norway region (c. 22%) and 216 km (c. 31%) in the paratectonic Caledonides of the British Isles.

The hypothesis that the Caledonide Orogen of the North Atlantic region is a collision orogen is supported by a wide variety of evidence which has been summarized by Dewey 1969a; Fitton & Hughes 1970; Briden et al. 1973; Skevington 1974; Williams 1976; Phillips et al. 1976 and other workers. Kvale (1977) has summarized evidence suggesting that the British Isles and Scandinavian sector of the orogen were bounded to the E by a rigid plate (Baltic Plate Fig. 1B) of the E European Platform, during late Precambrian and Lower Palaeozoic time. There is little doubt that the Greenland Shield and Hebridean Platform to the NW of the orogen formed part of a continuous N American Plate at this time.

In the Caledonides of E Greenland and W Norway and Sweden, there is a symmetrical thrust regime with westward directed thrusting in E Greenland (Higgins & Phillips 1980) and eastward directed thrusting in Scandinavia (Gee 1978 and references therein). Allowing for Cenozoic opening of the North Atlantic Ocean, this sector of the Caledonides shows an original regional strike of about 025°. In this paper it will be assumed that the main movement direction between the two bounding forelands was at 90° to this trend (i.e. 115–295°). This is supported by the strain analyses of McLeish (1971) in the Moine Thrust Zone of NW Scotland, indicating thrusting on this axis.

Acceptance of a rigid foreland frame to the British Isles-Scandinavia-E Greenland Caledonides requires a common plate convergence direction for this sector.

As the Caledonide Orogen is traced southwards from Scandinavia, the strike swings into a more E–W trend in the British Isles, where the collision suture strikes about 061° (Phillips et al. 1976). The strike curves back to about 014° in the northern Appalachians of the United States. These major strike swings must predate collision, otherwise there would be major accommodation structures such as grabens, oblique fold belts or major strike slip fracture systems transecting the forelands in the regions of strike swing. No such features have been recognized in the western margin of the N Appalachians where such features should be well exposed. If the more E–W strike of the Caledonides of the British Isles is a pre-collision feature, then there should be evidence of dextral transpression (Harland 1971) in the Caledonian deformation of this region (Fig. 1B). Evidence for an important component of dextral slip parallel to strike has been described for the Caledonides of central Ireland by Phillips et al. 1976, 1980), and Sanderson et al. (1980). The simple model for Caledonian plate movements shown in Fig. 1B will, therefore, be used in this paper. Table 1 summarizes distinctive features of the British

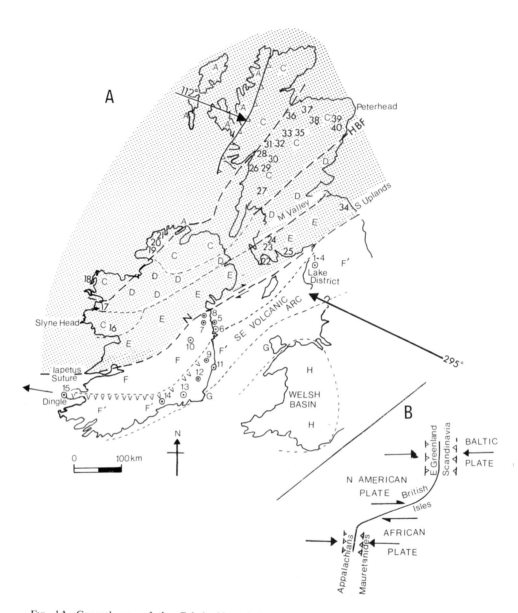

Fig. 1A. General map of the Caledonides of the British Isles showing the main structural-stratigraphic zones of Phillips *et al.* 1976. A. NW foreland, C. Moine and Dalradian Zone, D. NW Volcanic Arc, E. NW sedimentary Arc, F. SE Sedimentary Arc, F'. SE Volcanic Arc, G. Irish Sea Landmass, H. Welsh Basin and Midland Platform. Localities 1–15 in zone F' are used in Fig. 2. Localities 16–40 in zone C/E are used in Fig. 3. Northwestern (North American) Plate shaded, Southeastern (Baltic) Plate unshaded. Heavy arrows indicate probable vectors for plates. B. Summary of continental plate movements proposed for the Caledonide Orogen. Solid line represents the trend of the Caledonian–Appalachian Orogen. Barbed lines represent thrust zones.

TABLE 1. *A summary of features which are distinctive to the Caledonides of the British Isles with respect to the Caledonides of Scandinavia and E Greenland, and the significance of these features with regard to symmetrical compression and dextral transpression*

Distinctive features of the Caledonides of the British Isles	Relevance of dextral transpression	Distinctive features of the Caledonides of Scandinavia and E Greenland	Relevance of symmetrical compression
Post-Caledonian instability with widespread deposition of Carboniferous and younger cover rocks over positive and negative blocks	Restricted crustal thickening during the Caledonian Orogeny, which produced a mosaic of vertical fault blocks	Post-Caledonian stability with little subsequent deposition of cover rocks	Substantial crustal thickening during Caledonian orogenesis stabilizing the crust
Widespread preservation of late Caledonian rocks (Silurian–Lower Devonian). Scarcity of basement outcrops. Moho at about 30 km	Restricted crustal thickening during the Caledonian Orogeny and so restricted isostatic uplift and consequent erosion	Scarcity of late Caledonian rocks (Silurian–Lower Devonian). Widespread outcrops of pre-Caledonian basement. Moho at about 40 km	Substantial crustal thickening during Caledonian orogenesis caused substantial isotatic uplift and erosion
Abundant high angle strike faults	Caused strike slip faulting along the regional strike trends	Abundant large thrust faults	Favoured thrusting
Siluro-Devonian deformation produced upright folds	Caused a combination of lateral shortening and vertical extension with a component of dextral shear along strike (Phillips *et al.* 1980, Sanderson *et al.* 1980)	Siluro-Devonian deformation produced early recumbent folds	Folds associated with thrusting
Asymmetrical structural development with recumbent folds, thrusts and amphibolite facies metamorphism of Ordovician age only developed in the NW	Lateral (strike slip) movements between opposing plate margins brought together segments of different pre-collision history	Symmetrical structural evolution with W directed thrusting in E Greenland and E directed thrusting in Scandinavia	Result of symmetrical compression
Abundant granite plutonism	Availability of vertical fractures and generation of local pull-apart tectonics during strike slip movements facilitating the diapiric uprise of granite plutons	Relative scarcity of granitic plutonism	Inhibited formation of deep vertical fractures
Very low grade Siluro-Devonian metamorphism	Lack of crustal thickening	Widespread amphibolite facies regional metamorphism of Silurian age	Crustal thickening, heat retained by scarcity of plutonism
Asymmetric stratigraphical evolution e.g. thick late Precambrian and Cambrian sediments in the NW belong to the Caledonian cycle. In the SE the Caledonian cycle starts with Cambrian rocks. Contrasted Precambrian basement on opposing margins	Lateral strike slip movements between opposing plate margins brought together sections of contrasted plate margin history	Symmetrical stratigraphic evolution	Opposing plate margins opened and closed symmetrically

Isles and Scandinavian E Greenland sectors of the Caledonide Orogen, and indicates how this kinematic model can explain differences between the two sectors.

Methods of quantifying lateral

Diachronism and oblique collision

A model of oblique collision for the Caledonides of the British Isles was outlined by Phillips *et al.* (1976). A collision suture (Iapetus Suture) was recognized and stratigraphical-structural zones related to opposing margins of the Iapetus Ocean (zones E & F' Fig. 1A) were seen to diverge westwards suggesting that an oblique collision migrated westwards, like a scissors cut, with time. More specific evidence for this was obtained from showing that volcanism had ceased at progressively later times towards the W along zone F'. This was identified on geochemical evidence as an Andean type continental volcanic arc related to southeasterly subduction (Sd3 Fig. 4) of Iapetus oceanic crust. The westerly migration with time of the cessation of volcanism was interpreted as a response to oblique collision migrating W with time. Northwesterly directed subduction of Iapetus oceanic crust beneath zone E was inferred from the interpretation of this zone as an Ordovician–Silurian accretive prism (Mitchell & McKerrow 1975, McKerrow *et al.* 1977, Leggett *et al.* 1980) developed by such a subduction system (Sd2 Fig. 4). The progressively younger K/Ar cooling ages for granites in zones C–E when traced westwards was again interpreted as evidence for westerly migration of collision with time. It was argued that collision would terminate formation of granitic magma and initiate cooling and uplift. The rate of diachronism along strike of cooling ages was therefore used to measure the rate of collision migration along the suture.

Plate convergence rates calculated from these interpretations were hampered primarily by the absence of an adequate radiometric time scale for the Ordovician and Silurian. The consequences of the plate vector model outlined in Fig. 1B were also not used. Availability of a more detailed radiometric time scale for the Lower Palaeozoic (Gale *et al.* 1979) applied to this vector model, allows much more precise estimates of plate movements to be calculated.

Diachronous ending of volcanism

In Fig. 2 the times of the cessation of volcanism along zone F' (Williams *et al.* 1972, Brenchley *et al.* 1977) have been plotted as a function of distance along strike. At localities 9–14, erosion has removed younger sediments overlying the volcanic rocks and so the data points represent maximum ages for the ending of volcanism there. The regression line has been calculated without taking this into account, so that the line is for the greatest possible scatter in the data. Despite this, a 't test' shows that it is significant at the 1% level. An even better significance would result if the need to reduce the ages for localities 9–14 was taken into account. The slope of the regression line gives a rate of diachronism in the ending of volcanism along strike of 3.3 cm/year towards the W. The present angle (Fig. 1A) between the volcanic arc and the Iapetus Suture is 9° measured over 600 km along strike. If allowance is made for a 50% post-collision shortening normal to strike of the arc (Dewey 1969*b*), the angle is increased to 14°. Vector calculation for the 115–295° inferred plate convergence trend gives a convergence rate of 0.88 cm/year between 430 and 400 Ma. This rate will be reduced by any decrease in the age of data points 9–14.

In Fig. 3, K/Ar cooling ages for micas in granites of zones C–E (Fig. 1A) have been plotted as a function of distance along strike. The regression line shows a good correlation coefficient value with a significance of 0.1%. The slope of the regression line gives a rate of diachronism of cooling to the W of 1.48 cm/year on a line between Peterhead and Slyne Head, which strikes at 12° to the Iapetus Suture. Vector calculations give a rate of plate convergence of 0.88 cm/year on the trend 115–295°. The figures of 0.25 and 0.04 cm/year obtained by Phillips *et al.* (1976) for this vector depended upon using angles of 2 or 4° between Sd2 and the Iapetus Suture and did not include all the K/Ar data from Donegal. It is doubtful that such a small angle is suitable for vector calculations. If there were no time lag between

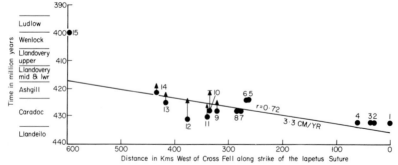

FIG. 2. Graph showing the ending times of volcanism in the Southeastern Volcanic Arc of the British Isles (zone F' Fig. 1) plotted against distance measured along strike. Localities 1–15 are shown in Fig. 1 and the data for them was obtained from Williams *et al.* 1972 and Brenchley *et al.* 1977. The time scale is from Gale *et al.* 1979.

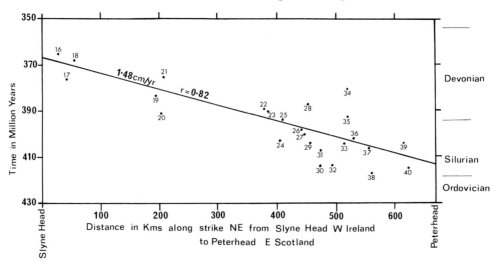

FIG. 3. Graph showing the K/Ar cooling ages for micas in late Caledonian granites of zone C to the S of the Great Glen Fault, plotted against distance along strike. Localities 16–40 are shown in Fig. 1. The data were derived from Brown *et al.* 1968 and Harper 1967.

the collision and cooling of granites through the blocking of temperatures for K/Ar in micas (*c.* 250°C) then the vector of 0.88 cm/year would be of late Llandovery–late Middle Devonian age. As there must be a time lag for this response, the vector must be older.

The inferred geometry and vectors for early Silurian plate margins of this part of the Caledonides are summarized in Fig. 4. Isotopic and geological evidence (Wilson *et al.* 1973) indicate that Caledonian deformation (collision tectonics) occurred in W Norway in late Llandovery–Wenlock times (*c.* 400 Ma.). Prior

to this, there was presumably some Iapetus oceanic crust separating the Baltic and Greenland Shields, as shown in Figs 4 and 6. This reconstruction then requires that collision first occurred in southern Norway and westwards towards the Lake District. This is consistent with the geological evidence (Sturt 1978; Moseley 1972) for significant Ordovician deformation being limited to these regions. When more data for dating volcanism and cooling of granites are available in zone F', it should be possible to estimate lateral shortening in these regions for this time.

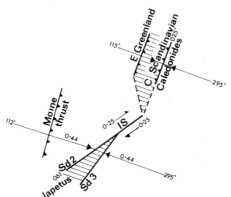

FIG. 4. A summary diagram of inferred Caledonian plate orientations and movements in the British Isles-Scandinavia-E Greenland sector in early Silurian times. Vector components are shown in cm/yr. The Iapetus oceanic plate is lined. IS Iapetus Suture.

Lateral offset of collision points

If collision of converging continental margins bounding the Iapetus Ocean is invoked to explain the ending of volcanism in the Lower Caradoc (*c.* 430 Ma.) of the Lake District (Fig. 1A) and hence the cessation of southeasterly subduction, then northwesterly subduction beneath the now opposed Southern Uplands (Zone E) might similarly be expected to have ended at the same time. The strong evidence that the Ordovician and Silurian rocks of the Southern Uplands represent an accretive prism produced by NW directed subduction (McKerrow *et al.* 1977 and Leggett *et al.* 1980 requires that this subduction continued until at least the end of the Wenlock (*c.* 400 Ma), for greywackes of this age outcrop there. This anomaly can be resolved by a component of post-collision dextral slip occurring along the suture (Figs 4 & 5). By this means,

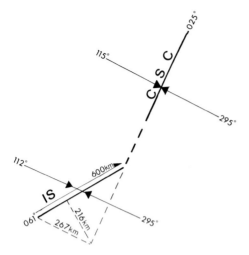

FIG. 5. A summary diagram showing inferred Caledonian plate vectors and their values in cm/yr for the British Isles-Scandinavian sector of the Caledonide Orogen for the end of Caledonian deformation (late Middle Devonian).

a younger collision point on the American Plate (Zone E) could have been moved E to abut against an older collision point on the Baltic Plate (Zone F'). The most conservative estimate for this translation is a 600 km dextral offset which is the present offset across the Iapetus Suture of 400 Ma collision points (Dingle on the S side, Southern Uplands on the N side). Though it is far from certain that the Lower Devonian calc-alkaline volcanism of the Midland Valley of Scotland can be interpreted as evidence for subduction continuing to this time (C. J. Stillman, pers. comm. 1979), a larger translation of about 980 km would be required if this were the case.

The minimum dextral offset of 600 km on the Iapetus Suture must be mostly accommodated within the period of 400 Ma to the end of the Devonian (c. 354 Ma), for uppermost Devonian and Dinantian rocks show broadly similar facies and thickness across the suture line in Central Ireland (MacDermott & Sevastopulo 1972.) There is, however, localized evidence of dextral strike slip movements in the suture zone continuing in post Denantian times at Navan and Silvermines (Phillips *et al.* 1977). A constraint of 600 km dextral offset occurring within 45 Ma (400–354 Ma) requires a slip rate of 1.3 cm/year on the suture. This rate decreases towards the 0.5 cm/year rate calculated prior to 400 Ma (Fig. 4), if offset continued during post-Devonian time. Fig. 5 shows that this slip rate of 1.3 cm/year gives a lateral

convergence of 267 km (c. 22%) in the Caledonides of W Norway–E Greenland during late Silurian–Middle Devonian orogenesis. This estimate can be resolved into a component of 216 km (c. 31%) of lateral convergence normal to the strike of the Iapetus Suture in the paratectonic Caledonides of the British Isles during orogenesis there. These estimates of lateral shortening during Caledonian orogenesis will be decreased by reducing the slip rate on the Iapetus Suture and extending slip on it in the British Isles into post-Devonian times. Conversely, the estimates are increased if the offset between inferred collision points in the British Isles was more than 600 km.

Discussion and conclusions

There are many obvious limitations to the accuracy of these methods. The most important factor is the question of scale. The size of the British Isles is probably about the smallest scale of unit for which plate tectonic calculations can be applied. The concepts of plate tectonics depend upon a set of rigid plates with narrow boundaries; clearly an orogenic belt up to 1000 km in width requires that plate tectonic calculations should be based on several thousand kilometres of strike length. On the scale of the British Isles, there is the possibility of the involvement of microplates and the possibility that diachronous cessation of volcanism along strike was caused by other factors than collision. The internal consistency of the model for this region makes this less likely. In the case of the cooling ages of granites, unless the scale of measurement is large enough, the pattern of ages may well reflect local hot spots, perhaps controlled structurally, rather than migration of collision. Recognition of the collision suture is particularly important to the methods. Such a suture is unlikely to be a sharp line. If there was strike slip movement over a broad zone, then there are likely to be complex braided patterns of rotated and translated blocks. The suture line must, therefore, be defined on a large (>500 km) scale. Accuracy of dating is another limiting factor which is well illustrated in the case of localities 9–14 (Fig. 2). Dating of vectors calculated from granite cooling is clearly difficult. The measurement of original distance along strike poses problems of allowing for subsequent strain-faulting or axial extension. In Fig. 2, the position of the data point for Dingle (15) takes no account of any possible Hercynian strain for instance. Allowance for post-collision strain is

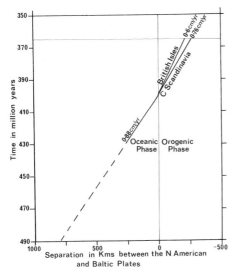

FIG. 6. Graph showing inferred separation of the North American and Baltic plates as a function of time. Negative values of separation measure lateral orogenic shortening, positive values measure the width of the Iapetus Ocean separating these plates.

track dating in granites on both side of the suture is an obvious test which awaits more data. The scarity of K/Ar mica dates in zone F′ prevented testing this method, until more data are available from the Leinster granite. The application of these methods elsewhere in the Caledonide Orogen will provide further tests.

The rather simple geometry of the model summarized in Fig. 1A, with two opposed volcanic arcs separated by *c.* 100–150 km, requires some comment in terms of estimating shortening of the lithosphere. If one could assume pre-collision widths for arc-trench gap units associated with both converging plate margins, then the present separation of the volcanic arcs might seem to offer a method of measuring post-collision shortening of the lithosphere. Factors which have an important control upon the width of arc-trench gaps are subduction rates, amount of sediment being accreted to the continental margin, and the presence or absence of tectonic erosion of the overriding plate during subduction. These are unknown quantities in the Caledonides of the British Isles. In addition to these difficulties, there is, clearly, the potential for large components of *apparent* shortening of the lithosphere between the opposed volcanic arcs being produced by the inferred post-collision strike-slip movements. This can arise both from the obliquity between the Iapetus Suture and the SE volcanic arc (F′), and from the probability that the post-collision strike slip displacements were not precisely parallel to the line of collision.

In conclusion, the methods described in this paper need to be applied on a large scale and the results cross-checked by many study areas. The methods are no less beset with inaccuracies than conventional strain analysis, but the two approaches together can compliment each other. Together they provide the potential of distinguishing components of horizontal from vertical shortening and, thus, the possibility of defining the extent of gravity tectonics. There is also the long term possibility of reconstructing plate vectors for pre-Mesozoic times.

essential, if the original angle between the collision suture and volcanic arc or line of granites is to be determined. In this paper, no correction for post-collision strain was made for the line between Peterhead and Slyne Head because of the absence of strain data from zone E.

The method of using offset of collision points depends upon dating these points. The difficulty of doing this is well illustrated in the case of the Caledonides of the British Isles. The use of offset-estimates in vector calculations depends upon knowing original angles between the strike slip sector and thrust sector. There is always the possibility of late changes in this angle. (see Briden *et al.* 1973).

Clearly, the results presented in this paper, summarized in Fig. 6, for the Caledonides should be treated with caution, at best they are order of magnitude estimates. Fortunately there is plenty of scope for testing these results. The use of Rb/Sr mineral and fission

ACKNOWLEDGMENT: I am particularly grateful to Dr P. S. Kennan for helpful discussions.

References

BRENCHLEY, P. J., HARPER, J. C., MITCHELL, W. I. & ROMANO, M. 1977. A re-appraisal of some Ordovician successions in Eastern Ireland. *Proc. R. Irish Acad.* **77B**, 65–85.

BRIDEN, J. C., MORRIS, W. A. & PIPER, J. D. A. 1973. Palaeomagnetic studies in the British Caledonides—regional and global implications. *Geophys. J. R. astron. Soc.* **34**, 107–34.

BROWN, P. E., MILLER, J. A. & GRASTY, R. L. 1968. Isotopic ages of late Caledonian granitic intrusions in the British Isles. *Proc. Yorkshire geol. Soc.* **36**, 251–76.

DEWEY, J. F. 1969a. Evolution of the Appalachian/Caledonian orogen. *Nature.* **222**, 124–9.

—— 1969b. Structure and sequence in paratectonic British Caledonides. *In:* KAY, M. (ed). *North Atlantic Geology and Continental Drift, a Symposium.* Mem. Am. Assoc. Petrol. Geol. **12**, 309–35.

FITTON, J. C. & HUGHES, D. J. 1970. Volcanism and plate tectonics in the British Ordovician. *Earth planet. Sci. Lett.* **8**, 223–8.

GALE, N. H., BECKINSALE, R. D., WADGE, A. J. & CHAMBERLAIN, V. E. 1979. A Rb-Sr whole rock isochron for the Stockdale rhyolite of the English Lake District and a revised mid-Palaeozoic time-scale. *J. geol. Soc. London,* **136**, 235–42.

GEE, D. G. 1978. Nappe displacement in the Scandinavian Caledonides. *Tectonophysics,* **47**, 393–419.

HARLAND, W. B. 1971. Tectonic transgression in Caledonian Spitsbergen; *Geol. Mag.* **108**, 27–41.

HARPER, C. T. 1967. The geological interpretation of potassium-argon ages of metamorphic rocks from the Scottish Caledonides. *Scott. J. Geol.* **3**, 46–66.

HIGGINS, A. K. & PHILLIPS, W. E. A. 1980. East Greenland Caledonides—an extension of the British Caledonides. *In:* HARRIS, A. L., HOLLAND, C. H. & LEAKE, B. L. (eds). *The Caledonides of the British Isles, reviewed.* Spec. Publ. geol. Soc. London, **8**, 19–32.

KVALE, A. 1977. Major features of the European Caledonides and their development. *In:* AGER, D. V. & BROOKS, M. (eds). *Europe from Crust to Core.* Wiley.

LEGGETT, J. K., MCKERROW, W. S., MORRIS, J. H., OLIVER, G. H. J. & PHILLIPS, W. E. A. 1980 The North-western margin of the Iapetus Ocean. *In:* HARRIS, A. L., HOLLAND, C. H. & LEAKE, B. L. (eds). *The Caledonides of the British Isles, reviewed.* Spec. Publ. geol. Soc. London, **8**, 499–522.

MACDERMOTT, C. V. & SEVASTOPULO, G. D. 1972. Upper Devonian and Lower Carboniferous Stratigraphical setting of Irish mineralisation. *Bull. geol. Surv. Ireland,* **1**, 267–80.

MCKERROW, W. S., LEGGETT, J. K. & EALES, M. H. 1977. Imbricate thrust model of the Southern Uplands of Scotland. *Nature,* **267**, 237–9.

MCLEISH, A. J. 1971. Strain analysis of deformed Pipe Rock in the Moine Thrust zone, Northwast Scotland. *Tectonophyics,* **12**, 469–503.

MITCHELL, A. H. G. & MCKERROW, W. S. 1975. Analogous evolution of the Burma orogen and the Scottish Caledonides. *Bull. geol. Soc. Am.* **86**, 305–15.

MOSELEY, F. 1972. A tectonic history of northwest England. *J. geol. Soc. London,* **128**, 561–98.

PHILLIPS, W. E. A., STILLMAN, C. J. & MURPHY, T. 1976. A Caledonian plate tectonic model. *J. geol. Soc. London,* **132**, 579–609.

——, —— & —— 1977. Discussion of a Caledonian Plate-tectonic model. *J. geol. Soc. London,* **133**, 497–9.

——, FLEGG, A. M. & ANDERSON, T. B. 1980. Strain adjacent to the Iapetus Suture in Ireland. *In:* HARRIS, A. L., HOLLAND, C. H. & LEAKE, B. L. (eds). *The Caledonides of the British Isles, reviewed.* Spec. Publ. geol. Soc. London, **8**, 257–62.

SANDERSON, D. J., ANDREWS, J. R., PHILLIPS, W. E. A. & HUTTON, D. H. W. 1980. Deformation. studies in the Irish Caledonides. *J. geol. Soc. London,* **137**, 289–302.

SKEVINGTON, D. 1974. Controls influencing the composition and distribution of Ordovician graptolite Faunal Provinces. *In:* RICKARDS, R. B., JACKSON, D. E. & HUGHES, C. P. (eds). *Graptolite Studies in Honour of O.M.B. Bullman.* Spec. Pap. Palaeont. London, **13**, 59–73.

STURT, B. A. 1978. The Norwegian Caledonides—Introduction. *In:* IGCP Project 27, Caledonian—Appalachian Orogen of the North Atlantic Region; *Pap. geol. Surv. Can.* **78–13**, 13–15.

WILLIAMS, A. 1976. Plate tectonics and biofacies evolution as factors in Ordovician correlation. *In:* BASSETT, M. G. (ed). *The Ordovician System: Proceedings of a Palaeontological Association Symposium, Birmingham, September 1974.* University of Wales Press and National Museum of Wales, Cardiff, 29–66.

——, STRACHAN, I., BASSETT, D. A., DEAN, W. T., INGHAM, J. K., WRIGHT, A. D. & WHITTINGTON, H. B. 1972. A correlation of Ordovician rocks in the British Isles *Spec. Rep. geol. Soc. London,* **3**, 74 pp.

WILSON, M. R., ROBERTS, D. & WOLFF, F. C. 1973. Age determinations from the Trondheim region Caledonides, Norway: a preliminary report. *Nor. geol. Unders.* **288**, 53–63.

W. E. A. PHILLIPS, Department of Geology, Trinity College, Dublin 2, Ireland.

Strain within thrust sheets

M. P. Coward & J. H. Kim

SUMMARY: The finite strains within the thrust sheets of the Moine Thrust Zone in NW Scotland have been factorized into components of simple shear and longitudinal strain. Variations in these strains have been examined in the Cambrian sediments in the Eriboll and Assynt areas and strain maps produced of the Glencoul Nappe, Assynt. There are heterogeneous simple shear strains parallel to the layering resulting from bending of the nappe over a step in the thrust plane and to frictional drag at the base of the thrust. Layer parallel shortening and associated layer parallel thickening occur in the front of the thrust zone at Eriboll, above a decoupling plane in the lower part of the Cambrian sequence. Within the Cambrian rocks of the Glencoul Nappe in Assynt, there is a steady eastward increase in intensity of layer parallel shortening together with local anomalous zones characterized by more intense shortening or extension. These anomalous zones overlie shear zones in the Lewisian basement. There are variations in shear strain on the plane which contains the normal to bedding resulting from differential movement of the nappe. These shear strains distort and fold the bedding planes. Combinations of these shear strains and the longitudinal strains result in a wide range of ellipsoid shapes from oblate to prolate and also explain the pattern and sequences of folds in the nappes and mylonite belts. The folds are formed by local variation in shear and longitudinal stress and, hence, there may be no simple correlation of fold phases along, or across, a thrust zone.

This paper aims to examine the states of strain within thrust sheets, taking examples from the Moine Thrust Zone, NW Scotland (Fig. 1). Intensely deformed Proterozoic sediments (the Moine Schists), deformed during the Caledonian Orogeny, were thrust over a foreland of early Proterozoic Lewisian Gneiss, unmetamorphosed late Proterozoic (Torridonian) and Cambro-Ordovician sediments (Peach *et al.* 1907). The Cambro-Ordovician sediments consist of a sequence of quartz-rich sandstones and grits (the Basal Quartzites) which pass up into well-bedded quartz-sandstones with bioturbation structures (the Pipe Rock). These quartzites are up to 150 m thick and are overlain by 15 m of dolomitic shales, sandstones and mudstones (the Fucoid Beds), followed by 10 m of quartz rich grit (the Serpulite Grit) and then a considerable thickness of limestone and dolomite (the Durness Limestone).

There are several thrust sheets stacked on top of each other. The lowermost thrust nappe contains an imbricated succession of Cambrian rocks (Figs 2 & 3) and the base of this nappe is termed the Sole Thrust (Peach *et al.* 1907). This thrust climbs down the stratigraphy from NW to SE; in the NW it lies in or above the Cambro-Ordovician sediments but to the E it must lie within the Lewisian complex as these gneisses are involved in the imbricate sequence. Above this imbricate zone are large thrust nappes of Lewisian and Cambrian rock,

including the Arnaboll Nappe at Loch Eriboll and the Glencoul Nappe in the Assynt area (Figs 1 & 5). The thrusts which bound these large nappes are not parallel, but converge and diverge and the nappes are lens-shaped in plan. The thrusts are not continuous; Bailey (1934) noted that the Glencoul Thrust at the base of the Glencoul Nappe dies out in central Assynt near Allt Poll an Droighninn (Figs 5 & 13). The most easterly thrust, the Moine Thrust, carries mylonite and the Moine Schists. This is, structurally, the highest major thrust though, locally, small faults thrust quartzites over the Moines from the underlying thrust nappes. The age of the thrusting is given by the Borrolan igneous complex on southern Assynt (Fig. 1) which was intruded during the thrust sequence and has given an Rb/Sr whole rock age of 430 ± 4 Ma. (van Breemen *et al.* 1979). The transport direction of the thrusts is to the NW, as seen from slickensides and listric faults. The total displacement of the Moine Nappe is unknown though Coward *et al.* (in press) have estimated a displacement of almost 40 km for the Glencoul Nappe from the offset of early Precambrian structures in the Lewisian Gneiss.

In the Cambro-Ordovician rocks, the Pipe Rock, Fucoid Beds and Serpulite Grit contain worm burrows ('pipes') of the genus Skolithus (Hallam & Swett 1966). In undeformed rock, the pipes are normal to bedding and circular on the bedding plane. They are, therefore,

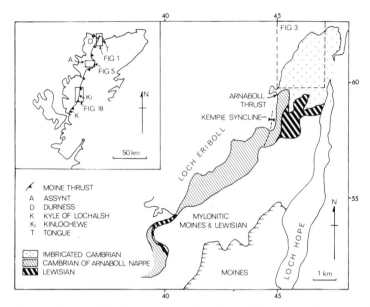

FIG. 1. Locality map for the Eriboll area showing the Arnaboll Nappe. Inset map: locality map, NW Scotland.

ideal strain markers for estimating layer-parallel strain ratios and layer-parallel shear. Where deformed, there is generally no cleavage refraction around the pipes; the grains within the pipes are similar to those outside though there may be differences in cement. Thus, there should be little ductility difference between pipe and matrix.

McLeish (1971) and Wilkinson *et al.* (1975) used the pipes to estimate strains within the thrust zone. They assumed plane strain deformation with no volume change and also assumed that the poles to bedding and the deformed pipes lay within the $\sqrt{\lambda_1}/\sqrt{\lambda_3}$ principal plane ($\sqrt{\lambda_1}$, $\sqrt{\lambda_2}$, $\sqrt{\lambda_3}$ are the principal strains, $\sqrt{\lambda_1} \geqslant \sqrt{\lambda_2} \geqslant \sqrt{\lambda_3}$ where $\sqrt{\lambda}$ is defined as final length of a line/original length). Wilkinson *et al.* (1975) also limited the deformation mechanism to that of simple shear. McLeish (1971) examined the strain in two areas: around a large syncline within the Arnaboll Nappe on the E side of Loch Eriboll and also beneath the thrust zone at Glencoul. Wilkinson *et al.* (1975) examined the strain at only one locality, at the Stack of Glencoul.

In this report the bedding parallel strain ratios have been measured from orientated photographs of deformed pipes on the bedding plane. At least 50 ellipses were measured on each photograph by use of a D-mac digitizer on line with a Digico Micro 16 V minicomputer at Leeds University to trace out the ellipse

shape (Siddans 1976), and then the strain ratio obtained using the method described by Dunnet (1969).

Variations in shear strain

Fig. 2 shows cross sections through the thrust zone at Eriboll. The majority of thrusts are parallel to bedding and where the thrusts climb, the beds above the thrust remain parallel to the thrust plane (Fig. 2). The thrusts are sharp discontinuities with no deformation of the beds above and below. The zone of brecciation on the imbricate faults is less than 1 cm wide and at the base of the larger thrusts such as the Arnaboll Nappe at Eriboll and the Glencoul Thrust at Assynt, the brecciated zone is only a few tens of centimetres wide. However, many of the overlying rocks show evidence of layer-parallel shear in that the pipes and cleavage are not normal to bedding but refract across bedding planes, and the changes in orientation of the pipes and cleavage are parallel to the bedding. Fig. 4 shows the variation in this shear strain across two sections of the imbricates at Eriboll. In Fig. 4A, across imbricated Fucoid Beds, Serpulite Grit and Limestone, the shear strain has been calculated from the orientation of the cleavage, as pipes show approximately circular cross sections on the bedding plane (cf. Ramsay & Graham 1970). In Fig. 4B, across Pipe Rock and Fucoid Beds,

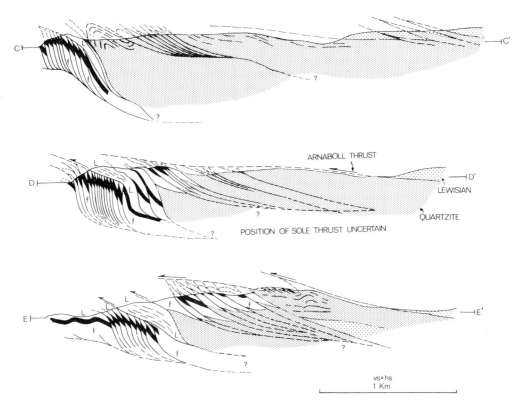

FIG. 2. Three sections through the imbricate zone. Loch Eriboll. The localities are shown in Fig. 3. f = Fucoid Beds. L = Durness Limestone, Serpulite Grit shown black.

the shear strain has been calculated from the deflection of the pipes.

Some of this shear strain may be due to flexural flow processes during climb of thrusts. The shear strain due to flexural flow has been calculated from the dip of the beds (Ramsay 1967, p. 393) and has been plotted on Fig. 4 along with the mean shear strain. It is evident that the shear is heterogeneous; in the quartzites it is less than that which should be caused by flexural flow but in the Fucoid Beds and in certain beds in the Pipe Rock, it is more intense. The mean strain is greater than that due to flexural flow and, hence, there must be extra shear strains throughout the rock. These may be due to a) the transmission of the shear due to thrusting to the overlying sediments or b) a distribution throughout the thrust pile of simple shear as a result of movement of the thrust over a step (cf. Elliott 1976a fig. 2).

The well bedded Fucoid Beds, Serpulite Grits and Durness Limestone show much higher shear strains than the Basal Quartzite and Lewisian Gneiss. Imbricate faults show much steeper dips in these well-bedded rocks

than in the quartzites and gneisses (Fig. 2) and possibly it is the ability to accommodate the internal strains due to thrust plane climb that has aided the development of these steep dips.

Within the Lewisian gneisses of the Arnabol and Glencoul Nappes there are shear zones which dip steeply to the E. These shear zones pass up into the steep limps of asymmetric inclined folds in the overlying quartzite and Pipe Rock and the amplitude of these folds decreases upwards in the Cambrian sediments. Ramsay (Tectonic Studies Group meeting, December, 1973) described an excellent example of this in the Arnaboll Nappe and McLeish (1971) recorded $\sqrt{\lambda_1}/\sqrt{\lambda_3}$ strain ratios of up to 9:1 from deformed pipes in the steep to overturned limb of this fold (the Kempie syncline, Fig. 1). Beneath the flat limb of this fold, the gneisses show little modified Lewisian structures but adjacent to the steep limb they attain an intensely developed new fabric. Similar shear zones with thrust sense occur in the eastern part of the Glencoul Nappe on the eastern slopes of Beinn Uidhe (Figs 5 & 6). In the gneisses the shear zones are only a few

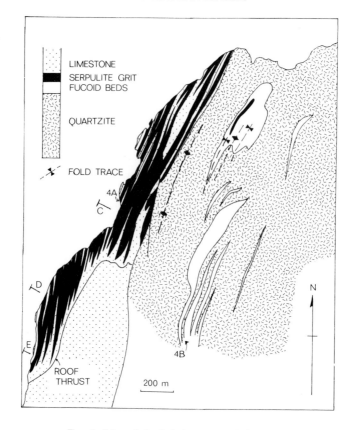

FIG. 3. Map of the imbricate zone, Eriboll.

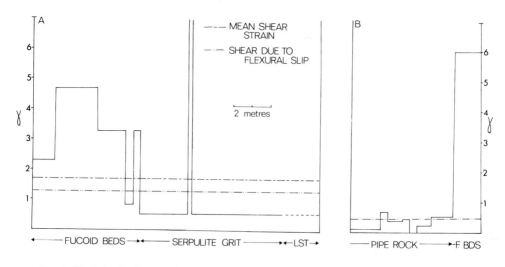

FIG. 4. Variation in shear strain across two sections of the imbricate zone at Eriboll. The localities are shown in Fig. 3.

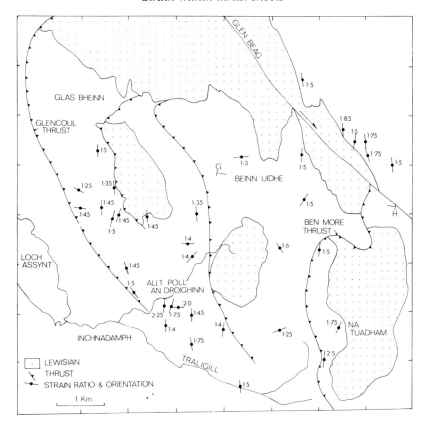

FIG. 5. Map of the N Assynt area showing localities, strain localities and orientations and the outcrops of Cambrian and Lewisian rocks. G–H section line of Fig. 6.

metres wide but some have vertical displacements of over 100 m. The total vertical displacement across this zone is over 900 m, a mean shear strain of $\gamma = 0.5$. Also on the E slopes of Beinn Uidhe there are steeply dipping ductile shears with an E side down-sense of displacement. They may represent ductile listric faults with normal fault displacement (Figs 5, 6 & 12). They produce a new fabric in the Lewisian Gneiss and pass up into drape folds in the overlying quartzites (Fig. 6).

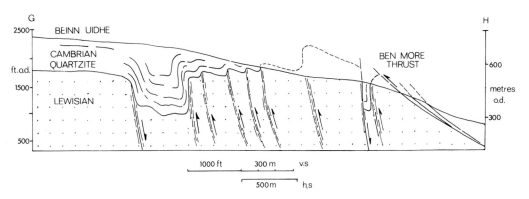

FIG. 6. Cross section through the eastern slopes of Ben Uidhe (section line shown in Fig. 5) showing shear zones in the Lewisian which pass up into folds in the Cambrian.

Strains due to layer parallel shortening

To the W of, and below, the main imbricate faults at Eriboll, on the SW side of the loch, the Pipe Rocks show evidence of layer parallel shortening strains. The pipes are normal to bedding but on the bedding planes the pipes make elliptical sections with ratios up to 2:1. The long axes of these ellipses on the bedding planes strike NNE, normal to the tectonic transport direction in the thrust zone. Assuming plane strain, with no change in length in this NNE ($\sqrt{\lambda_2}$) direction, the quartzites must have suffered up to 50% layer parallel shortening and hence, also, layer thickening. There is no evidence for this deformation in the underlying Lewisian Gneiss, where Lewisian dykes, pegmatites and gneissic foliation strike NW–SE and show no Caledonian folding. There must be a décollement zone beneath the Pipe Rock, presumably along bedding planes in the basal Cambrian Quartzite.

In the Fucoid Beds, Serpulite Grits and Durness Limestone of the imbricate zone at the NE shore of Loch Eriboll (Fig. 3) there is no evidence of layer parallel shortening; pipes still show circular sections on the bedding planes. However, in the imbricated Quartzite and Pipe Rock to the E, the pipes show strains due to layer parallel shortening, of up to 50%. The amount of layer parallel shortening shows little variation but certain beds suffered more intense layer parallel shearing strain (Fig. 4) and it is the variation in shear strain which caused the variation in the cleavage intensity in these rocks. Where the Sole Thrust lies within the well-bedded Upper Cambrian rocks, these rocks seem to have sheared and developed imbricate faults with relative ease. When the Sole Thrust is lower, in the quartzites, the thrust sheet suffered layer-parallel shortening during thrusting.

Similar layer-parallel shortening strains occur within the higher thrust nappes at Eriboll and Glencoul, where the pipes show strain ellipses on the bedding planes with ratios over 2:1. The deformation here is complicated by the addition of strains on the steeply dipping shear zones associated with the steep limbs of the folds.

Next to the Moine Thrust at Glencoul, Quartzites and Pipe Rocks are intensely deformed. The pipes show elliptical sections on the bedding planes, with ratios of about 5:1 (McLeish 1971; Wilkinson *et al.* 1975) but with the long axes plunging to the ESE, parallel to the transport direction, the pipes making

an angle of less than 2° with the bedding. Assuming plane strain, these rocks must have suffered considerable extension along the bedding and associated thinning of the beds. Johnson (1967) favoured irrotational deformation for these intense strains but Wilkinson *et al.* (1975) explain these strains as due to enormous shear strains acting obliquely on to overturned beds.

Layer parallel longitudinal strains due to differential movement of the thrusts

The Glencoul Thrust can be clearly traced from N of Loch Glendhu, across Loch Glencoul and around the W edge of the hill Glas Bheinn (Fig. 5). Along this section, Lewisian Gneiss has been thrust over imbricated Cambrian sediments. S of Glas Bheinn the thrust can be traced to near Inchnadamph but along this section Cambrian quartzites have been thrust on to limestones of the imbricate sequence. We agree with Bailey (1954), that the thrust dies out on the overturned limb of a fold in the quartzite SW of the waterfall on Allt Poll an Droighinn (Fig. 5).

Above the thrust plane the quartzites and Pipe Rock are folded and the pipes make elliptical sections on the bedding. However, the fold axes and long axes of elliptical pipe sections trend N–S to NNW–SSE; they are no longer normal to the tectonic transport direction (Fig. 5). To the S, in the imbricated Cambrian rocks S of Inchnadamph, the fold axes again trend NNE. The anomalous NNW trend occurs at the S edge of the Glencoul Thrust sheet and is presumably related to the increase in the amount of displacement on the Glencoul Thrust.

N of Glas Bheinn, the displacement on the thrust must be over 1.5 km as imbricated Cambrian rocks can be mapped beneath the Glencoul Nappe along the Glencoul and Glendhu valleys. Thus, between Glas Bheinn and where we believe the thrust dies out at Allt Poll an Droighinn there must be a mean sinistral shear strain, at least $\gamma = 0.35$, on a shear plane normal to the Glencoul Thrust but with a movement direction to the NW parallel to the transport direction of the nappe.

An idea of the variation in this shear strain may be obtained from the deformed pipes. The strain shown by these pipes may be due to combinations of layer-parallel shortening, as described previously, plus shear strains due to this differential movement of the Glencoul

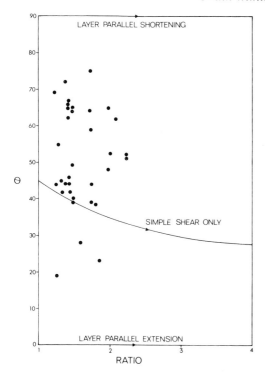

FIG. 7. Plot of θ, the current angle between the long axis of the ellipse and the shear direction, against ellipse ratio for the pipes in the Glencoul Nappe.

Thrust. The strike of the shear plane, due to differential movement of the thrust, has been estimated from i) isogons constructed for the change in orientation of cleavage, fold axes and long axes of the strain ellipses on the bedding plane and ii) the trend of a strike slip fault at Glen Beag (Fig. 5). This fault does not pass down into the underlying imbricate sequence, nor into the overlying Moines, though it affects Caledonian structures in the Cambrian rocks and must have been active during trans-

port of the Glencoul Nappe. About 1.5 km dextral displacement has been estimated from the offset of the structures.

In Fig. 7, θ, the angle between the long axis of the strain ellipse and the shear direction, has been plotted against the strain ratios given by sections of pipes on the bedding planes. It is evident that the strains are not the result of simple shear alone nor to layer parallel shortening alone but to combinations of these strains.

A model for the displacements within this zone is shown in Fig. 8. Assuming that there is no elongation of the thrust zone in the NE–SW direction, normal to the movement direction of the thrust, the possible strains may be considered as a combination of a) layer parallel shortening or extension (Fig. 8a) followed by b) layer parallel shear (Fig. 8b and c) shear on a plane normal to bedding but with the same shear direction as b (Fig. 8c).

Using the left-handed co-ordinate system shown in Fig. 8, the combined transformation is given by

$$\begin{bmatrix} \dfrac{1}{\sqrt{\lambda}} & 0 & 0 \\ \dfrac{\gamma}{\sqrt{\lambda}} & \sqrt{\lambda} & \gamma_2 \\ 0 & 0 & 1 \end{bmatrix} \quad (1)$$

assuming that the longitudinal strain precedes the shear strains. On the bedding plane this transformation simplifies to

$$\begin{bmatrix} \sqrt{\lambda} & \gamma_2 \\ 0 & 1 \end{bmatrix} \quad (2)$$

as this is a plane of no finite longitudinal strain during bedding parallel shear.

For a displacement of the form

$$\begin{bmatrix} a & b \\ c & d \end{bmatrix}$$

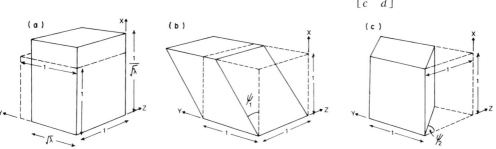

FIG. 8. The longitudinal strain (8a) and the shear strains (8b and 8c) relative to the (left handed) co-ordinate system, x, y and z. $\gamma_1 = \tan \psi_1$, $\gamma_2 = \tan \psi_2$. This particular co-ordinate system and convention has been used as it fits the Assynt structure.

the lengths of the principal axes of the finite strain ellipse may be obtained from the equation

$$\lambda_a \text{ or } \lambda_b = \frac{a^2+b^2+c^2+d^2}{2}$$
$$\pm\tfrac{1}{2}\sqrt{(a^2+b^2+c^2+d^2)^2-4(ad-bc)^2} \quad (3)$$

where the strain ratio $= \sqrt{\lambda_a}/\sqrt{\lambda_b}$ (after Jaeger 1956, p. 28).

The current orientation of the long axis of the ellipse may be determined from

$$\tan 2\theta = \frac{2(ac+bd)}{a^2+b^2-c^2-d^2}$$

(after Jaeger 1956, p. 27).

(4)

Thus, from this transformation (2) the values of the principal strains on the bedding plane and the current orientations of the long axes of the ellipses may be found from

$$\lambda_a \text{ or } \lambda_b = \frac{X}{2} \pm \tfrac{1}{2}\sqrt{X^2-4\lambda} \quad (5)$$

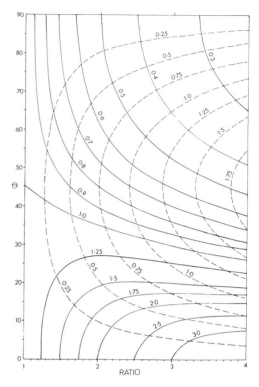

FIG. 10. As for Fig. 9, but derived from equation 7, assuming a sequence of simple shear followed by layer parallel shortening.

where

$$X = \lambda + \gamma_2^2 + 1$$

and the strain ratio

$$R = \sqrt{\lambda_a}/\sqrt{\lambda_b}$$

and

$$\tan 2\theta = \frac{2\gamma_2}{\lambda+\gamma_2^2-1}. \quad (6)$$

These equations have been evaluated for different values of γ_2 and $\sqrt{\lambda}$ and curves plotted of equal values of γ_2 and $\sqrt{\lambda}$ on a graph of resultant strain ratios R against θ (Fig. 9). From this graph the values of γ_2 and $\sqrt{\lambda}$ have been read off for the ellipse ratios of the pipes in the Glencoul Nappe and these values are shown in Figs 12 and 13. This procedure assumes a strain sequence of longitudinal strain followed by simple shear, an assumption which may be justified as the dextral shear displacement along the Glen Beag strike slip fault post-dates folds and faults in the Cambrian rocks. Similarly, at Eriboll, the longitudinal strains pre-date the shear strains due to

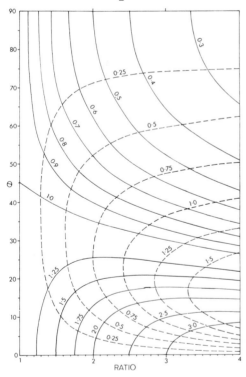

FIG. 9. Lines of equal value of layer parallel shortening, $\sqrt{\lambda}$, (solid lines) and lines of equal shear strain, γ_2, (dashed lines) plotted on a graph of θ against ellipse ratio. Evaluation from equation 2, assuming a deformation sequence of longitudinal strain followed by simple shear.

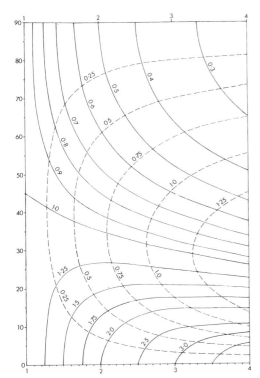

FIG. 11. As for Fig. 9, but derived from equation 21, assuming the simultaneous superimposition of simple shear and layer parallel shortening (see Appendix).

thrusting. Shear strain followed by longitudinal strain is given by the deformation

$$\begin{bmatrix} \sqrt{\lambda} & \sqrt{\lambda}\gamma_2 \\ 0 & 1 \end{bmatrix} \qquad (7)$$

From this transformation, the value of the principal strains and orientations of the long axes of the strain ellipse may be found from

$$\lambda_a \text{ or } \lambda_b = \frac{Y}{2} \pm \frac{1}{2}\sqrt{Y^2 - 4\lambda} \qquad (8)$$

where

$$Y = \lambda + \lambda\gamma_2^2 + 1$$

and

$$\tan 2\theta = \frac{2\sqrt{\lambda}\gamma_2}{\lambda + \lambda\gamma_2^2 - 1}. \qquad (9)$$

These equations have been solved for different values of γ_2 and $\sqrt{\lambda}$ and the strain ratios plotted against θ on Fig. 10. On this graph, the $\sqrt{\lambda}$ curves are identical to those on Fig. 9, though the curves for γ_2 differ. In Fig. 11 similar curves have been computed for the simultaneous superimposition of longitudinal strain and simple shear (see appendix for details). Thus,

for a specific ellipse ratio and orientation, the value of $\sqrt{\lambda}$ will have been the same no matter what sequence of strains produced the finite strain ellipse.

The strain field in the Assynt area

Figs 12 and 13 show the variations in layer parallel shear (γ_2) and in layer-parallel shortening ($\sqrt{\lambda}$) across the Glencoul Nappe, assuming the displacement given in equation (2). The contours on Figs 12 and 13 have been drawn assuming that shear strain varies across the nappe from SW to NE and $\sqrt{\lambda}$ varies from NW to SE. Obviously, there are many errors and assumptions involved in producing these maps. Apart from possible errors in strain measurement, there will be extra strains taken up by folding; locally tight folds occur in quartzites in the SW of the Glencoul Nappe. Thus, the total strain ratio should be greater than that measured from the deformed pipes. Such an underestimate of the strain ratio will give a low estimate of the shear strain (γ_2) and the layer parallel shortening ($\sqrt{\lambda}$). Within the Glencoul Nappe there are small thrusts which locally carry Lewisian rocks on to Cambrian quartzites (Fig. 5). Thus, within the nappe, the strain should not be continuous.

The shear strain is heterogeneous, with intense shear strains at locality A (Fig. 12) in the SW part of the nappe and also at locality B in the NE. The shear strains are dominantly sinistral, showing that the NE part of the nappe has moved more to the NW than has the SE part. However, in some areas, the shear strain has been reversed. At locality C (Fig. 12) there is localized dextral ductile shear while along Glen Beag there is a dextral fault. The strain is not continuous across the thrust faults from which we may infer that each fault has moved independently. Two extra strain discontinuities, shown by the thrusts with the (?) annotation in Fig. 12, are proposed from the pattern of shear strain.

In Fig. 14a, the shear strain is plotted against distance across the nappe. Integration of this shear strain gives a mean shear strain of $\gamma = 0.25$. This is less than that estimated from the overstepping of Lewisian rocks over imbricated Cambrian sediments along Glencoul. The shear strain must be greater than that estimated in Fig. 12 from the deformed pipes. Presumably most of this extra strain is taken up by folding or alternatively there may be layer parallel shortening simultaneous with or following the shear. Thus, Fig. 12 probably

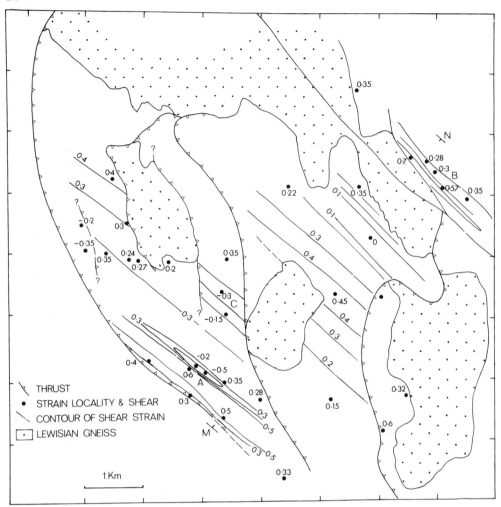

FIG. 12. The Glencoul area showing values of γ_2 calculated from the displacement in equation 2. The contour lines are only approximate and have been drawn assuming that the shear strain varies across the nappe from SW to NE. For locations A, B, C, see text.

gives an idea of the distribution of shear strains rather than their magnitude.

The intensity of layer parallel shortening is generally less at Assynt than at Eriboll. On the foreland and in the imbricate zone beneath the Glencoul Thrust, there is no evidence of layer-parallel shortening. In the frontal part of the Glencoul Thrust, the background longitudinal strain is small ($\sqrt{\lambda} = 0.95$). However, to the SE, this background strain increases to 20% layer parallel shortening (Figs 13 & 14b). There are zones of anomalous longitudinal strain; more intense layer-parallel shortening in zones A, B, C and D (Fig. 13) and layer-parallel extension in zones X and Y. The zones of more intense shortening overlie shear zones in the Lewisian Gneiss (Fig. 13). These zones

pass up into folds in the lower part of the Cambrian succession but into less folded though shortened and thickened beds in the upper quartzites and Pipe Rock (Figs 6 & 15). Elsewhere, dykes within the Lewisian complex maintain their Lewisian trend and there are no Caledonian fabrics. Thus, the anomalous strains may reflect shortening of the whole Glencoul Nappe while the background strains may only reflect layer parallel shorten-ing in the Cambrian rocks above a decoupling plane near the base of quartzites. Fig. 14b shows the variation in this longitudinal strain along a NW–SE section line. Integration of this strain (cf. Hossack 1978) gives a mean shor-tening of $\sqrt{\lambda} = 0.865$, that is a shortening of over 0.7 km across the Cambrian rocks of this

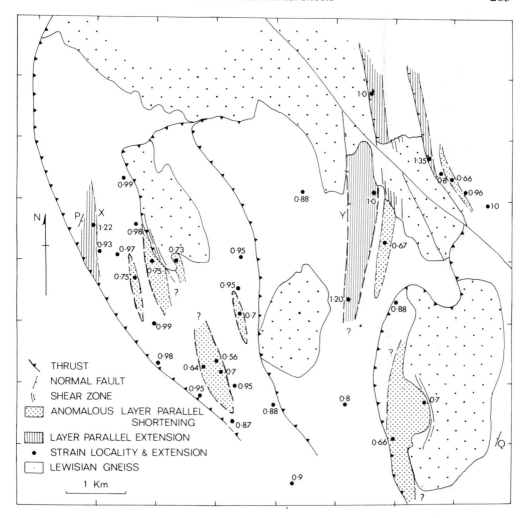

FIG. 13. The Glencoul area showing values of $\sqrt{\lambda}$ and the regions of anomalous layer parallel longitudinal strain. The main shears in the Lewisian Gneiss are shown.

nappe. This figure does not take into account any extra shortening due to thrusting. The ratio of shortening due to layer-parallel shortening versus shortening due to thrusting is large within the Glencoul Thrust sheet but may be small for the whole Moine Thrust Zone.

At localities X and Y (Fig. 13), layer-parallel extension and thinning is indicated. The zone of extension at Y does not extend across the Glencoul Nappe but dies out southwards. Extensions vary from $\sqrt{\lambda} = 1.0$ to $\sqrt{\lambda} = 1.35$. Along Glen Beag this zone is offset by the dextral fault. The extensional strains occur in the Pipe Rock overlying the normal listric faults in the Lewisian Gneiss (Figs 6 & 15)

and must be related to localized extension of the Glencoul Nappe.

Differential movement of the imbricate faults beneath the Glencoul Nappe

Along the Moine Thrust Zone, the imbricate faults generally strike N 20° approximately normal to the transport direction of the thrusts. However, at Assynt, the strike varies from N 60° in Glencoul to N 330° near Loch Assynt (Fig. 16). This change is not the result of later folding of the imbricates, as the underlying Cambrian and Torridonian sediments are

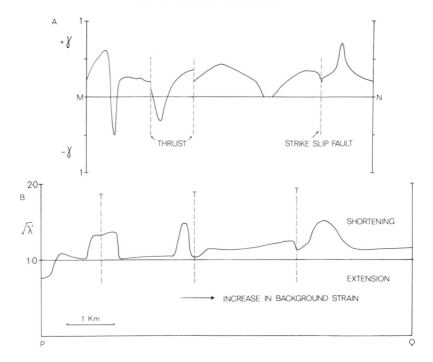

FIG. 14. (A) Plot of γ_2 against distance across the quartzites of the Glencoul Nappe. The section line is shown in Fig. 12. (B) Plot of $\sqrt{\lambda'} = 1/\sqrt{\lambda}$ against distance across the quartzites of the Glencoul Nappe. The section line is shown in Fig. 13. If l is the length of this section, the original (prestrain) length (l_0) has been found from the equation

$$l_0 = \int_0^l \sqrt{\lambda'}\, dl, \text{ after Hossack (1978).}$$

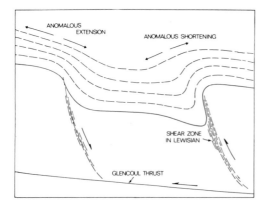

FIG. 15. Relationship of the anomalous layer parallel longitudinal strains in the Cambrian rocks to the shear zones in the underlying gneisses.

not folded and so it may be due to differential movement of the overlying Glencoul Nappe. Thus imbricates strike N 330° to the W and NW of the zone of sinistral shear in the Glencoul Nappe N of the place where the thrust plane dies out. In Glencoul, the change in trend of the imbricates does not correlate with ductile shear strains in the Glencoul Nappe but underlies a dextral strike slip fault. Presumably this fault was active during the later stages of nappe empacement during the formation of imbricate faults in the underlying Cambrian.

General considerations

Variation in shape of the finite strain ellipsoid

Assuming that the displacement within the thrust zone takes place by layer-parallel shortening or elongation followed by simple shear

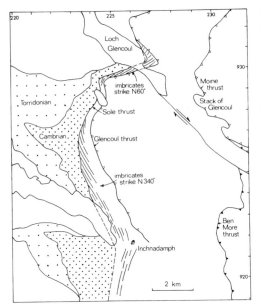

FIG. 16. Map of the Glencoul–Assynt area showing the change in strike of the imbricates beneath the Glencoul Thrust.

as shown in Fig. 8, the range of possible ellipsoid shapes and orientations may be computed from the transformation in equation (1). This procedure involves finding the eigenvalues and eigenvectors of the symmetric matrix formed by the multiplication of the transformation matrix in equation (1) by its transpose (cf. Means 1976, chapter 22; Eringen 1967, section 1.4). In Fig. 17 the resultant principal strains are plotted on a logarithmic deformation plot (cf. Ramsay 1967, p. 329) to show the variation in intensity and shape with different amounts of longitudinal strain $\sqrt{\lambda}$ and differing shear strains γ_1 and γ_2.

A combination of layer-parallel longitudinal strain $(\sqrt{\lambda})$ and layer-parallel shear (γ_1) results in a strain ellipsoid with a shape parameter $K = 1$, where

$$K = \frac{\ln\left(\frac{\sqrt{\lambda_1}}{\sqrt{\lambda_2}}\right)}{\ln\left(\frac{\sqrt{\lambda_2}}{\sqrt{\lambda_3}}\right)}$$

(cf. Ramsay 1967, p. 329). The orientation of the $\sqrt{\lambda_1}$ axis approaches the transport direction (y) with increase in γ_1 and increase in layer-parallel extension. (The co-ordinates x-y and z are shown in Fig 8.) With additional shear (γ_2) in the xy plane, normal to layering, the resultant finite strain ellipsoid is oblate ($K < 1$) if

there is shortening in the y direction ($\sqrt{\lambda} < 1$) but is prolate ($K > 1$) if there is extension in the y direction ($\sqrt{\lambda} > 1$). It is possible to produce a wide range of ellipsoid shapes, with K values from 0 to ∞ with different combinations of the above displacements. Thus, Fig. 17 shows how an oblate strain of $K = 0$ may be formed from a combination of layer-parallel shortening of $\sqrt{\lambda} = 0.8$ and a shear of $\gamma_1 = 0$, $\gamma_2 = 0.6$. A combination of the two shearing strains γ_1 and γ_2, where $\sqrt{\lambda} = 1$, results in an ellipsoid of shape $K = 1$. There must be some layer-parallel shortening or extension to produce a change in ellipsoid shape.

Finite strain ellipsoids which are oblate or prolate are common in thrust zones. Hossack (1968) reports a range in ellipsoid shapes from $K = 0$ to $K > 3$ from the Bygdin conglomerates in the Valdres Nappe beneath the Jotun Nappe in the Caledonian Thrust Zone of Norway. Hossack (1968) suggested that this variation in shape may be due to constriction or extension of the Valdres Nappe possibly due to movement over an irregular surface. Alternatively, the variation may be produced by a combination of the deformation as described above, without any change in length of the thrust sheet normal to the movement direction. Similar variations in ellipsoid shapes have been reported from the Funzie conglomerate of Shetland (Flinn 1956) and from conglomerates in the Caledonian nappes of northern Norway (Chapman *et al.* 1979). Within the Moines of NW Scotland, Mendum (1976) reports oblate strains of $K = 0.05$ from deformed conglomerates near Tongue, while Wood (1973) reports prolate strains of $K > 5.0$ from similar conglomerates on nearby Ben Hutig.

Fold axes in the thrust zones

Johnson (1960), Christie (1963) and Barber (1965) have shown that many of the folds in the Moine Thrust Zone, particularly within the mylonite zone beneath the Moine Thrust, have fold axes which plunge to the SE close to parallel to the transport direction. Indeed, Christie (1963) proposed a NE–SW transport direction parallel to the strike of the Moine Thrust Zone, on the basis of the folds. Many of these folds may have been initiated by layer-parallel shortening with their axes normal to the transport direction and then had their axes rotated towards the $\sqrt{\lambda_1}$ direction during deformation. Quinquis *et al.* (1978) have introduced the term 'Sheath-folds' for similar structures with curved hinges in the intensely deformed rocks of the Ile de Groix, S Brittany.

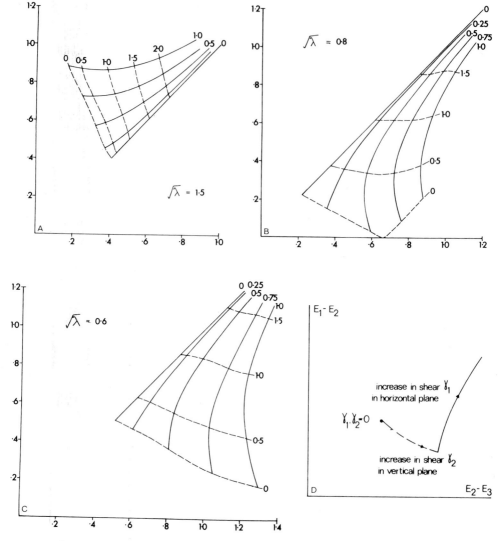

Fig. 17. Logarithmic strain plot $(\epsilon_1 - \epsilon_2)/(\epsilon_2 - \epsilon_3)$ where $\epsilon_1 = l_n\sqrt{\lambda}$, etc. for the finite ellipsoid shapes produced by deformation sequences of layer parallel shortening ($\sqrt{\lambda}$) followed by simple shears γ_1 (solid contour lines) and γ_2 (dashed contours). The ellipsoids produced by three different values of $\sqrt{\lambda}$ are shown here (A–C); others ranging from $\sqrt{\lambda} = 0.5$ to $\sqrt{\lambda} = 3.0$ will be provided on request. 17D shows the strain paths produced by increase in shear strains γ_1 and γ_2.

However, in the Moine mylonite zone there are many kink band and chevron type folds which also plunge to the SE. It is unlikely that these open folds have been rotated into this direction by intense deformation.

It has been shown at Assynt that folds formed oblique to the transport direction (y) where the rock carried a component of shear (γ_2) on the plane containing the normal to the layering. Thus if the mylonites formed at an early stage of thrust movement (cf. Barber,

1965), differential movement of the Moine Nappe would cause folds to form with hinges which plunge to the E or SSE.

Larger examples of these oblique folds occur S of Kinlochewe, in the southern part of the Moine Thrust Zone (Figs 1 & 18). In this area, the Kinlochewe-Kishorn Thrust carries Lewisian Gneiss with its cover of Torridonian Sandstones and Cambrian sediments over an imbricated Cambrian sequence. Near Kinlochewe the Torridonian is down-folded into

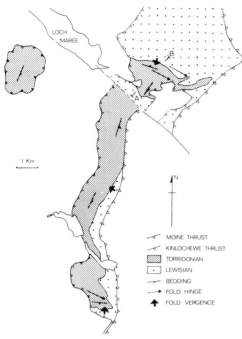

FIG. 18. Map of the Kinlockewe region (location on Fig. 1) showing the change in vergence of the folds in Torridonian rocks.

the Lewisian Gneiss to produce a SW facing inclined synform (Fig. 18) with a SE plunging hinge. The overlying Cambrian quartzites are also folded to produce SE plunging folds (Fig. 18). To the S near the Coulin Lodge, the Torridonian Sandstones are folded into the Lewisian Gneiss to produce a NE facing inclined syncline also with a SE plunging hinge. Thus, the Torridonian rocks trace out a sheath like synform whose hinges plunge to the SE closely parallel to the transport direction. On the overturned limbs of this sheath-like fold, the Torridonian rocks show a well-developed cleavage and there are shear zones in the adjacent Lewisian Gneiss. However, on the gently dipping right-way up limbs the Torridonian rocks often show little cleavage and the Lewisian rocks show no Caledonian deformation. Thus, it is unlikely that the fold hinges were rotated into their SE trend by intense deformation; the fold must have formed with SE plunging hinges, presumably because of differential movement of the Kinlochewe Thrust Nappe.

To the S, on Skye and by Kyle of Lochalsh, the Torridonian Sandstones are folded into a large gently incline syncline, the Lochalsh fold, with NE trending fold hinge normal to the

tectonic transport direction (Coward & Whalley, in press). On the overturned limb of this fold, between Lochalsh and Loch Carron, there is a later northward dipping cleavage which intersects the bedding to give an E–SE plunging lineation oblique to the fold hinge (Coward & Whalley, 1980). This cleavage may be due to extra shear strains set up by differential movement of the thrust nappe.

Thus, there is evidence for differential movement of thrust nappes along the length of the Moine Thrust Zone. There needs to be no correlation between the oblique structures along the Moine Thrust Zone or between different nappes in the same area; the oblique folds could be formed by a similar process in each area, but at different times.

The development of layer parallel longitudinal strains

Hudleston (1977) has shown how 'similar' type folds develop in glaciers where the layering has been deflected from the shear plane. Such folding could presumably occur in mylonite zones, where the mylonitic layering has been deflected by some rigid particles such as an augen or earlier fold hinge (cf. Quinquis *et al.* 1978). However, many of the folds appear to be regularly spaced and appear as fold trains rather than individual folds which have grown from some local deflection in the layering. Hence, we consider that many of the folds developed by layer-parallel shortening.

Elliott (1976*a*) applied the treatment by glaciologists (Nye 1969; Budd 1970, 1971) to deduce the longitudinal stress equations within a moving slab of material. Elliott used two parameters, termed the stress deviator gradient (G) and the variational stress (T), to describe the strain variations. Budd (1970) defined these parameters as

$$G = \int \frac{\delta \sigma_{yy}}{\delta_y} \, dx \qquad (10)$$

and

$$T = \int \int \frac{2\tau_{2y}}{\delta_{y^2}} \, dx \cdot dx \qquad (11)$$

where τ is the shear stress, σ the normal stress, the co-ordinates being those of Fig. 8. These are integrated from the surface of the nappe to the base and present the stress gradients parallel to layering. T may be considered as the resistance to shear, while $2G$ may be considered as the nett normal stress difference acting across a column of the nappe. Where

2*G* is negative (i.e. compressive) then layer-parallel shortening will take place by ductile deformation of thrust faults. Where 2*G* is positive then layer-parallel extension will take place. The gradient *G* will vary where the thrust changes dip and climbs a step; 2*G* will be negative in the cores of synclines but positive over anticlines. On a larger scale however, 2*G* may vary depending on the surface slope of the nappe. Budd (1971) has shown that

$$G = \rho \mathbf{g} H \alpha' + T \qquad (12)$$

where ρ is the density of the rock, $\mathbf{g}$ the gravitational acceleration, H the thickness of the nappe pile measured normal to the surface slope and α' the deviation of the surface slope from its average value. If there are only few steps in the thrust, that is, the steps are far apart, then the resistance to shear (T) will be negligible and G will vary with α'. Thus, the development of compressional or extensional structures within a thrust may vary with change in surface slope.

At Assynt and at Eriboll there must be changes in basal slope of the thrust pile, because progressively lower rocks are involved in the imbricate zone as it is traced to the SE and yet, generally, the thrust plane is parallel to bedding. Thus, the Sole Thrust must go down in steps to the E. Some of the changes in dip of the upper thrusts may be due to folding of the thrust layers above these steps. Some variations in longitudinal extension or compression may be due to such folding. However, in the Glencoul Nappe there is no direct correlation between a regional change in dip of the thrust planes and the compressional and extension zones shown in Fig. 13.

Within a thrust zone there could be changes in surface slope above a thrust due to the emplacement and later movement of higher level thrusts or to the erosion and deposition of the toes of higher level thrusts. During the emplacement of large thrust sheets these changes may take place not only across the thrust sheet but at the same point in the sheet with time. Thrust sheets, such as the Moine Thrust, which have been active over a relatively long period of time, may suffer changes from compressional to extensional longitudinal strains with time as it is unlikely that the upper slope of the Moine Thrust sheet remained constant with time. Changes from compressional to extensional strain, or vice-versa, with time, together with deformation due to differential movement of the Moine Nappe could lead to a complex strain history and,

hence, a complex fold history and this explains the numerous fold phases observed in the Moines and Moine mylonites (Johnson 1960; Barber 1965). As extensional and compressional longitudinal strains could be set up at different times along the length of the thrust zone it is unlikely that any of the fold phases can easily be correlated along, or across, each of the thrusts.

Conclusions

This paper has shown how the strain distributions within a thrust sheet may be considered in terms of combinations of simple shear and longitudinal strains. Within the Cambrian rocks of the Assynt Nappe there is a steady eastwards increase in amount of layer-parallel shortening together with local anomalous zones of more intense shortening and zones of extension. These anomalous zones overlie shear zones in the Lewisian basement. Variations in shear strain are due to folding of the nappe over steps in the basal thrust but there are also variations in shear strain in the plane which contains the normal to bedding, resulting from differential movement of the nappe.

Combinations of the shear strains and longitudinal strains result in a wide range of ellipsoid shapes from oblate to prolate. Oblate ellipsoids do not necessarily mean that there is extension of the nappe parallel to its length. These strain variations also explain the pattern and sequence of folds in the mylonite belts. The folds are formed by local variations in shear and longitudinal stress and hence there should be no simple correlation of fold phases along the length of a thrust zone.

ACKNOWLEDGMENTS. We would like to thank colleagues at Leeds for discussions during this work, in particular Dr Martin Casey for help with the computation and for critically reading the manuscript.

Appendix

The simultaneous superimposition of longitudinal strain and simple shear will give a set of curves between those of Figs 9 and 10. The simultaneous superimposition may be considered in two ways: (i) the step wise addition of small increments of longitudinal strain and simple shear, (ii) by considering the displacements in terms of strain rate.

To consider the step-wide addition, let a small extension along the *y* axis be δe, and a small shear along the *y* axis be $\delta \gamma$. Then the small strain along the *y* axis is $(1 + \delta e)$. The combined deformation may be considered as a displacement due to the small longitudinal strain followed by the displacement due to the small shear strain followed by a small longitudinal strain, this step wise process being continued a large number of times (Ramberg 1975). The first increments may be represented by:

1st increment

$$\begin{bmatrix} 1+\delta e & 0 \\ 0 & 1 \end{bmatrix} \begin{bmatrix} 1+\delta e & \delta\gamma \\ 0 & 1 \end{bmatrix},$$

2nd increment

$$\begin{bmatrix} 1 & \delta\gamma \\ 0 & 1 \end{bmatrix} \begin{bmatrix} (1+\delta e)^2 & \delta\gamma(1+\delta e) \\ 0 & 1 \end{bmatrix},$$

3rd increment

$$\begin{bmatrix} 1+\delta e & 0 \\ 0 & 1 \end{bmatrix} \begin{bmatrix} (1+\delta e)^2 & \delta\gamma(1+\delta e)+\delta\gamma \\ 0 & 1 \end{bmatrix}.$$

Thus after n increments the deformation is

$$\begin{bmatrix} [(1+\delta e)^n & \\ 0 & \\ & \delta\gamma[(1+\delta e)^{n-1}+(1+\delta e)^{n-2}+\ldots(1+\delta e)+1] \\ & 1 \end{bmatrix}$$

If the strain increments are very small, i.e. $\delta e \to 0$ and $n \to \infty$ then the above deformation may be expressed by

$$\begin{bmatrix} (1+e) & B \\ 0 & 1 \end{bmatrix} \qquad (13)$$

where $(1+e) = \sqrt{\lambda}$ and

$$B = \delta\gamma[(1+\delta e)^{n-1}+(1+\delta e)^{n-2}$$
$$+\ldots(1+\delta e)+1]$$

(after Ramberg 1975).

Ramberg (1975) has shown how simpler equations may be developed which express displacement as continuous functions of time. Thus if $\dot{\epsilon}$ is defined as the strain rate due to layer parallel shortening such that $\dot{\epsilon}t = \epsilon$ where ϵ is the finite natural strain, $\epsilon = \ln \sqrt{\lambda}$, and $\dot{\gamma}$ is the strain rate due to simple shear, such that $\gamma = \dot{\gamma}t$ then the simultaneous superimposition of shortening and simple shear may be expressed by

$$\begin{bmatrix} \dot{y} \\ \dot{z} \end{bmatrix} = \begin{bmatrix} \dot{\epsilon} & \dot{\gamma} \\ 0 & 0 \end{bmatrix} \begin{bmatrix} y \\ z \end{bmatrix} \qquad (14)$$

Following Ramberg (1975 p. 10–11) this may be developed to

$$\begin{bmatrix} y' \\ z' \end{bmatrix} = \begin{bmatrix} y+\dot{\gamma}/\dot{\epsilon}z & -\dot{\gamma}/\dot{\epsilon}z \\ 0 & y \end{bmatrix} \begin{bmatrix} \exp(\dot{\epsilon}t) \\ 1 \end{bmatrix} \qquad (15)$$

which simplifies to

$$\begin{bmatrix} y' \\ z' \end{bmatrix} = \begin{bmatrix} \exp(\epsilon t) & \dfrac{\dot{\gamma}}{\dot{\epsilon}}(\exp \dot{\epsilon}t - 1) \\ 0 & 1 \end{bmatrix} \begin{bmatrix} y \\ z \end{bmatrix}. \qquad (16)$$

As

$$\gamma = \dot{\gamma}t$$

then

$$t = \frac{\gamma}{\dot{\gamma}} \qquad (17)$$

where γ is the finite shear strain and as

$$\sqrt{\lambda} = \exp(\dot{\epsilon}t) \quad \text{and} \quad \ln \sqrt{\lambda} = \dot{\epsilon}t \qquad (18)$$

then

$$\begin{bmatrix} y' \\ z' \end{bmatrix} = \begin{bmatrix} \sqrt{\lambda} & \dfrac{\dot{\gamma}}{\dot{\epsilon}}(\sqrt{\lambda}-1) \\ 0 & 1 \end{bmatrix} \begin{bmatrix} y \\ z \end{bmatrix}. \qquad (19)$$

From (17) and (18)

$$\frac{\dot{\epsilon}}{\dot{\gamma}} \quad \text{may be expressed as} \quad \frac{\ln \sqrt{\lambda}}{\gamma} \qquad (20)$$

so that

$$\begin{bmatrix} y' \\ z' \end{bmatrix} = \begin{bmatrix} \sqrt{\lambda} & \dfrac{\gamma}{\ln \sqrt{\lambda}}(\sqrt{\lambda}-1) \\ 0 & 1 \end{bmatrix} \begin{bmatrix} y \\ z \end{bmatrix}. \qquad (21)$$

This is obviously a more manageable equation than that of (13) and the principal strains and orientations of the long axes may be found from substituting equation (21) into equations (3) and (4). These equations have been solved for different values of $\sqrt{\lambda}$ and γ and the results plotted in Fig. 11. Note this figure and equations 15 and 21 apply to deformation involving constant strain rates, that is constant $\dot{\epsilon}$ and $\dot{\gamma}$.

References

BAILEY, E. B. 1934. The Glencoul nappe and the Assynt culmination. *Geol. Mag.* **72**, 151–65.

BARBER, A. J. 1965. The history of the Moine thrust zone Lochcarron and Lochalsh, Scotland. *Proc. Geol. Assoc.* **76**, 215–42.

BUDD, W. F. 1970. The longitudinal stress and strain

rate gradient in ice masses. *J. Glaciol. London,* **9,** 19–27.

—— 1971. Strain variations within ice flows over undulations. *J. Glaciol. London,* **10,** 177–95.

CHAPMAN, T. J., MILTON, N. J. & WILLIAMS, G. D. (1979). Shape fabric variations in deformed conglomerates at the base of the Laksefjord Nappe, North Norway. *J. geol. Soc. London,* **136,** 683–91.

CHRISTIE, J. M. 1963. The Moine thrust zone in the Assynt region, northwest Scotland. *Univ. California Publ. geol. Sci.* **40,** 345–440.

COWARD, M. P. & WHALLEY, J. 1980. Textural and fabric studies across the Kishorn nappe, near Kyle of Lochalsh, Western Scotland. *J. Struct. Geol.* **1,** 259–273.

COWARD, M. P., KIM, J. A. & PARKE, J. 1980. A correlation of Lewisian structures across the lower thrusts of the Moine thrust zone, NW Scotland. *Proc. geol. Assoc. London,* (in press).

DAHLSTROM, C. D. A. 1970. Structural evidence of the eastern margin of the Canadian Rocky Mountains. *Bull. Can. Pet. Geol.* **18,** 332–406.

DUNNETT, D. 1969. A technique of finite strain analysis using elliptical particles. *Tectonophysics,* **7,** 117–36.

ELLIOTT, D. 1976a. The energy balance and deformation mechanisms of thrust sheets. *Philos. Trans. R. Soc. London* A 289–312.

—— 1976b. The motion of thrust sheets. *J. geophys. Res.* **81,** 949–63.

ERINGEN, A. C. 1967. *Mechanics of Continua.* John Wiley & Sons, London, 502 pp.

FLINN, D. 1956. On the deformation of the Funzie conglomerate, Fetlar, Scotland. *J. geol. Chicago.* **64,** 480–505.

HALLAM, A. & SWETT, K. 1966 Trace fossils from the Lower Cambrian Pipe Rock of the northwest Highlands. *Scott. J. Geol.* **2,** 101–6.

HOSSACK, J. R. 1968. Pebble deformation and thrusting in the Bygdin area (South Norway). *Tectonophysics,* **5,** 315–39.

—— 1978. The correction of stratigraphic sections for tectonic strain in the Bygdin area, Norway. *J. geol. Soc. London,* **135,** 229–41.

HUDLESTON, P. J. 1977. Similar folds, recumbent folds, and gravity tectonics in ice and rocks. *J. Geol. Chicago,* **85,** 113–22.

JAEGER, J. C. 1956. *Elasticity, Fracture and Flow.* Methuen, London 152 pp.

JOHNSON, M. R. W. 1960. The structural history of the Moine thrust zone at Lochcarron, Wester Ross. *Trans. R. Soc. Edinburgh.* **64,** 139–68.

—— 1967. Mylonite zones and mylonite banding. *Nature,* **213,** 246–47.

MCLEISH, A. J. 1971. Strain analysis of deformed Pipe Rock in the Moine thrust zone, northwest Scotland. *Tectonophysics,* **12,** 469–503.

MEANS, W. D. 1976. *Stress and Strain.* Springer Verlag, New York 339 pp.

MENDUM, J. 1976. A strain study of the Strathan Conglomerate; North Sutherland. *Scott. J. Geol.* **12,** 135–46.

NYE, J. F. 1969. The Effect of longitudinal stress on the shear stress at the base of an ice sheet. *J. Glaciol. London,* **8,** 207–13.

PEACH, B. N., HORNE, J., GUNN, W., CLOUGH, C. T. & HINXMAN, L. W. 1907. The geological structure of the North West Highlands of Scotland. *Mem. geol. Surv. U.K.*

QUINQUIS, H., AUDREN, Cl., BRUN, J. P. & COBBOLD, P. R. 1978.Intense progressive shear in Ile de Groix blueschists and compatibility with subduction or obduction. *Nature,* **273,** 43–4.

RAMBERG, H. 1975. Particle paths, displacement and progressive strain applicable to rocks. *Tectonophysics* **28,** 1–37.

RAMSAY, J. G. 1967. *Folding and Fracturing of Rocks.* McGraw-Hill, New York, 568 pp.

—— 1969. The measurement of strain and displacement in orogenic belts. *In*: KENT, P. E., SATTERTWAITE, G. W. & SPENCER, A. M. (eds.). *Time and Place Orogeny.* Spec. Publ. geol. Soc. London. **3,** 43–79.

—— & GRAHAM, R. H. 1970. Strain variations in shear belts. *Can. J. Earth Sci.* **7,** 786–813.

SIDDANS, A. W. B. 1976. Deformed rocks and their textures. *Philos. Trans. R. Soc. London,* **A 283,** 43–54.

VAN BREEMEN, O., AFTALION, M. & JOHNSON, M. R. W. 1979. Age of the Loch Borrolan complex, Assynt and late movements along the Moine thrust belt. *J. geol. Soc. London,* **136,** 489–95.

WILKINSON, P., SOPER, N. J. & BELL, A. M. 1975. Skolithus pipes as strain markers in mylonites. *Tectonophysics,* **38,** 143–57.

WOOD, D. S. 1973. Patterns and magnitudes of natural strain in rocks. *Philos. Trans. R. Soc. London,* **A 274,** 373–82.

M. P. COWARD, J. A. KIM, Department of Earth Sciences. The University, Leeds, LS2 9JT.

Tectonics of the Helvetic Nappes

J. G. Ramsay

SUMMARY: This paper gives a general account of the principal major nappes, fold and fault styles, and minor structural features of the Helvetic Nappes with particular emphasis on research results over the past few years. The principal stratigraphic variations are summarized and their influence on development of tectonic structures described. Measurements of strain variations throughout the nappe pile can be used to evaluate the significance of cleavage and linear fabrics. Pressure solution is a particularly important rock deformation process throughout the whole region and provides the source for the fibrous vein fillings which characterize much of this region.

The northern Calcareous Alps of Switzerland has been classic ground for the development of many of the basic ideas of nappe tectonics. A succession of Mesozoic and Tertiary sediments showing well-defined N–S changes of thickness and facies have been stripped from an underlying basement and moved northwestwards as the Helvetic Nappes. The aim of this contribution is to present a summary of our current knowledge of this classic region with particular emphasis on the results of research in tectonics over the past 10 years.

There is a vast geological literature on this region: memoirs, papers, map explanations and many unpublished dissertations and theses. Albert Heim's (1921) monumental summary of Alpine Geology has a general description of the Helvetic Nappes that is still hard to better. It provides a remarkably well-balanced description of the stratigraphy, large and small scale tectonic structure and is beautifully illustrated. For English language readers there is nothing so comprehensive in scope. Collet's book (1927) provides a summary of the main geological features of the region, and Bailey's Tectonic Essays give a perceptive and entertaining discussion of the history of research and the evolution of scientific ideas.

The Helvetic Nappes make up the calcareous mountain ranges of central Switzerland and are wonderfully exposed in high mountains and in deep valleys eroded by intense glacial and river erosion (Fig. 1). The Helvetic zone is more than 300 km in length, but is narrow, seldom exceeding 40 km in width. Towards the SE the zone passes into the structurally simpler Chaines subalpines, an external fold belt of the western Alps of France. To the NW the Helvetic zone continues into the Vorarlberg region of western Austria to disappear W of the Iller

river beneath the higher nappe units of the eastern Alps. Along the external or northern boundary, the Helvetic Nappes are overthrust onto Oligocene and Miocene sediments of the Molasse Basin (Fig. 2), but this contact is often hidden by overlying tectonic units of the Ultrahelvetic and Pre-Alpine Nappes. Along the internal southeastern boundary the Helvetic Nappes are overridden by the Penninic Nappes.

The nappes consist predominantly of limestones, marls and shales of Mesozoic and Tertiary age which were laid down on the southern edge of the European continental platform. In eastern Switzerland the nappes also contain a thick sequence of volcanoclastic sediments of Permo-Carboniferous age (Verrucano) originally deposited as fanglomerates in a 50 km wide NNE–SSW graben.

The nappes lie with tectonic contacts on Mesozoic and Tertiary sediments forming the autochthonous cover to a basement of crystalline metamorphic and igneous rocks and late Palaeozoic sediments. These basement masses form elongated domes (Fig. 2, Aiguilles Rouges, Mont Blanc, Mont Chétif, Aar, Tavetsch and Gotthard) which have been subjected to Alpine deformation and subdivided into compartments by cuspate synclines occupied by strongly deformed Mesozoic sediments. The most external (NW) of these basement massifs show comparatively little internal Alpine deformation, whereas the most internal (SE) show the development of Alpine shear zones with an intense new schistosity and metamorphism. The Gotthard Massif has been strongly displaced towards the Aar Massif so that it completely overlaps the Tavetsch along its western part: many geologists today prefer to link the Gotthard basement with the lobate

FIG. 1. The frontal folds of the Morcles Nappe exposed on the N face of the Grand Mulveran and L'Argentine. In the far distance are folded limestones forming the Diablerets Nappe. The thick pale stratum marking the folds of the Morcles front is the Urgonian limestone.

folded basement units of the Lower Penninic Nappes. The massifs form two main groups which occupy major structural highs or culminations. Between the Mont Blanc and Aar-Gotthard groups one finds a major depression. This depression controls not only the outcrop pattern of the Helvetic Nappes (the so called Wildstrubel depression, see Figs 2 & 3), but also distribution of units in the overlying Pre-Alpine klippen and high elements in the Penninic nappes (the Dent Blanche Klippe). It is generally accepted that the Mont Blanc and Aar Massifs are structurally homologous and link beneath the Wildstrubel depression, likewise the Aiguilles Rouges Massif is structurally linked with a small massif forming the northwestern units of the Aar Massif (the Gastern Massif).

Distribution of major nappe units

The major structural units of the Helvetic Nappes are shown in Fig. 2. There are important structural differences between the nappes of W, central and E Switzerland; there are also nomenclatorial differences whereby the same geometric unit may have different names at different localities. The main structural features from W to E along the Helvetic zone will now be described.

In W Switzerland the nappes show a pronounced plunge to the ENE, towards the Wildstrubel depression and the nappe order can be clearly established. A thin cover of *autochthonous Mesozoic sediments* to the Aiguilles Rouges Massif (Fig. 3, unit 1) is overlain by a large recumbent fold, the *Morcles Nappe* (Fig. 3, unit 2), and this is itself overlain by the thrust sheets of the *Diablerets Nappe* (unit 3) and *Wildhorn Nappe* (Fig. 3, unit 4, and Fig. 4). The overturned limb of the Morcles Nappe can be traced into the southern side of the synclinal zone between the Aiguilles Rouges and Mont Blanc Massifs (*the Chamonix–Martigny syncline*) whereas the normal limb of the Morcles fold continues with the sediment cover of the S side of the Mont Blanc Massif. The Mont Blanc Massif is therefore effectively a basement core of the Morcles Nappe. A complex of nappe units known as the *Ultrahelvetic Nappes* lie above the Wildhorn

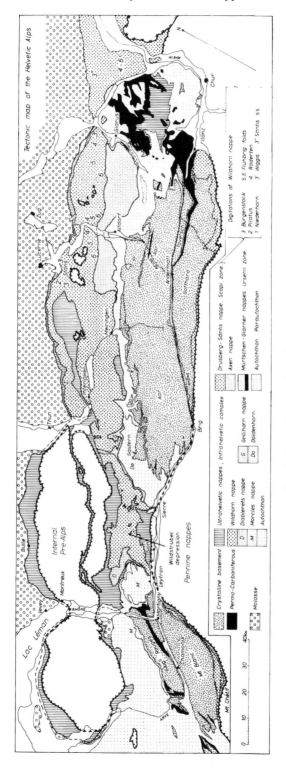

FIG. 2. Tectonic map of the Helvetic Nappes.

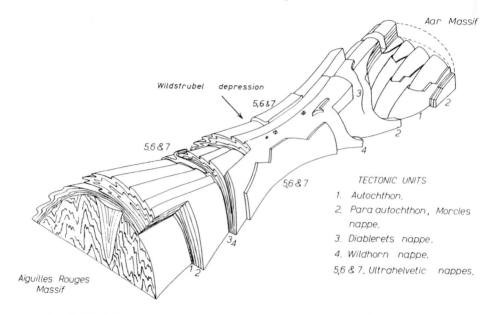

Fig. 3. Block diagram showing the geometric relations of the western Helvetic Nappes.

Nappe. These units emerge from a root zone on the N side of the Rhône Valley N of Sion (Figs 2 & 3). They are preserved as isolated klippen in the centre of the Wildstrubel depression and form the basal sheets of the internal Pre-Alpine Nappes. These Ultrahelvetic Nappes are folded with the frontal folds of the underlying Helvetic Nappes and occupy a great recumbent synform between the Morcles and Diablerets Nappes. These structural features indicate that the Ultrahelvetic Nappes were emplaced on top of a substratum of Mesozoic and Tertiary sediments that represented the, as yet, undeveloped

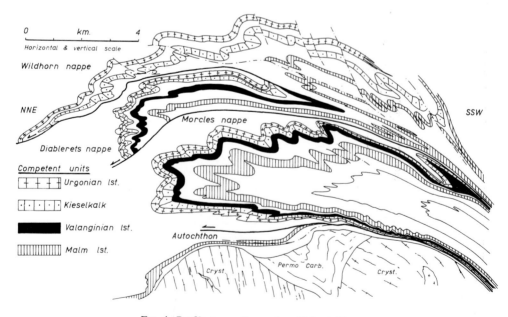

Fig. 4. Profile across the western Helvetic Nappes.

Helvetic Nappes. Subsequently, the shortening of the underlying units together with the overlying Ultrahelvetic Nappes led to the formation of the Helvetic Nappes and refolding and rethrusting of the Ultrahelvetic units. Stratigraphic relationships in Flysch and Molasse sediments suggest an Oligocene age for the early thrusting, and a Miocene age for the main development of the Helvetic Nappes. The Ultrahelvetic Nappes clearly have a more southern aspect than the underlying Helvetic units and their roots appear to link with the Mont Chétif Massif S of Mont Blanc.

Proceeding eastwards to the other side of the Wildstrubel depression, two nappes emerge from beneath the Wildhorn Nappe. These are the *Doldenhorn and Gellihorn Nappes*, which appear to be homologues of the Morcles and Diablerets units respectively.

Between Interlaken and Lake Lucerne the Wildhorn Nappe becomes the dominating structural unit. The northern part becomes geometrically separated from the main part of the nappe forming the *Randkette (border chain) of the Niederhorn* and is overthrust on Upper Cretaceous and Tertiary rocks of Ultrahelvetic aspect. Further E the Wildhorn Nappe undergoes a subdivision into two major units. The upper unit (*Drusberg–Säntis Nappe*) consists of Cretaceous and Tertiary strata which have slid sideways independently from the underlying Triassic and Jurassic units (*Axen Nappe*), the décollement taking place on the thick incompetent Lower Cretaceous shales. Large upward facing fold digitations are developed in the Drusberg Nappe (Räderten and Fluhbrig folds), while in the Axen Nappe spectacular downward facing folds are seen beneath the basal thrust of the Drusberg Nappe N of Altdorf.

In E Switzerland the autochthonous cover of the eastern Aar Massif is overlain by the so called *Infrahelvetic complex* (Milnes & Pfiffner 1977), slices of Tertiary Flysch and Mesozoic sediments that were probably emplaced earlier than, and overridden by, the Main Helvetic Nappes and which may be tectonic equivalents of the Ultrahelvetic Nappes further W. The lowest true Helvetic Nappe element is the *Glarner Nappe*, consisting of a thick basal mass of Permian Verrucano and overlying folded Mesozoic and Tertiary sediments. The Glarner Nappe is arched by a gently curving ENE plunging antiform. The thrust surface at the nappe base is extremely sharp and well defined; the overriding nappe is bounded by a fault cutting through a calc-mylonite—the well-known Lochseitenkalk. These are the classic localities that led to the acceptance of the nappe theory in the Alps (the best discussion in English of this famous controversy can be found in Bailey (1935); for more recent discussion of the significance of this mylonite see Schmid (1975). The mylonite layer, 10 cm–10 m in thickness, seems to have been derived from the intense shearing of Mesozoic limestones, and its homogeneity probably results from the extreme shear that took place at the nappe base during its 45 km northward advance. The Glarner Nappe is overlain by the *Mürtschen Nappe*, a unit which has close stratigraphic and tectonic resemblances to the Glarner unit, and these are in turn overlain by the *Säntis Nappe* (s.s.). The Säntis Nappe represents the detached Cretaceous and Tertiary cover of the underlying Permian, Triassic and Jurassic sediments of the underlying nappe units.

The overall sequence of initiation, main development and late history of the Helvetic Nappes is quite complex. The arguments to establish the tectonic sequence come first from stratigraphic observations (ages of Flysch and Molasse deposits), second from broad geometric criteria of the interactions of folds and thrusts, and third from a study of sequences of small scale structural features (Trümpy 1969, 1973; Schmid 1975; Milnes & Pfiffner 1977). Flysch deposits deposited before the nappe development include the well-known early Oligocene Engi-slates with their deformed fossil fish (Wettstein 1886). The first nappe emplacement began in mid-Oligocene times and the main movements were ended during the Miocene. Thus the total time for the major part of the nappe evolution here is about 5–10 Ma, and this figure gives average strain rates in zones of high strain of the order of $2 \times 10^{-14}\,\mathrm{s}^{-1}$ (Milnes & Pfiffner 1977).

Principal stratigraphic features

The Helvetic Nappes were derived from deformation of an original carbonate shelf sequence deposited on a subsiding basement of crystalline rocks and infolded and infaulted Upper Palaeozoic sediments. The region is a classic one for the development of ideas on how a tectonically disturbed region may be reassembled to establish the pretectonic positions of the strata. Arnold Heim (1916*a* & *b*) and Lugeon (1902) realized that the uppermost (and often most external) tectonic elements should be restored sequentially southwards to establish the original depositional locations, and in making these reconstructions they produced order out of what, at first sight, looked like chaos. Subsequent work has produced remarkably detailed palinspastic reconstructions (Alb. Heim 1921; Trümpy 1960, 1969; Ferrazzini & Schuler 1979). The erosion remnants of the various nappes can be reassembled, and although the resulting mosaic is incomplete, enough is present to see the overall picture of facies and thickness variations very clearly.

In broadest outline one sees that the Mesozoic successions of the autochthon of the basement massifs and the lowermost Helvetic Nappes represent the most shallow water successions originally deposited closest to the shoreline. Massive often poorly bedded limestones predominate in a total sediment thickness of less than 1500 m. In the uppermost Helvetic Nappes deeper water shelf successions become more marked; marls and shales become progressively better developed to the S, partly at the expense of facies changes in the massive shelf carbonates (which become better bedded), partly as an increase in thickness of shale content in the layers separating carbonate units. The total succession of Mesozoic sediments reaches more than 3000 m in which more than 50% is marl or shale.

Control of tectonic features of the nappes by stratigraphic variations

The stratigraphic variations set out above exert an extremely important control on the tectonic styles of the nappes.

Localization of thrusts

Thrusts are often localized by the positions of mechanically weak layers of shale and marl, and major nappe separations are frequently found where such thick weak horizons separate units containing more competent limestones (e.g. the separation of the Axen from Drusberg–Säntis Nappes). As thrust planes are traced from the internal to external part of a nappe they climb upward through the stratigraphic succession. Where they pass through a competent limestone they invariably steepen, and so the characteristic thrust surface style shows a well-defined flat-ramp-flat geometry.

Folding related to movements on thrust planes

Some folds in the Helvetic Nappes appear to be best explained as originating by movement of a nappe over an irregular flat-ramp surface. Folds generated at the front of a competent unit are geometrically fixed at a relatively early stage of nappe movement, and cease amplification once the competent layer has moved forward on to a flat thrust sector. These folds show bed inclinations related to the dip of the initiating ramp fault, and they show southward dipping axial planes. Other folds, generated as the thrust mass slides over an underlying ramp, are transient structures in that the moving layer is first folded and then unfolded. It seems possible that some of the small scale fractures that are very common in some localities may represent the imprint of deformations that take

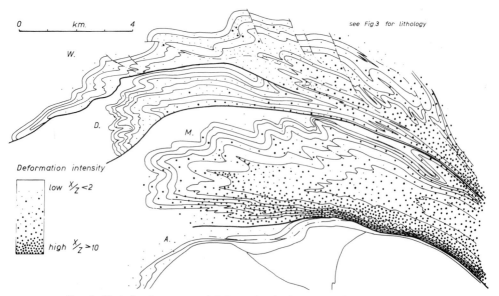

FIG. 5. Variation in amount of deformation in the western Helvetic Nappes.

place as the result of the migratory passage of such folds through competent layers.

Folds produced by strata shortening

Many folds in the Helvetic Nappes appear to be the result of contraction of the layers inside the main mass of the nappe. Such folds show forms characteristic of buckling instability, and show special geometric forms related to competence contrasts and layer thickness. The massive limestone layers are always more competent than the surrounding marls and shales and the folds that form generally have an almost constant layer thickness, with outer arc curvatures always less than inner arc curvatures. It has been noted above that competent limestones are most common in the autochthonous sediments and lowermost nappes. This feature gives rise to a general harmonic (or polyharmonic) style of folds throughout the whole sedimentary packet and a generally large main fold wavelength (Figs 4 & 6). In contrast to the lowest nappe units, the competent limestones are less well-developed in the uppermost nappes and the intervening incompetent marls are thicker. The competent layers often fold independently of one another and show disharmonic uncoupling of one layer from the adjacent layers. In the Wildhorn Nappe, the Urgonian limestone, Kieselkalk and Malm sometimes fold independently of one another. The Cretaceous part of the succession can also show a bulk shortening quite different from that of the underlying Jurassic limestones as a result of decoupling of separate folded packets.

One especially noteworthy feature of the folds produced by strata shortening is their geometric continuity along their axes. Many individual folds in the central and western Helvetic region can be followed for distances often exceeding 50 km.

Small scale tectonic features

Because of changes in plunge of the nappes it is possible to view at the surface different tectonic levels in the nappe pile. The maximum total thickness of the Helvetic Nappe pile was probably about 8 km, but there may have been several more kilometres of tectonic overburden provided by the Ultrahelvetic and Pre-Alpine Nappes. In general the nappes seem to have been formed in reverse order to that seen in the vertical pile that we see today. The Ultrahelvetic Nappes were the first to move northwards, and they were then carried 'piggyback' fashion by the mobilization of the underlying Helvetic Nappes, while the deformation of the autochthon appears to have been activated during later times in the tectonic history. Because of these geometric and temporal variations we are able to study how small scale deformation features such as cleavage and lineation vary with depth of formation and at different times.

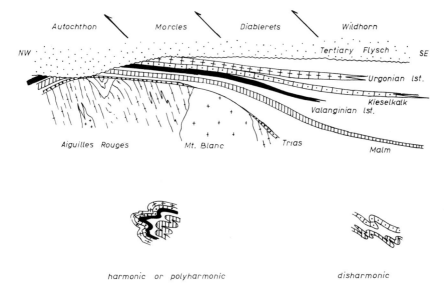

FIG. 6. Schematic diagram showing how fold style varies with stratigraphic thickness and facies.

Finite strain

In the past few years many finite strain studies have been carried out using the shapes of deformed marker objects embedded in the sediments (oolites, fossils, pebbles, etc.). The most important feature to emerge is that the values of total strain vary greatly. Fig. 5 illustrates schematically the variations seen in the western Helvetic Nappes; in general the bulk strain increases downwards in the nappe pile and southwards towards the root zone, but there are considerable variations in different parts of fold structures situated at the same tectonic level. Of particular interest is the extreme strain variation seen in the Morcles fold nappe. The lower limb of this fold shows intense deformation throughout all rock types, locally with strain showing $X:Z$ ratios (strain ellipsoid $X \geqslant Y \geqslant Z$) exceeding $100:1$. In contrast, the upper limb away from the root zone is comparatively weakly strained, and it is unusual to see strains with $X:Z$ ratios greater than $4:1$. The lower fold limb is in thrust contact with practically undeformed autochthonous sediments forming the southern flank of the Aiguílles Rouges Massif. The geometric boundary conditions here are those

of simple shear, and it would appear that this shear zone developed by northwesterly transport of the upper limb of the Morcles fold relative to the autochthon. Another especially interesting comparison that can be made between the upper and lower limbs of the Morcles folds concerns the mechanisms of rock deformation. A well-developed conglomerate is developed along the Cretaceous–Tertiary contact. Along the overturned fold limb the pebbles are extremely strongly deformed, the forms indicating plane strain with the deformation apparently achieved by plastic flow of the calcite forming the pebbles and their matrix (Fig. 7). In contrast the pebbles in the hinge region and upper fold limb show interlocking contacts with dark stylolitic seams oriented sub-parallel to the XY finite strain planes (Fig. 8). The pebbles are cut by many veins filled with fibrous calcite oriented approximately perpendicular to the maximum elongation direction X. These veins are themselves cut by the tectonic stylolites. It appears here that the dominant deformation mechanism was by pressure solution chemical transfer of calcite, and quite different from that seen on the inverted fold limb. Overburden pressure and temperature variation were probably not great

FIG. 7. Carbonate conglomerate strongly deformed by plastic flow, lower limb of **Morcles** fold, Salanfe.

FIG. 8. Carbonate conglomerate deformed by pressure solution, upper limb of Morcles fold, S of Val d'Illiez.

enough to account for the variations in mechanism. The differences in the enforced strain rate produced by the nappe transport that result in these variations are not understood but are probably related to the boundary conditions of the nappe and internal variation of effective stresses.

Cleavage

There are marked variations in cleavage through the nappe pile. The predominant cleavage is a typical slaty cleavage showing pervasive alignments of mineral grains in the cleavage plane accompanied by development of sub-parallel pressure solution seams. At some localities this slaty cleavage is redeformed by the development of crenulation cleavage. Such crenulation cleavages are well-developed throughout much of the inverted limb of the Morcles Nappe (Badoux 1972) through the root zones of the nappes and through much of the Glarner Nappe and the underlying Infrahelvetic complex and autochthon (Schmid 1975; Milnes & Pfiffner 1977), and clearly imply late compressions after the formation of the main cleavage.

The variations of intensity and orientations of the slaty cleavage accord well with the vari-

ations of finite strain intensity and orientation of the XY plane of the strain ellipsoid (Alb. Heim 1878; Tan 1976; Pfiffner 1978).

The lower limb of the Morcles Nappe (Fig. 9) is pervaded by a particularly intense cleavage, with cleavage fans related to layer competence contrasts. A strongly developed stretching lineation parallel to the X-axes of the strain ellipsoid is developed on this cleavage, and a well-developed cleavage-bedding intersection lineation runs parallel to the axes of the major folds. The folds show marked strata thinning in the limbs relative to that in the hinge zones.

The upper limb of the Morcles Nappe (Fig. 9) shows a much weaker cleavage than that seen on the lower limb, but with strongly convergent fans in the competent layers and divergent fans in the incompetent layers. Over most of this limb (with the exception of the root zone) little or no stretching lineation is found, although there is often a good cleavage-bedding intersection parallel to the fold axes.

In the structurally higher nappes (Diablerets and Wildhorn, Fig. 9) slaty cleavage is often very weakly developed, and at some localities it is replaced by a linear fabric, 'pencil-cleavage', oriented parallel to the fold axes (Fig. 10a). This pencil-cleavage is not an intersection lineation resulting from crossing planar fabrics

Small scale structural features   W. Helvetic nappes
Wildhorn

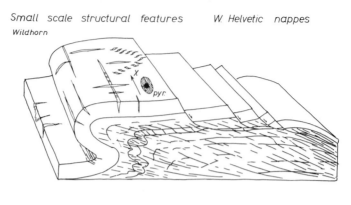

Upper limb Morcles

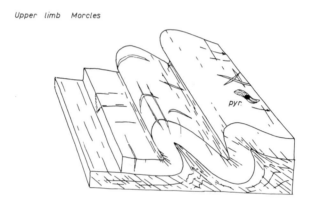

Lower limb Morcles

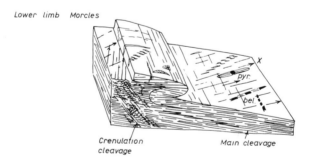

Crenulation   Main cleavage
cleavage

FIG. 9. Schematic diagram showing the main geometric features of small scale tectonic structures.

(bedding-cleavage). It appears only in slightly deformed rocks, and strain measurements show that the pencil-axes are parallel to the maximum total elongation X, and that the fabric is of constrictional type $(Y = Z)$. This fabric could possibly result from the superposition of initial diagenetic flattening fabrics with later tectonic strains, perhaps with progressive tectonic volume loss accompanying pressure solution (Ramsay & Wood 1973; Graham 1978).

A generally progressive sequence of increasing deformation and fabric development occurs from upper to lower levels in the nappe pile as follows: (a) planar sedimentary fabrics parallel to bedding, (b) pencil cleavage fabrics with X-axes parallel to fold axes, (c) weak slaty cleavage, no pronounced stretching lineation

($X = Y$), but with cleavage-bedding lineation parallel to fold axes, (d) strong slaty cleavage, strong stretching lineation 'X generally oriented SE and strong cleavage-bedding lineation parallel to fold axes.

Tectonic vein systems

One of the striking tectonic features of the Mesozoic and Tertiary rocks of the Helvetic Alps is the development of many differently oriented sets and systems of calcite-, quartz-, and chlorite-filled fissures or vein systems. Examples can be found in practically every outcrop. They occur through all levels in the nappe pile and its underlying autochthon, and there are many geometrically related vein systems in the crystalline basement massifs that were formed during Alpine orogenic events.

The veins vary in size from microscopic fissures to those visible in the field as fine hairline cracks to veins reaching tens of centimetres in width. The most frequently observed veins are about 0.5–2.0 cm wide and several metres in lateral extent.

In general, two main types may be recognized depending upon the relative differential movements of the walls and the structure of the fibrous crystalline infilling:

Extension veins (Fig. 10b) are those where the dilation is sub-perpendicular to the walls. These occur as extensive parallel systems or grouped into single or conjugate *en-echelon* arrays. In *en-echelon* arrays, individual veins may be sigmoidal and show rather complex bifurcations (Durney & Ramsay 1973, p. 84). The needle-like crystals infilling the veins are oriented in the sense of dilation and sub-perpendicular to the walls. In conjugate *en-echelon* arrays the maximum total shortening bisects the acute angle between the intersecting arrays.

Shear veins (Fig. 10c) are those where the dilation is sub-parallel to the walls. These are commonly developed along bedding and cleavage planes or along fault-like shears crossing these planar deformation features. The fibrous crystalline infill is oriented at a low angle to the vein walls, and usually shows a characteristic step-like form controlled by irregularities of the walls (Durney & Ramsay, 1973, p. 87).

Study of the progressive opening of these vein systems has been shown to offer a key to understanding the evolution of deformation at

FIG. 10a. Typical 'pencil cleavage' structure in Cretaceous marl of the Wildhorn Nappe, Lac de Tseuzier.

FIG. 10b. Extension vein in Middle Jurassic sandstone with fibrous calcite-quartz infilling, Wildhorn Nappe, Lammeralp, Gemmipass. The curved crystal forms relate to changes in the dilation history of the vein.

FIG. 10c. Shear vein in Urgonian limestone showing characteristic step structure in calcite fibres. Wildhorn Nappe, Six les Eaux Froides.

different levels in the nappe pile. Fibrous crystalline growth in veins and in pressure shadows around deformation resistant pyrite nodules appears to have started at the earliest periods of the deformation history and to continue up until the last stages. Durney (1972a) was able to show that the total strain calculated from fibrous growths in pressure shadows was the same as that from deformed oolites.

As a result of these studies, it is possible to show that in the western Helvetics the Autochthon and Morcles Nappe had a relatively simple extension history whereas the higher nappe elements and nappe roots show much more complex incremental strain sequences. This increasing complexity of deformation history has been attributed to three main factors:

1. The uppermost nappes have had a longer movement history than the lower units, and the deformation sequences have early parts not represented in the lower elements.

2. The uppermost nappes were displaced with lower confining constraints than the lower units, and individual nappe sectors had a higher degree of freedom to displace relatively independent from each other. As a consequence the strain pattern arising from more variable displacements is also complex.

3. The complexity of the root zone area may be connected with the proximity of the tectonically separate Penninic Nappe front.

The movement pattern emerging from these studies is that the earliest strains show a NNW elongation mostly connected with a subvertical shortening and the development of ENE–WSW oriented folds. In the upper nappes

there followed a period of quite marked extension along the fold axes also associated with a sub-vertical maximum shortening (see Fig. 9 for schematic representation of the geometry of these vein and pressure shadow systems).

A feature of particular interest related to the change from predominant NNW to ENE extensions is that at some localities the sequence proceeds in a clockwise sense, whereas at others it shows an anti-clockwise rotation. Fig. 11 illustrates a clockwise incremental extension sequence. The earliest veins here are of composite type with calcite margins (optically attached to the wall rock carbonate) and a central zone of quartz. In these composite systems new material is added along the internal carbonate-quartz interfaces, the fibre orientations being aligned with the dilation direction. The earliest formed veins relate to a NNW extension, and the increments show a progressive change towards the N (directions 1 and 2). At some time a critical stage appears to be reached where the original vein is no longer able to effectively accommodate the changing increments, and new veins are formed which cross-cut and displace the earlier formed veins. This new system also shows changing incremental extensions and it eventually becomes redundant as new veins take over the extension (directions 3 and 4). The reason for the clockwise or anticlockwise sense of the deformation increments has not been clearly established. The rotation sense may reflect small perturbations of local strain arising from differential displacement rates of different parts of the nappe sheet.

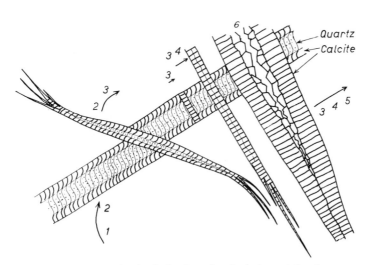

FIG. 11. Progressive sequences of veins indicative of a clockwise rotational sequence of extension increments, in Liassic slates from Leytron, Morcles Nappe root zone.

Composite Calcite-Quartz veins

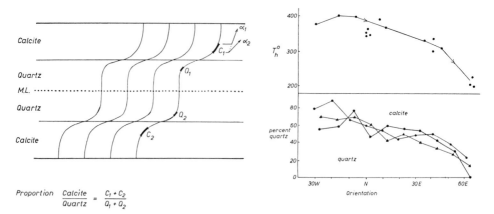

$$\text{Proportion} \quad \frac{Calcite}{Quartz} = \frac{C_1 + C_2}{Q_1 + Q_2}$$

FIG. 12. The proportion of quartz to calcite in composite veins compared to increment direction and homogenization temperature (T_h^0) of fluid inclusions in quartz, Leytron, Morcles Nappe root zone. Data after Durney (1972a).

The nature of the vein filling material changes with time. Durney (1972a) was the first to notice that the Leytron veins initiate with a high proportion of quartz relative to calcite, but later calcite dominates over quartz. In fact, the final increments give rise only of calcite-filled veins with the last gasp of deformation leading to open fissures which later became filled with vuggy calcite (Fig. 11, stage 6). By investigating homogenization temperatures of the fluid inclusions in the syntectonically growing quartz, Durney (1972a) was able to show that the compositional change went hand in hand with a temperature decrease of some 200°C (Fig. 12). There appears to be an excellent correlation of chemical activity, mineral deposition in veins and metamorphism, and Durney (1974) has been able to show how studies of vein system chemistry and homogenization temperatures of fluid inclusions can lead to an integration of deformation and thermal history.

Many of the syntectonic veins in the Helvetic Alps show features which indicate that the opening process was episodic, and that a sudden release of elastically stored energy formed a narrow crack which was subsequently filled by material crystallizing from the fluid which filled the crack. This process, termed 'crack-seal' (Ramsay 1980) is probably best explained by a process of hydraulic fracturing in a rock system with a high pore pressure, with transport of solid material in the fluid from sources undergoing pressure solution (Durney 1972b). The veins formed by this process often show regularly spaced wall-parallel inclusion bands (Fig. 13a & b). These bands result from progressive fracturing and tearing away of a part of the wall rock, the fragments then being later sealed into the vein system by the crystallization process. Studies of the geometry of the ubiquitous vein systems suggest that such a process of periodic release of energy and crack formation was not only one of the most important mechanisms for rock extension in the nappes, but that it produced significant extensions in the underlying crystalline basement. Fig. 13c & d show the appearance of plagioclase feldspar crystals in the Aar Massif gneisses. Fig. 13c shows the cloudy, altered (Hercynian) feldspar which are traversed by cracks containing new, (Alpine age) clear, unaltered feldspar. The same section under crossed polars (Fig. 13d) reveals a beautiful optical linkage of the albite twin planes between the old and new feldspar. At this particular locality the basement extensions by 'crack-seal' processes exceed 30%.

Faults

The development of faults varies through the nappe pile, and of special significance is the variable development of extension or normal faults developing late in the deformation history. In the lower nappes normal faults are uncommon, but in the higher Diablerets and Wildhorn Nappes normal faults become increasingly abundant and give rise to important regionally significant extensions (Figs 4 & 9).

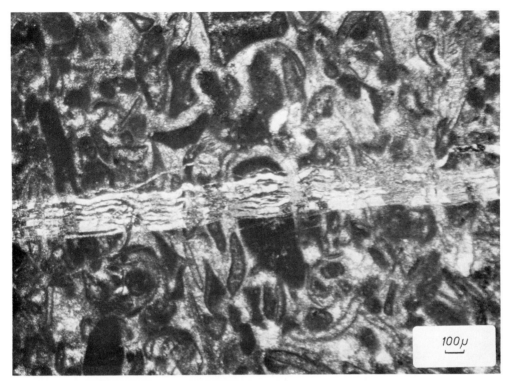

FIG. 13a. Thin section showing crack-seal calcite vein in organoclastic limestone of the Claridenkette, Aar autochthon.

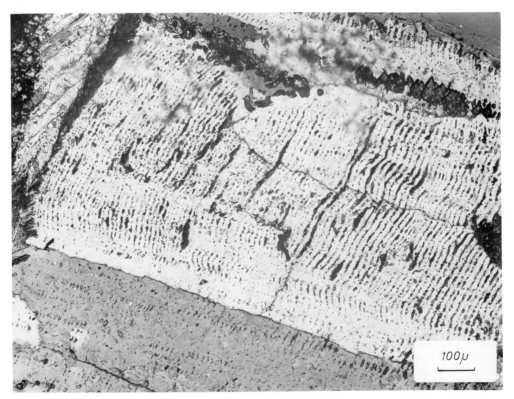

FIG. 13b. Thin section showing succession of inclusion bands in quartz crystals in a tectonic vein from the Windgällen, Autochthonous Dogger limestone, Aar Massif.

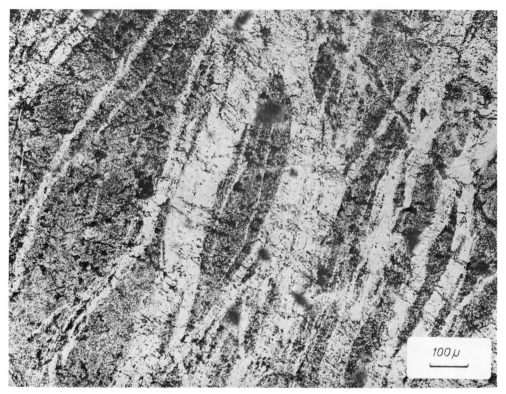

FIG. 13c. Thin section of crack-seal structure in deformed plagioclase, Aar Massif gneisses, Innertkirchen.

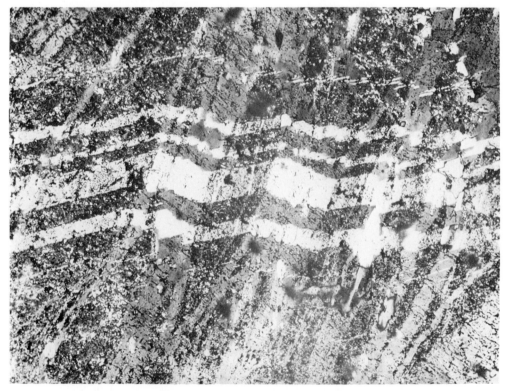

FIG. 13d. As 13c under crossed polars.

The fault systems lead to extensions both perpendicular and parallel to the fold axes. Extensions normal to the fold axes were the earliest to develop. These normal faults show only one set of the potentially available two conjugate directions, the dominant movement being a down throw on the SE side of southeasterly dipping faults. These were followed by E–W or SE–NW striking conjugate normal faults giving extensions parallel to the fold axes. It would appear that such faulting was taking place in the higher brittle levels of the moving nappe pile when more ductile deformations were proceeding below. The present seismic activity of the Helvetic Nappes shows release of seismic energy at locations close to many of the geological faults (Pavoni & Maya-Rosa 1978) and it seems possible that some of these faults are actively moving today.

Concluding remarks

This paper has attempted to relate some of the main geometric features of the Helvetic Nappes to stratigraphic features, and to indicate the relationship of small scale and large scale tectonic features. Recent work has added much to the understanding of the tectonic evolution, and in particular it has shown how the often complex small-scale structural features that developed during the nappe transport provide the key to unravelling the movement history of the nappe complex.

ACKNOWLEDGMENTS. Much of this work was carried out with support from the Schweizerischer Nationalfonds (Grant 2.859–0.77) and on ETH Forschungsprojekt. I would also like to express my appreciation of valuable help and discussion with my colleagues Dorothee Dietrich, Roy Kligfield, William Lowrie, Adrian Pfiffner and Stefan Schmid.

References

ARBENZ, P. 1912. Der Gebirgsbau der Zentralschweiz. *Verh. Schweiz. naturforsch. Ges. Zurich*, **95/2**, 95–122.

BAILEY, E. B. 1935. *Tectonic Essays, mainly Alpine.* Oxford University Press, 200 p.

BADOUX, H. 1972. Tectonique de la nappe de Morcles entre Rhône et Lizerne *Mat. Carte Géol. de la Suisse*, NS 143, 1–78.

COLLET, L. W. 1927. *The Structure of the Alps*, Arnold, London, 289 p.

DURNEY, D. W. 1972a. *Deformation History of the Western Helvetic Nappes. Valais, Switzerland.* Ph.D. thesis, London Univ. 372 (unpubl.).

—— 1972b. Solution transfer, an important geological deformation mechanism. *Nature*, **235**, 315–7.

—— 1974. Relations entre les températures d'homogénéisation d'inclusions fluides et les minérals métamorphiques dans les nappes hélvétiques du Valais. *Bull. Soc. géol. Fr.* **14**, 269–72.

—— & RAMSAY, J. G. 1973. Incremental strains measured by syntectonic crystal growths. *In*: DEJONG, K. & SCHOLTEN, R. (eds), *Gravity and Tectonics*, Wiley, New York, 67–96.

FERRAZZINI, B. & SCHULER, P. 1979. Eine Abwicklungskarte des Helvetikums zwischen Rhone und Reuss. *Eclog. geol. Helv.* **72**, 439–54.

GRAHAM, R. H. 1978. Quantitative deformation studies in the Permian Rocks of Alpes Maritimes. *Goguel Symposium, B.R.G.M.* 220–38.

HEIM, ALB. 1878. *Unterschung über den Mechanismus der Gebirgsbildung im Anschluss an die Geologische Monographie der Tödi-Windgällen Gruppe.* Schwaber, Basel.

—— 1921. *Geologie der Schweiz.* **2/1**, 259–476. Tauchnitz, Leipzig.

HEIM, ARN, 1916a. Monographie der Churfirsten—Mattstock gruppe. *Beitr. geol. Karte Schweiz, N. F.* **20**, 1–4.

—— 1916b. Ueber Abweicklung und Fazieszusammenhang in den Decken der nördlichen Schweizer Alpen. *Verh. Schweiz. naturforsch. Ges. Zürich*, **61**, 474–87.

LUGEON, M. 1902. Les grandes nappes de recouvrement des Alpes du Chablais et de la Suisse. *Bull. Soc. géol. Fr.* **1**, 723–825.

MILNES, A. G. & PFIFFNER, O. A. 1977. Structural development of the Infrahelvetic complex, eastern Switzerland. *Eclog. geol. Helv.* **70**, 83–95.

PAVONI, N. & MAYER-ROSA, D. 1978. Seismotektonische Karte der Schweiz 1 : 750'000. *Eclog geol. Helv.* **71**, 293–5.

PFIFFNER, O. A. 1978. Der Falten- und Kleindeckenbau im Infrahelvetikum der Ostschweiz. *Eclog geol. Helv.* **71**, 61–84.

RAMSAY, J. G. 1980. The "crack-seal" mechanism of rock deformation. *Nature*, **284**, 135–9.

—— & WOOD, D. 1973. The geometric effects of volume change during deformation processes. *Tectonophysics*, **16**, 263–77.

SCHMID, St. 1975. The Glarus overthrust: field evidence and mechanical model. *Eclog. geol. Helv.* **68**, 247–80.

TAN, B. K. 1976. Oolite deformation in Windgällen, Canton Uri, Switzerland. *Tectonophysics*, **31**, 157–74.

TRÜMPY, R. 1960. Palaeotectonic evolution of the Central and Western Alps. *Bull. geol. Soc. Am.* 843–908.

—— 1969. Die helvetischen Decken der Ostschweiz. *Eclog. geol. Helv.* **62**, 105–42.

—— 1973. The timing of orogenic events in the Central Alps. *In*: DEJONG K. A. & SCHOLTEN R. (eds.), *Gravity and Tectonics*, Wiley, New York, 229–51.

WETTSTEIN, A. 1886. Ueber die Fischfauna des Tertiären Glarner Schiefers. *Abh. Schweiz. Paläontol. Ges.* **13**, 1–101.

J. G. RAMSAY, Geologisches Institut, ETH Zentrum, CH–8092, Zürich, Switzerland.

The 3D propagation of décollement in the Jura

H. P. Laubscher

SUMMARY: The sequence of instabilizations leading to the formation of shallow nappes may be illustrated by the kinematics of the embryonic Jura Nappe. On the first order arc, due to regional boundary conditions, are superposed second and third order arcs that developed around more local irregularities in the distribution of strength. Successive instabilization of the Rheintal part of the Jura Décollement Nappe generally proceeds from S to N. Location of ramps where décollement climbs to the surface is largely influenced by pre-existing Rhinegraben structures. These also convey a certain anisotropy to the sedimentary cover which seems to be responsible, at least partly, for a different aspect of sinistral and dextral shear zones. Whereas sinistral shears are usually along discrete faults, mostly reactivated Rhinegraben faults, the dextral shears commonly are diffuse zones. Arcuate elements, convex to the N, connect the sinistral and dextral shear zones frontally. Regionally, the shear zones accommodate the divergence of movement, with lateral elongation, within the overall Jura Arc. More locally, they bound arcuate segments of ever smaller dimensions, and also seem to ease diverging movements in these smaller arcs.

The premises of this paper are that the Jura is a décollement nappe on Triassic evaporites, of uppermost Miocene–Lower Pliocene age, with displacements up to 30 km due to a push of some kind from the Alps. I consider these premises proved beyond reasonable doubt as argued elsewhere (Laubscher 1961, 1965, 1979*b*).

Here we are concerned with the sequence of instabilizations (fracture and yielding by cataclastic flow and pressure solution) and their relation in space and time as the nappe began to form. This sequence is a problem even under the controlled conditions of rock deformation experiments. Under the complex geological conditions manifest in the Jura a thorough theoretical understanding will not be possible for many years, and inductive reasoning on the strength of incomplete field information is required.

In a former paper (1977) I have dealt with some aspects of this problem in a cross-sectional view. Here, emphasis is on the map view, but the essence of cross-sectional aspects will be summarized first.

Initial instabilities seem to be thrusts emanating from irregularities—stress concentrators—in the decollement layer, primarily small pre-existing Oligocene faults of the Rhinegraben system. They often degenerate upwards into kink bands. On the metre-scale, systems of shears with Mohr-relationships and tectonic stylolites play a role (Laubscher 1979*a*).

In 3 dimensions some geometrical features are obvious even to the casual observer. The Jura is an inhomogeneous fold belt, the folds and thrusts are discontinuous, largely non-parallel, and unevenly spaced. How did these irregularities arise in space and time? Answers to this question are sought in the analysis of detailed mapping, particularly in the Rheintal Jura S of the Rhinegraben where the control on inherited geometry, possibly guiding nucleation of Jura structures, is best observed.

The Rheintal Jura (particularly the northern and western margin of the Delémont basin, Fig. 1)

The Delémont basin is a Lower Tertiary structure built into the uppermost Tertiary Jura folding. In the Lower Tertiary it was part of the Rhinegraben or its southern prolongation, a southward tilted block of subsidence bounded by normal faults and flexures (Fig. 2). At that time it was a basement structure, with the faults displacing, though probably not entirely interrupting, the Triassic evaporite layers that, in the Upper Tertiary, acted as a basal décollement layer.

This inherited geometry set up boundary conditions for Jura folding. In a general way, the influence is obvious—folding was deflected around the basin which moved as a fairly rigid mass, with the Rhinegraben faults reactivated as sinistral strike-slip faults—but in detail this influence is highly intriguing.

Some years ago (1966) I attempted a kinematic analysis of the area, using the cutting and displacing of correlatable folds by wrench faults and the deformation of thrusts

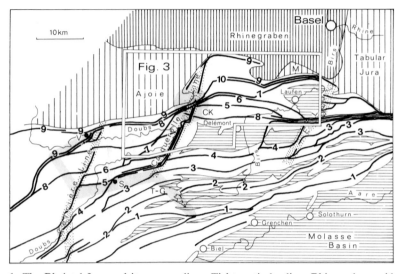

FIG. 1. The Rheintal Jura and its surroundings. Tight vertical ruling: Rhinegraben: wide vertical ruling: Tabular Jura bordering the Rhinegraben. Horizontal ruling: Tertiary (mostly Oligocene) basins S of the Rhinegraben. Stippled: mains zones of sinistral wrench faults, mostly along pre-existing Rhinegraben faults. Heavy lines: successive (Numbers 1–10) compressional fronts (ramps), simplified, particularly in the area outside of Fig. 3; very schematic in the S. Addition of successive fronts to form large anticlinal zones is shown in some places for exemplification. Particularly striking is the development of the frontal thrust in the E. M = Plateau of Metzerlen-Mariastein; CK = Caquerelle knot; V = Vaufrey; S = Saignelégier; T–G = Tavannes–Les Genevez dextral zone; EL = Erschwil line.

by folds as guidelines for a kinematic sequence which, at every step, was constrained by requirements of material balance as set forth in Laubscher (1965, fig. 6).

Such a kinematic sequence, though inferred on incomplete evidence, is indispensable for guiding our inquiring into the possible mechanisms that prompted nucleation of this highly irregular pattern of deformation.

Fig. 3 is a schematic illustration of the distribution of compressional quantities, thrusts and folds grouped together into belts whose width is a quantitative measure of compression, arrived at by the analysis of cross sections. Coming from the W, the salient feature is a confluence of several such belts into the 'Caquerelle knot' (cf. Fig. 1) and then, going E, a redistribution of compression into an altogether different system of belts.

How did this happen? Taking the latest step first—displacement of an anticline by a strike-slip fault of 250 m—subtracting it from total deformation, and so on, going back step by step through a process of kinematic inversion—a very laborious trial and error procedure—the sequence of events illustrated in Fig. 3 appears to fit the information best.

The first recognizable instability (Fig. 3a) arose in a compressional belt that reached the

SW corner of the Delémont basin from the W (5 in Fig. 1); then, instead of passing through the Delémont basin, reactivated a bundle of pre-existing Rhinegraben faults as sinistral wrench faults permitting it to by-pass the basin; and finally, to the N of the basin, continued in a generally eastern direction, as a northward convex arc.

This geometry of the first compressive belt that was confronted with the inherited geometry of the Delémont basin, has 3 particularly typical features that have been found in this part of the Jura: the segmentwise reactivation of Rhinegraben faults as discrete sinistral wrench faults; the arcuate shape of the frontal compressional belt, convex to the N; and a diffuse dextral shear zone at the eastern end, where compression is transferred backwards.

On the whole (stages b & c of Fig. 3), the slipped region subsequently expands farther and farther into the foreland. It is bounded by new, more external arcs which are, as a rule, at some distance from the inactivated arcs. Again and again, Rhinegraben fault segments are reactivated as sinistral strike-slip elements of the arc; the new arc frequently uses some sections of the old arc, and it seems quite unpredictable which of them is chosen.

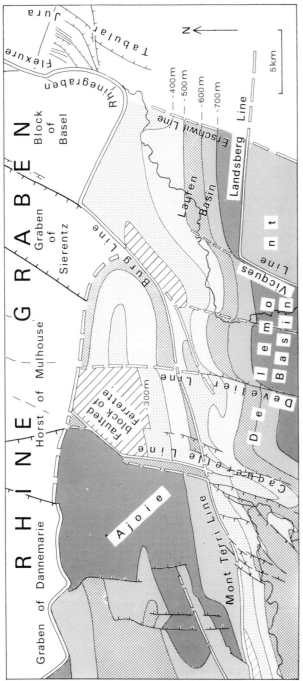

FIG. 2. Top of basement configuration in the northern Rheintal Jura as estimated from cross-sections and extrapolation of tabular synclines. There are many uncertainties in detail but the general distribution of highs and lows and their bounding basement steps (double lines; faults and flexures not differentiated) are believed realistic. Single lines are surface faults (barbs on downthrown side), exact location and geometry in basement unknown. Typical for the southern end of the Rhinegraben, which strikes NNE, are E–W elements (comprising WSW and WNW segments). They are believed to be a part of a sinistral transform zone connecting the Rhine and Bresse graben. The interference of ENE and EW elements forms complex patterns; but note that the graben of Sierentz (substructure of the Rhinegraben), after interference with the Burg line, continues into the central part of the Delémont basin. The fronts of Fig. 3 are obviously influenced by these pre-existing structures (boundary conditions), although because they are represented as mapped on the surface and simplified, there is no exact correspondence. Compare Laubscher *et al.* (1967); Laubscher (1970); Liniger (1967).

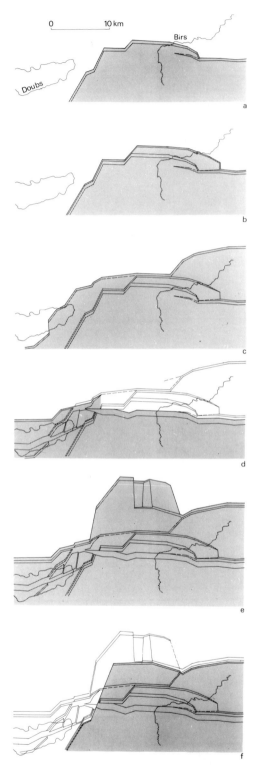

Probably the most puzzling feature is stage d. It is defined as that stage, creating the Vorbourg anticline (compare Fig. 4) which is beautifully exposed in the Birs gorge NE of Delémont. To account for the full compression of this anticline I have found it necessary to distribute it, W of the Caquerelle knot, among a series of individual features. The situation at the knot (Fig. 4) is quite complicated. Axial plunge, i.e. decay of compression in one anticline (Mont Terri a.) is associated with cross-linking features which build up complementary compression in another anticline (Vorbourg a.).

In a general way, the complications in this area are understandable. Between the SE corner of the rigid Ajoie mass and the NW corner of the rigid Delémont basin compression must somehow be concentrated into 'knots'. However, why the distribution of compressional belts in stage d took place in this particular way is hard to say. It involves dextral backstepping from the Mont Terri knot to the Les Rangiers knot across the sinistral deformation belt of stages a and b and, contrary to the general rule, a reduction of the slipped area in this region with a front behind those of stages a to c. This dextral backstepping is a requirement of the simplified kinematic model, but by which mode of deformation it was achieved is quite puzzling.

FIG. 3. The kinematic sequence in the northern Rheintal Jura, simplified quantitative model. Shaded: slipped domain. Heavy line: front of slipped domain at each stage. Spacing of double line at front gives amount of slip. Distributed dextral shear is shown by complementary linear changes in width. The final result, stage f is from Laubscher (1965). The overall kinematic model governing material balance for this figure is simple rotation around a pivot at the eastern end of the Jura. Except for stage d, it is assumed that only one front was active at a given time interval. This is an oversimplification for the benefit of the model; from experiments and the distribution of earthquake foci in tectonically active zones it would appear more realistic to weight the importance of the different fronts for the given time interval (on the order of 10^5 years): movement would then be concentrated in those fronts shown as active in the figure. However, information does not permit this degree of sophistication.

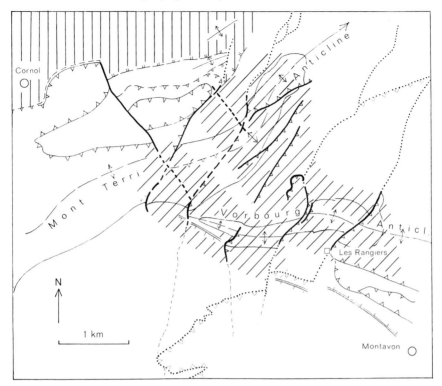

FIG. 4. Elements of distributed dextral shear in the Cornol–Les Rangiers zone (heavy lines). Double lines with barbs: fold limbs with WNW–NW strike. Dotted: main elements of sinistral Caquerelle zone. Lines with triangles: thrusts and reverse faults including strike-slip segments with a reverse component. Shaded: Lower Bajocian and older rocks in cores of anticlines. Dashes with double barbs: non-thrust border of tabular Jura of Ajoie (vertically ruled). The Caquerelle-knot of Fig. 1 may be subdivided into a Mont Terri-knot and a Rangiers-knot.

In Fig. 4 I have emphasized on a simplified geological map (sheet St. Ursanne of the Geological Atlas of Switzerland 1 : 25 000) those features which strike the eye as unexpected for N–S compression and sinistral movement and which conceivably might be meaningful for dextral backstepping. At the NW end of the postulated dextral zone, near Cornol, there is a segment of a dextral fault which displaces the frontal thrust (Tschopp 1960). Another dextral segment is postulated farther E, as frontal thrusting there stops altogether. However, it is not visible because these thrusts have been folded and eroded away on top of the fold; their roots in the poorly exposed Triassic core of the anticline are impossible to pinpoint.

Such dextral faults are an oddity in the area, and their occurrence in a part of the dextral backstepping zone is considered significant.

In the W, the first traces of the Vorbourg fold are found at the SE projection of the main dextral fault, and they have an E–SE strike— again a rare occurrence in the area. More segments of this strike are found farther SE within the postulated dextral belt. As the Mont Terri anticline loses compression to the NE, the Vorbourg anticline increases its compression to the E, and both phenomena are associated with a peculiar behaviour of the Rhinegraben faults. In the Vorbourg fold they seem to be bent or kinked, with a thrust component, and there seems to be another *en échelon* belt of such Rhinegraben fault segments converted into reverse faults that connects the decaying northeastern tip of the Mont Terri anticline with the growing Vorbourg anticline.

If we accept this association of peculiar features with the dextral zone as inductive evidence of a probably causal connection, we arrive at a highly complex mechanism.

In the frontal thrusts which are dissociated from the Triassic décollement layer, newly formed dextral faults played a role, whereas in those zones farther S where the moving cover was still based on Triassic evaporites the inherited anisotropy due to the Rhinegraben faults played a more important role. These faults were used as a sort of Riedels shear— in a manner similar to bedding planes in a kink band—to distribute the dextral shear. Note that the same faults on other occasions were reactivated as sinistral wrench faults.

This area is one of the few places where it has been possible to gain some insight into the complex nature of distributed dextral shear, though there are many others where it is kinematically inevitable. More of them are under study, and all seem to behave quite individualistically. The abundant pressure solution in these zones may have been helpful in distributing the dextral shear. The strain rate drops to an estimated $10^{-14} \sec^{-1}$, less than one hundredth of that along sinistral fault zones, which would move it well into the pressure solution field for calcite deformation (Rutter 1976, fig. 8), provided there is a sufficient microfracture density.

We may speculate further why the Vorbourg fold developed where it did behind the arcs of stages a to c (Fig. 3).

Inspection of Fig. 2 suggests the following answer. The fold and thrust zone S of the Laufen basin, which develops farther E into the main frontal thrust zone of the Jura (Fig. 1), seems to be due to an important obstacle at the basal décollement layer (Landsberg line) which was overcome only after some delay. N of the Delémont basin such obstacles seem to exist farther N.

The northern stress concentrators having played their part and the thrusts they initiated having been inactivated, there was a choice of alternative procedures: either create the Vorbourg fold by propagating the Landsberg line instability westward and incur the difficulties of connecting the Mont Terri and Les Rangiers knots, or expand the area of slip to a new and more external set of stress concentrators and zones of weakness.

The solution was sequential: Vorbourg in stage d, expansion of slipped area in stage e, with a very peculiar return to a more internal front of slip in stage f.

We may summarize pro tempore the growth of instabilization—area of slip—in the Rheintal part of the Jura décollement nappe as follows.

Areas of slip of the decollement nappe are limited at each stage by a heterogeneous set of obstacles: stress concentrators provoking ramping, and weak spots such as minimal thickness of the cover which were unable to sustain a level of stress necessary for the expansion of slip. As thrusting and folding reinforces these weak spots, and flow of evaporites mitigates the stress concentrators, the area of slip expands to another limiting set of obstacles (stress concentrators and weaknesses). In this process the inherited anisotropy due to predominantly NNE striking Rhinegraben faults plays a decisive role. They are normally reactivated as sinistral strike-slip segments, but occasionally they may serve as *en échelon* elements in distributed dextral shear (which is always combined with compression). Internal deformation of Lower Tertiary basins is generally avoided by sinistral shear along their lateral margins; sometimes, as in the case of the Laufen basin, both dextral and sinistral shear are involved. The tendency to form forward convex arcs is attributed to the indenter effect which would favour an arcuate expansion of slipped area between points fixed by obstacles. Because of asymmetric conditions—anisotropy due to inherited geometry seemingly the most important in the area—the sinistral western flank of the arc has evolved differently from the dextral eastern flank. The distribution of horizontally striated joints in these arcs points to locally divergent movements.

Regional generalization

In Fig. 1 I have tentatively expanded the model of kinematic sequences without quantifying. The role of the Rhinegraben faults in the Vaufrey knot (V in Fig. 1) and along the Ferrière Line in the west (Bailly 1979; Suter 1979) is similar to that of the Rheintal faults of the Caquerelle zone and the Mont Terri and Les Rangiers knots, and there are other zones of similar kinematics. Note that the smaller arcs which have been discussed so far are parts of arcs of higher regionality (e.g. front 10). Again, sinistral faults are obvious, whereas dextral zones are often hidden, and in the rare instances where they are easily spotted they are puzzling. One of these dextral zones is that of Tavannes–Les Genevez (T–G in Fig. 1). Here, a limited cluster of dextral faults and thrusts with a dextral component make their appearance. At Tavannes there is a conspicuous inherited flexure with thick Oligo-Miocene sediments in the E and Upper Miocene in places directly on the Jurassic in the W (Rothpletz 1933; Forkert 1933). The details, particularly the direction of this flexure, are not known. It may be the direct or indirect cause for this dextral path which is crossed and overwhelmed by later anticlines that have been subjected to all kinds of contortions in the area of interference. I have a suspicion, however, that it is only a part of a more extensive but hidden dextral zone, made visible because of favourable local circumstances.

The Jura as a whole is arcuate, but the changeover from one direction to another is usually not smooth. One of the zones of rather abrupt divergence is the Tavannes–Les Genevez dextral zone; another patch is near Saignelégier, and the third is near Vaufrey. Together they mark the main boundary between the eastern Jura, with its predominantly E trends, and the central Jura, with its predominantly SW trend. This boundary is not straight and seems to have shifted with successive stages. The important consideration here is that this divergence in trend seems to result from a divergence of the transport vector, as indicated by various geometric elements (Laubscher 1972). This, however, requires lateral stretching of the slipped cover which is achieved by the wrench faults. The sinistral faults often seem to have different effects on their E and W flanks. The E flanks have a tendency to move forward obliquely to the fault, thereby displacing it with respect to basement and simultaneously pushing the W flank to the NW. Transport vectors of the two flanks point in divergent directions. Thus, the sinistral faults seem to play the largest part in helping to push the W flank towards the Salins zone and the border of the Bresse Graben. The dextral ones permit directly NW movement of their SW flank. The Ferrière Line (Fig. 1) seems to accommodate divergence by sinistral movements, as does the Saignelégier patch (S in Fig. 1), particularly in the domain of the Gipou thrust (Suter 1976). Between the latter and the Tavannes–Les Genevez zone there is a belt several kilometres wide, where E and SW trends in the folds are superposed. There are scattered vestiges of small dextral faults throughout the area.

The Rheintal Jura is a special case in as much as the preexisting faults have a favourable direction for sinistral strike-slip during subsequent folding. This relationship does not hold for the main SW part of the Jura, where new wrench faults were formed according to the Mohr angle within the changing strike of the Jura arc (Laubscher 1972).

Conclusions

Successive instabilization of the Rheintal part of the Jura decollement nappe generally proceeds from S to N. Location of ramps where decollement climbs to the surface is largely influenced by pre-existing Rhinegraben structures. These also convey a certain anisotropy to the sedimentary cover which seems to be responsible, at least partly, for a different aspect of sinistral and dextral shear zones. The sinistral shears are usually along discrete faults, mostly reactivated Rhinegraben faults. The dextral shears are diffuse zones and often involve diverse *en échelon* elements in addition to possibly important pressure solution. Arcuate elements, convex to the N, connect the sinistral and dextral shear zones frontally. The sinistral connection is often achieved by a series of relays. The sinistral movement is transferred from the northern, frontal end of more westerly rails to the southern, rear end of more easterly rails. Regionally, the shear zones accommodate the divergence of movement within the overall Jura arc. More locally they bound arcuate segments of ever smaller dimensions, and also seem to ease diverging movements in these smaller arcs.

References

BAILLY, CH. 1979. *Etude géologique de la vallée du Doubs et de ses abords à l'est de St. Hippolyte (Doubs)*. Ph.D. thesis, Besançon. 122 p., (unpubl).

FORKERT, E. 1933. Geologische Beschreibung des Kartengebietes Tramelan im Berner Jura. *Eclog. geol. Helv.* **26**, 1–41.

GEOLOGISCHER ATLAS DER SCHWEIZ. 1 : 25 000, Blatt 1085, St Ursanne.

LAUBSCHER, H. 1961. Die Fernschubhypothese der Jurafaltung. *Eclog. geol. Helv.* **54**, 221–80.

—— 1965. Ein kinematisches Modell der Jurafaltung. *Eclog. geol. Helv.* **58**, 232–318.

—— 1966. Zur Kinematik und Dynamik des nördlichen rheintalischen Juras. *Eclog. geol. Helv.* **59**, 957–9.

—— 1970. Grundsätzliches zur Tektonik des Rheingrabens. *In: Graben Problems, International Upper Mantle Project, Scientific Report* **27**, 79–87.

—— 1972. Some overall aspects of Jura dynamics. *Am. J. Sci.* **272**, 293–304.

—— 1977. Fold development in the Jura. *Tectonophysics*, **37**, 337–62.

—— 1979a. Elements of Jura kinematics and dynamics. *Eclog. geol. Helv.* **72**, 467–83.

—— 1979b. Die Entwicklung des Faltenjuras—Daten und Vorstellungen. Beiheft zum Deutschen Handwörterbuch der Tektonik, (in press).

——, THEOBALD, N. & WITTMANN, O. 1967. Le prolongement S du fossé rhénan. *Abh. geol.*

318 H. P. Laubscher

Landesamt Bad.-Wurttemb. **6,** 59–66. Mém.
Serv. Carte géol. Als.-Lorr. **26,** 59–66.
LINIGER, H. 1967. Pliozän und Tektonik des
Juragebirges. Eclog. geol. Helv. **60,** 407–90.
ROTHPLETZ, W. 1933. Geologische Beschreibung
der Umgebung von Tavannes im Berner Jura.
Verh. natf. Ges. Basel, **43,** 12–150.
RUTTER, E. H. 1976. The kinetics of rock deforma-
tion by pressure solution. Philos. Trans. R. Soc.
London, **A 283,** 203–19.
SUTER, M. 1976. Tektonik des Doubstals und der
Freiberge in der Umgebung von Saignelégier

(Faltenjura). Ecolg. geol. Helv. **69,** 641–70.
—— 1978. Geologische Interpretation eines reflex-
ionsseismischen W-E-Profils durch das Dels-
berger Becken (Faltenjura). Eclog. geol. Helv.
71, 267–75.
—— 1979. Strukturelle Geometrie des Faltenjuras
im nördlichen bereich der Ferrière-Linie. Eclog.
geol. Helv. **72,** 375–400.
TSCHOPP, R. 1960. Geologie des Gebietes von Sieg-
friedblatt Miécourt (Berner Jura). Beitr. geol.
Karte Schweiz (NF) **110.**

H. P. LAUBSCHER, Geological Institute of the University of Basel, Bernoullistrasse
32, CH 4056 Basel.

Fold-and-thrust tectonics in the Helvetic Nappes (E Switzerland)

O. A. Pfiffner

SUMMARY: The Helvetic Nappes in E Switzerland form an example of décollement nappes. The Säntis Thrust represents both an upper and a lower detachment. In the units underlying this detachment shortening is accomplished by a combination of folding and thrusting and is strongly influenced by the occurrence of 2nd order décollement horizons. Nappe-internal deformation resulted in the reorientation of folds (development of a fold arc) and smoothing out of ramps and flats in thrust surfaces. Two types of folds can be recognized: true buckle folds and folds due to ramps and flats.

The movement direction of the thrust sheets was S–N and fold axes oblique to this direction developed probably due to initially ENE striking ramps. Transverse faults with a strike slip component allow changes in displacement along individual thrust surfaces.

The purpose of this paper is to show the relationship between folds and thrusts in the example of the Helvetic Nappes in E Switzerland. For more detailed descriptions of the area discussed (Fig. 1), including profiles and reference lists, the reader is referred to Oberholzer (1933), Helbling (1938), Staub (1954) and Trümpy (1969).

The tectonic units discussed here consist of a sedimentary sequence ranging from Permian to Tertiary in age and containing lithological units with strongly contrasting mechanical properties which allow the development of décollement structures (see Fig. 2).

The area investigated is characterized by two important structures: the Glarus Overthrust separating the Infrahelvetic complex (below) from the Helvetic Nappes (above) and, occurring within the latter, the Säntis Thrust, defined here as the basal thrust of the Säntis (Churfirsten) Nappe ('nappe supérieure glaronnaise' of Lugeon 1902). The nappe complex between these two thrusts is here referred to as the Lower Glarus Nappe complex ('nappe inférieure glaronnaise' of Lugeon 1902); traditionally it is subdivided into the Glarus (s.s.), Mürtschen and Axen Nappe, a practice only partly followed here.

The rocks studied suffered a well-defined sequence of deformation phases (Trümpy 1969; Schmid 1975; Milnes & Pfiffner 1977; Pfiffner 1977, 1978). A first phase of deformation, the Pizol phase (cf. Milnes & Pfiffner 1977; Pfiffner 1977), is characterized by the emplacement of exotic strips of flysch (Fig. 2, sections 1–4). The folds and thrusts within the Lower Glarus Nappe complex and the Säntis Nappe, as well as the initial development of the Glarus Overthrust, are related to an axial planar, thrust parallel cleavage which may be attributed to a second, Calanda, phase defined in the Infrahelvetic complex (op. cit.; Pfiffner 1978). Displacements along the Glarus Overthrust with passive transport of these Calanda phase structures during a third, Ruchi, phase (op. cit.) led to an inversion of the metamorphic zonation (Frey et al. 1974). In the following, the nappe-internal structures are discussed first, followed by a discussion of displacements along faults.

Fold-and-thrust tectonics

The Säntis Thrust

The Säntis Thrust represents a lower detachment for the Cretaceous limestones of the Säntis Nappe (see Fig. 2, section 4) and an upper detachment for the thrusts and folds in the underlying Malm (Upper Jurassic) limestones. It follows the lowermost Cretaceous marls over the entire map area.

The synformal structure of the thrust surface immediately N of the map area (Fig. 2) is due to the fact that the Säntis Nappe sheet travelled farther N than the underlying Lower Glarus Nappe complex (onto the S-dipping Subalpine Molasse Thrust sheets) and that the Glarus Overthrust as well as the various thrusts within the Lower Glarus Nappe complex, cut up-section.

Imbricate thrusts and folds in the Lower Glarus Nappe complex

The imbricate thrusts and folds below the Säntis Thrust (Fig. 2) occur within the level of the Malm limestones and give rise to irregularities in the thrust's smooth overall topography. The imbricate thrusts meet the Säntis

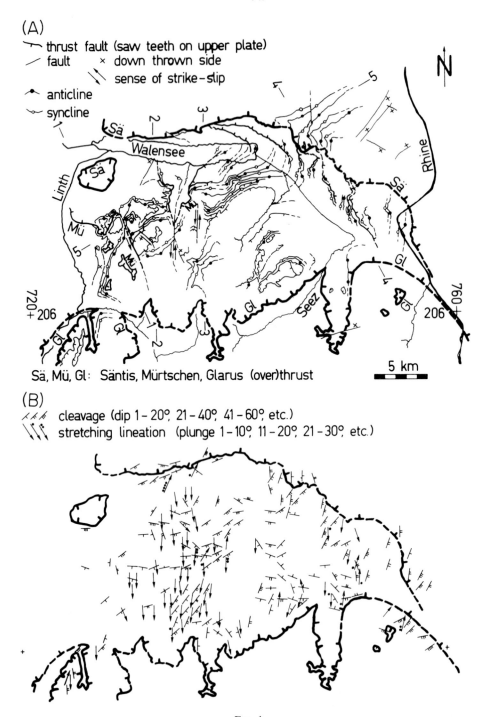

FIG. 1.

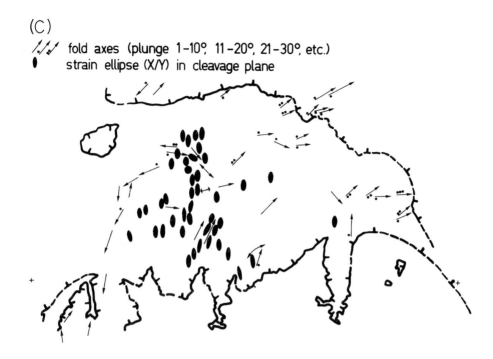

(C)

/./. fold axes (plunge 1–10°, 11–20°, 21–30°, etc.)
● strain ellipse (X/Y) in cleavage plane

FIG. 1. Structural data. The values in B represent means of domains 1 km² in size. Included are data from Huber (1964); Schielly (1964); Ryf (1965); Kühn (1966); Markus (1967) and Richter (1968).

Thrust at low angles similar to the situation near the roof thrust of a duplex structure (Boyer 1976). As one traces the imbricate thrusts down-section, shortening is transferred to folding, partly because, in the lower part, the Malm limestones are relatively well-bedded and thus more suited for folding, with bedding plane slip allowing the necessary internal deformation. Further down-section, two mechanically weak units (the base of the Dogger (Middle Jurassic) and the Lower Lias (Lower Jurassic)/Upper Triassic) allow considerable decoupling (the 'Lias-nappe' postulated by Helbling 1938; see also Trümpy 1949, p. 91). These 2nd order décollement horizons partly inhibit a direct correlation between the imbricate thrusts and fold-and-thrust structures at the level of the Triassic. In any case, the imbricate thrusts do not run all the way down-section to meet the Glarus Overthrust, i.e. there is no clear floor thrust as in an idealized duplex structure. Furthermore, none of these imbricate thrusts show a major displacement such as to allow a correlation with the Axen thrust of central Switzerland (for a discussion of this correlation see also Trümpy 1969).

The imbricate thrusts cut at variable angles through the stratigraphical section (ramps and flats) but, in contrast to true staircase geometry, the thrust surfaces are smoothed out and thus, besides anticlines above hanging-wall ramps (cf. Fig. 5 and Rich 1934), one also finds synclines below foot-wall ramps (Fig. 2, section 4).

To the S, these imbricate thrusts become replaced by a fold complex consisting of a sequence of anticline/syncline pairs (Figs 1A, 2, section 4, & Fig. 5) representing true buckle folds.

At the level of the Malm, fold axes of both buckle folds and folds due to ramps and flats show a constant trent of N60°E–N120°W (Fig. 1C).

The Mürtschen Thrust

The Mürtschen Thrust located in the W (Fig. 1A) divides the Lower Glarus Nappe complex into two blocks (Glarus Nappe s.s. and Mürtschen Nappe). To the S, its trace is lost in the Permian (Verrucano group); it seems likely

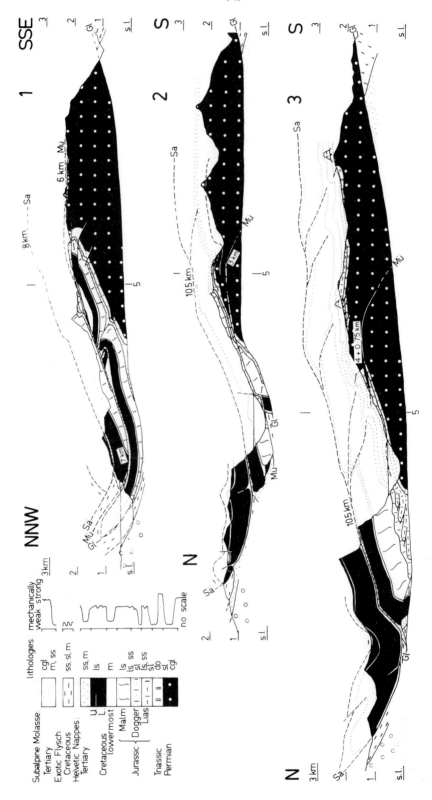

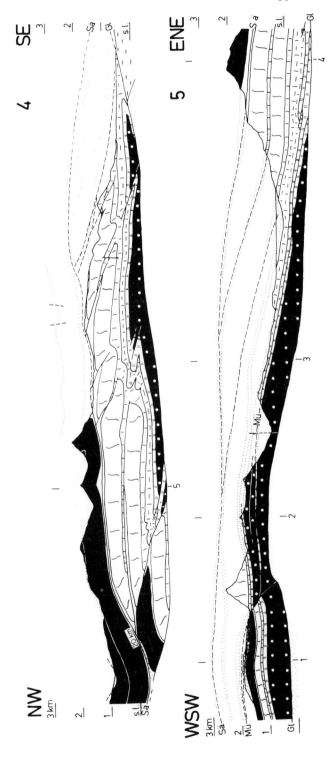

Fig. 2. Vertical cross sections drawn as to minimize internal inconsistencies concerning bed lengths and displacements (for location of cross sections and Sä, Mü and Fig. 1A). Lithologies: cgl (conglomerate), do (dolomite), ls (limestone), m (marl), sl (slate) and ss (sandstone).

that the Mürtschen Thrust branches up to the S
and that part of the thrust displacement is
transferred into additional shear strains in the
adjacent rocks, as is indicated by the slightly
higher strain ellipse axial ratios S of its re-
entrant S of Walensee in Fig. 1C (see also Ryf
1965, p. 91). As the lowermost Cretaceous is
developed in a more calcareous facies
(Oberholzer 1933), both the Mürtschen Thrust
and the Glarus Overthrust, unlike the Säntis
Thrust, ramp up through this horizon (Fig. 2,
section 1).

To the E, the Mürtschen Thrust branches up
(Figs 1A & 2, section 3); the upper branch
connecting via folds with the lowermost of the
imbricate thrusts (base of the Walenstadter
Zwischendecke of Heim 1917).

The displacement along the Mürtschen
Thrust in cross section 1 of Fig. 2 is 6–7 km,
depending on whether one takes the Triassic
or the base of the Cretaceous limestones as a
marker; the missing displacement of 1 km is
taken up by the subsidiary thrust in the foot-
wall (S of Fronalpstock). If this section was
drawn parallel to the probable movement direction, i.e. S–N (see below), these displacement values would be increased by about 10%.
The next cross section to the E (2 in Fig. 2)
shows a displacement at the level of the Triassic along the same thrust of only 3 km. This
discrepancy is explained by a transverse fault
in the foot-wall (Murgsee transverse fault, Fig.
2, section 5) for which a sinistral strike-slip
component of 3 km can be deduced from the
offset of the ramp of the Mürtschen Thrust
through the Triassic dolomite. As is evident
from cross section 5, the transverse fault lines
up with, and was possibly predetermined by, a
transverse foot-wall ramp through the Jurassic
(striking roughly N–S) and a rise of the surface
of the Glarus Overthrust below (Fisch 1961;
Schmid 1975), which is, as yet, poorly understood.

The tectonic level of the Triassic

In the W part of the map area, shortening at
the level of the Triassic dolomites is mainly
accomplished by low angle thrusting (see Fig.
2, sections 1 and 2, hanging-wall of Mürtschen
Thrust), whereas in the E the Triassic dolomite
is partly thrown into folds. This contrast seems
to arise from facies changes: in the W the Lias
is missing (Trümpy 1949) and the Dogger is
reduced (Dollfus 1965). Both Lias and Dogger, when present, have mechanically weak
lower parts which allow some decoupling and

the geometrically necessary contact strains for
folding in the dolomite.

The level of the Triassic defines a fold arc:
In the SW folds of this level trend roughly N–S
closing to the W; towards the NE (Walensee),
fold axes turn around into an EW direction
closing to the N and then to the SE into a N–S
direction (near the 90° bend of the Seez) closing to the E. The fold axes in the central part
of the map area scatter strongly, due to complicated strain accommodations at thrust and
transverse fault terminations (see below; see
also the fold at the W termination of the thrust
defining the klippe, 4 km NW of the word Seez
in Fig. 1).

Displacement along faults

Movement direction of thrust sheets

This difficult problem is treated in the following way: first the structural data of the
nappe-internal deformation are discussed and
the resulting possible movement directions are
then checked with 'balanced cross-sections'
(Dahlstrom 1969).

The fold arc at the level of the Triassic,
bulging out to the N, the N–S oriented stretching direction (Fig. 1B & 1C), and the sense
of asymmetry of the folds is compatible with a
northward movement of this level of the
Lower Glarus Nappe complex during the
Calanda phase. Structural data from the underlying Infrahelvetic complex are also compatible with a northward movement along the
Glarus Overthrust during the subsequent
Ruchi-phase. Small-scale Ruchi-phase folds
scatter along a great circle identical with the
Ruchi-phase cleavage (Fig. 3 and Pfiffner 1977
& 1978) but, as one approaches the Glarus
Overthrust, these fold axes become oriented
N–S, the cleavage retaining its orientation
(Schmid 1975, Fig. 4C). The most reasonable
explanation for this change of orientation is a
northward movement direction (Sanderson
1973; Escher & Watterson 1974).

The movement direction often inferred is
the shortening direction indicated by the con-
stantly oriented fold axes at the level of the
Malm and Cretaceous limestones, i.e. a direction N30°W. Cross section 4 in Fig. 2 is drawn
in that direction, and for the Säntis Thrust a
displacement of 20 km results. If a cross section in the same direction is drawn 9 km
farther to the WSW (along section 9 of Herb

1962), a displacement of only 8–9 km is obtained. There are no transverse faults (tear faults of Dahlstrom 1969) immediately above, or below, the Säntis Thrust which could allow for this 11–12 km difference in displacement. A broad shear zone would have rotated the fold axes, which is, in fact, not observed. Thus, it is concluded that the movement direction could not have been perpendicular to these fold axes. If the trace of the cross section is chosen in a N–S direction (Fig. 2, sections 2 & 3), thrust displacements remain consistent and are thus more likely to coincide with the movement direction. Why could those folds be oblique to this possible movement direction? A possible explanation for this is that the ramps formed at an angle of *c.* 60° to the movement direction (see Fig. 4): (i) The footwall ramp at the level of the Triassic of the Mürtschen Thrust can be shown to strike about NE–SW (see e.g. Huber 1964, p. 108). (ii) Folds due to ramps and flats of thrust surfaces (Rich 1934) trend N60E and include folds in the Malm limestones of the Lower Glarus Nappe complex and possibly the frontal folds of the Säntis Nappe (see Kempf 1968, plate II) and such folds (and possibly also nearby buckle folds) will have their axes parallel to the ramp, not perpendicular to the movement direction.

For the Säntis Thrust the obliquity of the ramp through the Cretaceous limestones with

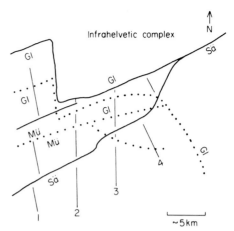

FIG. 4. Palinspastic sketch map showing future thrust (ramp) traces oblique to the S–N movement direction (Sä, Mü, Gl: see Fig. 1A); solid and dotted lines: base of ramp through Lower Cretaceous limestones and Triassic dolomite, resp. The transverse ramp followed by the Glarus overthrust was subsequently used as transverse fault (Murgsee transverse fault explained in text) and its expression in the Infrahelvetic complex is most probably found in the Panixerpass transverse fault (cf. e.g. Pfiffner 1978). 1–4: traces of cross sections.

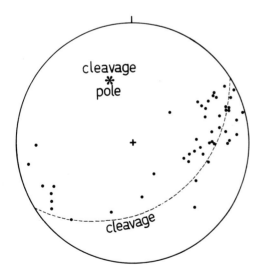

FIG. 3. Ruchi phase minor folds and cleavage in the Infrahelvetic complex (Wulff net, lower hemisphere). The cleavage represents a regional average of the data in Pfiffner 1977 & 1978.

regard to the movement direction could be explained by the orientation of the isopic line of the lowermost Cretaceous, marking the change from a marly to a more calcareous facies (Heim 1916, p. 463). Another possibility, i.e. a regionally penetrative sinistral shear, is less probable from a structural point of view (cf. orientation of stretching lineation and nature and degree of internal deformation).

Transverse faults

Three major sinistral transverse faults, active mainly during the Calanda phase, are recognized in the map area (Fig. 1A), the most western of which (Murgsee transverse fault) has been discussed in some detail in connection with the Mürtschen Thrust. One prominent feature that needs to be added here is that the sinistral shear extends into the rocks adjacent to the fault, resulting in a rotation of bedding and cleavage strikes and fold trends of up to 60°.

FIG. 5. The transition from imbricate thrusting (NNW) to folding (SSE) below the Säntis Thrust (Sä) in the Gonzen (G) and Alvier (A) area. Note anticline due to hanging-wall ramp through Middle (1) and Upper (2) Jurassic formed by the southernmost imbricate thrust (x). 1: Middle Jurassic (Dogger), 2: Upper Jurassic (Malm; Quinten limestone forming cliffs), 3: lowermost Cretaceous, 4: Lower Cretaceous (for lithologies and mechanical stratigraphy cf. Fig. 2); a: anticline, s: syncline.

The next, to the E, (Murgtal transverse fault) marks a change in the nappe-internal structure, shows a strike-slip component of 1 km (see Ryf 1965, p. 74), and may represent a reactivated Mesozoic fault (Trümpy 1949; Dollfus 1965).

The third one is found S of the place where the Mürtschen Thrust branches up (Fig. 1A). S of its map termination in the S, the strike-slip displacement must be transferred into penetrative shear in the adjacent rocks, as indicated by a fold train running across its would-be S continuation (Fig. 1A) whose axes seem to be rotated into a NNE direction (Fig. 1C). The perturbation in the orientation of strain ellipses (Fig. 1C) and cleavage planes (Fig. 1B) is compatible with a transfer into a shear zone diverging to the S. The N continuation of the fault is somewhat more complex (joining the map intersection of the branching Mürtschen Thrust?) and the orientations of fold axes and strain ellipses N of its map termination are not easy to explain. This transverse fault, however, could explain some of the increase in displace-

ment along the Mürtschen Thrust from 3 to 4+0.75 km between cross sections 2 and 3.

Conclusions

Mapping traces of axial surfaces of folds and drawing 'balanced cross sections' by minimizing internal inconsistencies prove to be useful tools in understanding nappe-internal deformations and in deriving possible movement directions of thrust sheets. In the area studied, the orientation of fold axes is influenced by a whole variety of factors (geometric effects of thrust and transverse fault terminations, orientation of ramps and rotation during nappe emplacement) and is by itself not adequate to deduce the movement direction of thrust sheets.

ACKNOWLEDGMENTS. The author wishes to thank Roy Kligfield, Geoff Milnes, Stefan Schmid and R. Trümpy for critically reading the manuscript, Bill Chapple, Dave Elliott and John Ramsay for stimulating discussions of fold and thrust terranes. The work was financed by the Swiss National Foundation (project 2.859–0.77).

References

BOYER, S. E. 1976. Formation of the Grandfather Mountain window, North Carolina, by duplex thrusting. *Abstr. Geol. Soc. Am. with Prog.* **8**, 788–9.

DAHLSTROM, C. D. A. 1969. Balanced cross sections. *Can. J. Earth Sci.* **6**, 743–57.

DOLLFUS, S. 1965. Ueber den Helvetischen Dogger zwischen Linth und Rhein. *Eclog. geol. Helv.* **58**, 453–554.

ESCHER, A. & WATTERSON, J. 1974. Stretching fabrics, folds and crustal shortening. *Tectonophysics*, **22**, 223–31.

FISCH, W. P. 1969. Der Verrucano auf der Nordost-Seite des Sernftales (Kt. Glarus). *Mitt. geol. Inst ETH u. Univ. Zürich Ser. C*, **84**, 1–88, and *Mitt. natf. Ges. Glarus* **11**, 1–88.

FREY, M., HUNZIKER, J. C., FRANK, W., BOCQUET, J., DAL PIAZ, G. V., JAGER, E. & NIGGLI, E. 1974. Alpine metamorphism of the Alps: a review. *Schweiz. mineral. petrogr. Mitt.* **54**, 247–90.

HEIM, ARN. 1910, 1913, 1916, 1917. Monographie der Churfirsten-Mattstock-Gruppe. *Beitr. geol. Karte Schweiz. N.F.* **20/1–4**, 1–662.

HELBLING, R. 1938. I. Die Anwendung der Photogrammetrie bei geologischen Kartierungen II. Zur Tektonik des St. Galler Oberlandes und der Glarneralpen. *Beitr. geol. Karte Schweiz. N.F.* **76**, 1–133.

HERB, R. 1962. Geologie von Amden mit besonderer Berücksichtigung der Flyschbildungen. *Beitr. geol. Karte Schweiz. N.F.* **114**, 1–130.

HUBER, R. 1964. Etude géologique du massif du Gufelstock avec stratigraphie du Verrucano. *Mitt. Geol. Inst. ETH u. Univ. Zürich N.F.* **23**, 1–154.

KEMPF, T. A. 1966. Geologie des westlichen Säntisgebirges. *Mitt. Geol. Inst. ETH u. Univ. Zürich N.F.* **61**, 1–82.

KÜHN, H. 1966. *Observations géologiques dans la région du Spitzmeilen.* Diploma-thesis ETH-Zürich, 122 p. (unpubl).

LUGEON, M. 1902. Les grandes nappes de recouvrement des Alpes du Chablais et de la Suisse. *Bull. Soc. géol. Fr* **4/I**, 723–825.

MARKUS, J. H. 1967. Geologische Untersuchungen in den Flumserbergen (St. Galler Oberland). *Mitt. Geol. Inst. ETH u. Univ. Zürich N.F.* **71**, 1–119.

MILNES, A. G. & PFIFFNER, O. A. 1977. Structural development of the Infrahelvetic complex, eastern Switzerland. *Eclog. geol. Helv.* **70**, 83–95.

OBERHOLZER, J. 1933. Geologie der Glarner Alpen. *Beitr. geol. Karte Schweiz. N.F.* **28/I + II**, 1–626.

PFIFFNER, O. A. 1977. Tektonische Untersuchungen im Infrahelvetikum der Ostschweiz. *Mitt. geol. Inst. ETH u. Univ. Zürich N.F.* **217**, 1–432.

—— 1978. Der Falten- und Kleindeckenbau im Infrahelvetikum der Ostschweiz. *Eclog. geol. Helv.* **71**, 61–84.

RICH, J. L. 1934. Mechanics of low-angle overthrust faulting as illustrated by Cumberland thrust block, Virginia, Kentucky and Tennessee. *Bull. Am. Assoc. Petrol. Geol.* **18**, 1584–96.

RICHTER, H. 1968. Die Geologie der Guschagruppe im St. Galler Oberland. *Mitt. Geol. Inst. ETH u. Univ. Zürich N.F.* **99**, 1–111.

RYF, W. H. 1965. Geologische Untersuchungen im Murgtal (St. Galler Oberland). *Mitt. Geol. Inst. ETH u. Univ. Zürich N.F.* **50**, 1–104.

SANDERSON, D. J. 1973. The development of fold axes oblique to the regional trend. *Tectonophysics*, **16**, 55–70.

SCHIELLY, H. P. 1964. Geologische Untersuchungen im Deckengebiet des westlichen Freiberges (Kt. Glarus). *Mitt. Geol. Inst. ETH u. Univ. Zürich N.F.* **44**, 1–293, and *Mitt. natf. Ges. Glarus* **12**, 1–293.

SCHMID, S. M. 1975. The Glarus overthrust: field evidence and mechanical model. *Eclog. geol. Helv.* **68**, 247–80.

STAUB, R. 1954. *Der Bau der Glarneralpen und seine prinzipielle Bedeutung für die Alpengeologie.* Verlag Tschudi & Co. Glarus, 1–187.

TRÜMPY, R. 1949. Der Lias der Glarner Alpen. *Mitt. Geol. Inst. ETH u. Univ. Zürich Ser. C*, **36**, 1–192, and *Denkschr. schweiz. natf. Ges.* **79/1**, 1–192.

—— 1969. Die helvetischen Decken der Ostschweiz: Versuch einer palinspastischen Korrelation und Ansätze zu einer kinematischen Analyse. *Eclog. geol. Helv.* **62**, 105–42.

O. A. PFIFFNER, Institut de Géologie, Université de Neuchâtel, Rue Emile-Argand 11, CH-2000 Neuchâtel, Switzerland.

Some observations on the development of thrust faults in the Ultradauphinois Zone, French Alps

A. Beach

SUMMARY: The Ultradauphinois Thrust Nappe involved a westerly movement of external autochthonous Jurassic and Eocene sedimentary sequences by décollement on the Trias. A complex thrust belt evolved at its southern end as the movement was hindered by the upfaulted Pelvoux basement massif. All of the Jurassic rocks exhibit strong, penetrative ductile strains—in the lowermost thrust slices (most westerly part of the sheet) forward spreading strains (NE–SW stretching) involving a combination of simple and pure shear, and in the uppermost thrust slices a NW–SE stretching and rearward compression as the main nappe continued to move past to the N of the hindrance. As the resistance to movement increased in the S, the completely distributed ductile strain became localized in numerous zones, characterized by the formation of many veins and strong local deformation of these veins. This marks the onset of stratigraphic imbrication and repetition. The progress from penetrative ductile to localized ductile to discrete brittle strain is recorded by the sequence of structures observed in the field. The main discrete, brittle thrust surfaces represent the last major stage in a continuous sequence of deformation.

The Ultradauphinois Thrust Nappe consists of para-autochthonous Mesozoic and Tertiary external sedimentary sequences that moved from E to W across the external basement surface by décollement on Triassic horizons. The thrust nappe terminates in the S against the northern margin of the Pelvoux Massif, where there is a 15 km. long complex thrust belt striking NW–SE and consisting of thrust sheets of strongly deformed Jurassic rock beneath the (para-) autochthonous Eocene flysch. In this paper, I will discuss the field observations which suggest that an early ductile penetrative strain was succeeded by more localized deformation in zones, which in turn, gradually evolved into discrete and brittle thrust surfaces as the last stage of a continuous deformation.

The stratigraphy of the region was described by Ramsay (1963). The thin Triassic sequence lacks gypsum nearly everywhere in the area of complex thrusting, and passes upwards through the shales into the distinctive limestone-shale facies of the Lower Lias, and then into the less distinctive Lower–Middle Jurassic shales. Isolated masses of Triassic dolomite and limestone from 10 m to 1 km in length occur along some thrusts. Thrusts within the uniform Lower–Middle Jurassic shales are difficult to assess since no lithological contrast exists. The northern margin of the Pelvoux basement dips to the NE, with its deformed autochthonous cover, beneath the thrust belt (Fig. 1).

Direction of movement of thrust sheets

The present-day traces of the thrusts strike NW–SE (Fig. 1), and there is no reason to suppose that these have been strongly modified, and thus they are interpreted to be perpendicular to the direction of movement (Elliott 1976a, b). Thrusts commonly climb section from NE to SW with sub-horizontal thrust plane-bedding intersections, indicating a movement from the NE (cf. Dahlstrom 1970, Elliott 1976a, b). The autochthonous strata immediately below the lowermost thrust shows a strong component of simple shear deformation with the stretching lineation plunging NE (Fig. 1), and cleavage-bedding relations indicating movement from the NE. The Lower Lias limestone-shale facies is often deformed by asymmetric s-folds (looking NW) with sub-horizontal or gently plunging hinge lines running NW–SE. These are thought to have been generated as early folds with axes perpendicular to the direction of movement, their asymmetry indicating movement from the NE.

Relation of thrust belt to regional nappe structure

The central part of the Ultradauphinois Thrust Nappe (S of St. Jean de Maurienne) presents a simple sequence of a Lower-Middle

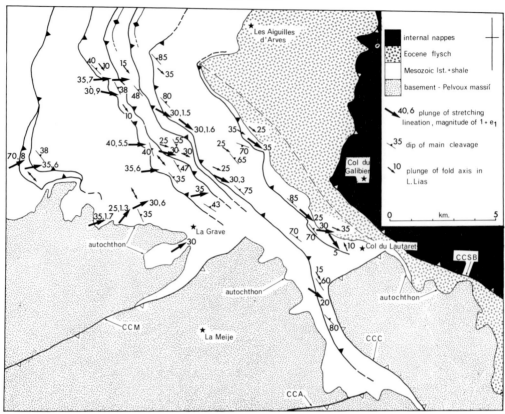

FIG. 1. The area around La Grave, Hautes Alpes, France, Showing the Ultradauphinois Thrust
Belt, the southern termination of the Ultradauphinois Thrust Nappe, consisting of Jurassic and
Eocene sedimentary sequences resting on Pelvoux basement and overlain by the lower internal
nappes of the sub-Brianconnais Zone (based in part on 1/50 000 sheet no. 798 published by
BRGM) Thrusts in the Jurassic are ornamented by solid triangles; they die out across the northern
margin of the map into folds. Other thrusts are ornamented by open triangles and lettered as
follows: CCM—La Meije Thrust; CCA—Arsine Thrust; CCC—Combeynot Thrust; CCSB—basal
sub-Brianconnais Thrust. The dashed line in the flysch represents the position below which the
flysch is strongly and penetratively deformed; the cleavage here is close to bedding and a stretching
lineation generally plunges SE.

Jurassic stratigraphy, overlain by Eocene
flysch, not affected or duplicated by imbricate
thrusts, and recording a low penetrative strain,
resting on a thick, strongly deformed Triassic
gypsum layer. The westerly movement of this
part of the nappe, over a basement surface of
unknown dip, was thus accomplished by deformation of the basal gypsum. The Jurassic sequence thins and the gypsum dies out rapidly
southwards. Thus the southern end of the
thrust nappe (Fig. 1) is not only affected by the
absence of the weak basal gypsum, but also by
an increase in the dip (to the NE) of the
basement surface as it rises to the upfaulted
northern margin of the Pelvoux Massif (Fig. 1).
The Faulting occurred prior to nappe movement
(Bartoli et al. 1974). The presence of a strong

penetrative deformation throughout the Jurassic
sequence and the complex imbrication of this
sequence is attributed to these factors.

It is considered that in the absence of a basal
gypsum, the whole of the (much thinner)
Jurassic sequence, dominated by shale and
with no horizons of high competence contrast,
acted as the weak basal layer to the nappe of
Eocene flysch. In addition it is suggested that
during the early stages of nappe movement,
the autochthonous cover along the northern
margin of the basement underwent penetrative
strain due to forward spreading up the
steepened basement surface (cf. Price 1973;
Elliott 1976a, b; Ramberg 1977; Chapple
1978), these strains decreasing in intensity
away from the basement in the NE direction

(i.e. as observed up the thrust sequence now). Furthermore as the central part of the nappe continued to move westwards, the southern margin was increasingly hindered by the up-faulted basement, and the more easterly parts of the Jurassic (para-) autochthon underwent a NW–SE stretching and a NE–SW shortening as the central part of the nappe moved more freely. The intensity of this strain decreases down the thrust sequence and is absent in the autochthon. Thus the uppermost thrust slices record a NW–SE stretching and the auto-chthon a NE–SW stretching. The transition from one to the other is reflected by the gradual change in orientation of the X direc-tion (stretching lineation) and the XY plane (assumed parallel to the slaty cleavage) of the finite strain ellipsoid and is recorded on Fig. 1.

The postulated hindrance by the upfaulted basement not only caused a change in the type of ductile strain in the Jurassic rocks, but also is considered to have resulted in the initiation of localized heterogeneous strain and the even-tual formation of thrust surfaces as the incom-patibility between the arrested southern end of the nappe and the still moving central portion increased. The analogy (Elliott 1976a) of thrusts propagating as screw dislocations, northward from this hindrance, and dying out as the displacement is transferred to the basal gypsum, seems valid.

Ductile deformation and fabrics

Deformation of the Jurassic rocks occurred by a pressure solution mechanism throughout the sequence, producing penetrative fabrics by grain to grain solution and grain overgrowth in the limestone beds and slaty cleavage in the shales. Stretching lineations within the cleav-age are recorded by oriented fossil debris (spines etc.) in the limestones, and deformed chlorite spots in the shales. Strain measure-ments have been made using extended belem-nites which are often abundant in the Lower Lias limestone-shale facies. These provide data on the actual changes in dimensions in the plane of the bedding.

In the present-day autochthonous sequence, a flat lying cleavage is seen dipping to the NE slightly more steeply than bedding. This cleav-age contains a strong down dip stretching line-ation (Fig. 1). Higher up in the sequence of thrusts, the cleavage steepens until it makes an angle of 40–50° with bedding, still dipping NE or overturned and dipping SW, while the stretching lineation gradually changes to a SE

plunge (Fig. 1). This SE lineation is continuous into the basal part of the overlying flysch. The magnitude of the maximum extension $(1 + e_1)$ in the plane of the bedding varies from up to 8.0 in the autochthon to between 1.5 and 3.0 in the upper thrust slices (Fig. 1). Values of $1 + e_2$ in the bedding plane are usually about 1.0 decreasing to 0.7 in the upper thrust slices. This ductile strain is present throughout the Jurassic sequence. The magnitude varies con-tinuously throughout these rocks, and dies out rapidly into the underlying Triassic limestones. Strains in the Jurassic shales and within the deformation zones described in the next sec-tion are thought to be more intense than in the Lower Lias limestone-shale facies where the extended belemnites are found.

The strains in the autochthon beneath the lowermost thrust are not consistent with a deformation accomplished entirely by simple shear parallel to bedding plane since the bed-ding is itself a plane of intense strain. Thinning of the limestone shale facies of up to 85% (assuming no volume change) is implied. This type of strain cannot maintain continuity with the underlying undeformed rocks and may be characteristic of the forward edge of a gravity spreading sheet. As explained, the ductile strain in what are now the upper thrust sheets built up in a different way and involved a component of rearward compressive (shorten-ing) strain. This is an example of the mechan-ism proposed by Chapple (1978) whereby the surface slope of a nappe may be increased to maintain its forward motion.

The development of inhomogeneous deformation zones

During the evolution of the thrust belt there was a transition from the distributed, penetra-tive strain described above to a brittle defor-mation on discrete thrust surfaces. This transi-tion is recorded in the development of numer-ous deformation zones. These are the first expression of the developing incompatibility from S to N in the thrust nappe and represent the beginning of imbrication and stratigraphic repetition of the Jurassic sequence. The forma-tion of heterogeneous deformation zones over-laps with the penetrative ductile strain.

The deformation zones are easy to recognize—they are characterized by swarms of variably deformed quartz—carbonate veins, and demonstrably represent thust zones where

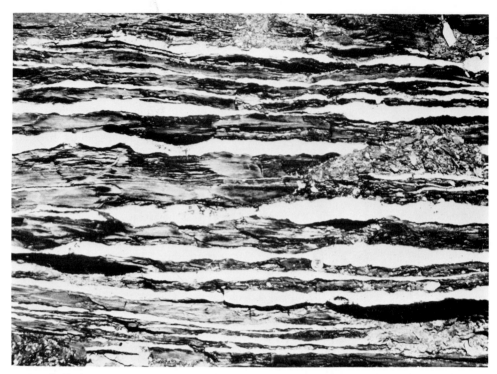

FIG. 2. Typical zone of intense deformation characterized by abundant quartz-carbonate veins parallel to the cleavage. This zone is about 90 cm. wide, consisting of approximately 35% vein material, and the slate above and below is barren of veins for several metres until the next deformation zones are encountered.

they separate the characteristic Lower Lias limestone shale facies from underlying younger shales. The veins are laterally very extensive and run subparallel to the slaty cleavage, occurring singly or in groups of up to 20 subparallel veins in zones up to 3 m wide, separated by 5–40 m of barren slate. Vein minerals constitute between 30 and 40% (by volume) of the material in these zones. A typical example is illustrated in Fig. 2. Such zones are common in many areas of low grade metamorphism and slate development, and can still be identified when such rocks has been further deformed and metamorphosed.

The slaty cleavage is often cut by irregularities along the margins of veins in these zones and by the blunt often rectangular ends of the veins (Fig. 3); however, the veins are just as frequently strongly deformed by the cleavage into pinch and swell shapes (Fig. 3). These rather ambiguous relations are interpreted as indicating that the veins developed towards the end of a period of ductile strain, but were affected and modified by continued strong deformation in these zones. Such zones

are also the preferred sites for the development of folds deforming the slaty cleavage and for the formation of crenulation cleavage. The veins are often folded by these structures, but may also truncate them, and continued development of veins during localized ductile strain is implied.

Field studies indicate that the veins developed by very large, lateral extension, opening and infilling of short, subvertical cross-cleavage boudin necks within the slates. The veins evolved through a rectangular geometry into strongly modified and elongated pinch and swell shapes, with modified boudin slate-vein interfaces. These commonly observed features necessitate the occurrence of slip on the cleavage surfaces bounding the original boudin (Fig. 3). In his model of thrust development, Price (1977) interpreted abundant sub-horizontal concordant veins at thrust surfaces as hydraulic fractures in which the fluid pressure jacked up the overburden during thrusting; unfortunately, there is no description of the geometrical relations of these veins with which to compare those described here. Careful field

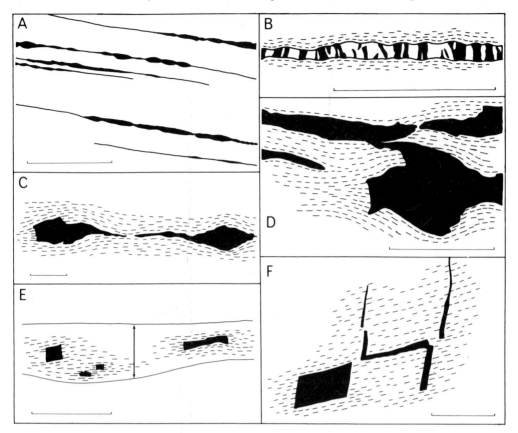

FIG. 3. Details showing the geometry of veins in deformation zones such as that illustrated in Fig. 2; all are drawn from photographs and the scale bar in each represents 10 cm. With the exception of *B*, the veins are shown completely black, and with the exception of *A*, the trace of the cleavage is shown around the veins only by thin dashed lines. *A*. Extreme thinning and development of pinch and swell in early veins parallel to the cleavage. *B*. An early vein (probably parallel to bedding and possibly pretectonic in origin) of dark grey calcite (shown black) subsequently boudinaged, with the necks filled with white calcite and quartz (uncoloured). The extension of these veins can be measured in the same way as for extended belemnites—in this example, $1 + e = 2.0$. *C*. Pinch and swell structure in a typical vein in a zone, also showing truncation of the cleavage at the left-hand end. *D*. Irregular vein geometry commonly observed to consist of parts where the cleavage is truncated, with here a modified boudin interface in the slate, and cleavage wrapped around a swell. *E*. A zone of deformation defined by numerous very thin cleavage parallel veins (not shown, but the width of the zone is indicated by the arrows) and containing unmodified rectangular veins formed by extension and accompanied by marginal slip on the cleavage. These veins formed late in the deformation and are considered to represent the geometry from which the much modified veins in *C* and *D* developed. *F*. A combination of rectangular geometry as in *E*, and vertical cross-cleavage extension veins, both formed late in the deformation and showing how the vertical growth of extension fractures is no longer limited by discontinuity and slip on the cleavage in the closing stages of the deformation.

observation in the Ultradauphinois Thrust Belt suggests that the veins did not develop as concordant hydraulic fractures, but rather by the process of extension described. Thus it may not be possible to use Price's (1977) model as a basis for the interpretation of the Ultradauphinois Thrust Belt in the area described. Furthermore, the veins studied do not show the vertically developed fibres that would characterize horizontal hydraulic fractures by which the overburden was jacked up (cf. Shearman *et al.* 1972); the vein infilling is usually massive quartz and carbonate—where elongate 'fibrous' crystal growth occurs (e.g. in Fig. 3B) it is developed parallel to the wall of the vein as lateral extension occurs. The quartz and carbonate probably originated locally within or close to the deformation zones (e.g. Kerrich *et al.* 1978) as a result of pressure solution and low grade metamorphism in the slates (cf. Beach 1979).

The extension direction recorded by the original slate boudins and that recorded by their subsequent opening and stretching is generally NW–SE and clearly relates to the extension of the rocks as thrusting developed due to the hindrance of the upfaulted basement block. The generally later formed second folds and cleavages have an asymmetry implying movement from SE to NW which is consistent with this interpretation.

The development of discrete thrust faults

The continued localization of deformation eventually resulted in the production of entirely discrete and brittle surfaces of movement—thrust faults. Small scale flat lying shear surfaces are common within the movement zones discussed above, and usually deform and displace the veins and the second folds and cleavages, and are thus inferred as a record of the last stages of the deformation. Similarly, large scale thrust surfaces are also late stage structures. Thrust faults clearly truncate the first folds, seen in the limestone shale facies, to which the main slaty cleavage is axial planar.

Disrupted slices of Triassic rock occur along the thrust faults, and in some the fault breccias known as cargneules (Warrak 1974) are seen. These breccias usually contain fragments of Liassic limestone with strong ductile strain fabrics and veins, and abundant fragments of slate. Thrust faults also truncate the main cleavage in the Lower Lias of the underlying thrust sheet. Thus it is considered that the discrete thrust faults characterized by the presence of isolated strips of Triassic material along them represent the latest structures to develop in the thrust belt.

Summary

A complex thrust belt evolved as the movement of the external autochthonous cover was hindered by the upfaulted Pelvoux basement. The whole of the Jurassic sequence present acted as the deforming basal layer, undergoing penetrative ductile strain first at its leading edge due to forward spreading and thinning, and subsequently, as the resistance to movement increased, by rearward compression and lateral extension. Ductile strain gradually became concentrated in more discrete movement zones causing imbrication of the stratigraphy, and eventually thrust surfaces developed as brittle strain features, the last stage in a continuous sequence of deformation.

ACKNOWLEDGMENT. This work is part of a NERC supported research project and grant GR3/3472 is gratefully acknowledged.

References

BARTOLI, F. PECHER, A. & VIALON, P. 1974. Le chevauchement Meije-Muzelle et la repartition des domaines structuraux alpins du massif de l'Oisans. *Geol. Alpine,* **50,** 17–26.

BEACH, A. 1979. Pressure solution as a metamorphic process in deformed terrigenous sedimentary rocks. *Lithos,* **12,** 51–8.

CHAPPLE, W. M. 1978. Mechanics of thin-skinned fold- and thrust-belts. *Bull. geol. Soc. Am.* **89,** 1189–98.

DAHLSTROM, C. D. A. 1970. Structural geology in the eastern margin of the Canadian Rockies. *Bull. Can. Pet. Geol.* **18,** 332–406.

ELLIOTT, D. 1976a. The energy balance and deformation mechanisms of thrust sheets. *Philos. Trans. R. Soc. London,* **A283,** 289–312.

—— 1976b. The motion of thrust sheets. *J. geophys. Res.* **81,** 949–63.

KERRICH, R., BECKINSALE, R. D. & SHACKLETON, N. J. 1978. The physical and hydrothermal regime of tectonic vein systems: evidence from stable isotope and fluid inclusion studies. *Neues Jahrb. Mineral. Abhandlungen,* **131,** 225–39.

PRICE, N. J. 1977. Aspects of gravity tectonics and the development of listric faults. *J. geol. Soc. London,* **133,** 311–27.

PRICE, R. A. 1973. Large scale gravitational flow of supracrustal rocks, southern Canadian Rockies. *In* DE JONG, K. A. & SCHOLTEN, R. (eds), *Gravity and Tectonics.* 491–502. Wiley, New York.

RAMBERG, H. 1977. Some remarks on the mechanism of nappe movement. *Forh. geol. Foren. Stockholm,* **99,** 110–7.

RAMSAY, J. G. 1963. Stratigraphy, structure and metamorphism of the western Alps. *Proc. Geol. Assoc. London,* **74,** 357–91.

SHEARMAN, D. J., MOSSOP, G., DUNSMORE, H. & MARTON, M. 1972. Origin of gypsum veins by hydraulic fracture. *Trans. Instn. Ming. Metall.* **81,** B149–55.

WARRAK, M. 1974. The petrography and origin of dedolomitized, weinded or brecciated carbonate rocks, the 'cornieules', in the Frejus region, French Alps, *J. geol. Soc. London,* **130,** 229–47.

A. BEACH, Department of Geology, The University, Liverpool, L69 3BX.

Gravity sliding in the Maritime Alps

R. H. Graham

SUMMARY: Fallot's 'intercutaneous' Tinée Nappes are interpreted as gravity slides initiated by uplift of the Argentera Massif and emplaced partly by the ductile deformation of slate horizons, and partly by movement on discrete shear planes. Together, the structures stack between 8 and 11 km of Jurassic and Lower Cretaceous strata—the telescoped cover of the Argentera Massif. The lowest nappe is the furthest travelled.

Sliding on a larger scale may have contributed to shortening in the more external parts of Provence.

In general, deformation in Alpes Maritimes is less intense and complicated than it is elsewhere in the western Alps. The nappe structures of the external zones of the Maritime Alps, which form the subject of this paper, are smaller, simpler and less far travelled structures than the Helvetic Nappes which occupy an analogous structural position (immediately external of the massifs) 250 km away around the Alpine Arc.

The structures discussed here are located in the country SW of the Argentera Massif, between the Tinée and Var rivers (Figs 1 & 2). Particular attention is paid to the area around the village of Roya 44°12′ 5°11′ where nappe structures, thrusting and stratigraphic duplication have been perceptively described by Fallot (1949), and Fallot & Faure-Muret (1949 c, d). Fallot called the structures here 'intercutaneous' because, although he considered them to post-date the deposition of the whole stratigraphic sequence, he saw that they duplicate only the lower part of it, and that Upper Cretaceous rocks overlie the duplications as an unbroken cover (an 'envelope' in Fallot's terminology; one might nowadays refer to the structures as 'blind').

Geological background

General stratigraphy and structure

Alpes Maritimes has a 'tectonic stratigraphy' of basement, autochthon and allochthon similar to that seen elsewhere in the Alps (Figs 2 & 3). Crystalline basement rocks cropping out in the Argentera Massif show Alpine faulting and cataclasis superimposed on Hercynian ductile deformation. Lying unconformably on the basement are autochthonous Permian clastic sediments with upright folds and steeply dipping cleavage (shortening which is taken up in fault zones or by cataclastic deformation in the crystalline basement). The Permian sequence begins with sandstones and passes up into 1 km of red slates. Permian rocks crop out on the S side of the Argentera Massif and in an inlier known as the Dôme de Barrot some 10 km S of the massif proper.

A thin basal Trias (Werfenian) quartzite, locally unconformable on lower formations (Graham 1978 b), forms the top unit of the autochthon. Above it are thin shales with gypsum overlain by a massive dolomite (100 m thick, but highly variable), then a thin sequence of alternating limestone and shale bands which passes up into the Lias. Commonly the shaly horizons above and below the dolomite are converted to cavenous breccia (cargneule), and the dolomite itself is also locally brecciated. The cargneules are the lowest and most important of a number of décollement horizons. In regional terms the lower one marks the boundary between the autochthon and overlying allochthonous or decollé Mesozoic rocks. The cleavage of the autochthon does not penetrate the higher unit. In some places deformation dies out within the Permian red pelites, in others (e.g. SW of Isola, in the Vionene valley) the lower cargneule is involved in the folds of the autochthon (e.g. A, Fig. 3). Some folds in the dolomite are harmonic with autochthon folds, (cf. Bordet 1949), others are not (points B and C respectively, Fig. 3) but all the structures above the dolomite are independent of those below.

Stratigraphy above the Trias

Triassic dolomite and cargneule are succeded by Jurassic and Cretaceous limestone and shale/slate formations which vary considerably in thickness across the region. The main mapable formations are given in Table 1, their approximate stratigraphic limits are inferred from 1:50 000 and 1:80 000 B.R.G.M. maps since the author has made no palaeontological study. Thicknesses given are the maxima in the

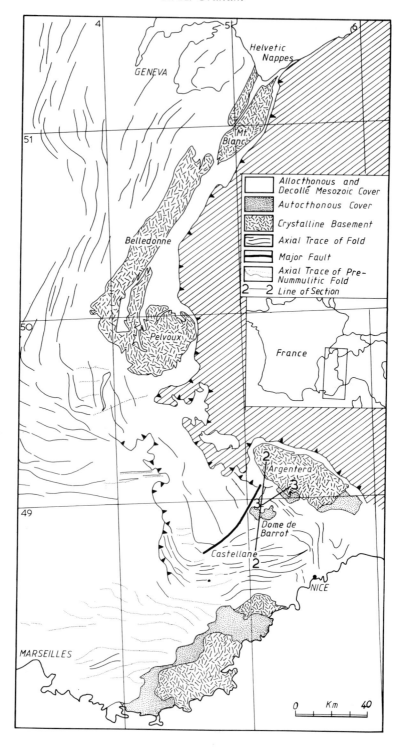

FIG. 1. Location map.

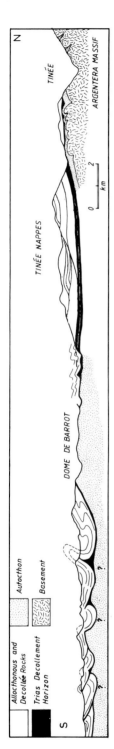

FIG. 2. Generalized section from the Sub-Alpine chains of Haute Provence.

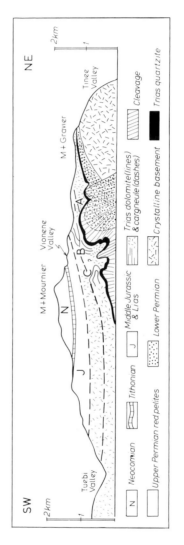

FIG. 3. Relations between autochthon and allochthonous Mesozoic cover on the SW border of the Argentera Massif. Note overstep of basal Trias quartzite (heavy black line) over underlying Permian.

TABLE 1.

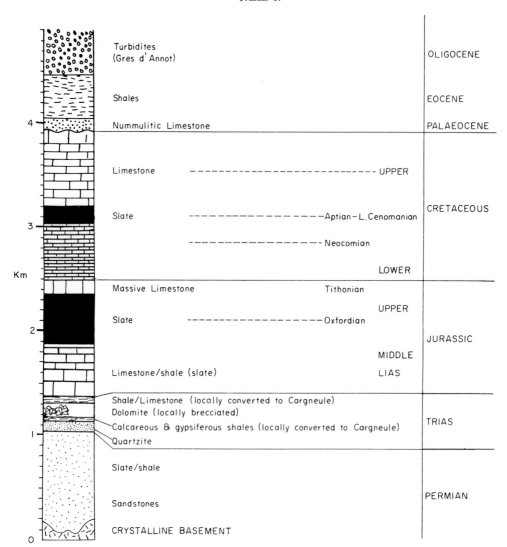

ground between the Tinée and the Var. The total thickness is over 3 km. Most passages from one formation to another are gradational.

Structures above the Trias

'Thin-Skin' tectonics prevail in the Mesozoic rocks of Alpes Maritimes and Provence. Structures are controlled by décollement horizons in the Trias (Cargneules) and Cretaceous (Aptian shale/slate) and to a lesser extent the Jurassic (Oxfordian shale/slate). Two distinctly different kinds of structure exist. Remote from the Argentera Massif, in the country S and W of the Dôme de Barrot, the dominant structures are asymmetrical but essentially upright folds associated with reverse faults and thrusts (Figs 1 & 2). N and E of the Dôme de Barrot, adjacent to the massif, are found the stratigraphic duplications associated with recumbent folds and sub-horizontal cleavage, which form the main topic of the present paper.

Fig. 2 shows the spatial relationship between the two kinds of structures. Bordet (1949) suggested that the upright structures were produced by shortening at the front of a gravity-slide sheet, and the similarity between the section and the models of Blay et al. (1977)

or the diagrams of Price (1977) is evident. There is a distinct possibility that the Mesozoic and Tertiary cover of Provence slid *en masse* on the Trias and that the upright folds, listric reversed faults and thrusts of the Sub-Alpine chains in Provence developed at the front of the moving sheet. However the main concern of this paper is with smaller scale nappe structures near the Argentera Massif (The Tinée Nappes) which would lie within any larger scale translated rock mass. The movement direction of these nappes is judged from the general orientation of their fronts, from the orientation of stretching lineation in the tail of the lower nappe, and from the asymmetry and the general orientation of the hinges of associated minor folds. Use of these last two criteria involve an assumption of ductile deformation associated with nappe movement.

The Tinée Nappes

As Fallot (1949) pointed out, the Tinée Nappes are known only because erosion has cut through their apparently undisturbed envelope. Except at the nappe fronts, the envelope itself gives no clue to the presence of the structures beneath.

Erosion is deepest in the Roya valley S of St Etienne de Tinée, a window into crystalline basement through the whole nappe pile. NW of the Roya, successively higher stratigraphic units are encountered (the result of regional updoming on a NE–SW axis), and the duplications of the Tinée are buried.

The main tectonic units of the Tinée area are shown on Figs 4 & 5. The lowest stratigraphic duplication is the Roya Nappe whose basal movement plane contours the Roya valley, and whose front is visible above the village of Les Tourres in the Barlatte valley (44°10′30″ 6°50′34″) and on the S side of Montagne de l'Alp (Fig. 6). The Roya Nappe is the structure figured in Fallot's (1949) cross sections of the area SW of the Tinée. It repeats stratigraphy between the Trias and the Aptian.

The basal movement plane is almost flat, cutting gently up section from Trias to Lower Cretaceous in both the hanging-wall and the foot-wall. E of the present outcrop, movement was probably parallel to bedding in the Trias. In current terminology, the Roya Nappe is a hanging-wall ramp. Its foot-wall is a ramp in the NE part of the outcrop, but southwest wards and with a concomitant decrease in dip it changes to a bedding parallel flat. Fallot, of course, did not use this terminology, but his

sections and text clearly show that he appreciated the geometry.

The front of a Higher Tinée Nappe is visible below Mt Rion (44°12′50″ 6°52′) and Mt Riounet, (44°12′50″ 6°52′90″) and in the Valon de Demandols (Fig. 7). For the length of its exposure on Mt Riounet this structure is a hanging-wall ramp in Oxfordian to Lower Cretaceous on a foot-wall ramp in Neocomian, Aptian and Upper Cretaceous. On the N side of the Demandols valley, behind the hanging-wall ramp no duplication is evident (Fallot called this sort of situation, 'false autochthon').

The highest stratigraphic duplication in the Tinée area is visible on the top of Mt Chavalet, (44°12′40″ 6°54′) N of Roya, but exposure is very limited and the structure is not discussed further in this paper. The base of the Upper Cretaceous is invariably a movement plane which is locally discordant to structures beneath—probably one should refer to an 'Upper Cretaceous nappe' although no significant stratigraphic repetition is involved.

A major listric normal fault running from the Pas de Roya (44°11′30″ 6°34′) through the Col de Crous (44°9′50″ 6°54′) and down the Tuebi valley marks the eastern boundary of another translated rock mass—the Col de Crous unit (Figs 8 & 9). No stratigraphic duplication is involved, but the Col de Crous fault interferes with the Roya Nappe, increasing its displacement and causing marked thinning of formations at the Pas de Roya (Figs 5, 6 & 9).

Slices of Tithonian limestone lie out of stratigraphic sequence beneath both the Higher & Lower Tinée Nappes. One forms the summit of Les Donnes, 44°15′20″ 6°54′30″, the other is visible on the N side of the Roya valley.

Amounts of displacement

Fallot (1949) estimated 15–20 km of translation of the cover on the SW side of the Argentera Massif. Fallot & Faure-Muret (1949 *b*) suggest 20 km for the movement of the whole cover and 6 km for the Roya Nappe at Pas de Roya, (decreasing SE-wards).

Amounts of displacement are most easily estimated by piecing together disrupted Tithonian limestone in the movement direction, and on this basis Fallot & Faure-Muret's estimates for movement of the Roya Nappe are easily confirmed. In the northern part of its outcrop (within the Col de Crous Unit) the Roya Nappe has moved 6 km (Tithonian at the nappe front at Les Tourres matched with

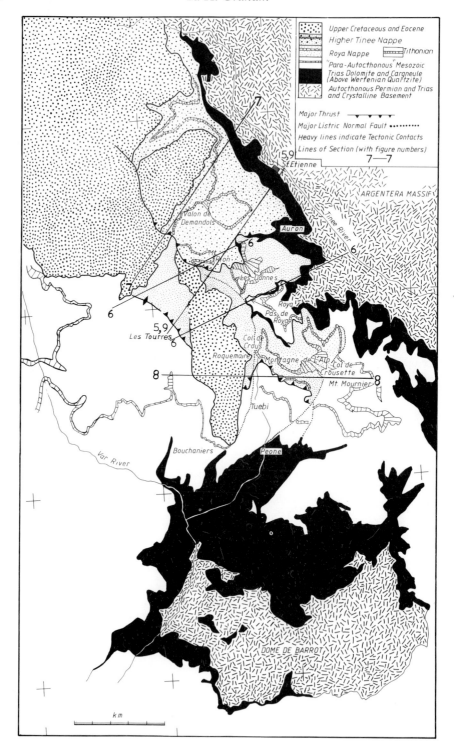

FIG. 4. Map of the area SW of the Argentera Massif. Showing the main tectonic units and locating the sections.

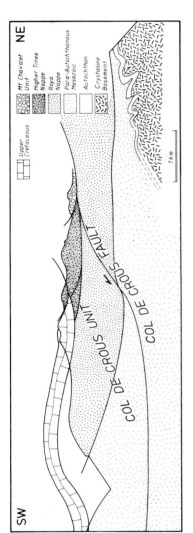

FIG. 5. Generalized section through the Tinée area naming the main tectonic units.

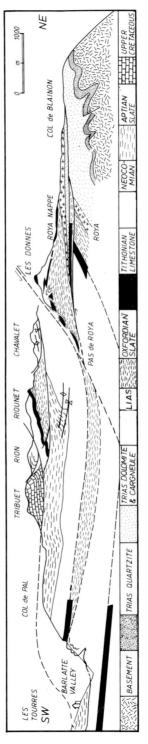

FIG. 6. Compilation of sections on the N side of the Roya valley and SW of Auron. Note listric normal faults below the Tithonian on Mt. Rionnet and above Pas de Roya, and discordant base of Upper Cretaceous.

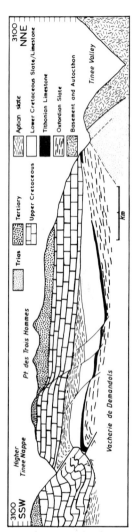

FIG. 7. Section along NW side of Demandols valley. Note listric normal faults of two ages and discordant base of Upper Cretaceous, and doubling of Cretaceous thickness in the foot-wall of the Higher Tinée Nappe front. For interpretation see Fig. 12.

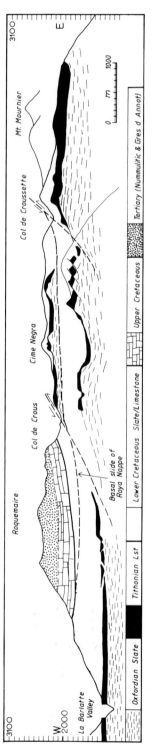

FIG. 8. Section from Mounier to Roquemaire. Note listric normal faults.

Tithonian below the basal movement plane at Roya). Assuming the structure at Les Tourres to be the genuine nappe front (not merely a splay from a main thrust) this figure represents the real displacement of the Roya Nappe at this point, not a minimum.

E of the Col de Crous fault, measured between Montagne de l'Alp and the Roya valley, the movement on the Roya Nappe (now a minimum estimate) is about 3 km. The present author does not agree with Fallot & Faure-Muret (1949 *a*) that movement on the Roya Nappe dies out completely at the Col de Crousette. True, 1 km S of Roya (44°11′ 5°10′) apparently para-autochthonous Tithonian becomes the Tithonian of the nappe, but this is merely the differential erosion of the nappe tail.

The Higher Tinée Nappe has moved between a minimum of 1.7 km and maximum of 3 km (uncertainty is created by inadequate exposure near Auron). The imbricate slab below the Higher Nappe has moved a minimum of 1.5 km, to a maximum of 3 km, and that below the Tinée Nappe has moved about 0.5 km.

Excluding the topmost unit on Mt Chavalet, between 9.7 and 12.5 km (11 km average) of strata are stacked in the Tinée Nappes—at least this is true locally around Roya— the way the amount of movement varies laterally is uncertain because of lack of exposure.

Minor structures

A NE–SW trending lineation is visible on cleavage surfaces in the NE part (the tail) of the Roya Nappe (Fig. 10, 1). The structure is both a bedding/cleavage intersection and a stretching direction. The cleavage is strong. At the nappe front stretching lineation is not usually visible—in some places a NW–SE trending pencil cleavage can be seen, in others a bedding/cleavage intersection is visible (trending in the same direction), in still others one sees only cleavage. The cleavage is weaker than in the tail of the nappe.

Minor fold hinges in the Roya Nappe are highly variable in orientation in detail, though tend to run generally NW–SE at the front of the Roya Nappe and nearer NE–SW in the nappe tail (Fig. 10, 2 & 3). It is tempting to associate this phenomenon with higher strain in the nappe tail and rotation towards the stretching (movement) direction. While this may be true in the Oxfordian slates, it cannot be the general case, for the orientation also exists in massive limestone lithologies (Tithonian, Neocomian) where the stain is clearly

very weak. Evidently fold hinges and intersection lineations were generated near parallel with the stretching direction in the area around Roya.

In the Higher Tinée Nappe cleavage is not usually so intense as in the Roya Nappe, and no stretching lineation is visible. This may relate to greater displacement of the Roya Nappe and implies that the two structures have travelled together, (piggy-back fashion). Linear structures in this nappe are shown in Fig. 10 (4).

The nappe fronts

The front of the Tinée Nappe is visible on the S side of Crete de Montagne de l'Alp, and in a window on the E side of the Barlatte valley near Les Tourres. Between these two localities it is hidden by Upper Cretaceous rocks, draped over the nappe front as an asymmetrical anticline where the hanging-wall ramp of the Tinée Nappe ends and movement switches a higher bedding parallel décollement in Aptian slates.

At Les Tourres, Aptian and Neocomian formations beneath the thrust plane are intensely folded, the folds dying out upwards towards the anticlinal drape (Fig. 11). Problematically, there is no obvious break in the fold trains which succeed the Tithonian outcrop laterally (at the tips of the eroded window). Various possible interpretations exist for the Les Tourres structures, some are shown on Fig. 11. Interpretation B implies that the Roya Nappe has moved more than 6 km.

An important change of trend takes place N of Les Tourres where NW–SE folds associated with the nappe front swing into an E–W orientation which persists westwards for some distance (across the Var Valley). Movement on the Col de Crous structure may have contributed to this change of trend, E of the fault the orientation again comes close to E–W.

Structures at the front of the Upper Tinée Nappe are also complex. In the Demandols valley (Fig. 7) the basal movement plane (or, more likely, a reversed splay from it) throws Tithonian and Lower Cretaceous formations against Upper Cretaceous rocks. The Upper Cretaceous is doubled in thickness in the footwall of the thrust, but the base of the overlying Nummulitic limestone maintains more or less constant level across the structure. The base of the Upper Cretaceous is discordant to underlying Aptian and Neocomian strata and cuts across listric normal faults (dipping and downthrowing NE) in these rocks. Fig. 12 gives a suggested interpretation for all these

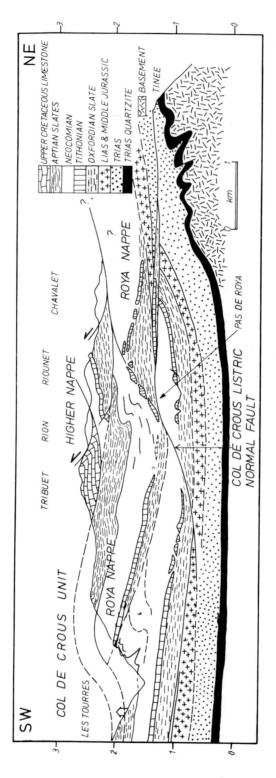

FIG. 9. Compilation of Tinée Nappes in downplunge section. For interpretations of the Roya Nappe front at Les Tourres see Fig. 11.

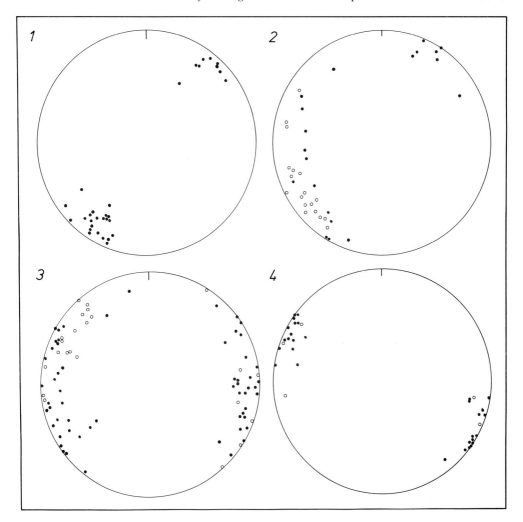

FIG. 10. Stereograms showing the orientation of linear structures in the area SW of Argentera. 1. Stretching directions in the tail of the Roya Nappe. 2. Fold hinges (open circles) and bedding/cleavage intersection in the tail of the Roya Nappe (Roya). 3. Fold hinges (open circles) and bedding/cleavage intersection at the front of the Roya Nappe (Les Toures and S of Montagne de l'Alp). 4. Fold hinges (open circles) and bedding/cleavage intersection in the Higher Tinée Nappe.

phenomena in a sequence where movement on a listric reverse splay is later transferred to the base of the Upper Cretaceous. An alternative possibility is that movement preceded deposition of the Nummulitic limestone, but even though the unconformity at the base of the Nummulitic lends some credence to this idea, it is rejected on regional grounds. The significance of these particular listric normal faults is not fully understood.

Listric normal faults

Small scale listric normal faults are common throughout the Tinée area. Movement planes which cut down section in the movement direction are visible on Mt. Rionet (Fig. 6), at Pas de Roya (Fig. 6) and at the Col de Crousette (Fig. 8).

In addition to minor structures, two large scale listric normal faults cut the nappes—one

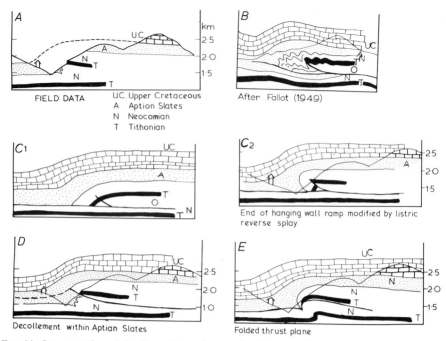

FIG. 11. Interpretation of the Roya Nappe front at Les Tourres. C_1 and C_2 are in sequence. The village of Les Tourres is marked.

passes through the Col de Crousette (48°8′ 6°57′), E of which the Roya Nappe is not exposed, another runs from Pas de Roya through the Col de Crous and down the Tuebi valley. The Col de Crous structure drops Upper Cretaceous and Tertiary Rocks to exposure level on Roquemaire, and these rocks face Jurassic formations across the Col (Fig. 8).

The Col de Crous and Col de Crousette Faults find décollement in the Trias—hence their apparent abrupt terminations on the B.R.G.M. maps on the Tinée region. Both structures involve considerable ductile strain and formations are thinned and highly deformed in the movement zones. 400 m. of Jurassic rocks are thinned to a few metres by the Col de Crous structure (Figs 6 & 9). Competent Tithonian limestone is thinned, boudinaged, strung out into rubble or smeared out altogether in the movement zones. No significant internal strain is visible in this particularly competent rock type, and thinning seems to have been accomplished by the slip of lensoid beds over each other.

The total downthrow on the listric fault system is 1100 m. The horizontal movement cannot be estimated because no significant stratigraphic duplication is involved. A gap in the outcrop of the 'authochthonous' Tithonian of about 0.5 km (across the Tubei valley) repres-

ents the minimum horizontal ductile extension.

E of the Crousette Fault, 'para-autochthonous' Necomian rocks reach an elevation of 2800 m on Mt Mournier. Presumably the Roya Nappe once lay above this, but has been removed by erosion (except for one small klippe). Mt Mournier forms part of a NE–SW trending elevated zone which also includes the Permian inlier of the Dôme de Barrot. The Col de Crousette and Col de Crous structures, and the regional NW dip are all assumed to have formed in response to the elevation of this zone rather than to elevation of the Argentera Massif itself. A ductile listric normal fault more or less continuous with the Col de Crous structure runs SW from here as far as Castellane (Fig. 1). Gypsiferous Trias is locally diapiric along it, and displaced slabs of Nummulitic limestone lie to the NW of it. N–S trending listric normal faults occur N, but not S of this line.

Time relationships of the nappes

In general higher nappes cut lower ones—the Roya Nappe is cut by the Higher Tinée Nappe which is in turn cut by the structure on Mt Chavalet. The Upper Cretaceous 'nappe' cuts

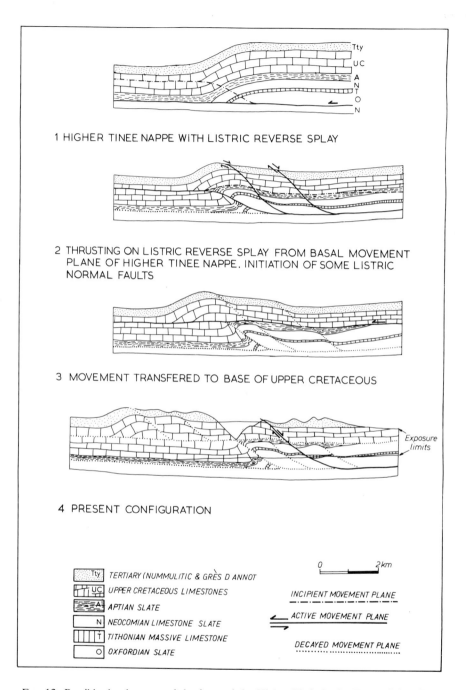

1 HIGHER TINEE NAPPE WITH LISTRIC REVERSE SPLAY

2 THRUSTING ON LISTRIC REVERSE SPLAY FROM BASAL MOVEMENT PLANE OF HIGHER TINEE NAPPE. INITIATION OF SOME LISTRIC NORMAL FAULTS

3 MOVEMENT TRANSFERED TO BASE OF UPPER CRETACEOUS

4 PRESENT CONFIGURATION

Exposure limits

Tty	TERTIARY (NUMMULITIC & GRÈS D ANNOT
UC	UPPER CRETACEOUS LIMESTONES
A	APTIAN SLATE
N	NEOCOMIAN LIMESTONE SLATE
T	TITHONIAN MASSIVE LIMESTONE
O	OXFORDIAN SLATE

0   2 km

INCIPIENT MOVEMENT PLANE

ACTIVE MOVEMENT PLANE

DECAYED MOVEMENT PLANE

FIG. 12. Possible development of the front of the Higher Tinée in the Demandols valley.

stratigraphy in both the Roya Nappe and the Higher Tinée Nappe (Fig. 7). At the same time, the intensity of deformation undoubtably increases downwards. The cleavage and stretching lineation in Oxfordian and Neocomian slates near the base of the Roya Nappe are noticeably stronger than those of the equivalent formations in the Higher Tinée Nappe (unfortunately there are no strain markers). Presumably these facts are explained by higher nappes which travelled "piggy-back" fashion on lower ones after their emplacement.

The emplacement of the nappes and their relationship with the massif

Fallot (1949) recognized that his 'intercutaneous' thrusts formed within cover which was slipping en masse (Fig. 13). He considered that they were initiated by some irregularity ('grippage') in the basal décollement plane which held back the lower levels of the gliding cover. He saw that his structures died out upwards but reference to a discrete higher level of décollement is obscure.

On the question of the ultimate cause of nappe movement Fallot favoured gravity slid-

ing from the Argentera Massif while Goguel (1949) suggested a push from the internal zones.

There are, of course, three possibilities: the nappes could pre-date the elevation of the massif (Fig. 15), they could have slid from a rising massif (Fig. 16), or they could have been translated over an existing massif. There is no totally convincing evidence for any argument. The title of this paper betrays the author's belief that the weight of evidence lies on the side of gravity sliding. Significant arguments are as follows:

Slope

Price (1973) has pointed out that most low angle thrust faults have always sloped in the wrong direction for gravity sliding, but the argument seems inapplicable in the Maritime Alps. The present-day watershed of the Argentera Massif is about 3 km high, with an average 10° slope over 6—7 km to the NE of nappe exposure. The present-day orientation of the principal ramps of the Tinée Nappes is horizontal while the 'flats' dip away from the massif.

Whether or not these dips existed when the nappes formed is, of course, uncertain. One can only point out that the Argentera Massif has had a tendency to be positive through the

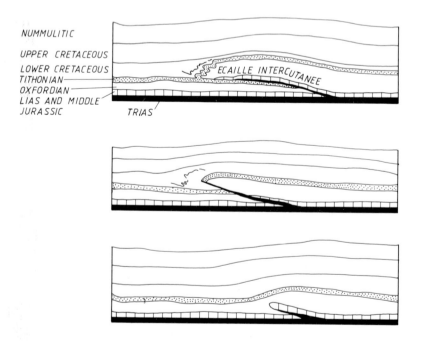

FIG. 13. Fallot's interpretation of the development of an 'intercutaneous' nappe.

geological history of the area—(e.g. the Trias quartzite oversteps underlying Permian towards basement).

Shape and strain state of the nappes

Stratigraphic thinning associated with higher strain towards the backs of the nappes (giving a 'tear drop' shape to the Roya Nappe) might be expected if they had slid from the massif like large scale rotational landslips (Fig. 14). Equally, however, the shape and strain state would be visible if the nappes were horses in a duplex re-oriented by the later elevation of the massif (Fig. 15) or by their passage across the massif. There is nothing conclusive here.

Stratal length

The nappes telescope about 11 km of Jurassic and Cretaceous strata at Roya. In addition, about 15 km of Triassic stratigraphy appears to be duplicated between the massif and the Dome de Barrot, making 24 km of slipped cover in total. 6–7 km of basement separates the backs of the nappes from the Argentera watershed, while the total width of massif here is about 20 km. The amount of Alpine shortening of the basement is difficult to assess—one is dealing with polyphase crystalline rocks re-deformed by faulting or more general cataclasis, and there are no strain markers. A figure of 3 km (33%) Alpine shortening across the SW border of the massif near St Sauveur has been suggested on the basis of displaced Trias Quartzite (Graham 1978 *b*). If this figure is applicable across the whole massif, there would seem to be a rough balance between the cover stacked in the nappes and the rock potentially available from the Argentera Massif. Certainly there is no enormous discrepancy; no cause to use excessive strata length as an

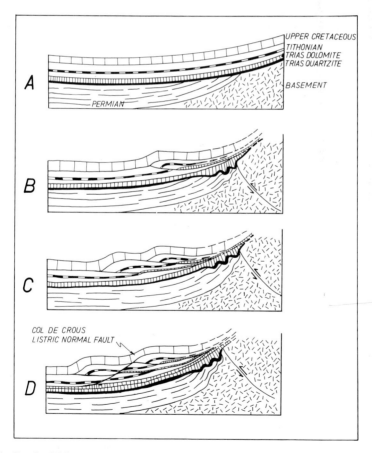

FIG. 14. Gravity Sliding model for the Tinée Nappes. A. Initial configuration. B. Emplacement of Higher Tinée Nappe. C. Emplacement of Roya Nappe with higher nappe on it. D. Development of Col de Crous Fault. The backs of the nappes are eroded, and the structure there interpretive.

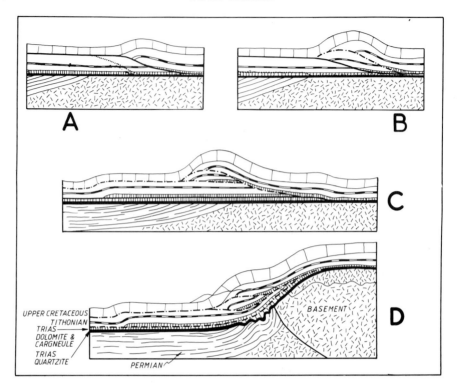

FIG. 15. Possible sequence of emplacement of the Tinée Nappes assuming thrusting followed by basement elevation. Dotted lines are incipient movement planes, heavy lines are active movement planes, dash-dot lines decayed movement planes. Trias dolomite and cargeneule is shown in brick ornament. It is underlain by quartzite which oversteps Permian onto crystalline basement.

argument *against* the derivation of the nappes from the massif, and consequently no argument against gravity sliding on grounds of stratal length.

Location

If the nappes have been translated from beyond the Argentera Massif, their present position, adjacent to it, must be regarded as coincidence (Fig. 16A). If, however they have slipped from the massif, then the siting of the ramps in the area where regional dip begins to flatten away from the massif is probably no accident. Presumably, a decrease in dip exerted a buttressing effect which initiated the ramps (Fig. 16B). This is the strongest argument for gravity sliding.

Listric normal faults

Three types of listric normal faults can be envisaged. Some represent the backs of gravity slides, others are developed where a sheet

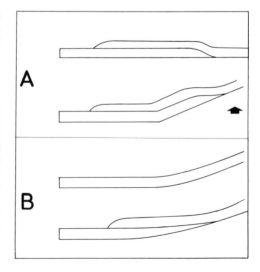

FIG. 16. Location of ramps. A. Assumes basement elevation after emplacement, B. is a gravity sliding model.

moving downslope cuts *downwards* through underlying stratigraphy, while others are conventional ramp structures re-oriented in a duplex.

The first two types are simple normal faults which put younger rocks in the hanging-wall against older rocks in the foot-wall. The last type puts older rocks in the hanging-wall over younger rocks in the foot-wall and is associated with downward facing structures.

The Alpes Maritimes listric normal faults belong in one or the other of the first two categories, and therefore must be associated with stratal extension and movement downslope. However, most of them post-date the emplacement of the two main Tinée Nappes, thus the existence of listric normal faults suggests only that gravity sliding has been important in the Tinée area, but says nothing definite about the Tinée Nappes themselves. The Col de Crous unit, backed by a major listric normal fault, must be a large gravity slide, but the backs of the Tinée Nappes themselves have been eroded, and uncertainty remains.

A realistic view might be that even if the Tinée Nappes existed before basement elevation, it is highly likely that they continued moving during that elevation, and that then, at least, gravity was the principal driving mechanism.

The nature of the décollement

Cleavage and folding suggest that some of the movement of the Tinée Nappes was accomplished by ductile shear in incompetent units (cf. Kehle 1970). Distinct movement planes also exist, of course. In some places these are parallel to cleavage, in others they cut cleavage.

No matter how strong the cleavage in the overlying formations, the Triassic rocks are not cleaved, they show only chaotic brecciation. Clearly, a different type of décollement existed in the Trias than in the higher formations, and it may be that high pore fluid pressures were important. Water derived from underlying Permian pelites suffering volume loss during their deformation (Graham 1978 b) may have contributed to this.

Regional considerations

The 26 km of translation seen in the Trias of Alpes Maritimes means that higher formations (Upper Cretaceous) not duplicated adjacent to the massif must somewhere show 26 km shortening. 15 km must be recorded in the Jurassic and Lower Cretaceous strata. Presumably the folds and thrusts of the external Alpine zones of Haute Provence record this shortening. These structures change their trend in two conspicuous geniculations and it has been suggested (Graham 1978 a) that they formed above transcurrent basement faults, decolle cover fed into the deforming zone. If this did occur it would have facilitated cover translations of the cover in areas nearer the massif.

It is obviously important to see if shortening in the external zones balances internal translation. Work is in progress to discover the answer.

ACKNOWLEDGMENTS. I have benefitted considerably from discussions with Drs D. Elliott and N. Fry. I thank Dr Fry and Dr J. Grocott for reading the manuscript, and Mrs V. Jenkins for typing the text. A Royal Society travel grant is gratefully acknowledged.

References

BLAY, P., COSGROVE, J. W. & SUMMERS, J. M. 1977. An experimental investigation of the development of structures in multilayers under the influence of gravity. *J. geol. Soc. London,* **133,** 329–42.

BORDET, P. 1949. Sur l'allure des plis de couverture au Sud-Quest du massif de l'Argentera-Mercantour. *C.r. Seances Acad. Sci. Fr.* **228,** 408–10.

—— 1950. Le dôme Permien de Barrot (Alpes-Maritimes) et son auréole de terrains secondaries. *Bull. Serv. Cart géol. Fr.* **XLVIII, 228,** 51–89.

FALLOT, P. 1949. Les chevauchements intercutanés de Roya (A.-M.). *Ann. Hébert Haug Lab. Géol. Fac. Sci. Univ. Paris,* **7,** 161–170.

—— & FAURE-MURET, A. 1949 a. Sur la géologie de l'ouest du Mounier (Alpes-Maritimes). *C.r. Seances Acad. Sci., Fr.* **228,** 523–5.

—— & —— 1949 b. Sur l'extension du décollement de la série de couverture subalpine. *C.r. Seances Acad. Sci. Fr.* **228,** 616–9.

—— & —— 1949 c. Sur un mode particulier de charriage. *C.r. Seances Acad. Sci. Fr.* **228,** 789–92.

GOGUEL, J. 1949. A Propos du glissement de la couverture au Sud-Quest du massif de l'Argentera. *C.r. Seances. Acad. Sci. Paris* **228,** 698–9.

—— 1952. *Tectonics* (*English trans.*). Freeman & Co., San Francisco, 348 p.

GRAHAM, R. H. 1978 *a*. Wrench faults, arcuate fold patterns and deformation in the Southern French Alps. *Proc. Geol. Assoc.* 125–42.

—— 1978 *b* Quantitative deformation studies in the Permian rocks of Alpes-Maritimes. *Proc. Symposium in honour of Prof. J. Goguel B.R.G.M. Paris*, 212–38.

KEHLE, R. O. 1970. Analysis of gravity sliding and orogenic translation. *Bull. geol. Soc. Am.* **81,** 1641–64.

PRICE, N. J. 1977. Aspects of gravity tectonics and the development of listric faults. *J geol. Soc. London*, **133,** 311–327.

PRICE, R. A. 1973. Large scale gravitational flow of supracrustal rocks, southern Canadian Rockies *In*: DE JONG, K. A. & SCHOLTEN R. (eds), '*Gravity and Tectonics*', Wiley, New York.

R. H. GRAHAM, Department of Geology, University College, Swansea.

Sutures, thrusts and nappes in the Variscan Arc of western Europe: plate tectonic implications

Ph. Matte & J. P. Burg

SUMMARY: The Variscan Arc of western Europe, convex to the W, links the Iberian and the middle European Variscides. It is characterized by nappes and thrusts with converging vergences towards the inner part of the arc. This is illustrated by two cross-sections, one roughly E–W in northwestern Spain, the other N–S in the French Massif Central. This segment of the Variscan belt appears to be a typical collision belt whose plate tectonic evolution may be explained in the following stages: (i) consumption of a Lower Palaeozoic ocean by an intraoceanic subduction towards the NW, (ii) choking of subduction by underthrusting of continental crust beneath the oceanic lithosphere (obduction), (iii) intracontinental deformation during which the arcuate form results from the progressive impingement of a southern continental promontory (part of Africa?) into the northern Laurasian continent.

The Variscan belt extends into Europe over 3000 km from southern Spain to the Bohemian Massif. It is a wide (700–800 km), asymmetric orogen which presents a tight syntaxis convex to the W: the Ibero-Armorican Arc (Matte & Ribeiro 1975). The main thrusts and nappes are displaced towards the inner part of the arc. The main Variscan deformation (F1) changes in age and style from the external* part (Middle Carboniferous superficial décollement and/or gravity nappes without metamorphism) to the internal part (synmetamorphic pre-Carboniferous fold nappes and ductile thrusts). This evolution is illustrated by two cross-sections across the arc, one E–W in northwestern Spain, the other N–S in the French Massif Central (Fig. 1).

The N Spain cross-section

The arcuate shape of the Variscan belt appears clearly in northern Spain where the Iberian arc tightens eastwards so that the structures facing inwards are bent through 180° in the Cantabrian Mountains (Matte 1968). These mountains and the Galician coast provide an excellent E–W cross-section across the Iberian structures. Four zones through deeper and deeper structural levels are found from E to W (Fig. 2A).

Zone I: (Cantabrian Mountains)

Cambrian–Lower Carboniferous rocks (mainly limestones, shales and quartzites) are involved

---

* External and internal are defined regarding the vergence of the folds and the displacement of the nappes from the internal towards the external part of the belt.

---

in décollement type nappes, like the Appalachian Plateau or Cordilleran foothills (Julivert 1971). The structures are superficial and without cleavage: décollement occurred mainly along the Middle Cambrian marly plastic layer. Nappe emplacement, folding of the thrusts and cross folding occurred during Middle Carboniferous, and resulted in the progressive tightening of the arc. Regional metamorphism and granites are absent.

Zone 2: (western Asturias)

Cambro-Ordovician pelitic/clastic sequence overlies unconformably the Upper Precambrian (slates and greywackes). The rocks are deformed in the greenschist facies with folds overturned to the E. A steeply westwards dipping slaty cleavage becomes more and more flat towards the W with a down-dip stretching lineation.

Zone 3: (eastern Galicia)

Upper Precambrian and Cambro-Silurian rocks are involved in large synmetamorphic (greenschist–amphibolite facies) fold nappes of Helvetic style, recumbent to the E with well preserved inverted limbs (up to 25 km) (Matte 1968). A stretching lineation is parallel to the sense of displacement (i.e. normal to the fold axes) of the nappes. The strain and metamorphism increase from the front towards the roots of the fold-nappes where local mesoscopic EW synfolial 'a' folds develop parallel to the stretching.

In Zones 2 and 3, the axial plane cleavage steepens progressively along the strike of the structures towards the S and SE, so that on the

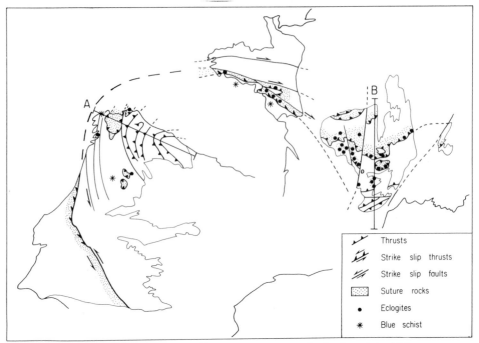

Fig. 1. Structural sketch map of the Ibero-Armorican Arc and distribution of the high pressure metamorphism.

southern branch of the syntaxis the folds be-come upright, more open and more or less parallel to the stretching lineation. The thrusts pass progressively into ductile dextral shear-zones.

Zone 4: (western Galicia)

Two units may be distinguished in this zone: (i) a lower parautochtonous epizonal unit com-posed mainly of Silurian metasediments and metavolcanics (red and green schist, cherts, basalts, keratophyres). The upper part which includes mainly gabbros, basalts, amphibolites, limestone lenses and serpentinites, closely re-sembles an ophiolitic mélange (Van Der Meer Mohr 1975; Bayer & Matte 1979). (ii) An upper allochtonous high grade unit including gneisses, mafic and ultramafic rocks metamor-phosed in high pressure–high temperature con-ditions (eclogites, pyrope-garnetites, flaser gab-bros) (Den Tex & Engels 1972). This unit is thrust towards the E onto Zone 3 over at least 100 km (Ries & Shackleton 1971; Bayer & Matte 1979). Some of the mafic rocks have a composition of oceanic tholeites and the HP–HT metamorphism occurred around 390 Ma. (Van Carlsteren *et al.* 1979). Zones 3 and 4 are characterized by the widespread occurr-ence of many kinds of Variscan granitoids.

The Massif Central cross-section

The French Massif Central displays nappe and thrust tectonics comparable with that of north-ern Spain (Burg & Matte 1978). From S to N it may be subdivided into three main zones (Fig. 2B).

Zone I (Montagne Noire)

Lower Cambrian–Lower Carboniferous rocks are involved in fold nappes of Helvetic type displaced towards the S (Arthaud 1970). Deformation occurred in non-metamorphic (frontal parts of the intermediate and lower nappes) to epizonal and mesozonal conditions (upper nappes and root zones). As in the Helvetic nappes (Ramsay, this volume) the strain increases towards the roots of the nappes. The stretching lineation is well developed and strikes N–S along the basal thrusts of the different units; it is less marked (flattening) and E–W (parallel to the fold axes) in the upper and frontal parts.

Zone II (Cévennes–Rouergue)

This zone which is thrust over Zone I in-cludes a thick series of undated (probably Cambro-Ordovician) highly deformed schists

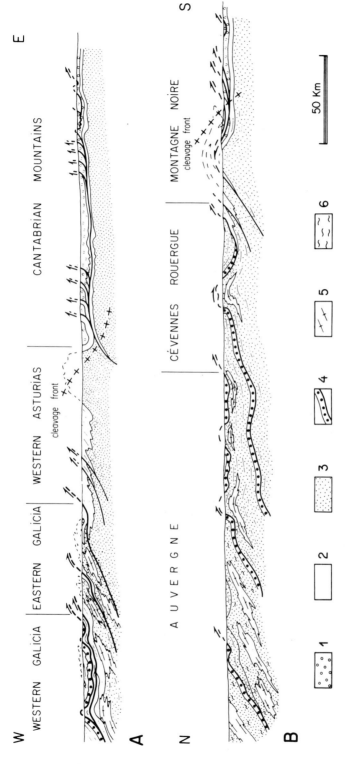

FIG. 2. Schematic cross sections across the Ibero-Armorican Arc. (A) NW Spain. (B) French Massif Central. (1) Devono-Carboniferous. (2) Dated Lower Palaeozoic. (3) Upper Precambrian (Spain), Upper Precambrian + undated Lower Palaeozoic (Massif Central). (4) High grade mafic/ultramafic complexes. (5) Anatexites. (6) Syntectonic Variscan Granites. Pre-Variscan and late Variscan Granites are not represented.

overlying a high grade mafic-ultramafic complex which contains early HP/HT assemblages
(Nicollet *et al.* 1979). Zone II is characterized
by a flat-lying composite (S1+S2) slaty cleavage (or foliation) affecting a thick pile of rocks
(10 km). Isoclinal folds F1 and F2 (refolding
S1) develop with various orientations. Some of
them lie parallel to a prominent NS stretching
lineation. Polymetamorphism varies from
greenschist to amphibolite facies (high pressure
to intermediate type). At the northern limit of
Zone 2 with Zone 3 the isograds (intermediate
type) are inverted below a main thrust (Briand
& Gay 1978).

Zone III (Auvergne)

This zone includes mainly pre-Lower Carboniferous high grade rocks (micaschists,
gneisses, anatexites, mafics and ultramafics
(Lasnier 1977)). The mafics and ultramafics
show early HP/HT assemblages. As in western
Galicia, this high grade complex is thrust onto
Zone II towards the S over 100–150 km. At
the base of the main thrust, lenses of serpentinized peridotites have been stretched and
squeezed.

Further information on Zones 2 and 3 is
given by the westward continuation of this

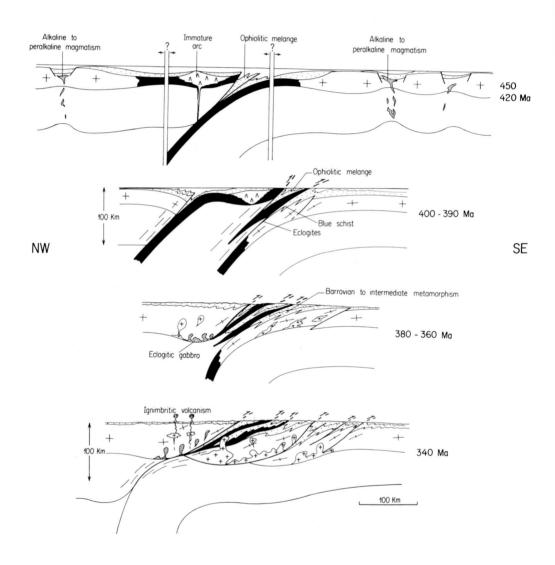

Fig. 3. Plate tectonic interpretation for the Ibero-Armorican Arc.

main thrust in southern Brittany. There, an allochthonous unit considered as island arc tholeites (Jahn *et al.* 1977) metamorphosed in blue schist conditions is squeezed between Zone 2 and 3 (Matte & Mattauer 1978; Audren & Lefort 1977). Blue schist metamorphism is dated at Ile de Groix between 420 and 350 Ma. (Carpenter & Civetta 1976; Peucat & Cogné 1977) and the overlying anatectic rocks similar to those of the northern Massif Central give an age of 376 ± 12 Ma for the metamorphic climax (Vidal 1973).

Zone III is also characterized by the widespread development of syntectonic anatectic granites emplaced mainly between 360 and 320 Ma.

Plate tectonic implications

The Variscan Arc of western Europe shows most typical features of a collision belt: (a) large nappes (décollement and Helvetic types) and great overthrusts comparable in size with Alpine and Himalayan thrusts, (b) polyphase metamorphism with an early (400–380 Ma) high pressure stage and a late intermediate to low pressure stage (with local inversion of isograds, (c) decreasing age of the tectono-metamorphic events from the internal part of the belt towards the external part, (d) widespread development of peraluminous mesocrustal anatectic granites in relation with the main thrusts.

The major thrusts between Zone 4 and 3 in Galicia and between Zones I & II and II & III in Massif Central along which tectonic mélanges, mafic rocks of tholeitic oceanic composition (meta-ophiolites: Montigny & Allegre 1974) high pressure metamorphism and upper mantle rocks are found, may be considered to be superposed to oceanic sutures separating a northern and a southern continent.

The characteristics of the Variscan Arc may be explained by an obduction model, as proposed by Dewey (1976), for the Appalachians of Newfoundland and by Mattauer *et al.* 1980 for the Alps and Himalayas.

In this model, we assume that the main nappe and thrust tectonics result from the progressive underthrusting of a southern (African?) promontory below a northern continent. This evolution includes the following stages (Fig. 3): (a) Consumption of a Lower Palaeozoic ocean during late Ordovician and Silurian by intraoceanic subduction towards the NW and possible creation of an immature intraoceanic arc. (b) Subduction of the southern continental crust below the oceanic lithosphere (eclogite and blue schist metamorphism) during Silurian and Lower Devonian and possible second subduction below the northern continent. (c) Collision with overriding of the northern continent over the southern continent prior to the Lower Carboniferous. Retrogradation of initial high pressure assemblages into Barrovian and intermediate type metamorphism and formation of mesocrustal anatectic granites. (d) Increasing intracontinental deformation with rising of granitic anatectic magma accompanied by low pressure metamorphism, migration of the deformation and metamorphism from the internal towards the external part of the belt and rise of many granitoids (from the deeper parts of the thickened continental crust).

In this model, we assume that the sense of the initial subduction may be inferred from the sense of vergence and nappe displacement, since the intracontinental deformation results from the blocking of the subduction by underthrusting of continental crust (Mattauer & Proust, 1976; Mattauer & Tapponnier 1978).

We propose that the arcuate form of the belt is entirely acquired after collision by progressive impingement of a southern continental promontory into the northern continent as proposed by Tapponnier & Molnar 1977 for the western syntaxis of the Himalayas.

ACKNOWLEDGMENTS. We are indebted to J. P. Bard, M. Mattauer and P. Tapponnier for helpful discussion. This work has been carried out with the financial support of the C.N.R.S. L.A. N° 266.

References

ARTHAUD, F. 1970. Etude tectonique et microtectonique comparée de deux domaines hercyniens: les nappes de la Montagne Noire (France) et l'anticlinorium de l'Iglesiente (Sardaigne). *Publ. de l'Université des Sciences et Techniques du Languedoc série Géologie Structurale*, 175p.

AUDREN, C. & LEFORT, J. P. 1977. Géologie du plateau continental sud armoricain entre les îles de Glénan et de Noirmoutier. Implications géodynamiques. *Bull. Soc. geol. Fr.* **19**, 395–404.

BAYER, R. & MATTE PH. 1979. Is the Mafic/ultramafic massif of the Cabo-Ortegal (NW Spain) a nappe emplaced during a Variscan obduction? A new gravity interpretation. *Tectonophysics*, **57**, T9–T18.

BRIAND, B. & GAY, M. 1978. La série inverse de St Geniez d'Olt: évolution métamorphique et structurale. *Bull. Bur. Rech. geol. min Paris* **1**, 167–86.

BURG, J. P. & MATTE, PH. 1978. A cross-section through the French Massif Central and the scope of its Variscan Geodynamic Evolution. *Z. Deutsch. geol. Ges.* **129**, 429–60.

CARPENTER, M. S. N. & CIVETTA, L. 1976. Hercynian high pressure/low metamorphism temperature in the Ile de Groix Blueschists. *Nature*, **262**, 276–7.

DEN TEX, E. & ENGELS, J. P. 1972. A high-pressure intermediate temperature facies Series in the Precambrian at Cabo-Ortegal (NW Spain). *Proc. 24th Int. geol. Congr.* **2**, 64–73.

DEWEY, J. F. 1976. Ophiolite obduction. *Tectonophysics*, **31**, 93–120.

JAHN, B. M., PEUCAT, J. J. & CARPENTER, M. S. N. 1977. Géochimie des terres rares de Glaucophanites et roches associées de l'Ile de Groix (France) et de Taiwan. *Réun. Ann. Sci. Ter. Rennes*, 280.

JULIVERT, M. 1971. Décollement Tectonics in the Hercynian cordillera of Northwestern Spain. *Am. J. Sci.* **270**, 1–29.

LASNIER, B. 1977. *Persistance d'une série granulitique au coeur du Massif Central français (Haut-Allier). Les termes basiques, ultrabasiques et carbonatés.* Thèse d'État, Nantes, 351 p.

MATTAUER, M. & PROUST, F. 1976. La Corse alpine: un modèle de genèse du métamorphisme haute pression par subduction de croûte continentale sous du matériel océanique. *C.r. Seances Acad. Sci. Paris*, **282D**, 1249–52.

——, —— & TAPPONNIER, P. 1980. *Tectonic mechanism of obduction in relation with high pressure metamorphism.* Colloque CNRS, N° 272 Grenoble 197–201.

—— & TAPPONNIER, P. 1978. Tectonique des plaques et tectonique intracontinentale dans les Alpes franco-italiennes. *C.r. Seances Acad. Sci. Paris.* **287D**, 899–902.

MATTE, PH. 1968. La structure de la virgation hercynienne de Galice (Espagne). *Géol. Alpine*, **44**, 157–280.

—— & MATTAUER, M. 1978. Tectonique des plaques et chaîne hercynienne. Les "schistes bleus" de la côte sud-armoricaine sont-ils les témoins d'une obduction. *Réun. Ann. Sci. Ter. Orsay* 270.

—— & RIBEIRO, A. 1975. Forme et orientation de la virgation hercynienne de Galice. Relations avec le plissement et hypothèses sur la genèse de l'arc Ibero-Armoricain. *C.r. Seances Acad. Sci. Paris*, **280D**, 2825–8.

MEER MOHR, G. G. VAN DER. 1975. The Paleozoic strata near Moeche in Galicia. (NW Spain). *Leidse geol. Meded.* **49**, 487–97.

MONTIGNY, R. & ALLEGRE, C. J. 1974. A la recherche des océans perdus: les éclogites de Vendée, témoins métamorphisés d'une ancienne croûte océanique. *C.r. Seances Acad. Sci. Paris*, **279D**, 543–5.

NICOLLET, CH., LEYRELOUP, A. & DUPUY CL. 1979. Petrogenesis of high pressure trondhjemitic layers in eclogites and amphibolites from Southern Massif Central, France. *In*: BARKER, F. (ed), *Trondhjemites, Dacites and Related Rocks* Elsevier, Amsterdam, 43–63.

PEUCAT, J. J. & COGNE J. 1977. Geochronology of some blueschists from Ile de Groix, France. *Nature*, **268**, 131–2.

RIES, C. A. & SHACKLETON, R. M. 1971. Catazonal complexes of north-west Spain and north Portugal remnants of a hercynian Thrust plate. *Nature, Phys Sci.* **234**, 65–8.

VAN CALSTEREN, P. W. C., BOELRIJK, N. A. T. M., HEBEDA, F. H., PRIEM, H. N. A., DEN TEX, E. VERDURMEN, R. A. TH. & VERSCHURE, R. H. 1979. Isotopic dating of older elements (including the Cabo Ortegal Mafic-ultramafic complex) in the Hercynian orogen of NW. Spain. Manifestations of a presumed early Paleozoic Mantle Plume. *Chem. Geol.* **24**, 35–56.

TAPPONNIER, P. & MOLNAR, P. 1977. Rigid plastic indentation: the origin of syntaxis in the Himalayan belt. *Colloque Himalaya CNRS*, **268**, 431–2.

VIDAL, PH. 1973. Premières données géochronologiques sur les granites hercyniens du Sud du Massif Armoricain. *Bull. Soc. géol. Fr.* **15**, 239–45.

MATTE PH., BURG, J. P. L. A. CNRS N° 266 Labo. Géol. Structurale, U.S.T.L., Place Bataillon, 34060. Montpellier, Cedex, France.

Wrench related thrusting along a Mesozoic–Cenozoic continental margin: Antalya Complex, SW Turkey

N. H. Woodcock & A. H. F. Robertson

SUMMARY: An imbricate thrust belt and a geometrically related wrench-fault terrain are reported from the Antalya Complex, SW Turkey. The deformation occurred between late Cretaceous and Miocene time along a former Mesozoic rifted continental margin. The thrusting appears to have been temporally and mechanically related to at least the early stages of wrench tectonics.

A short preliminary report is given here of complex thrust and wrench tectonics recently mapped by us in part of the Antalya Complex, SW Turkey. The geometric and possible genetic relationships of the thrust belts with major wrench faults are of general interest. Our main results are summarized here: a detailed description and illustration of the structural geology of this area will be presented elsewhere.

Geological setting

The Antalya Complex (Woodcock & Robertson 1977, the Antalya Nappes of previous authors) is an extensive assemblage of dominantly Mesozoic igneous and sedimentary rocks cropping out essentially S of the Tauride Mesozoic carbonate massifs of S Turkey (Fig. 1, Inset). It has been interpreted as a former Mesozoic passive continental margin sequence (Dumont et al. 1972; Delaune-Mayere et al. 1977, Woodcock & Robertson 1977) which, prior to its deformation in late Cretaceous to Tertiary time, formed part of the northern edge of a Mesozoic Troodos Ocean (Robertson & Woodcock in press a). The Tauride platform carbonate sequences represent the more proximal shallow water deposits on the autochthon of this margin.

Fig. 1 shows the geology of the southern part of the main Antalya Complex outcrop W of Antalya Bay, where we have distinguished five tectonic zones, striking N–S. Between platform carbonates and cover (Bey Dagları Zone) in the W and a partial ophiolite sequence (Tekirova Zone) in the E margin sediments occur either on pre-Triassic continental basement (Kemer Zone), on Triassic mafic crust (Gödene Zone), or on an unknown basement (Kumluca Zone).

Structure

The map (Fig. 1) and section (Fig. 2) illustrate our interpretation of the structure, which differs substantially from previous views of the complex as a stack of low-angle 'nappes' (Brunn et al. 1971, Delaune-Mayere et al. 1977). Of primary interest here is the imbricate thrust belt of the Kumluca Zone. N striking, E dipping thrusts repeat a thin (c. 250 m) allochthonous sedimentary sequence as many as ten times in an across-strike distance between 2 and 4 km. Fold asymmetry data imply westward thrusting towards the Bey Dagları Zone carbonates.

The Gödene Zone to the E shows a markedly different structural style dominated by N–S striking, sub-vertical, anastamosing, sheared serpentinite screens. These are interpreted as cold diapiric serpentinite intrusions into a braided array of strike-slip faults, contemporaneous with fault displacement. The serpentinites separate large lozenges of often strongly contrasting sequences, including an assemblage of imbricated sediments which closely resembles the Kumluca Zone in lithology and structure. The high-angle faults separating the Gödene, Kemer and Tekirova Zones may also have dominant strike-slip components and be part of a wide wrench tectonic belt. Sporadic occurrences of coarse ophiolitic clastic sediments within this belt probably represent erosional debris deposited in small strike-slip generated basins (Robertson & Woodcock, in press b). This wrench belt has been traced continuously, and the thrust belt discontinuously, along strike for a total N–S distance of about 80 km.

Interpretation

Both the thrust and wrench belts reflect the deformation of a previously passive continental

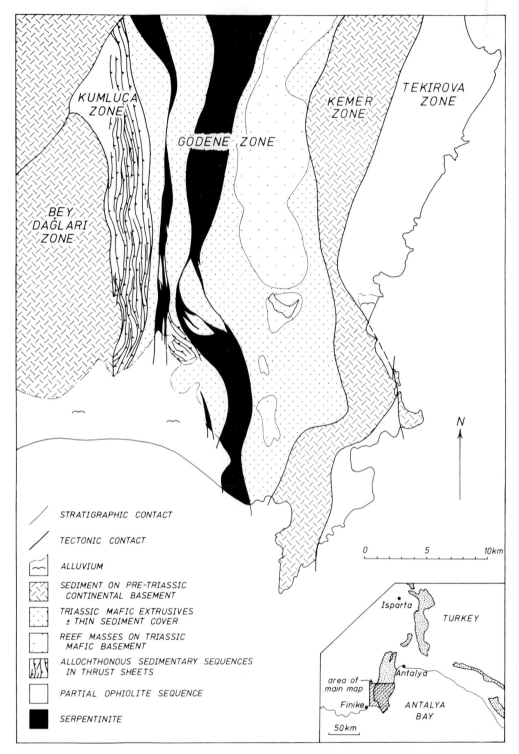

FIG. 1. Geological map of the southern segment of the Antalya Complex outcrop W of Antalya Bay showing main tectonic zones. Inset shows Antalya Complex outcrops in S Turkey and location of main map.

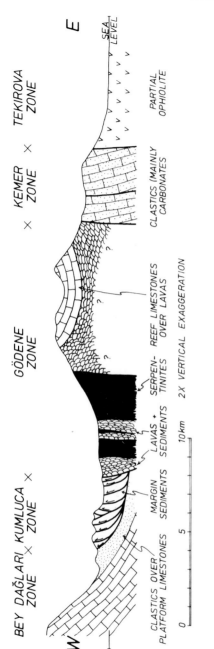

FIG. 2. Structural E–W cross-section of the Antalya Complex.

margin and the juxtaposition of different segments of ocean floor and margin sequences with the platform sequence. The precise timing is unknown. Both belts could have been active from the late Cretaceous, the time of last deposition of margin sediments, into the early Tertiary, which is marked by post-orogenic deposition of Oligocene and Miocene ophiolitic clastics in the axis of the 'Isparta Angle'. The imbricated sliver within the wrench terrain suggests that thrusting predated at least some strike-slip faulting.

Two interpretations of the structural relationships are possible. Either a discrete thrust event preceded the wrench event, or else both were broadly contemporaneous within a major transpressive episode along the deforming continental margin. In the second model, the Kumluca Zone would represent an interesting example of a small thrust belt developed within a strike-slip belt, kinematically analogous to, for example, the Transverse Ranges in the San Andreas system or to parts of the Spitsbergen Orogen. The particular interest of the Antalya example is the involvement of both continental and oceanic basement.

In a regional context, the structural history displayed in Antalya is part of a more widespread late Cretaceous-Cenozoic event that disrupted the northern continental margin of the Troodos Ocean. We speculate elsewhere (Robertson & Woodcock, in press *a*) that this event involved the strike-slip rearrangement of lithospheric fragments above a N-dipping subducting slab, possibly resulting from impingement of the Arabian and Turkish continental edges further E. A major element in this rearrangement was the 90° anticlockwise rotation of Cyprus, possibly in part achieved by strike-slip displacements along or parallel to the Antalya lineament.

ACKNOWLEDGMENTS. Our field work in Turkey was supported by the Natural Environment Research Council, U.K. and by Maden Tetkik ve Arama Enstitüsü, Ankara.

University of Cambridge, Department of Earth Sciences, publication No. ES8.

References

BRUNN, J. H., DUMONT, J. F., DE GRACIANSKY, P. C., GUTNIC, M., JUTEAU, T., MARCOUX, J., MONOD, O. & POISSON, A. 1971. Outline of the geology of the western Taurides. *In*: CAMPBELL, A. S. (ed), *Geology and History of Turkey*, Petrol. Explor. Soc. Libya, 225–55.

DELAUNE-MAYERE, M., MARCOUX, J. PARROT, J.-F. & POISSON, A. 1977. Modèle d'evolution Mesozoique de la paleomarge Tethysienne au niveau des nappes radiolaritiques et ophiolitiques du Taurus Lycien, d'Antalya et du Baër-Bassit. *In*: BIJU-DUVAL, B. & MONTADERT, L.

(eds), *Structural History of the Mediterranean Basins*, Éditions Technip, Paris, 79–94.

DUMONT, J. F., GUTNIC, M. MARCOUX, J., MONOD, O. & POISSON, A. 1972. Le Trias des Taurides occidentales (Turquie). Définition du bassin pamphylien: Un nouveau domaine à ophiolithes à la marge externe de la chaine taurique. *Z. Deutsch. geol. Ges.* **123**, 385–409.

ROBERTSON, A. H. F. & WOODCOCK, N. H. in press *a*. Tectonic setting of the Troodos Massif in the East Mediterranean. *Proc. Int. Ophiolite Symp., Cyprus.*

—— & ——, in press *b*. Strike-slip related sedimentation in the Antalya Complex, SW Turkey. *Spec. Publ. Int. Assoc. Sediment.* **4**.

WOODCOCK, N. H. & ROBERTSON, A. H. F. 1979. Imbricate thrust belt tectonics and sedimentation as a guide to emplacement of part of the Antalya Complex, SW Turkey. *Proc. 6th Coll. Aegean Geol. Izmir,* 1977.

N. H. WOODCOCK. Department of Geology, University of Cambridge, Cambridge CB2 3EQ, U.K.

A. H. F. ROBERTSON, Grant Institute of Geology, University of Edinburgh, Edinburgh EH9 3JW, U.K.

Thrust and strike slip fault interaction along the Chaman transform zone, Pakistan

R. D. Lawrence, S. H. Khan, K. A. DeJong, A. Farah, & R. S. Yeats

SUMMARY: The interaction between thrust and strike slip fault systems is well detailed in Pakistan where the Chaman transform zone connects the Makran and Himalayan convergence zones and contains an internal convergence zone in the Zhob district. The transform zone contains numerous strike slip faults of which the Chaman fault proper is the westernmost. We can demonstrate at least 200 km of left lateral displacement along the Chaman fault alone. In the Zhob belt N–S shortening by folds and a major thrust fault amounts to several dozen kilometres. The 400 km wide Makran convergence zone is now being shortened by E–W oriented folds, thrust faults, and reverse faults. As these faults in the Makran zone approach the transform zone, their traces bend to the N and motion on each of them becomes oblique, combining reverse and left lateral slip. They merge continuously with the strike slip faults of the Chaman transform zone. The Makran thrust system and the Chaman transform zone first became active in the late Oligocene or early Miocene. Later (Pliocene?), a component of left lateral shear occurred across the entire Makran Zone in association with the opening of the newly identified Haman-i-Mashkel fault trough S of the Chagai Hills and W of the Ras Koh. The total displacement and displacement rate across the Chaman transform zone varies in response to the rates of convergence in the plates E and W of the zone.

The interaction of major fault systems, particularly where one type of fault terminates against another, is a subject of considerable interest (Hobbs *et al.* 1976, p. 309), but one that is only rarely subject to direct field investigation. The termination of normal faulting in the Basin and Range Province of the W United States in strike slip faults (Davis & Burchfiel 1972; Lawrence 1976) and the interaction of thrust and high angle reverse faulting in the California Transverse Ranges with the San Andreas Fault (Crowell 1968) are examples of such situations. Another exceptionally well exposed example is in W Pakistan where strike slip faults of the Chaman transform zone interact with thrust and reverse faults in convergent zones (DeJong & Farah, 1978). This area (Fig. 1) is located between the Indian plate and the Afghan block (Stocklin 1977). The Chaman transform zone connects the Makran convergence zone where oceanic lithosphere is being subducted beneath the Lut and Afghan microplates (White & Klitgord 1976; Farhoudi & Karig 1977; Jacob & Quittmeyer 1979; White 1979), and the Himalayan convergence zone, where the Indian continental lithosphere is underthrusting Eurasia (Powell & Conaghan 1973). The Zhob thrust belt is an internal convergence zone within the Chaman transform zone. We became aware of the importance of the interaction between thrust and strike slip faulting in this region during studies of the Chaman fault in Pakistan (Lawrence & Yeats 1979).

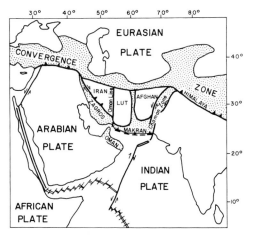

FIG. 1. Present tectonic setting of the Chaman transform zone, South Asia.

The Chaman transform zone

The transform character of the Chaman fault was first recognized by Wilson (1965). However, the Chaman fault is only the W margin of a wide zone of strike slip faults and related features that together constitute the Chaman transform zone (Fig. 2). The main strike slip faults composing the transform zone are the Chaman, Gardez, W and E Waziristan, Sulaiman, Ghazaband, and Ornach-Nal faults. Numerous smaller faults are present. The zone

364   R. D. Lawrence et al.

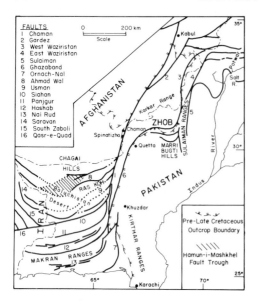

FIG. 2. Major structural features of the
Chaman transform zone and adjacent convergence zones. Where possible, fault
names follow Kazmi (1979).

is almost coextensive with the outcrop of the
Khojak flysch (Oligocene–Lower Miocene) of
Vredenburg (1901) which was subdivided into
the Murgha Faqirzai and Shaigalu Formations
by the Hunting Survey (Jones 1961). Similar
units, collectively the Turbat Group* (Jones
1961), make up the Makran Ranges between
the Siahan and Nai Rud Faults (Jones 1961;
Bakr & Jackson 1964). The width of the transform zone varies markedly. It is about 100 km
wide in the S, W of the Ornach Nal fault. From
about Khuzdar to just N of Quetta it narrows
to 25–40 km. At the Zhob belt, it widens
abruptly to over 200 km and then narrows
gradually to around 175 km near Kabul.

The eastern margin of the transform zone is
marked by the westernmost outcrops of
Mesozoic rocks and the Las Bela and Muslim
Bagh ophiolite occurrences (Fig. 2). N of the
town of Zhob this boundary is within the Chaman transform zone between the two Waziris-

*The name Turbat group was introduced by the
Hunting Survey for undifferentiated Oligocene–
Miocene sandstone, siltstones, mudstones, and shales
equivalent to all or part of the Panjgun, Binga,
Parkini, Diz, Hoshob, and Siahan formations and is
thus a convenient collective term herein.

tan and Sulaiman faults. It is thought to mark
the W edge of the Indian plate (Sillitoe 1976;
Farah pers. comm. 1978). The W margin of the
zone is marked by the easternmost outcrops of
pre-late Cretaceous rocks in Afghanistan N of
the obscuring sands of the Dasht-i-Margo. A
small outcrop of these pre-Cretaceous rocks is
probably present in the mountains of Spinatizha W of Quetta (Lawrence & Yeats 1979).
From Spinatizha to the Usman fault the transform zone is bounded on the W by Upper
Cretaceous to Eocene andesitic arc material
(Jones 1961; Bakr 1963; Ahmed 1964). This
arc was built on, or accreted to, the S edge of
the Afghan block at least as far S as the Chagai
Hills. Thus, the transform zone mainly occupies a gap between continental lithospheric
plates which filled with Khojak flysch during
the Oligocene.

The Chaman fault proper is marked by a
zone of gouge including an assemblage of red
and green clastic sedimentary rocks of the
Kamerod and Rakhshani formations, ultramafic rocks, and foraminiferal limestones of
the Eocene Kharan formation (Lawrence &
Yeats 1979). The Kamerod formation is a unit
of locally derived, subaerially deposited red,
green and grey clastic sediments of Miocene–
Pliocene age similar to the Siwaliks, while the
Rakhshani formation is a marine assemblage
of red, green, and brown clastic sediments of
Palaeocene–Lower Eocene age. Conglomerates
of these units can be distinguished by their
clast assemblages. The assemblage is widely
exposed in, and enters the fault zone from, the
E Ras Koh. Most of the material in the fault
zone is derived from the W side; fragments of
flysch are rare. Kharan limestone was confirmed (Yin Chi-hsiang, per. comm. 1978) near
Khwaja Amran in the Spinatizha area over
100 km N of the source. Conglomerate clast
assemblages at Loe Boghra E of the town of
Chaman confirm the presence of both
Rakhshani and Kamerod Formations in addition to ultramafic fragments over 200 km N of
the Ras Koh. These units all first enter the
fault zone at the Usman fault. How far this
assemblage extends into Afghanistan, is unknown, but sizeable bodies of ultramafic rock
first appear E of the fault about 400 km N of
the Usman fault (Wittekindt & Weippert
1973). Thus, between 200 and 400 km of left
slip along the Chaman fault alone seems probable. No units are yet matched across the
entire zone, and as a plate boundary it is likely
that none exist. Therefore, the total displacement across the zone will probably have to be
derived from regional tectonic reconstructions
rather than measured displacements.

The convergent zones

There are three zones of convergence that interact with the Chaman transform zone (Fig. 2). The N. zone, the Himalayan convergence zone, has its S boundary at the thrust faults of the Salt and Trans-Indus Salt Ranges. The southward overthrusting may be as much as 50 km (Sarwar & DeJong 1979) and is marked by décollement thrusting on salt beds (Wadia 1957; Gansser 1964; Powell 1979). The exact nature of the connection between strike slip and thrust faults in Waziristan has not yet been studied.

The Zhob convergence zone is of special interest because much of it is developed within the transform zone. E of Chaman at Khojak Pass, the flysch is sericitized and tightly folded but not known to be thrust faulted. In the Karkar area, folds in the flysch are much more open and have a greater wavelength. Shortening in the Zhob area was mainly achieved by southward thrusting along the Zhob fault. The tectonic superposition of coeval formations of completely different facies suggests a minimal displacement of several tens of kilometres. The thrusting was probably synchronous with the 50° counterclockwise rotation of the Loralai Ranges (C. T. Klootwijk, *et al.* in prep.), occurring in the Pliocene–early Pleistocene.

The Makran convergence zone has been of particular interest to us. Our field studies have been in the E Ras Koh and ranges to the N. One visit was made to Tuscan Pass near to the point where the Siahan fault branches W from the Chaman fault. Farhoudi & Karig (1977) supported by Jacob & Quittmeyer (1979) have interpreted this zone as a modern arc-trench gap. They place the slope trench break at the Siahan fault (Fig. 2) and consider the sedimentary fill of the Baluchistan Desert to be the forearc basin. The model is intended to explain a very low angle of subduction suggested by the distance of about 600 km between the andesitic volcanoes, Koh i Sultan and Koh i Taftan, and the buried Makran trench. This model is much oversimplified because the pre-Holocene development of the area is only now becoming understood, but only a brief account of our results can be included here (Lawrence, unpubl. data). We find four major stages in the development of the area.

Development of the Makran convergence zone

Early andesitic arc

Vigorous andesitic arc activity occurred during rapid subduction as the Indian plate moved northward at as much as 20 cm/yr (McKenzie & Sclater 1971; Powell 1979). This late Cretaceous–Middle Eocene igneous episode is recorded in both the Chagai Hills and Ras Koh (Jones 1961; Bakr 1963; Ahmed 1964). Trenches related to subduction during this time may have been located approximately along the N Ras Koh in the Palaeocene and near the present Siahan fault in the Late Eocene. Evidence for arc activity at this time is also present along the E Afghan block (Wittekindt & Weippert 1973; Sillitoe, 1976). This episode climaxed when the Indian plate first contacted Eurasia and the rate of sea floor spreading in the Indian ocean slowed or even stopped in late Palaeocene–Middle Eocene time (McKenzie & Sclater 1971; Powell & Conaghan 1973; Dewey & Burke 1973; Powell 1979).

Clastic sedimentation

During the period from the late Eocene to the early Miocene clastic sedimentation dominated. The Khojak flysch accumulated E of the Afghan block in what subsequently became the Chaman transform zone. The Turbat group formed simultaneously S of the Afghan block and is now present in the central and N Makran Ranges. These units accumulated during very slow subduction (Powell 1979). The outcrop width of the Turbat group is now 200 km and before folding and thrusting was much wider (perhaps over twice the present width). Accretion of this enormous Middle Cenozoic sedimentary prism would produce a very large seaward migration of the locus of subduction, according to the Karig (1974) model, and may, therefore, be the reason for the extremely low angle of subduction currently observed here.

Renewed subduction, thrusting and transform faulting

In the Middle Miocene more rapid sea floor spreading resumed, and continental lithosphere of the Indian plate began to underthrust Eurasia. Subduction was rejuvenated S of the Makran coast. This change is most clearly marked by folding and thrust faulting of the Khojak flysch, Turbat group, and Palaeogene and older sediments of the Ras Koh and Dalbandin trough. Miocene–Recent sediments S of the Nai Rud faults have developed only open folds. Strike slip faulting in the transform zone began at this time, simultaneously with the thrust faulting. The thrust faults curve from nearly E-W trending thrust faults to NE trending left oblique thrusts to

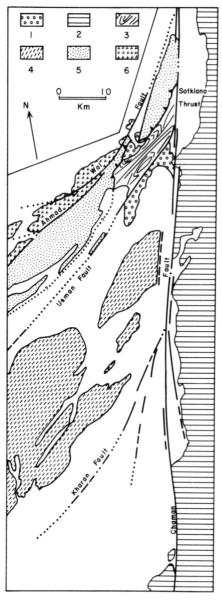

FIG. 3. Structural geology of the eastern Ras Koh and Chaman fault. Units: No pattern = Quaternary deposits of alluvial fans, pediments, sand dunes, hamuns (playas) and other materials; 1. = Pliocene and/or Miocene Kamerod formation; 2. = Oligicene Khojak flysch; 3. = Eocene (?) sandstones and siltstones, perhaps the Kullen formation of Bakr (1963) and Ahmed (1964); 4. = Eocene Nauroz formation; 5. = Palaeocene Rakhshani formation; 6. = Cretaceous (?) to Palaeocene (?) Kuchakki volcanics. Units 5 & 6 are probably combined as the Bunap formation by Bakr (1963) and Ahmed (1964).

N–S trending left lateral strike slip faults of the Chaman transform zone.

The Siahan fault–Chaman fault and Hoshab fault–Ghazaband fault connections clearly illustrate this interaction at present (Figs 2 & 4). Other faults showing this relation are the Ahmad Wal, Usman, Panjgur, and Nai Rud faults. Other less well-known faults intervene between these. Virtually all these faults have evidence of recent activity. Thus, thrusting is spread over a very wide zone (over 400 km) above the subducting slab of the Arabian plate (Jacob & Quittmeyer 1979). The accretionary prism is carried N on the subducting slab as well as being thrust S over the slab (partially coupled motion). Complete decoupling occurs somewhere not far N of the Ahmad Wal fault.

The E Ras Koh (Fig. 3) shows the pattern of this interaction through two generations of faults. The older Sotkiano thrust is sub-horizontal, at least where we have seen it in the N part of the map area. The Kamerod formation (locally derived and Miocene–Pliocene in age) may, in part, have been shed off the front of this thrust and then overridden by it. R. S. Arthurton (pers. comm. 1979) has found similar thrusts involving Kamerod and older units in the Dalbandin trough between Ras Koh and the Chagai Hills. If the NE bend of the E Ras Koh is a tectonic drag feature associated with the Chaman fault, the Sotkiano thrust may be an early pre-drag structure developed when this portion of the Ras Koh was oriented nearly E–W and the stress field was favourable to thrust faulting.

The younger Ahmad Wal, Usman, and Kharan faults are all steeply dipping to the NW. All three show evidence of Quaternary activity based on offsets of fan and pediment gravels. These faults appear to have oblique motion, reverse slip that is up on the N combined with left lateral slip. They may continue into thrust or high angle reverse faults in the W Ras Koh (Bakr 1963) and form the contemporary transition element between thrust and strike slip motion. Their gradual merger into the Chaman fault without loss of continuity is best exposed on the Usman fault.

Recent pattern: oblique slip element

The current pattern of faulting between the Makran thrust belt and the Chaman transform zone is shown in Fig. 4. It is worth noting that the traces of many of the thrust faults have a bulge to the E where they rotate into the transform zone. This is clearly shown by the Panjgur and Ornach-Nal faults and is present

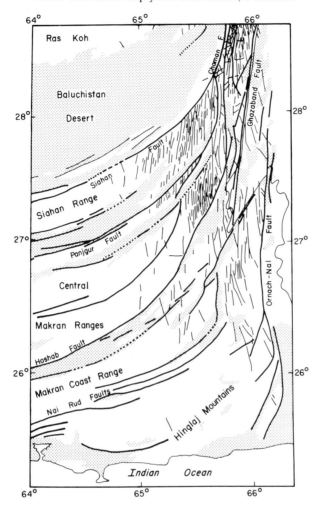

FIG. 4. Structural pattern of the present interaction of the Makran convergence zone and the Chaman transform zone. Heavy lines are major faults; light lines, minor faults and fractures. Continuous light line near Ornach-Nal and Ghazaband faults gives western boundary of Mesozoic outcrops. Dot pattern indicates major areas of Quaternary cover. Figure drawn from Landsat mosaic.

on most of the major faults between them. One suspects that the smooth curve of the Siahan fault is the original configuration and that the bulge is a later development. Thus, the Siahan is one of the youngest faults in the area. These bulges imply that material is being transported from the Makran convergence zone into the transform zone.

Concentrated at the intersection of the two fault systems are a series of fractures between the major faults. These are most intensely developed between the Siahan and Hoshab faults where they are oriented approximately

N–S. They are oblique to fold axes at 30–40°. Folds are tighter than farther W and cleavage is very intensely developed in these fracture zones. To the W cleavage is poorly developed. S of the Hoshab fault, the fractures are less abundant and are oriented up to 15° W of N. These fractures are probably related to the concentration of stress that occurs at the intersection between structures.

The W boundary of the outcrops of Mesozoic rocks at the edge of the Indo-Pakistani subcontinent is displaced at the Nai Rud faults (Fig. 2). The offset of the boundary

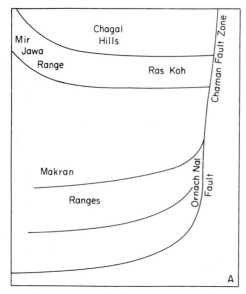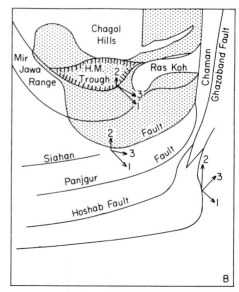

FIG. 5. Oroclinal bending of Ras Koh-Mir Jawa Range and opening of Hamun i Mashkel fault trough. A. Structural configuration before opening of fault trough (Miocene?). B. Structural configuration after opening of fault trough. Vectors resolve hypothetical displacements acting at three locations. (1) Displacement related to fault trough opening, decreasing to the SE. (2) Displacement related to convergence, decreasing to N. (3) Net displacement. Pattern indicates area of Quaternary cover to emphasize the lack of surface expression of suggested structures.

reflects approximately the position of the bulging fault traces.

The presence of oblique slip is also indicated by a recently discovered tectonic depression S of the Chagai Hills and W of the Ras Koh (Fig. 2). The Hamun i Mashkel fault trough is beautifully defined by aeromagnetic data (A. Farah *et al.*, in prep.). It is almost entirely concealed by Quaternary sediments of the Baluchistan Desert from which one may infer that it formed in the Pliocene or Miocene. The fault trough is bounded on the S by the Ras Koh and Mir Jawa Ranges which contain equivalent stratigraphy and are probably continuous under the Baluchistan Desert. Opening of the fault trough resulted from left lateral movement across the Makran convergence zone and was superimposed on or interrupted the northward directed fold and thrust regime. This oblique motion (combined left lateral and thrust) produced different tectonic results in different areas, perhaps depending on the nature of the underlying lithosphere. In the Makran Ranges, the main obvious result is the bulging eastward of thrust traces (Fig. 4). In the area N of the Ras Koh–Mir Jawa Range no effect is seen except perhaps bending of Chaman fault trace (Fig. 2). Between these areas the Mir Jawa Range has pulled loose from the

Chagai Hills and moved southeastward as a coherent block, leaving the Hamun i Mashkel fault trough in its wake (Fig. 5).

The cause of this oblique motion is uncertain. It may result from collision of the Arabian plate with Iran in the Pliocene (Fig. 1) which imposed an eastward directed component of motion on the central Iran and Lut blocks that could produce left slip across the Makran convergence zone.

Conclusion: motion of the transform and convergence zones

The discussion above shows that the rate of motion and total displacement across the Chaman transform zone is closely related to the convergence adjacent to the zone. S of the Ahmad Wal fault, plates are moving N on both sides of the transform zone, and the rate of left slip is determined by the differential ratio of plate motion plus the partial decoupling by thrusting of the Makran surface rocks. Total displacement across the transform may be quite small in the S but increases to the N. From the Ahmad Wal fault to just N of Quetta no convergence occurs within the plates and the transform zone is narrow. Thus, constant total displacement and displacement rate might be anticipated for this area. From the Zhob N, the transform zone is very wide. Part of the displacement is absorbed in the Zhob fold and thrust belt. Thus, displacement rate is decreased by being distributed over more structures and total displacement on individual faults decreases. All, or nearly all, transform motion is finally absorbed in the N on the extensions of the Himalayan, Hindu Kush, and other thrust systems of the great Himalayan convergence zone.

ACKNOWLEDGMENTS: Support for this work was provided by NSF EAR 78–15476 and NSR Int. 76-22304 grants and the Geological Survey of Pakistan. Mr Asrarullah, Director General of the Geological Survey of Pakistan extended every facility and cooperation. Landsat imagery was provided by the Missions Utilization Office of the National Aeronautics and Space Administration through the courtesy of Charles Bohn and Stanley C. Freden.

References

AHMED, W. 1964. Iron-copper deposits of Bandgan, Kimri, and Jadino; Raskoh Range, Chagai district, West Pakistan. *Symposium on Mining Geology and the Base Metals, Ankara, Turkey.* 181–90.

BAKR, A. 1963. Geology of the western Ras Koh Range, Chagai and Kharan districts, Quetta and Kalat divisions, West Pakistan. *Rec. geol. Surv. Pak.* **10**, 1–28.

—— & JACKSON, R. O. 1964. *Geological Map of Pakistan* 1:2,000 000. Geological Survey of Pakistan, Quetta.

CROWELL, J. C. 1968. Movement histories of faults in the Transverse Range and speculations on the tectonic history of California. *In:* DICKINSON, W. R. & GRANT, A. (eds), *Proceedings of the Conference on Geologic Problems of the San Andreas Fault Systems.* Stanford Univ. Publ. Geol. Sci. **11**, 323–41.

DAVIS, G. A. & BURCHFIEL, B. C. 1973. Garlock fault; and infracontinental transform structure, Southern California, *Bull. geol. Soc. Am.* **84**, 1407–22.

DEJONG, K. A. & FARAH, A. 1978. The plate boundary west of the Indo-Pakistan subcontinent. *Geol. Soc. Am. Abst. with Prog.* **10**, 387.

DEWEY, J. E. & BURKE, K. C. A. 1973. Tibetan, Variscan, and precambrian basement reactivation: products of continental collision. *J. Geol. Chicago,* **81**, 683–92.

FARHOUDI, G. & KARIG, D. E. 1977. Makran of Iran and Pakistan as an active arc system. *Geology,* **5**, 664–8.

GANSSER, A. 1964. *The Geology of the Himalayas.* Wiley-Interscience, New York, 289 p.

—— 1966. The Indian Ocean and the Himalayas. A geological interpretation. *Eclog. geol. Helv.* **59**, 931–48.

HOBBS, B. E., MEANS, W. D. & WILLIAMS, P. F. 1976. *An Outline of Structural Geology.* Wiley, New York, 571 p.

JACOB, K. H. & QUITTMEYER, R. C. 1979. The Makran region of Pakistan and Iran: trench-arc system with active plate subduction, *In:* FARAH, A. & DEJONG, K. A. (eds), *Geodynamics of Pakistan.* Geological Survey of Pakistan, Quetta 305–18.

JONES, A. G. (ed.) 1961. *Reconnaissance Geology of part of West Pakistan, a Columbo Plan Cooperative Project.* Oshawa, Government of Pakistan, 550 p. (Hunting Survey Report).

KAZMI, A. 1979. Active fault systems of Pakistan. *In:* FARAH, A. & DEJONG, K. A. (eds), *Geodynamics of Pakistan.* Geological Survey of Pakistan, Quetta, 285–94.

KARIG, D. E. 1974. Evolution of arc systems in the western Pacific. *In:* DONATH, F. (ed.), *Annual Review of Earth and Planetary Sciences,* **2**, 51–75.

LAWRENCE, R. D. 1976. Strike slip faulting terminates the Basin and Range province in Oregon. *Bull. geol. Soc. Am.* **87**, 846–50.

—— & YEATS, R. S. 1979. Geological reconnaissance of the Chaman fault in Pakistan. *In:* FARAH, A. & DEJONG, K. A. (eds), *Geodynamics of Pakistan,* Geological Survey of Pakistan, Quetta 351–8.

MCKENZIE, & SCLATER, J. G. 1971. The evolution of the Indian Ocean since the late Cretaceous. *Geophys J. R. astron. Soc.* **24**, 437–528.

POWELL, C. M. A. 1979. A speculative tectonic history of Pakistan and surroundings: some constraints from Indian Ocean, *In:* FARAH, A. & DEJONG, K. A. (eds), *Geodynamics of Pakistan,* Geological Survey of Pakistan, Quetta 5–24.

—— & CONAGHAN, P. J. 1973. Plate tectonics and the Himalayas. *Earth planet. Sci. Lett.* **20**, 1–12.

SARWAR, G. & DEJONG, K. A. 1979. Arcs, oroclines, syntaxes: the curvature of mountain belts of Pakistan. *In:* FARAH, A. & DEJONG, K. A. (eds), *Geodynamics of Pakistan,* Geological Survey of Pakistan, Quetta, 341–50.

SILLITOE, R. H. 1976. Metallogenic evolution of a collisional mountain belt in Pakistan (a preliminary analysis). *Rec. geol. Surv. Pak.* **34**, 1–16.

STOCKLIN, J. 1977. Structural correlation of the Alpine ranges between Iran and Central Asia. *Mem. h. Ser. Soc. Geol. France,* **8**, 333–53.

VREDENBURG, E. W. 1901. A geological sketch of the Baluchistan desert and part of eastern Persia. *Mem. geol. Surv. India* **31**, 179–302.

WADIA, D. N. 1957. *Geology of India.* 3rd ed. MacMillan, London, 536 p.

WHITE, R. S. 1979. Deformation of the Makran

continental margin, *In:* FARAH, A. & DEJONG, K. A. (eds), *Geodynamics of Pakistan*, Geological Survey of Pakistan, Quetta, 295–304.

—— & KLITGORD, K. 1976. Sediment deformation and plate tectonics in the Gulf of Oman. *Earth planet. Sci. Lett.* **32,** 199–209.

WILSON, J. T. 1965. A new class of faults and their bearing on continental drift. *Nature*, **207,** 343–7

WITTEKINDT, H. & WEIPPERT, D. (compilers) 1973. *Geological map of central and eastern Afghanistan, 1:500 000.* Geological Survey of the Federal Republic of Germany, Hannover and Kabul.

R. D. LAWRENCE, & R. S. YEATS, Geology Department, Oregon State University, Corvallis, Oregon.

S. H. KHAN & A. FARAH, Geological Survey of Pakistan, Quetta.

K. A. DE JONG, University of Cincinnati, Ohio.

Active thrusting and the evolution of the Zagros fold belt

J. A. Jackson, T. J. Fitch & D. P. McKenzie

SUMMARY: Earthquake locations and fault-plane solutions reveal the spatial distribution and kinematics of strain release by faulting; information that is difficult to infer from geological evidence alone. In the Alpine-Himalayan belt, thrust faulting can be classified into one of three distinct types, each of which illustrates a particular aspect of continental deformation. Some thrusts are mechanically linked to strike-slip faults. Low angle thrusting is observed in regions where intermediate depth earthquakes and volcanism show that subduction is or was occurring. High angle reverse faulting at shallow depths is seen in the Zagros and it is suggested that this is the result of rejuvenation of old normal faults which stretched and thinned the basement of a Mesozoic continental margin.

The purpose of this paper is to point out three different types of thrusting occurring today in the Alpine-Himalayan belt. Since most seismic deformation is accounted for by relatively infrequent large earthquakes, a detailed examination of the fault plane solutions, aftershock distributions, and surface faulting associated with these larger events is thought to be representative of the brittle deformation occurring in broad regions of continental crust.

Recent studies of active continental deformation show that large horizontal motions often take place on narrow strike-slip systems whose function appears to be to move large blocks of continental material away from zones of collision, thereby avoiding the shortening and thickening of continental crust (e.g. McKenzie 1972; Molnar & Tapponnier 1975). Where crustal shortening is taking place, the seismic deformation is spread over broad regions in contrast to the seismic activity on major strike-slip faults, which is narrowly confined and often bounds relatively aseismic blocks. The first type of thrusting discussed is that which occurs at the ends of some strike-slip faults and is associated with continental block movements. Examples are then shown of active low-angle thrusting and high-angle reverse faulting and their tectonic implications.

Thrusting associated with strike-slip faults

The Dasht-e-Byaz earthquake of 1968 in E central Iran was associated with an 80 km E–W left-lateral strike-slip fault. Its principal aftershocks were both thrusts with NW–SE trend to the N of the western end of the strike-slip fault (Fig. 1). This N–W trend is delineated by smaller aftershocks, the topography, and associated surface faulting (Berberian 1979). These earthquakes are discussed in detail by Jackson & Fitch (1979), but of particular interest here is the mechanics of block faulting. If the faulting represents slip on the W and S sides of a westwards moving block (see inset, Fig. 1), then no major internal deformation of the block is necessary if the horizontal components of the slip vectors on both faults are the same. At Dasht-e-Byaz the control on the fault plane solutions is insufficient to ascertain whether this is so. In practice, some internal deformation is likely because slip by strike-slip and thrusting is not likely to be of the same magnitude.

The Markansu Valley earthquake of 1974 exhibits a similar behaviour (Jackson et al. 1979). The mainshock, which was strike-slip, was followed by aftershocks showing strike-slip and thrust faulting (Fig. 2). The faulting inferred from the trends of the larger aftershocks and fault plane solutions (inset A, Fig. 2) is consistent with that described by Burtman et al. (1963) and Rushentsev (1963) for the NE Pamir. In particular, the large right-lateral NW–SE strike-slip faults which enter the source region from the SE are intimately associated with the E–W thrust faults of the Pamir (see inset B, Fig. 2). The N–S faulting suggested by the aftershocks and fault plane solution of 27.8.74 is supported by the satellite imagery of the area though not reported by field geological observations. Significant internal deformation on the blocks of inset A, Fig. 2 is suggested by the locations of the smaller aftershocks which are diffuse and not confined to the trends shown by the larger aftershocks (Jackson et al. 1979). This appears to be a general phenomenon seen in other continental aftershock sequences (e.g. Whitcomb et al. 1973; Jackson & Fitch 1979) and probably

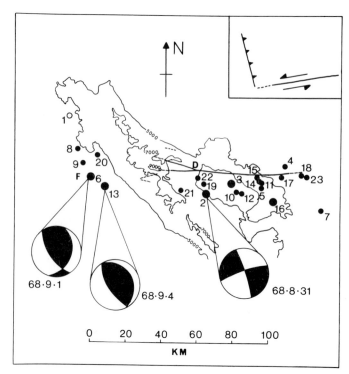

FIG. 1. The aftershock sequence at Dasht-e-Byaz, eastern Iran, after Jackson & Fitch (1979). Large symobls are the larger shocks with $m_b \geqslant 5.2$. Uncertainties for these larger events are about 5 km increasing to 10 km for the smaller. The heavy line marks the surface break mapped by Ambraseys & Tchalenko (1969). Contours are in feet. Numbers are sequential and the open circle is an earlier shock of 1964. Inset shows a cartoon description of the faulting. In this paper fault plane solutions are mostly from McKenzie (1972, 1978a). Those which are not are new and will be published elsewhere. Black quadrants are compressional.

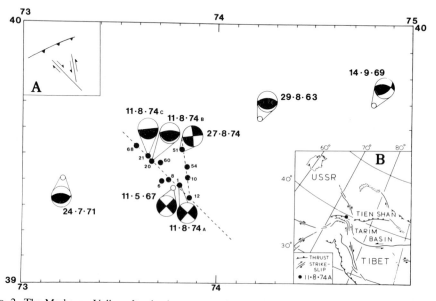

FIG. 2. The Markansu Valley aftershock sequence after Jackson et al. (1979). Closed symbols and sequence numbers are for the 1974 series, open symbols are earlier shocks. Inset A shows a cartoon description of the faulting, and inset B the relation of this source area to the tectonic structure of Central Asia. Uncertainties in relative locations are c. 5 km for the 1974 series.

indicates that most small aftershocks represent minor internal deformation in blocks whose overall motion is controlled by major faults on which the larger earthquakes occur. However, uncertainties in location are greater the smaller the earthquake, so this is easier to demonstrate with local network data (which have better control) than teleseismic data.

Internal deformation of fault-bounded blocks is probably not very significant in the oceans. The curvature of the transform faults and reliability of plate reconstructions allow a kinematic description of oceanic motions in which rigidity is maintained. This will clearly not be the case where movement on strike-slip faults reactivates older faults of only approximately the right orientation to take up the motion at their ends. It should be mentioned that strike-slip faults can also be seen to reactivate neighbouring normal faults, e.g. at Mudurnu, Turkey (McKenzie 1972), Tangshan, China (Butler *et al.* 1979), and Guatemala (Plafker 1976), and that reactivation of other faults can occur anywhere along the length of a pre-existing strike-slip fault.

Low angle thrust faulting

The southern Ionian Sea marks the northern limit of the thrusting associated with the Hellenic Trench (McKenzie 1978*a*). Fig. 3A shows the available fault plane solutions for the area and the locations of the larger earthquakes during the period 1964–1977. This shows a western area of thrusting seaward of the Ionian Islands, which comes ashore at *c.* 39°N and, E of this, an area of predominantly normal faulting. Fig. 3B shows the more reliable earthquake locations for the area and suggests the two regions are separated by an area of relative quiescence. The separation of the normal and thrust faulting is also apparent on the satellite imagery of an area further N in Greece, where the thrusting comes on land (McKenzie 1978*a*). The thrusting solutions, like those by Crete, all have shallow planes dipping NE beneath the Aegean and western Greece. The Hellenic Arc has many features of a subducting system, and, though hard to prove, it is likely that these shallow dipping planes are the active fault planes (McKenzie 1978*a*). Most of the larger shocks in the W of Fig. 3B occur at the base of a steep submarine escarpment with undulating outline (McKenzie 1978*a*) which is possibly the intersection of a low angle thrust plane with the surface. McKenzie (1972) suggested that low angle thrusting occurs over a broad area in this reg-

ion, and this idea is reinforced by the aftershocks of a large (magnitude 7.2) earthquake in 1953 near Kefallinia (Fig. 3C) which spread out over a large area in the northern part of the quiet zone in Fig. 3B. This is in strong contrast to the aftershocks of earthquakes in the Zagros, Iran, shown later.

Further S along the Hellenic Arc near Crete (Fig. 4) most of the big earthquakes have fault-plane solutions that show a low angle plane dipping beneath the Aegean, which is presumably the fault plane (McKenzie 1978*a*). As in Fig. 3 these thrusts are in close spatial proximity to normal faulting (65.4.27) and geological evidence of recent normal faulting has been described from the NW corner of Crete by Angelier (1977)

A similar situation exists in the eastern Himalaya, where fault plane solutions show a shallow dipping plane beneath the Himalaya and normal faulting to the N in southern Tibet (Molnar & Tappionnier 1978).

The Zagros mountains

High angle thrust faulting

The Zagros Mountains of Iran have long been thought of as a classical fold mountain belt resulting from the collision of the Arabian continental plate to the SW with Central Iran to the NE. The area is seismically very active, with earthquakes spread over an area up to 300 km wide with a distinct NE boundary roughly coincident with the Zagros Thrust Line (Falcon 1969, and others). This seismicity is probably all shallower than 40 km (see Jackson 1980 for discussion) and there is no reliable evidence that it increases with depth towards the NE margin of the Zagros. Consequently, there is no convincing evidence of seismic shortening on a single inclined shallow-dipping plane, as is commonly assumed for areas of oceanic underthrusting. Fault plane solutions in the Zagros consistently show thrusting with comparatively high angle (40–50°) fault planes (Figs 5 & 6). It appears that the seismic activity of the Zagros reflects high angle reverse faulting on a large number of faults distributed across the whole width of the belt.

This inference is further supported by the aftershock distributions of two destructive earthquakes in the southern Zagros. Fig. 7 shows the aftershocks from the Ghir earthquake of 1972 which not only lie along a linear trend parallel to the strike of its fault plane solution and the regional structure but

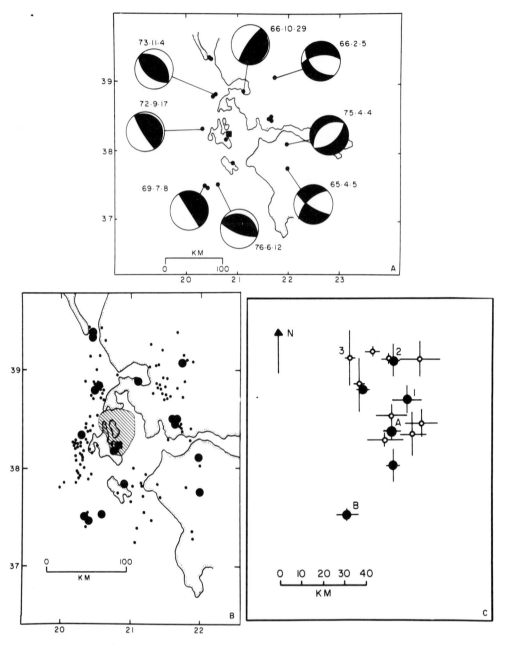

FIG. 3. (A) Major shocks in the southern Ionian Sea during 1964–77. All are greater than m_b5.2. Locations are those determined by the International Seismological Center (ISC) from more than 200 arrival times. The square is the location of the 1953 shock marked by A in Fig. 3C. Hypocentral depths are not well controlled, but are all shallower than 50 km. (B) All shocks in the same area as Fig. 3A with more than 50 arrival times used in their ISC locations. Large symbols are those in Fig. 3A. The 1953 shock is marked by a square in the hatched area which denotes the extent of its aftershock sequence shown in Fig. 3C. (C) the 1953 sequence off Kefallinia covering the hatched area of Fig. 3B. Numbers 1–3 were foreshocks of the mainshock, A of magnitude 7.2 (1953.8.12). B is a magnitude 6.6 shock of 1959.11.5. Errors bars in the locations are shown. McKenzie (1972) reported focal mechanisms for A and B that are not well controlled and contain many inconsistencies. Consequently these solutions are not reproduced here.

continue into the epicentral region of an earlier shock in 1968 which had an identical fault plane solution (Jackson & Fitch 1979). This is in marked contrast to the aftershock distribution of a probable low angle thrust in the Ionian Sea (Fig. 3C). A similar behaviour is seen in the 1977 sequence at Khurgu (Fig. 8). Five fault plane solutions all show faulting on planes dipping 40–50° and a concentrated aftershock distribution elongated parallel to both the regional structure and the fault plane solutions.

In general, the dip of fault plane solutions in the Zagros is well controlled, even in cases where the strike is not. Fig. 6 shows histograms comparing the dips of the planes from fault plane solutions in the Zagros and the Hellenic Trench. They are very different. This difference is manifest not only in the fault plane solutions, but also in the distribution of seismicity, which definitely increases to intermediate depth beneath the Aegean Sea (McKenzie 1978a; Berckhemer pers. comm. 1978).

The evolution of the Zagros fold belt

We propose that the current seismicity of the Zagros is explained by the reactivation of older normal faults as high angle thrusts. There is much evidence that during the Mesozoic and early Tertiary what is now the simply folded belt of the Zagros was a subsiding continental margin (e.g. Stocklin 1968; Haynes & McQuillan 1974; Stoneley 1976). This subsidence began in Permian time (Stocklin 1968), and it is likely that subsidence was preceeded by stretching and thinning of the continental crust

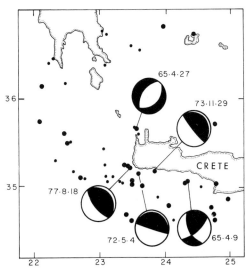

FIG. 4. Seismicity of western Crete during 1964–1975. The large and small symbols represent ISC locations based on more than 100 and more than 50 arrival times respectively.

by normal faulting, as is the case in intracontinental sedimentary basins (McKenzie 1978b). The normal faulting was probably listric, as is observed in the Great Basin (Proffett 1977) and the North Sea and inferred in the Aegean and W Turkey (McKenzie 1978a). Thus, the thick sedimentary column of the Zagros was deposited on thin crystalline basement which was cut through by normal faults. When lateral compression began in the Tertiary, the listric faults in the basement may have been

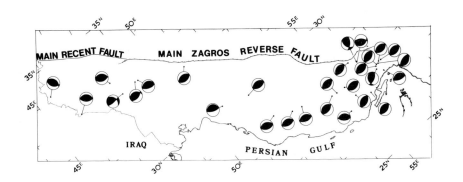

FIG. 5. Fault plane solutions from the Zagros, to illustrate the high angle nature of the thrusting W of the Gulf of Oman. Some of the solutions are from McKenzie (1972), the rest will be published elsewhere.

reactivated as high angle reverse faults, tending to return the basement to its original thickness while causing the younger sedimentary column to take up the shortening by folding. Helwig (1976) showed that sediment deposition on a distended basement removes the space problem caused by alternative hypotheses (e.g. Haynes & McQuillan 1974; Bird *et al.* 1975) in which only the sedimentary cover is shortened and the basement underneath it is removed by low angle thrusting or subduction. Neither the depth nor the focal mechanisms of the earthquakes supports this removal of the basement. In our model, the sedimentary cover is, therefore, passively adjusting to movements in the basement beneath, which takes up the lithospheric convergence by thickening. This possibility has also been suggested by Lees (1952) and Falcon (1969), though the former regarded basement folding as more important than faulting. We believe the available seismic evidence supports such an origin for the folded belt.

This suggestion has a number of implications and consequences. If the sediments of the folded belt formed on a rifted continental margin with oceanic crust to the NE, then most of

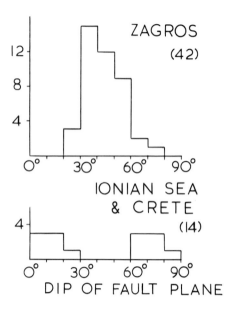

FIG. 6. Histogram comparing the dips of the fault plane solutions in the Zagros with those in the Hellenic Trench. Only those for which the dip was well controlled were used in the dataset.

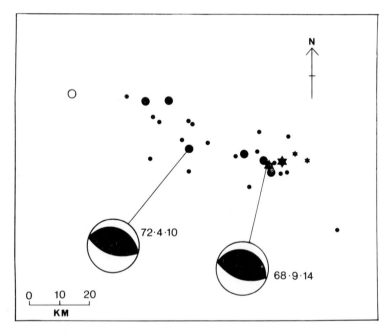

FIG. 7. Aftershocks of the Ghir sequence of 1972.4.10 in the southern Zagros. Large symbols are the bigger events of $m_b \geqslant 5.0$. Stars mark an earlier sequence in 1968 and the open circle an event of 1970. The ISC epicentre for 72.4.10 is 28.39°N, 52.78°E (see Fig. 5 for location). The linearity of the trend paralleled to the strike of the fault plane solutions contrasts with the broad nature of the distribution in Fig. 3C. Uncertainties are for the larger and small symbols are about 5 and 10 km respectively.

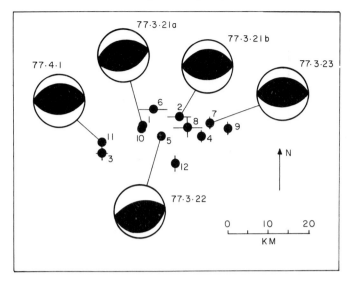

FIG. 8. Aftershocks of the Khurgu earthquake of 1977.3.21 in the southern Zagros. Numbers are sequential and all shocks are greater than m_b 5.0. The ISC epicentre for 77.3.21a is 27.59°N, 56.37°E (see Fig. 5 for location). Errors bars are shown where they are larger than the size of the symbols.

the orignal normal faults in the basement would dip NE. This predominance of one dip direction is seen elsewhere in regions where much stretching has occurred by normal faulting, such as the W part of the Great Basin (Proffett 1977) and the North Atlantic margin (Charpal *et al.* 1978). Most of the thrusts exposed in the northeastern part of the folded and imbricated belt do indeed dip NE (Falcon 1969).

The presence of salt in both the Tertiary sedimentary sequence and at the base of the Palaeozoic sedimentary cover (Stocklin 1968), probably ensures that the surface structures are not related to basement motions in any simple way. The Tertiary salt (Gach Saran Formation) is responsible for the well known disharmonic folding in the Zagros (e.g. Lees 1952; Falcon 1969) and effectively decouples the structures above it from those below. Furthermore, any seismic faulting originating on the basement faults would probably not propagate upwards through the Precambrian Hormuz salt, thus accounting for the lack of surface breaks in the Zagros (e.g. Berberian 1976, 1977). There is also certain to be some dècollement between the basement and the Cambrian caused by the Hormoz Salt Formation (Falcon 1969), so that the structures in the sediment cannot be a simple passive adjustment to basement movement. It is quite possible that the Hormuz salt was itself deposited

on a faulted basement, and that these faults were reactivated in the late Palaeozoic by normal faulting. This possibility was mentioned by Falcon (1969). Stocklin (1968) cites evidence for Precambrian fault structures of the Zagros trend and points out that the Zagros Thrust Line itself was an active Precambrian structural feature which controlled the northern limit of the southern salt plug area. Thus it is likely that several different faulting episodes have affected the Zagros since the late Precambrian.

Discussion and conclusions

The reactivation of old faults and planes of weakness appears to be an important process in continental deformation and is illustrated by the examples shown here. Sykes (1978) also mentions several examples where faults have been reactivated with a different sense of motion from that which first occurred on them. Winslow (this volume) cites geological evidence for reactivation of basement normal faults as high angle reverse faults. In the oceans the rigidity of the plate allows simple kinematic discriptions of their motions which impose severe restrictions on the processes which occur on plate boundaries. On the continents it is therefore important to understand the deformation which occurs at the ends of the long linear strike-slip faults which commonly join regions of compression or extension. It appears that, at the ends of these strike-slip faults, older faults of the most favourable orientation are reactivated, thereby approximately maintaining the direction of motion in the region but causing some internal deformation in the blocks involved. This internal deformation is manifest as the diffuse distribution of minor aftershocks in the blocks defined by the larger earthquake faults

In the Hellenic Trench, Makran and Eastern Himalaya shortening occurs by low angle underthrusting, and the sesimicity of these regions differs markedly from that of the Zagros. Intermediate depth earthquakes are common under Greece and occur, though infrequently, in the Makran. Behind all the areas of low angle thrusting, the existence of volcanism suggests that subduction has occurred in the past also. In the eastern Himalaya, where oceanic crust has completely disappeared, and in the Hellenic Trench, where, if it exists, it is covered by thick sediment (Makris 1975), thrusting may be occurring on the low-angle planes which were active during subduction as in the Makran today (White 1978). It is curious that, behind both the Hellenic Trench and the Himalaya, extension by normal faulting occurs close to the underthrusting and on a trend perpendicular to it.

In the Zagros, shortening is occurring by shallow high-angle reverse faulting spread over a wide area. There is no evidence to support active subduction here and it is suggested that the present-day activity is occurring on reactivated normal faults which stretched and thinned the basement of a continental margin on which the Mesozoic sedimentary cover was deposited. Although the present seismicity is explained by faults with a dip of 40–50°, these probably flatten with depth as they do in other areas where normal faulting has led to subsidence of sedimentary basins (e.g. McKenzie 1978b) and continental margins (e.g. Charpal *et al.* 1978). This particular geometry allows considerable extension and crustal thinning to take place so that, when the faults are regenerated as thrusts, shortening of the sedimentary cover can occur without creating abnormally thick continental crust. It is unlikely that this origin explains all the active high-angle reverse faulting in continental regions, some of which is remote from present or Palaeozoic continental margins (e.g. Molnar & Tapponnier 1975; Tapponnier & Molnar 1979). The asymmetry of the folds and thrusts in the Zagros is presumably caused by the consistent dip directions of the faults on a rifted continental margin. A more chaotic pattern would be expected if an intracontinental sedimentary basin was compressed, as the faults in such basins commonly dip in two directions. If the pattern of normal faulting which created the Great Basin of western Turkey were later covered in sediment following subsidence (e.g. North Sea, Aegean), it might yield the structures observed in the Tien Shan and Nan Shan (Tapponnier & Molnar 1977, 1979) when compressed.

ACKNOWLEDGMENTS. We thank P. Molnar for helpful criticism. D. McGregor of the ISC provided arrival time data for the Khurgu sequence. This work was supported in part by the advanced Research Projects Agency of the Department of Defence and in part by USGS contract 14-08-001-16758. J. J. gratefully acknowledges a scholarship from the Shell Oil Company.

References

AMBRASEYS, N. & TCHALENKO, J. 1969. The Dasht-e-Byaz (Iran) earthquake of August 31, 1968: a field report, *Bull. Seismol. Soc. Am.* **59**, 1751–92.

ANGELIER, J. 1977. Sur l'évolution téctionique depuis le Miocene Supériér d'un arc insulaire Méditerranean: L'arc Egeen., *Rev. geogr. phys Geol. dyn.* **19**, 271.

BERBERIAN, M. 1976. Contributions to the seismotectonics of Iran (part 2). *Rep. Geol. Surv. Iran.* **39**

—— 1977. Contributions to the seismotectonics of Iran (part 3). *Rep. Geol. Surv. Iran.* **40**

—— 1979. Earthquake faulting and bedding thrust associated with the Tabas-e-Golshan (Iran) earthquake of September 16, 1978. *Bull. Seismol. Soc. Am.* **69**, 1861–87.

BIRD, P., TOKSOZ, M. & SLEEP, N. 1975. Thermal and mechanical models of continent-continent convergence zones. *J. geophys. Res.* **80**, 4405–16.

BURTMAN, V. S., PEIVE, A. V. & RUSHENTSEV, S. V. 1963. The main strike-slip faults of the Tien Shan and Pamir. *In: Faults and Horizontal Movements of the Earth's Crust.* Transactions of the Institute of Geology, Academy of Sciences of the USSR, Issue **80**.

BUTLER, R., STEWART, G. S. & KAHAMORI, H. 1979. The July 27, 1976 Tangshan, China Earthquake—a complex sequence of intraplate events. *Bull. Seismol. Soc. Am.* **69**, 207–20.

CHARPAL, O., MONTADERT, L., GUENNOC, P. & ROBERTS, D. G. 1978. Rifting, crustal attenuation and subsidence in the Bay of Biscay. *Nature*

London, **275**, 706.

FALCON, N. L. 1969. Problems of the relationship between surface structure and deep displacements illustrated by the Zagros Range. *In:* SPENCER. A. M. (eds), *Time and Place in Orogeny*, Spec. Publ. geol. Soc. London, **4,** 9–22.

HAYNES, S. J. & McQUILLAN, H. 1974. Evolution of the Zagros Suture Zone, Southern Iran, *Bull. geol. Soc. Am.* **85,** 739–44.

HELWIG, J. 1976. Shortening of continental crust in orogenic belts and plate tectonics. *Nature London,* **290,** 768–70.

JACKSON, J. A. 1980. Errors in focal depth determination and the depth of seismicity in Iran and Turkey, *Geophys. J. R. astron. Soc.* (in press)

—— & FITCH, T. J. 1979. Seismotectonic implications of relocated aftershock sequences in Iran and Turkey. *Geophys. J. R. astron. Soc.* **57,** 209–29.

——, MOLNAR, P., PATTON, H. & FITCH, T. J. 1979. Seismotectionic aspects of the Markansu Valley, Tadjikstan earthquake of August 11, 1974. *J. geophys. Res.* **84,** 6157–67.

LEES, G. M. 1952. Foreland folding. *Q. J. geol. Soc. London,* **108,** 1–34.

MAKRIS, J. 1975. Crustal structure of the Aegean Sea and Hellenides obtained from geophysical surveys. *J. Geophys.* **41,** 441.

McKENZIE, D. P. 1972. Active tectonics of the Mediterranean Region. *Geophys. J. R. astron. Soc.* **30,** 109.

—— 1978a. Active tectonics of the Alpine-Himalayan belt: the Aegean Sea and surrounding regions. *Geophys. J. R. astron. Soc.* **55,** 217–54.

—— 1978b. Some remarks on the development of Sedimentary Basins. *Earth planet. Sci. Lett.* **40,** 25–32.

MOLNAR, P. & TAPPIONNIER, P. 1975. Cenozoic tectonics of Asia, effects of continental collision. *Science,* **189,** 419–25.

—— & —— 1978. Active tectonics of Tibet. *J. geophys. Res.* **83,** 5361–75.

PLAFKER, G. 1976. Tectonic aspects of the Guatemala earthquake of 4 February 1976, *Science,* **93,** 1201–8.

PROFFETT, J. M. 1977. Cenozoic geology of the Yerington district, Nevada, and implication for the nature and origin of Basin and Range faulting. *Bull. geol. Soc. Am.* **88,** 247–66.

RUSHENTSEV, S. V. 1963. Transcurrent fault in the South East Pamir. *In: Faults and Horizontal Movements of the Earth's Crust,* Transactions of the Institute of Geology, Academy of Sciences of the USSR, Issue **80**.

STOCKLIN, J. 1968. Structural history and tectonics of Iran: a review. *Bull. Am. Assoc. Petrol. Geol.* **52,** 1229–58.

STONELEY, R. 1976. On the origin of ophiolite complexes in the southern Tethys region, *Tectonophysics,* **25,** 303–22.

SYKES, L. R. 1978. Intraplate seismicity, Reactivation of Pre-existing Zones of Weakness, Alkaline Magmatism, and other Tectonism past-dating continental fragmentation. *Rev. Geophys. Space Phys.* **16,** 621–88.

TAPPONNIER, P. & MOLNAR, P. 1977. Active faulting and tectonics in China. *J. geophys. Res.* **82,** 2905.

—— & —— 1979. Active faulting and Cenozoic tectonics of the Tien Shan, Mongolia and Baykal Regions. *J. geophys. Res.* **84,** 3425–59.

WHITCOMB, J. H., ALLEN, C. R., GARMANY, J. D. & HILEMAN, J. A. 1973. San Fernando earthquake series, 1971: focal mechanism and tectonics. *Rev. Geophys. Space Phys.* **11,** 693–730.

WHITE, R. S. 1978. Deformation of the Makran continental margin. *In: Geodynamics of Pakistan,* Mem. geol. Surv. Pak. **11.**

J. A. JACKSON & D. P. McKENZIE, Department of Geodesy & Geophysics, Madingley Rise, Madingley Road, Cambridge, CB3 0EZ.

T. J. FITCH, Applied Seismology Group, MIT Lincoln Laboratory, 42 Carleton Street, Cambridge, Mass. 02142. U.S.A.

An overview of thrusts and nappes of western Himalaya

V. C. Thakur

SUMMARY: The Shali-Deoban Parautochthon, Krol Berinag Nappes and Outer
Crystallines Nappes are the main lithostructural units of the Lesser Himalaya of
Kumaun, Garhwal and eastern Himachal. Two thrust sheets, the Chail Nappe and the
Jutogh Nappe are recognized in the Outer Crystallines Nappes. The Chail Nappe forms a
separate thrust sheet, and the Jutogh Nappe overlying it represents a southward
extension of the Central Crystallines Nappe of the Higher Himalaya. The Chail Nappe
rocks constitute the base of the Palaeozoic–Mesozoic sequence of the Kashmir-Chamba
Parautochthon, whereas the Central Crystallines Nappe forms the basement for the late
Precambrian–Cretaceous sequence of the Tethyan Zone in the Kumaun, Spiti and
Zaskar regions. The Central Crystallines Nappe shows a progressive regional
metamorphism, chlorite to sillimanite grade, whereas the metamorphism of the Chail
Nappe is mainly confined to the greenschist facies. Metamorphic inversion is a characteristic feature of the Jutogh Nappe which occurs as crystalline klippen in the Lesser
Himalaya Zone. The ophiolite suite of rocks of the Indus-Tsangpo suture occurs also as
klippen above the sediments of the Tethys Himalaya and metamorphics of the Tso
Morari Dome. They appear to have resulted from squeezing out from the root zone and
subsequent gravity gliding. The Indus Suture Zone is unique with regard to its thrust
tectonics, in that, whereas all the principal thrusts elsewhere in the Himalaya are
directed towards the S, within this zone they are directed only toward the N.

The western Himalaya comprises the part of
the Himalaya lying to the W of Nepal, and
includes the regions of Kumaun, Garhwal,
Himachal and Kashmir (Fig. 1). It has been
studied more extensively than the other parts,
both by earlier and later workers. Among the
significant early contributions to unravel
the structural framework and tectonic evolution of this part of the Himalaya, are the works
of Pilgrim & West (1928), Auden (1934,
1937), Wadia (1928; 1938) and Heim & Gansser (1939). In subsequent years, a large volume
of data on the structure and tectonics has been
generated by workers from Geological Survey
of India, the Wadia Institute of Himalayan
Geology and various universities. These
geologists have confined their studies largely to
the regional geology, to structural and tectonic
analysis and to the metamorphic history. The
author has undertaken several N–S traverses in
Kumaun, Garhwal, Himachal and Kashmir,
and has also made some detailed studies of the
Central Crystallines of the Higher Himalayan
Zone in Kumaun and of the Indus Suture
Zone in Ladakh.

Six structural zones can be recognized in the
western Himalaya (Fig. 1). They are: (1) the
Tertiary belt of the Sub-Himalaya; (2) the
platform sediments and crystalline klippen of
the Lesser Himalaya; (3) the Kashmir-Chamba
Parautochthon; (4) the Central Crystallines of
Higher Himalaya; (5) the Upper Precambrian–
Cretaceous sequence of the Tethys Himalaya;

and (6) the ophiolitic melange with flysch,
molasse and intrusives of the Indus Suture
Zone. No major thrusts or nappes have been
observed in the Sub-Himalaya or the Tethys
Himalaya zones. An overview of the main
tectonic features of the other four zones follows.

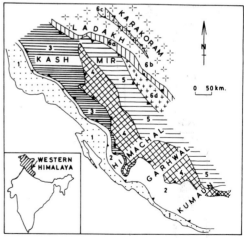

FIG. 1. Structural zones of western
Himalaya. 1) Sub-Himalaya, 2) Lesser
Himalaya, 3) Kashmir-Chamba Par-
autochthon, 4) Higher Himalaya, 5)
Tethys Himalaya, 6a) Indus Suture, 6b)
Ladakh and Karakoram Batholiths, 6c)
Shyok Ophiolitic Melange, 6d) Tso
Morari Dome.

Nappes of the Lesser Himalaya

The Lesser Himalaya Zone is delimited by the Main Central Thrust to the N and the Main Boundary Fault or the Krol Thrust to the S. It thus forms a broad NW–SE trending belt between Lower Tertiaries to the S and Central Crystallines to the N. This belt narrows towards the N–W from the Simla Hills to the Jammu area of Kashmir (Fig. 2). Although the lithostratigraphy and the major structural units of the zone have been established, a lack of fossil control has given rise to divergent opinions about the age and stratigraphic positions of various lithostratigraphic units. Three principal lithostructural divisions have been recognized in the Lesser Himalaya Zone on the basis of their lithostratigraphy and tectonic setting (Table 1).

Shali-Deoban Parautochthon

The rocks of the Shali-Deoban unit are exposed between the Sub-Himalayan Lower Tertiary sediments and the metamorphics of the Chail Nappe, in a narrow belt extending from Jammu in the NW to Shali in the Simla Hills in the SE (Fig. 2). Their extension further to the SE appears to be concealed in the Chor mountain region as a result of overlap of the crystallines of the Chail and Jutogh Nappes. They reappear near Deoban and can be traced as a continuous belt SE to Pithoragarh. Another, inner, belt of the unit appears to the N in Eastern Kumaun.

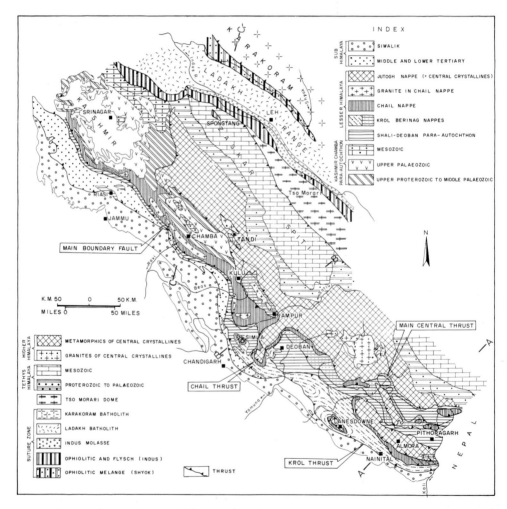

FIG. 2. Tectonic map of western Himalaya (compiled on the basis of author's own work and other published data).

The rocks of Shali-Deoban Parautochthon form the lowermost tectonic unit of Lesser Himalaya; its base is not clearly exposed. The lower part consists of quartzites and slates with intercalcated volcanic flows of spilitic composition. These rocks are overlain by orthoquartzites and carbonates with shales, siltstones and halite, characterized by prolific stromatolites of Riphaean age. Some workers (Valdiya 1964; Srikantia & Bhargava 1976) have correlated the orthoquartzite-carbonate rocks of the Shali-Deoban unit with rocks of the Vindhyan System of the Peninsular shield of India, suggesting an extension of the sediments of the Indian platform into the Himalaya.

Krol-Berinag Nappes

Two structural units have been recognized above the Shali-Deoban Parautochton: the Berinag Nappe in the inner belt and the Krol Nappe in the outer belt (Fig. 3).

The Berinag Nappe consists of a thick succession of quartzites and basic volcanics. They are exposed in the Rampur window and also extend as a continuous belt from the River Tons in the W to the River Kali in the E, where they overlie the orthoquartzite-carbonate sequence of the Shali-Deoban unit. The quartzite of Berinag Nappe is characterized by occurrence of sporadic uranium mineralization and also contains large sills, of deformed granite a few kilometres in length.

The Krol Nappe, however, consists of greywacke, shale, siltstone quartzite and volcanics in the lower part (Jaunsars = Simlas) and diamictite, shale, carbonate and quartzite in the upper part (Krols). It also extends as a belt from Krol Hill in the Simla area in the W to the Nepal border in the E. The occurrence of Eocene nummulitic beds in windows beneath the Krol Nappe proves its allochthonous nature (Auden 1934; Bhargava 1976).

The lower part of the Krol Nappe, the Nagthat Formation, is correlated with the quartzites of Berinag Nappe (Rupke 1974; Valdiya 1976). The Berinag Nappe is therefore considered to be the northern prolongation of the Krol Nappe (Fig. 4a & b). The upper part of the Krol Nappe, comprising diamictites, carbonates, shales and quartzite, is not represented in the Berinag Nappe. This suggests

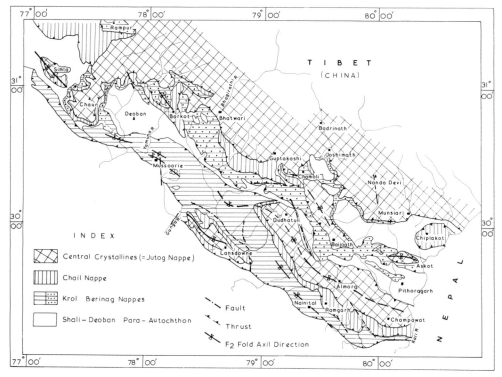

FIG. 3. Lesser Himalaya of Kumaun, Garhwal and eastern Himachal showing principal thrusts, folds and faults in different structural zones (modified after Valdiya 1976).

TABLE 1: *Lithostructural zones of Himalaya and southern part of Trans Himalaya in western Himalaya.*

Main divisions	Principal structural zones	Sub-divisions of structural zones	Lithostratigraphic and other features	Age
Trans Himalaya	Shyok Suture Zone	Karakoram Batholith	2 Mica granite, tonalite, hornblende granite and migmatoid gneiss	Precambrian, Oligocene and Miocene?
		——— Thrust ———		
		Shyok Ophiolitic Melange	Basic volcanics, serpentinites, pyroxenites, diorite and sediments.	Permian fauna in limestone
		——— Thrust ———		
		Khardung Volcanics	Dacite, rhyolite, ignimbrite, agglomerate, limestone	Palaeocene–Eocene
		——— Intrusive Junction ———		
	(Indus Suture Zone)	Ladakh Intrusives	Tonalite, hornblende granite, diorite	Upper Cretaceous and Oligocene
		——— Transgressive Contact ———		
(Indus Suture Zone)		Indus Molasse	Conglomerate, sandstone, shale	Miocene
		——— Thrust ———		
		Ophiolitic Melange, ophiolite with flyschoid sediments.	Melange of basic volcanics, serpentinites, pyroxenites, sediments: Ophiolite has mappable units of ultrabasic, gabbro, pillow lavas with chert and jasper. Alternation of shale and limestone, sandstone and shale constitute flyschoid sediments.	Cretaceous
		——— Zaskar Thrust ———		
Tethys Himalaya	Tethyan Zone	Cambrian–Cretaceous	A fairly complete sequence, Cambrian–Cretaceous; richly fossiliferous; orthoquartzite, carbonate and shale.	Cambrian–Cretaceous
		Haimanta (= Martoli)	Phyllite and quartzite; lowermost unit of Tethyan zone	Late Precambrian

			Lithology / Description	Age
Higher Himalaya	Central Crystallines		15–20 km thick crystalline sheet forming basement for late Precambrian–Cretaceous sequence of Tethyan Zone. Metasediments, granitoids, migmatites, amphibolites and granite. Progressive regional metamorphism, chlorite to sillimanite grade.	Precambrian, remobilized during Caledonian and Tertiary orogenic cycles.
			——————— Main Central Thrust ———————	
Lesser Himalaya	Outer Crystallines	Jutogh Nappe	Upper crystalline sheet of the crystalline klippen, representing southern extension of Central Crystallines in the Lesser Himalaya. Metasediments with granite bodies showing inverted metamorphism ranging from biotite to sillimanite grade.	Precambrian
			——— Jutogh Thrust (=Main Central Thrust) ———	
		Chail Nappe	Lower crystalline sheet of the crystalline klippen of the Lesser Himalaya. Epigrade metasediments, retrogression prevalent. Gneissose granite bodies within metasediments.	Lower–Middle Cambrian?
			——————— Chail Thrust ———————	
	Krol, Berinag Nappes	Tal, Krol, Infra-Krol, Blaini.	Sandstone, quartzite, phosphate, limestone, dolomite, shale, diamictite	Upper Palaeozoic —Mesozoic
		Nagthat, Chandpur, Mandhali (=Simla Group=Berinag)	Orthoquartzite, sandstone, siltstone, shale, limestone	Lower Palaeozoic
			——————— Thrust ———————	
	Shali-Deoban Parautochthon	Upper / Lower	Shale, siltstone, quartzite, limestone, dolomite, salt / Quartzite, slate, phyllite and basic volcanics	Precambrian (Riphaen)
			——————— Main Boundary Fault ———————	
Sub-Himalaya	Neogene	Siwalik	Conglomerate, sandstone, shale (Molasse type sediments)	Middle Miocene Pleistocene Lower Miocene
	Palaeogene	Dharamsala	Sandstone, greywacke, siltstone, shale with plant fossils	
		Subathu	Shale and limestone	Eocene– Palaeocene

that the rocks of the Krol and Berinag Nappes were deposited in two separate basins; the absence of the upper formations from the Berinag Nappe is probably due to Hercynian uplift.

Outer crystallines nappes

Several thrust sheets of metamorphic rocks occur as klippen above the sediments of the Lesser Himalaya in eastern Himachal, Garhwal and Kumaun (Fig. 3). The major klippen are those of Simla, Lansdowne, Almora, Baijnath and Askote. They occupy the highest structural level of the Lesser Himalaya zone, and two separate thrust sheets, referred to as the Chail and Jotogh Nappes, are recognized (Pilgrim & West 1928; Valdiya 1976; 1978).

The Chail Nappe

The Chail Nappe, the lower metamorphic thrust sheet, is thrust over the sediments of the Krol and Berinag Nappes as well as over the Shali-Deoban Parautochthon. It is made up of phyllites and quartzites with some acidic and basic volcanics. The metamorphism is mainly of greenschist facies but the metasediments contain bands of mylonitic gneiss and large bodies of granite: the Dalhousie Granite and the Mandi Granite have been dated (Rb/Sr), giving whole rock isochron-ages of 500 ± 100 Ma and 456 ± 50 Ma respectively. The Chail Nappe is overlain with a thrust contact by the metamorphics of the Jutogh Nappe in the klippen units. A similar structural relationship also exists in the Simla and Kulu areas of eastern Himachal but, further NW in the regions of Chamba and Kashmir, the rocks of the Chail Nappe form the basement to the Cambrian–Triassic sequence in the Kashmir and Chamba synclinoria (Fig. 2).

The Jutogh Nappe

The upper thrust sheets of the crystalline klippen form the Jutogh Nappe. They consist of metasediments with bands of basic rocks and large bodies of gneissic granite, showing progressive regional metamorphism from the biotite to the sillimanite zone. Inversion of metamorphism, i.e. an upwards increasing metamorphic grade, is the most characteristic feature of the Jutogh Nappe in the Lesser Himalaya.

Previously, the Jutogh Nappe was considered to be a tectonic unit separated from the Central Crystallines Nappe of the Higher Himalaya. However, recent investigation by the author has shown that the rocks of the Jutogh Nappe extend northwards from the Chaur Mountain area (E of Simla) to the Satluj valley, where they join the Central Crystallines Nappe N of the Rampur window. It is, therefore, evident that the upper crystalline klippen in the Lesser Himalaya represents detached remnants of the Central Crystallines Nappe of the Higher Himalaya. It is only for purposes of nomenclature that the term Central Crystallines Nappe is restricted to the main belt of the Higher Himalaya and that its extension in the klippen of Lesser Himalaya zone is referred to as the Jutogh Nappe.

Structural history of the Lesser Himalaya

The structural histories of all the units in the Lesser Himalaya have not yet been investigated; however, some data exist from the Krol and Berinag Nappes and from the Chail and Jutogh Nappes. The Chail and Jutogh Nappes have undergone at least three episodes of ductile folding (Ray & Naha 1971; Virdi 1976; Merh 1977). The first phase produced both recumbent and reclined isoclinal folds and an axial plane schistosity. The second phase folds have a NW–SE trend and open to close style. The third phase folds are similar in style to the F_2 folds, but their axes trend NE–SW to N–S. The rocks of the Krol Nappe have also suffered three phases of folding, somewhat similar to those of the Chail Nappe (Bhattacharya & Niyogi 1971; Pal & Merh 1974).

The second phase of folding is predominant. It produced synformal and antiformal structures of regional dimensions, such as the Simla synform, the Lansdowne synform, the Krol and Naini Tal synforms, the Almora synform and others (Fig. 3). It also folded the major Krol Thrust, Chail Thrust, Jutogh Thrust and others, indicating that the thrust movements predated the F_2 episode. These thrusts appear to have been generated as a result of parallel or subparallel shearing during the development of large F_1 recumbent folds. The third phase of deformation produced major transverse culminations and depressions: it is in the depressions that the higher tectonic units of the crystallines klippen are preserved as large basinal structures, and in the regions of culmination that the lowermost structural units of Lesser Himalaya are exposed.

The Sub-Himalaya and Lesser Himalaya zones are affected by several transverse faults (tear faults), tens of kilometres in length (Valdiya 1976). These faults postdated the F_3

folding and are probably related to the uplift of Himalaya.

Kashmir-Chamba Parauthochthon

The Kashmir-Chamba Zone appears to be the NW extension of the Lesser Himalaya Zone of Kumaun, Garhwal and eastern Himachal (Fig. 2), although it differs in its stratigraphic and tectonic setting. It lies between Main Central Thrust in the N and the Chail Thrust (= Panjal Thrust) in the S, but has biostratigraphic affinities with the Tethys Himalaya Zone. In Kashmir, a gigantic synclinorium comprises a basement of rocks of the Chail Nappe (= Salkhalas) overlain by a thick sequence of sediments and volcanics ranging in age from Cambrian to Triassic. The Chamba synclinorium has a similar stratigraphy and structural setting, and represents the SE extension of the Kashmir synclinorium (Thakur & Tandon 1976). The concept of a 'Kashmir Nappe' was proposed by Wadia (1931) and later reinterpreted by Srikantia (1973). However, the Kashmir-Chamba structural zone is not widely allochthonous: the basement of Chail Nappe rocks and its cover sediments are thrust, as a para-autochthonous unit, over the Shali-Deoban belt of the Lesser Himalaya (Fig. 2). Evidence of limited southwards movement over the Shali-Deoban belt is supported by the presence of bands of mylonitized gneiss and metamorphic retrogression in the metasediments of the Chail Nappe, as well as by the development of 'schuppen' structures in the Shali-Deoban belt.

Central Crystallines Nappe

The crystalline rocks of the Higher Himalaya occur as a great thrust sheet, referred to as the Central Crystallines Nappe, with an approximate thickness of 15–20 km. These rocks form the basement to the sequence of Upper Precambrian–Cretaceous sediments of the Tethys Himalaya Zone and extend as a continuous NW–SE belt from western Kashmir to eastern Kumaun. The immensely thick slab of crystalline rocks has been thrust S over the Shali-Deoban and Berinag units in Kumaun and Garhwal, and over the rocks of the Chail Nappe in Himachal Pradesh. The basal thrust is referred to as the Main Central Thrust (Fig. 2), and is of great tectonic significance since it brings a deep level of basement up over the sediments of Lesser Himalaya Zone.

The rocks of the Central Crystallines Zone show a progressive regional metamorphism.

From the Main Central Thrust at the base of the Nappe, metamorphism increases upwards to the anatectic sillimanite zone; it then progressively decreases upwards through the overlying rocks to the chlorite and anchi zones (Thakur 1976). In the overlying cover sediments the metamorphism is largely restricted to the Upper Precambrian Haimanta Formation (= Martoli Formation), and most of the Tethyan Cambrian to Cretaceous sequence remains unaffected; only in the Tandi region of Lahaul are the Mesozoic sediments metamorphosed to amphibolite facies. Stratigraphic evidence (Powell & Connaghan 1973) and radiometric dating (Jaeger et al. 1971; Mehta 1977) have indicated late Tertiary phases (Mio-Pliocene) of metamorphism. However, a 8.30 Ma whole-rock age (Rb-Sr) from gneiss of the Central Crystallines Nappe in Kumaun (Bhanot et al. 1976), and 581 ± 9 Ma (Mehta 1977) from the gneisses of Western Himachal Pradesh, confirm that the rocks of the Nappe formed an old Precambrian basement that has been reactivated during different orogenic epochs (Thakur, in press).

At least two generations of granitic activity can be recognized. The earlier phase is represented by deformed granites occurring as intrusive sheets within the metamorphosed sediments. The later unfoliated leucocratic granites appear to have been associated with anatexis and regional metamorphism.

Three phases of ductile deformation, similar to those described for Jutogh Nappe, are recognised. The first phase is represented by recumbent and reclined isoclinal folds associated with an axial plane schistosity. The widespread folds of second phase have a NW–SE axial trend, and the third phase is transverse (NNE–SSW). The first phase folds affect a metamorphic layering, indicating a pre-F 1 metamorphic and tectonic episode that may be Pre-Alpine in age. The mineral lineation, defined by chlorite, biotite, quartz-fibres and rarely kyanite, indicates a stretching fabric transverse (NNE–NE) to the regional Himalayan trend.

Tso Morari Dome

Schists, gneisses, metabasics and granites occupy a NW–SE trending belt in Ladakh, between the Mesozoic sediments of Tethyan Zone to the S and the ophiolitic melange and ophiolite of the Indus Suture Zone to the N. The boundaries of the belt are thrust faults (Figs 1, 2). The metamorphics occupy a very large, doubly plunging anticlinal fold, referred to as the Tso Morari Dome. The distribution

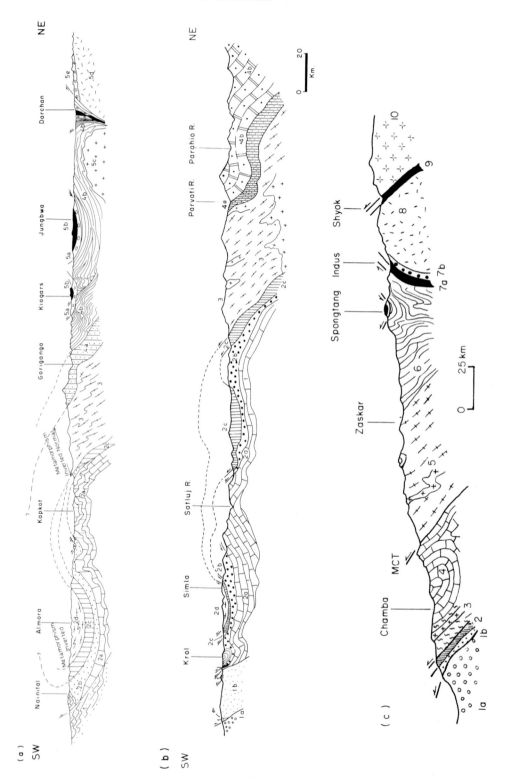

of metamorphic isograds appears to have been controlled by the domal structure: metamorphism is highest (kyanite and sillimanite zones) near the core and decreases progressively to the garnet and biotite zones towards the edges of the fold (Thakur & Virdi 1978). In contrast to the rocks of the Central Crystallines Nappe, which form the Precambrian basement to the Tethyan sediments, the crystalline rocks of the Tso Morari Dome are metamorphosed Palaeozoic sediments (Virdi *et al.* 1978).

Another domal structure, the Gurla Mandhata Dome (Heim & Gansser 1939), has been described in a similar tectonic setting to the E of Tso Morari Dome in southern Tibet.

Thrusts and nappes of Indus-Tsangpo Suture Zone

The Indus-Tsangpo Suture Zone has been studied in Ladakh (Tewari 1964; Ravi Shanker *et al.* 1976; Frank *et al.* 1977; Thakur & Virdi 1978) and its developments in Malla Johar and Kiogar in N Kumaun, and in the adjoining areas of Raksas Lake and Mansarovar in Tibet (China) are known from the early accounts of Von Krafft (1902) and Heim & Gansser (1939). The main litho-structural units of Ladakh, including the regions of the Indus valley, Ladakh Range, Nubra and Shyok valleys and the S slopes of the Karakoram, are given in Table 1.

In all the five structural zones (1–5) of the Himalaya (Fig. 1), the major thrusts dip towards the NE and all of the major folds have a S vergence, except where the thrusts have been folded by second phase folds as in the Almora, Simla and Lansdowne synforms. In the Indus Suture Zone (6a & d), however, all the principal thrusts dip towards the SW and the major folds have a N vergence. Recent investigations in Shyok region, zone 6c (Thakur *et al.* in press), which lies N of the Indus Suture Zone,

has revealed that all the principal lithostructural units, as well as the principal thrusts, again dip NE at a moderate angle. The Indus Suture Zone, therefore, is unique in that all of its major thrusts dip towards the SW (Fig. 4c).

The ophiolitic melange and ophiolite of the Indus-Tsangpo Suture Zone probably represent obducted slabs of oceanic lithosphere. Their structural setting is described below.

Ophiolitic melange and ophiolite nappe of Ladakh

In the area W of Leh, flyschoid sediments of Early as well as late Mesozoic age, together with the ophiolitic melange and volcanic rocks, have been thrust steeply to the N over the molassic sediments of Indus Formation. To the S they have been overthrust by the Mesozoic sediments of Tethyan Zone of Zaskar range (Fig. 4c). The flysch often contains imbrications of platform rocks as well as some of the overlying ophiolites, which have slumped into the flysch (Gansser 1979). The ophiolitic units are disrupted as a result of strong tectonism. 30 km S of the Indus Suture Zone, the 'Spongtang Nappe' or Klippe (Fuchs 1977), consisting of flysch and ophiolitic melange, overlies the Tethyan Mesozoic platform sediments of the Zaskar range (Fig. 2).

The ophiolitic melange unit occurs as a narrow band, a few hundred metres thick, in the region E of Leh. Here the ophiolitic melange belt is overridden by a thick (approx. 5 km) slab of ophiolites, consisting of mappable units of ultramafites, gabbros, dykes and pillow lavas with cherts and jaspers (Thakur & Virdi 1978). This entire belt of ophiolitic melange and ophiolite is thrust over the rocks of the Tso Morari Dome to the S and over the Indus Formation to the N. Small klippen of ophiolitic melange also occur above the metamorphics of the Tso Morari Dome. The steeply dipping

FIG. 4a Section (A–A), generalized, across Kumaun and southern Tibet based on Tectonic map (Fig. 2) and Gansser (1964). (1) Tertiaries (Sub Himalaya). (2a) Shali-Deoban Parautochthon, (2b) Krol Berinag Nappes, (2c) Chail Nappe, (2d) Jutogh Nappe (Lesser Himalaya). (3) Central Crystallines Nappe (Higher Himalaya). (4a) Martoli Formation (Precambrian). (4b) Cambrian to Cretaceous (Tethys Himalaya). (5a) Ophiolitic Melange, (5b) Ultrabasic, (5c) Gurla Mandhata Dome, (5d) Kailash Granite, (5e) Kailash Conglomerate (Indus Tsangpo Suture Zone).

b. Section (B–B) across eastern Himachal based on Tectonic map (Fig. 2). (1a) Siwalik, (1b) Middle and Lower Tertiary, (Sub-Himalaya). (2) Shali-Deoban parautochthon, (2b) Krol Berinag Nappes, (2c) Chail Nappe, (2d) Jutogh Nappe (Lesser Himalaya). (3) Central Crystallines Nappe (Higher Himalaya). (4a) Haimanta, (4b) Cambrian–Cretaceous (Tethys Himalaya).

c. Section (C–C) across Western Himachal and Ladakh based on Tectonic map (Fig. 2). (1a) Siwalik, (1b) Middle and Lower Tertiary. (2) Shali-Deoban Parautochton. (3) Chail Nappe with Dalhousie Granite. (4) Palaeozoic–Mesozoic of Chamba Synclinorium. (5) Central Crystallines Nappe (Higher Himalaya). (6) Palaeozoic–Mesozoic of Zaskar Tethyan zone, (7a) Indus ophiolite and flysch, (7b) Indus molasse. (8) Ladakh Batholith. (9) Shyok ophiolitic melange. (10) Karakoram Batholith.

nature of the Indus Suture Zone, and the klippen which indicate 20–30 km transport of the thrust sheet to the S, suggest that strong tectonism in the Suture Zone resulted in squeezing out and consequent gravity gliding of the ophiolite nappe.

Another belt of ophiolitic melange lies N of the main Indus Suture Zone, in the Shyok area (Thakur *et al.* in press). The Shyok ophiolitic melange belt consists of thrust slices of serpentinites, volcanics, sediments and pyroxenites, and is sandwiched between the Karakoram Batholith to the N and the Ladakh Batholith to the S.

Ophiolitic melange and ultrabasic nappes of Kiogar and Jungbwa

Between the Indian–Tibetan (China) border and the Kailas mountain, Gansser (1974) recognized three major structural units: (1) the Tethys Himalayas, (2) the Kiogar Ophiolitic Melange Nappe, and (3) the Jungbwa Ultrabasic Nappe. The Kiogar Ophiolitic Melange Nappe is thrust over the folded Mesozoic sediments of the Tethys Himalaya cross-cutting pre-existing folds in the sediments, and hence indicates that the thrusting of the nappe postdated the Tethyan folding phase. The ophiolitic melange of Kiogar consists of limestone blocks of Triassic age, Permian–Liassic and Upper Jurassic radiolarites, siliceous shales and limestones, glauconitic sandstones, peridotites, serpentinites, diabase and ophi-carbonates. Some of the limestone blocks have very large dimensions, such as the Kiogar limestone with an area of 20 km^2. The Kiogar ophiolitic melange is again overthrust by the highest structural unit of the entire Himalaya, the Ultrabasic Jungbwa Nappe (Fig. 4a). This nappe is made up predominantly of harzburgites with some local serpentinization in the form of antigorite: its composition indicates original mantle conditions of high temperature and pressure. The area of this sheet is 3500 km^2 with a minimum thickness of 500 m. The Jungbwa Ultrabasic Nappe is interpreted as having originated by the obduction and subsequent S thrusting of a large mantle slab, squeezed out from the line of collision along the Indus Suture Zone between the Indian and Tibetan continental blocks.

Conclusions

Palaeogene sediments of continental to marine environment and the Neogene molasse of the Siwalik Group form the autochthonous belt of the Sub-Himalaya. In the Lesser Himalaya, the sediments of the Shali-Deoban Parautochthon and Krol Berinag Nappes represent the northwards extension of the platform sediments on the margin of the Indian shield. They probably originally overlay the crystalline basement of the shield, and later were detached to move relatively southwards as thrust sheets. The Shali-Deoban Parautochthon is thrust over the Lower Tertiary sediments, and the Krol Nappe has tectonically overlapped the Shali-Deoban and the Lower Tertiary belts, so that, in some areas, it rests directly on the Siwalik sediments. The basement to the Shali-Deoban Parautochthon, which is the lowermost structural unit, is not observed in the Lesser Himalaya: it is presumed, however, that the crystalline rocks are present at depth beneath the cover of sediments.

The thrust sheets of the crystalline klippen of the Lesser Himalaya, the Chail Nappe and the Jutogh Nappe can be traced back to their parental nappes. The Jutogh Nappe is continuous N into the Central Crystallines Nappe of the Higher Himalaya, which has been shown to be a thrust sheet of considerable thickness (15–20 km) that has moved some 80 km to the S along the Main Central Thrust. The sediments of Tethys Himalaya in turn form an autochthonous cover to the basement of Central Crystallines Nappe. The nappes of ophiolitic melange and ophiolite, preserved as klippen above the Mesozoic sediments of the Tethys Himalaya, show a southwards displacement of at least 25 km and are rooted in the Indus-Tsangpo Suture Zone.

In contrast to the Indus-Tsangpo Suture Zone, the nappes of the Lesser Himalaya and the Central Crystallines Nappe have no autochthonous root zone in the sense of classical Alpine geology. The Himalaya have developed as a result of continent-continent collision between the Indian Plate and Tibetan block along the line of the Indus-Tsangpo Suture (Dewey & Bird 1970; Gansser 1977). It is along this zone that a large segment of the Tethyan Ocean was consumed as a result of subduction. It is suggested that the Central Crystallines Nappe of the Higher Himalaya and the nappes of Lesser Himalaya have developed as a result of the collision between the two continental plates. The Main Central Thrust, which is responsible for the relative southwards movement of the Central Crystallines Nappe together with its thick cover of Tethys Himalayan sediments, initially developed as a reversed fracture in the basement as a result of N–S compression arising from the collision of the northern edge of Indian continent with the Tibetan block. The thrusts of Lesser Himalaya were developed in a similar fashion and they were subsequently folded as a result of continued N–S compression.

ACKNOWLEDGMENTS: I thank Dr S. C. D. Sah, Director, Wadia Institute of Himalayan Geology for permission to publish this paper. Mr Rajeev Banga helped me in preparing the manuscript.

References

AUDEN, J. B. 1934. Geology of the Krol Belt. *Rec. geol. Surv. India*, **67**, 357–454.

—— 1937. The structure of the Himalaya in Garhwal. *Rec. geol. Surv. India*, **71**, 407–33.

BHANOT, V. B., SINGH, V. P., KANSAL, A. K. & THAKUR, V. C. 1977. Early Proterozoic, Rb-Sr, whole-rock age for Central Crystalline geniss of Higher Himalaya, Kumaun. *J. geol. Soc. India*, **18**, 90–1.

BHARGAVA, O. N. 1976. Geology of the Krol belt and associated formations: A reappraisal. *Mem. geol. Surv. India*, **106**, 167–234.

BHATTACHARYA, S. C. & NIYOGI, D. 1971. Geological evolution of the Krol belt in Simla Hills, H. P. *Himalayan Geology*, **1**, 178–212.

DEWEY, J. F. & BIRD, J. M. 1970. Mountain belts and the new global tectonics. *J. geophys. Res.* **75**, 2625–47.

FRANK, W, GANSSER, A. & TROMMSDORFF, V. 1977. Geological observations in the Ladakh area (Himalayas)—a preliminary report. *Schweiz. Mineral. petrogr. Mitt.* **57**, 89–113.

FUCHS, G. 1977. Traverse of Zanskar from the Indus to the valley of Kashmir—a preliminary note. *Jahrb. geol. Berg. Akad. Berlin*, **120**, 219–29.

GANSSER, A. 1964. *Geology of the Himalayas.* Wiley Interscience, London, 289 p.

—— 1974. The Ophiolitic Melange, a worldwide problem on Tethyan examples. *Eclog. geol. Helv.* **67**, 479–503.

—— 1977. The great suture zone between Himalaya and Tibet—a preliminary account. *Eclog. geol. Himalaya*, **268**, 181–92.

—— 1979. The ophiolitic suture zones of the Ladakh and the Kailas region—a comparision. *J. geol. Soc. India*, **20**, 277–81.

HEIM, A. & GANSSER, A. 1939. Central Himalaya: geological observations of the Swiss expedition 1936. *Denkschr. Shweiz. naturfoch. Ges.* **73**, 1–245.

JAEGER, E., BHANDARI, A. K. & BHANOT, V. B. 1971. Rb-Sr age determinations on biotites and whole rock samples from the Mandi and Chor granites, Himachal Pradesh, India. *Eclog. geol. Helv.* **64**, 521–7.

KRAFFT, A. V. 1902. Notes on the exotic blocks of Malla Johar in the Bhot Mahals of Kumaun. *Mem. geol. Surv. India*, **32**, 127–85.

MEHTA, P. K. 1977. Rb-Sr. geochronology of the Kulu-Mandi belt: its implication for the Himalayan tectogenesis. *Geol. Rdsch.* **66**, 156–288.

MERH, S. 1977. Structural studies in parts of Kumaun Himalaya. *Himalayan Geology*, **7**, 26–42.

PAL, D. & MERH, S. 1974. Stratigraphy and structure of the Nainital area in Kumaun Himalaya. *Himalayan Geology*, **4**, 547–62.

PILGRIM, G. E. & WEST, W. D. 1928. The structure and correlation of the Simla rocks. *Mem. geol. Surv. India*, **53**, 1–140.

POWELL, C. MC. A. & CONAGHAN, P. J. 1973. Polyphase deformation in Phanerozoic rocks of the Central Himalayan gneiss, Northwest India. *J. Geol. Chicago*, **81**, 127–43.

RAVI SHANKER, PADHI, R. N. GYAN PRAKASH, THUSSU, J. L. & WANGDUS, C. 1976. Recent geological studies in upper Indus valley and the plate tectonics. *Misc. Publ. geol. Surv. India*, **34**, 41–56.

RAY, S. K. & NAHA, K. 1971. Structural and metamorphic history of the "Simla Klippe"—a summary. *Himalayan Geology*, **1**, 1–24.

RUPKE, J. 1974. Stratigraphic and structural evolution of the Kumaon Lesser Himalaya. *Sediment. Geol*, **11**, 81–265.

SRIKANTIA, S. V. 1973. The tectonic and stratigraphic position of "Panjal Volcanics" in the Kashmir Himalaya—a reappraisal. *Himalayan Geology*, **3**, 59–71.

—— & BHARGAVA, O. N. 1976. Tectonic evolution of the Himachal Himalaya. *Misc. Publ. geol. Surv. India*, **34**, 217–36.

TEWARI, A. P. 1964. On the upper Tertiary deposits of Ladakh Himalayas and correlation of various geotectonic units of Ladakh with those of the Kumaon-Tibet region. *Proc. 22nd. Int. geol. Congr.* **11**, 37–58.

THAKUR, V. C. 1976. Divergent isograds of metamorphism in some parts of Higher Himalaya zone. *Eclog. geol. Himalaya*, **268**, 433–42.

—— Tectonics of the Central Crystallines of Western Himalaya. *Tectonophysics* (in press).

—— & TANDON, S. K. 1976. Significance of pebble and mineral lineation in the Chamba syncline of Punjab Himalaya. Himachal Pradesh, *India*, *Geol. Mag.* **113**, 141–9.

—— & VIRIDI, N. S. 1978. Lithostratigraphy, structure and tectono-metamorphic history of SE part of Ladakh, Kashmir Himalaya. *IX Himalayan Geology Seminar* (Abs.), 96–7.

——, ——, RAI, H. & Gupta, K. R. A note on the geology and structure of Nubra-Shyok area of Ladakh, Kashmir Himalaya. *J. geol. Soc. India*, (in press).

VALDIYA, K. S. 1964. The unfossiliferous formations of the Lesser Himalaya and their correlation. *Proc. 22nd. Int. geol. Congr.* **6**, 15–36.

—— 1976. Himalayan transverse faults and folds and their parallelism with subsurface structures of North Indian Plains. *Tectonophysics.* **32,** 353–86.

—— 1976. Structural set up of Kumaun Lesser Himalaya. *Eclog. geol. Himalaya,* **268,** 449–62.

—— 1978. Extension and analogous of the Chail Nappe in the Kumaun Himalaya. *Indian J. Earth Sci.* **5,** 1–19.

VIRDI, N. S. 1976. Stratigraphy and structure of the area, around Nirth, district Simla, Himachal Pradesh. *Himalayan Geology,* **6,** 163–75.

——, THAKUR, V. C. & AZMI, R. K. 1978. Discovery and significance of Permian microfossils in the Tso Morari Crystallines of Ladakh, J & K. India. *Himalayan Geology,* (in press).

WADIA, D. N. 1928. The geology of Poonch state (Kashmir) and adjacent portions of the Punjab. *Mem. geol. Surv. India,* **51,** 185–320.

—— 1931. The syntaxis of NW Himalaya—it rocks, tectonics and orogeny. *Rec. geol. Surv. India,* **65,** 189–220.

—— 1938. The structure of the Himalaya and of the North Indian foreland, Presidential Address. *Indian Sci. Congr. 25th Session,* 91–118.

V. C. THAKUR, Wadia Institute of Himalayan Geology, Dehra Dun 248001, India.

Ambiguity in interpretation of seismic data from modern convergent margins: an example from the IPOD Japan Trench transect

R. von Huene, M. Arthur & B. Carson

In the plate tectonic theory, crust generated at mid-ocean ridges is disposed beneath the continents at convergent margins. The first half of the theory is firmly substantiated by seemingly uncontrovertible evidence for generation of ocean crust. Consequently, crustal disposal is often assumed *per se*. The absence of early Mesozoic and older crust in the ocean basins is a strong indication that ocean crust is indeed disposed, but the processes of this disposal are poorly known. Structural models of convergent margins are largely deduced from what are presumed to be ancient convergent margins and subaerially exposed collision zones. The structure of modern convergent margins is observed in marine seismic reflection records most of which have poor resolution (50–100 m) even in the zone 1–5 km below the sea floor. Geological structure commonly featured in models or cross-sections of the large volume of rock lying between that detected in seismic reflection records and the seismically delineated Benioff Zone are necessarily based more on inference than observation (e.g. Hamilton 1977). One model has been used extensively to guide interpretation. This model involves an imbricate stack of thrust sheets lying above a master thrust, which is the interface between material being added to the upper plate and the top of the downgoing slab (e.g. Coates 1962; Seely *et al.* 1974; Karig & Sharman 1975). It has since been discussed and applied by many authors, and the necessary concepts were recently summarized by Dickinson & Seely (1979). We will refer to this model as the 'imbricate accretionary model.' The greatest deficiency in many studies that support the imbricate accretionary model is temporal and petrologic data. Despite the extensive assumptions on which it is based, the 'imbricate accretionary model' is now commonly the only model considered in the interpretation of data collected along ancient and modern convergent margins. The study of some recently obtained drillcore samples at convergent margins casts doubt on the validity of interpreting seismic records only in terms of

the 'imbricate accretionary model.' In this paper, we present two examples of data from IPOD Leg 57, that suggest a tectonic evolution that differs from that expected in the simple imbricate accretionary process in several significant respects. The first example shows how the interpretation of seismic records alone—records that illustrate well the structure expected from the imbricate accretionary model—must be changed when litho- and biostratigraphic information are added. The second shows that considerable material added to the continental margin, even near the Japan Trench, is derived from the continent rather than being scraped tectonically from the ocean basin.

In this paper, we use the term *subduction* to denote the tectonic process whereby oceanic lithosphere is thrust beneath the leading edge of the margin (e.g. see Scholl *et al.* 1977). *Accretion* denotes a tectonic process whereby material is added to the continental margin (e.g. Karig & Sharman 1975). Accretion may occur as a result of *offscraping* (e.g. Seely *et al.* 1974), which involves the tectonic skimming of rock from the ocean lithosphere. During and after offscraping, the trench fill and some slope sediments, that are deposited in structural basins or as a veneer over 'tectonically accreted' materials, are also structurally deformed and are carried along with the deposits tectonically scraped from the ocean lithosphere. The term *accretionary complex* is used to include tectonically offscraped deposits as well as the slope sediment that has been tectonically deformed and ultimately kneaded into the material added to the continental margin.

Overview of Japan Trench transect data

The Japan Trench (Fig. 1a) is associated with the present magmatic arc of Honshu Island, an arc that first developed during Oligocene time. From the relation of arc volcanism to subduction, therefore, it is assumed that the present

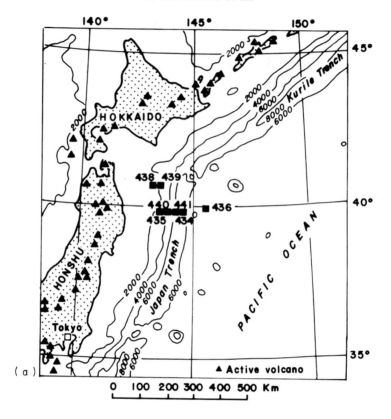

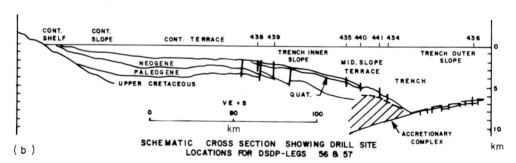

FIG. 1. Location of sites drilled on the Japan Trench transect (1a) and schematic section showing drill sites (1b). Section is on basis of Ishiwada & Ogawa (1977) and JPDC multichannel data.

subduction episode off northern Japan also began in Oligocene time.

The continental margin off Honshu has a configuration typical of many island arc settings with some local exceptions (Fig. 1b). The continental terrace in this region is 140 km broad and in places 1600 m deep; it is divided into a narrow continental shelf and a deep-sea terrace (Fig. 1b) (Nasu 1964). The trench upper slope dips about 4°; a pronounced mid-slope terrace at 4200 m separates the upper and lower trench slope, and the lower slope is commonly inclined greater than 4°. The trench averages about 7300 m deep and there is generally no trench fill. The absence of significant trench fill may result from the trapping of most continentally derived sediment on the broad continental terrace and in up-slope basins, as well as from the sweeping of trench fill against or beneath the margin as the result of rapid (9 cm/yr) convergence (Minster & Jordan 1978).

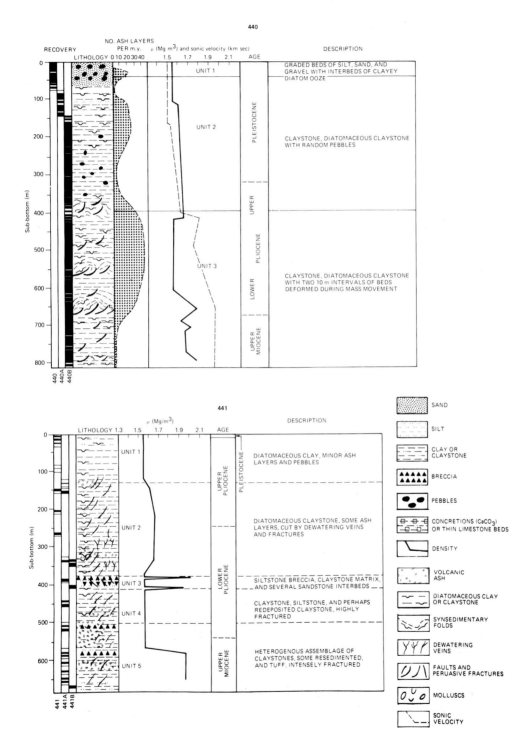

FIG. 2. Summary of lithology, age, and paleo-environment of core from the landward reference site, Japan Trench transect.

Geophysical data from the Japan Trench transect consist of a grid of single-channel seismic reflection data (Honza *et al.* 1977) and subsequent multichannel records (Nasu *et al.*, in press). A series of sites for *Glomar Challenger* drilling on the Japan Trench transect were selected from these records to sample a reference site on either side of the inferred accretionary complex and four sites within it

(Fig. 1a,b), (Langseth & Okada 1978; von Huene & Nasu 1978). The following briefly summarizes the preliminary results of the study of seismic records and drill core.

At the continental terrace reference site (438–439), the drilling penetrated a Neogene hemipelagic section (Fig. 2) in an area where no compressional folds or reverse faults are seen in multichannel seismic records. At the

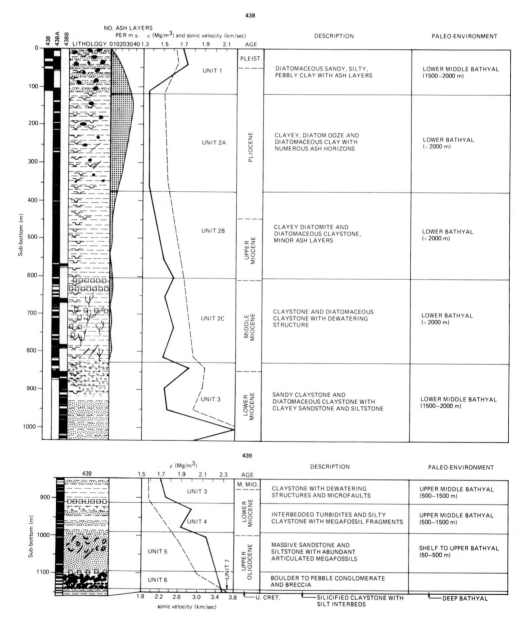

FIG. 3. Summary of lithology and age of core from sites above the accretionary complex, Japan Trench transect.

ocean basin reference site on the outer swell (436), the drilling also penetrated a section without seismically observed compressional structure consisting of Neogene hemipelagic sediment overlying Cretaceous pelagic sediment on oceanic crust (Langseth & Okada 1978). These sites are used to establish the lithostratigraphy and structure outside the accretionary complex. Sites within the accretionary complex include the midslope terrace site (440), where Neogene hemipelagic sediment was recovered. The cores are cut by small normal and reverse faults and are highly fractured, but the orderly stratigraphic sequence sampled indicates no major displacement or repetition by faults (Fig. 3). The same lithology was recovered from the trench lower slope only 15 km landward of the trench axis (Sites 434 & 441), although the recovery here was poor owing to the more highly microfractured nature of the rock (Fig. 4). Despite the position of sites on the lower trench slope on presumed accreted material, none of the material recovered from these sites could be definitely identified as ocean basin deposits transferred tectonically from the ocean plate to the continental plate. In fact, it is difficult to differentiate between the cover of hemipelagic sediment deposited on the incoming oceanic plate (Site 436; Langseth & Okada 1978) from hemipelagic slope sediment in Sites 440 or 441. At all sites, most of the material older than Pleistocene is a uniform hemipelagic mudstone of Miocene and Pliocene age with varying amounts of diatoms and volcanic ash. The uniform lithology of these sections minimizes the difficulty of distinguishing the effect of different lithology and age on the development of structure.

Interpretation of seismic records

Near shore, regional geological mapping and seismic reflection records indicate a basement of folded Cretaceous rock unconformably overlain by a Cenozoic continental shelf sequence (Ishiwada & Ogawa 1977) (Fig. 4). The unconformity is of regional extent (Fig. 1) and has been detected in multichannel seismic reflection records used in this study. In these records, it is characterized acoustically by many diffractions indicating a rough surface. Faint landward dipping reflections are recorded from below this surface and above it Cenozoic beds lap downward against the unconformity, relations indicating that the basal part of the Cenozoic section grows younger in a seaward direction. The unconformity and overlying Cenozoic sequence extend seaward, at least as far as the mid-slope terrace (Fig. 1). Father seaward, between the mid-slope terrace and the trench, faint reflections paralleling the sea floor are interpreted as a veneer of slope deposits. Below the slope deposits are landward dipping reflections, interpreted as tectonically accreted oceanic and deformed slope accretionary-complex deposits. The accretionary complex lies above a westward dipping, strong reflector, interpreted as the top of the downgoing slab of igneous ocean crust.

The acoustically resolved structure of the margin described above is consistent with the imbricate accretionary model. The model requires uplift and continued seaward growth of a continental margin through tectonic accretion of oceanic rocks. The seismic records show progressive seaward growth of the downlapping slope deposits; the uplift is seen in the landward tilted (sub-unconformity) reflections below the unconformity representing a rising, imbricated stack. At the seaward edge of the margin, development of the imbricated stack from offscraped oceanic rock is indicated by the landward tilting of beds under the trench lower slope. Above the imbricate stack are slope deposits resting on a rough surface formed by the uplifted ends of imbricate slices as modelled by Moore & Karig (1976). The essential geometric aspects of the model are clearly illustrated in seismic records from the Japan Trench.

Cores from the landward reference sites (438–439; Fig. 1), however, give lithological and temporal evidence of overall subsidence of the continental terrace since the early Miocene rather than uplift, as indicated by interpretation of the seismic data in accordance with the imbricate accretionary model. The sections drilled at these sites consist of terrigenous diatomaceous claystone (Pleistocene–Lower Miocene) underlain by Lower Miocene silt and sand turbidites and claystone. This Neogene section is underlain by a thick, massive Oligocene and Miocene sandstone containing numerous articulated megafossils. This sandstone, in turn, overlies an unfossiliferous sedimentary breccia-conglomerate made up largely of dacite boulders. The boulder bed unconformably overlies steeply dipping black silicified claystone of Cretaceous age. The unconformity was formed by subaerial erosion, and it represents a hiatus of 40–50 Ma (von Huene & Nasu 1978).

The geological history interpreted from this

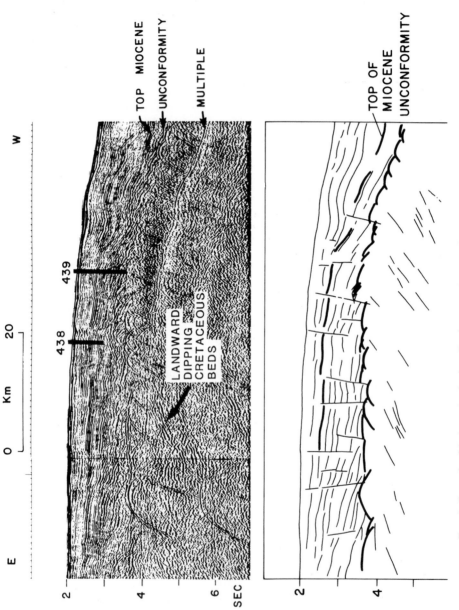

Fig. 4. Part of a 24-channel seismic reflection record across the landward reference site showing the unconformity on landward dipping Cretaceous rocks and downlap of overlying Cenozoic section against the unconformity. Reflector corresponding to top of the Miocene in the core from DSDP sites 438–439 is emphasized by a black line.

litho- and biostratigraphy begins in Oligocene and Miocene time with an emergent terrane of silicified Upper Cretaceous claystone and dacite intrusions in the area of the drill site. The Palaeogene subaerial terrane was covered in late Oligocene and early Miocene time by sand, tranported from a nearby surf zone into quieter marine water that foraminiferal assemblages indicate was less than 500 m deep (von Huene & Nasu 1978). The terrane continued to subside throughout early Miocene time as layers of interbedded turbidite sand and clay were deposited. Greater distance from sources, or decreasing availability of coarse-grained source material, is indicated by a change from deposition of sand–silt turbidite units in early Miocene time to deposition of clay and diatomaceous clay in the Middle Miocene. The rocks penetrated at the landward reference sites (438 and 439) are presently at about 1600 m water depth and have an upper and middle bathyal (500–1500 m) early Miocene foraminiferal assemblage, and a lower bathyal (>2000 m) late Miocene assemblage (Keller, in press).

This geological history can be extrapolated to areas on either side of the sites in seismic records where beds of a particular age can be traced and which, in turn, join with the continental margin section published by Ishiwada & Ogawa (1977). Thus, a complete reconnaissance geological cross section of the margin can be made. The geological development of part of the margin is shown in Fig. 5. Inundation of the Cretaceous landmass, named the Oyashio ancient landmass, began in early Cenozoic time, near the present eastern shoreline of northern Honshu, and progressed seaward through late Cenozoic time, passing Sites 438 & 439 in late Oligocene and early Miocene time. The ancient landmass began subsiding during the initial period of magmatic arc activity. If it is assumed that arc volcanism is related to subduction, then subduction and forearc subsidence must have occurred concurrently. During subduction, it appears that material was also tectonically accreted, although not necessarily continuously, to the continent immediately landward of the trench. If it is assumed that regional subsidence involves some sort of crustal thinning, then it is significant to know whether a net addition or removal of material has occurred in the outer forearc area since Middle Miocene time. The imbricate accretionary model (e.g. Karig & Sharman 1975; Dickinson & Seely 1979) would predict that if material is accreted, the outer forearc should be uplifted.

An estimate of the age and the cross-sectional area of the accretionary complex can be made and compared with a cross-section of the area that subsided during the equivalent period. The area of the accretionary complex defined on the basis of the seismic record across the Japan Trench transect is indicated in Fig. 1. The sediment penetrated at Sites 434, 440 & 441 are, on the basis of seismic and lithologic evidence, considered to be slope sediment deposited on top of the complex, although the lower strata in Site 434 & 441 dip steeply. Thus, a minimum late Miocene age of most of the accretionary complex can be established, as this was the oldest sediment recovered and age should increase with greater depth in the slope deposits. The mid-slope terrace (Site 440) marks the landward edge of the sediment tectonically accreted since possibly Middle Miocene time. The forearc area that subsided below sea level since the Miocene age can be established by tracing the lowest reflection of that age seaward from Sites 438 & 439. The minimum cross-sectional areas of subsidence and maximum of accretion since the late Miocene are shown in Fig. 6. It is apparent that subsidence greatly exceeds accretion, especially when it is noted that no allowance is made in Fig. 6 for slope deposits in the accretionary complex nor for added subsidence of the area already below, or that above, sea level in the Upper Miocene, factors that would only increase the area of subsidence and reduce the area of accretion. Since at least late Miocene time, then, subsidence has been dominant along the transect; therefore, net removal rather than addition of crustal material may have occurred in the outer forearc area during the past 10 Ma.

This conclusion is contrary to the initial interpretation of the seismic data, which was done without benefit of drill core stratigraphic information. As pointed out earlier, the seismic evidence alone can be interpreted as showing continuous accretion at the leading edge of the Japan upper plate. However, the evidence from drill cores constrains estimates of the age and volume of the accretionary complex and suggests that very little accretion of material scraped from the downgoing oceanic plate has occurred since late Miocene time (von Huene & Nasu 1978). Some earlier accreted material may have been removed—subducted or tectonically eroded—as proposed by Murauchi (1971). This hypothesis is in line with the observed subsidence just described, which indicates crustal thinning or removal of material.

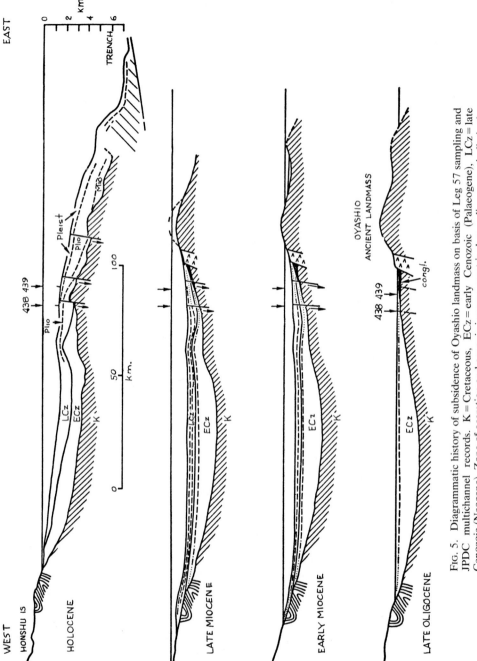

FIG. 5. Diagrammatic history of subsidence of Oyashio landmass on basis of Leg 57 sampling and JPDC multichannel records. K = Cretaceous, ECz = early Cenozoic (Palaeogene), LCz = late Cenozoic (Neogene). Zone of accretion and oceanic igneous crust is shown diagrammatically in the Holocene section.

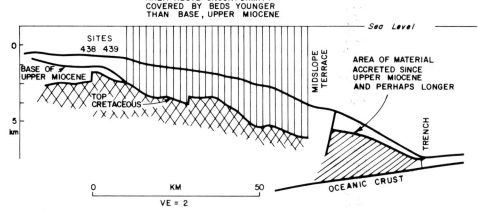

AREA ABOVE UNCONFORMITY
COVERED BY BEDS YOUNGER
THAN BASE, UPPER MIOCENE

FIG. 6. Indication of the relative amount of subsidence and accretion since late Miocene time along the Japan Trench transect. A slanted line pattern denotes the area of accreted material as defined from seismic records whose minimum age is established from cores of the overlying slope deposits. A vertical line pattern indicates the area that has subsided during the corresponding time as defined by the depth to the erosional unconformity covered by deposits younger than the beginning of late Miocene time. The minimum area of subsidence is greater than the maximum area of accretion.

Small structures not detected in seismic reflection records

The cores reveal structures that are too small to be detected with standard seismic reflection techniques. These structures are significant in interpreting the tectonics of the margin. Cores from the Japan Trench lower slope probably did not sample tectonically accreted ocean basin deposits, but the slope deposits are highly fractured and deformed. The fracturing and consolidation of these sediments occur at much shallower depths on the trench slope than at the reference sites. This sequence, documented in greater detail elsewhere, (Arthur *et al.* in press) is briefly described here.

At all sites, the seismic records show coherent reflections in the section penetrated by drilling, although on the trench lower slope the reflections are faint, nearly horizontal and laterally continuous. Small normal faults with vertical displacements of about 50 m are distinguishable at 1–1.5 km intervals along the records across the deep sea terrace.

In the upper part of the sediment sequence at all drill sites, the diatomaceous mud gradually changes to mudstone with depth, becoming brittle and fractured when strained (Fig. 7). At depth where the mudstone begins to deform in a brittle manner, dewatering veins are observed. The depth of vein development appears to depend on the stress environment.

A gradational progression of small structures is described in three phases (Fig. 7). In the first

(veining) phase (Fig. 8), dark, anastomosing, thin veins begin to appear locally and, with greater depth, these veins increase in length and number per unit volume of core. Vein patterns are anastomosing to unidirectional and are commonly separated by less veined or unveined intervals. Cross-cutting relations at lower levels indicate a polyphase development.

In the second phase, microfaulting begins along the veins (Fig. 9). Where first observed, the faults have many orientations; at Site 440 they have apparent both normal and reverse senses of motion. Where microfractures became more numerous, conjugate fracture directions and crossing sets of faults were observed. The intensity of shearing varied within a 10 m section, but the overall intensity increased with depth. In late Miocene and younger deposits at Sites 441 & 434 on the trench lower slope, the microfaults were open in the recovered core and the core fell apart when handled. This was associated with poor core recovery and hole instability. In the extreme case, the core disintegrated into coarse, angular fragments if taken out of the core liner.

In the final phase, most faults and fractures are closed and perhaps rehealed. The zones of healed, of open, and of closed fractures may overlap. Open fractures *in situ* are inferred from down hole logging data. Open fractures observed in the core may have been closed *in situ*.

The sequence of microstructures appears to

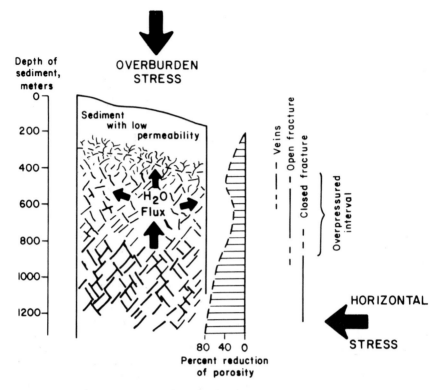

FIG. 7. Schematic diagram of response of hemipelagic slope sediment to burial compaction and horizontal stress.

reflect initial veining and then microfracturing; in some settings, as on the trench lower slope, the fractures remain open or unhealed. This structural sequence was penetrated at increasingly shallower sub-bottom levels and over a compressed interval at sites close to the trench. At the continental reference site (438 & 439), veins were first observed at 700 m in mid-Miocene rocks, well below the level at which rocks are consolidated sufficiently to deform in a brittle manner; whereas at the mid-slope terrace (Site 440), veining begins at 387 m in Pliocene rocks, about 200 m below the upper limit of brittle deformation. On the trench lower slope (Site 441), the sequence progresses to the open fracture phase at shallower depth and in rock which is younger than at the sites higher on the trench slope. Veins begin at 132 m in Pliocene rocks. Veining may, in part, be influenced by the emplacement of the local sedimentary breccias assumed to have formed from slumps or slides that came to rest at the site.

From these observations, the following sequence is inferred: plastic mud in the upper layer dewaters in response to lithostatic load and any added stress. The dewatering produces widely spaced veins that, under continued stress, eventually form fractures. The veins and fractures become more numerous and influence the initiation of faulting that produces microbreccia. Continued dewatering may produce more water than can permeate the overlying unlithified, relatively impermeable muddy sediment, and this upper section becomes an effective cap over a highly fractured, more consolidated zone. In this circumstance, abnormal pore pressure may develop and keep fractures open. There is evidence of abnormal pressure at the mid-slope terrace and trench lower slope sites. At these sites, bulk density decreases with depth, concurrent with fracturing (Arthur et al., in press; Carson & Bruns, in press). This decrease can be interpreted as development of fracture porosity. However, the single velocity log obtained does not show a corresponding velocity decrease as would be expected. Nonetheless, most of the evidence indicates a zone of low shear strength at about 600 m or deeper, which is consistent with the high Poisson ratio observed by Nagumo (1979) in seismic refraction studies.

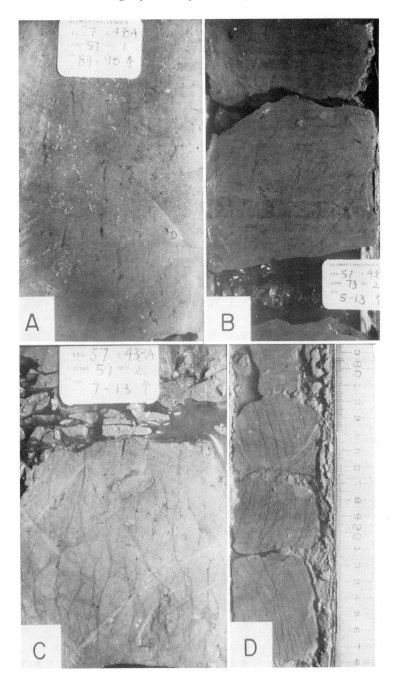

FIG. 8. Development of veins as seen in core from Site 438: A. Dark, short, vertical veins in massive claystone; an example of initial vein development (core 59, section 1, 89–98 cm). B. Thin veins branching upward from a horizontal burrow in claystone (core 73, section 2, 5–13 cm). C. Vertical veins, developed preferentially to veins with low inclinations (core 59, section 2, 7–13 cm). D. Veins with a strongly developed orientation (core 71, section 1, 79–98 cm).

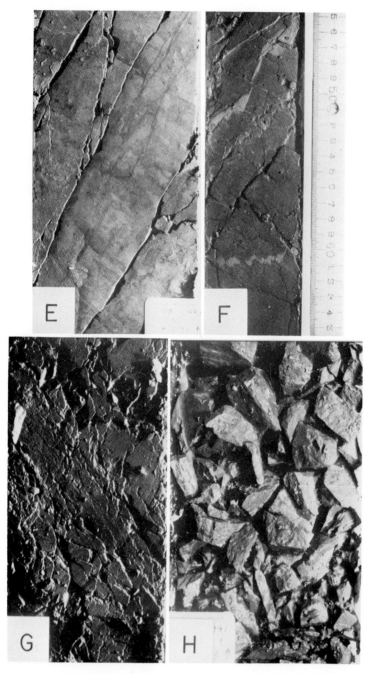

Fig. 9. Development of fractures along veins: E. Fractures, both open and healed, and veins in parallel orientation (Site 440, core 55, section 5, 85–97 cm). F. Open, conjugate fractures and deformed horizontal calcareous bands (Site 434B, core 9, section 2, 45–65 cm). G. Open fractures, closely spaced and well developed (Site 434, core 15, section 3, 24–37 cm). H. Fragmented core, commonly the only material recovered on trench lower slope (Site 441, core 9, section 1, 13–23 cm).

If a weak, fluid-charged breccia zone develops, it produces conditions similar to those observed along delta fronts where slides break loose on the upper surface over pressured zones. In a tectonically active area, greater opportunity for sliding exists during earthquakes, when instantaneous high fluid pressures are observed and the earthquake vibrations also tend to decrease shear strength. Evidence for slumping has been noted on the Japan Trench transect (Langseth & Okada 1978; von Huene & Nasu 1978).

The potential for extensive downslope movement emphasizes a point made by other authors (Scholl *et al.* 1977; von Huene 1972; Elliot 1976) regarding the interpretation of features on trench lower slopes. The products of intense comprehensive deformation are commonly difficult to distinguish from the products of mass movement: in deep water the seismic record across both a tectonic melange and a chaotic slump mass contain both diffractions and few coherent reflections (von Huene & Shor 1969). Morphological criteria such as lobes, slump scars, and associated canyons are commonly used to supplement seismic interpretation (Piper *et al.* 1973; Moore 1977). The problem is similar to the interpretation of chaotic deposits on land where it may be difficult to distinguish between olistostromes and tectonic melange.

Conclusions

These two examples illustrate some problems of interpreting seismic data from the Japan Trench transect in accordance with only the imbricate accretionary model. We recognize that the model may be applied to many convergent margins, but other models must also be considered. The pervasive unconformities seen in some convergent margin seismic records might result from simple large vertical motion as well as from a rising imbricated ocean basin sequence (Seely *et al.* 1974). Diffuse seismic character can result either from complex tectonic melange or olistostromes. Clearly, lithostratigraphical and biostratigraphical data are needed to improve the constraining of such interpretations. As we and our colleagues have pointed out (von Huene & Nasu 1978), there are alternative interpretations and a great deal more variability of convergent margin structure than have been generally recognized.

References

ARTHUR, M., CARSON, B. & VON HUENE, R. in press. Initial tectonic deformation at terrigenous sediment at the leading edge of the Japan Trench convergent margin: *Initial Rep. Deep Sea drill. Proj.*, **57**.

CARSON, B. & BRUNS, T. R. in press. Physical Properties/Legs 56 and 57; *Initial Rep. Deep Sea drill. Proj.*, **57**.

COATES, R. R. 1962. Magma type & crustal structure in the Aleutian arc. In: MCDONALD, G. A. & KUNE, H. (eds), *The crust of the Pacific basin*, Am. geophys. Union Mon. 6. **1035**, 92–109.

DICKINSON, W. R. & SEELY, D. R. 1979. Structure and stratigraphy of forearc regions: *Bull. Am. Assoc. Petrol. geol.* **63**, 2–31.

ELLIOTT, D. 1976. The motion of thrust sheets: *J. geophys. Res.* **81**, 949–63.

HAMILTON, W. 1977. Subduction in the Indonesian region: *Maurice Ewing Series*, **1**, Island Arcs, Deep Sea Trenches and Back-Arc Basins, 15–31.

HONZA, E. KAGAMI, H. & NASU, N. 1977. Neogene geological history of the Tohoku Island arc system: *J. Oceanographic Soc. Japan*, **33**, 297–310.

ISHIWADA Y. & OGAWA, K. 1977. Petroleum geology of offshore areas around the Japanese Islands. *United Nations Asian Committee for Offshore Prospecting, Technical Bulletin*, **10**, 23–34.

KARIG, D. E. & SHARMAN, G. E. III, 1975. Subduction and accretion in trenches. *Bull. geol. Soc. Am.* **86**, 377–89.

KELLER, G., in press, Benthic foraminfera, Leg 57. *Initial Rep. Deep Sea drill. Proj.* **57**.

LANGSETH, M. & OKADA, H. 1978, Near the Japan Trench: transects begun. *Geotimes*, 22–26.

MINSTER, J. B. & JORDAN, T. H., 1978, Present-day plate motions. *J. geophys. Res.* **83**, 5331–54.

MOORE, D. G. 1977. Submarine slides. *In:* VOIGHT, B. (ed), *Rockslides and avalanches*, **4**, Natural Phenomena, Developments in Geotechnical Engineering, **14A**, 563–604.

MOORE, G. F. & KARIG, D. E. 1976. Development of sedimentary basins on the lower trench slope. *Geology*, **4**, 693–7.

MURAUCHI, S., 1971. The renewal of island arcs and the tectonics of marginal seas: *In: Island arc and marginal sea*, Tokai Univ. Press, Tokyo, 39–56.

NAGUMO, S. in press, OBS-arigun seismic refractor survey near the sites 441 and 434 [J-1A], 438 and 439 [J-2B], *Initial Rep. Deep Sea drill. Proj.* **57**.

NASU, N. 1964. The provenance of the coarse sediments on the continental shelves and the trench slopes off the Japanese Pacific coast. *In:* MILLER, R. L. (ed), *Paper in marine geology*, Macmillan Co., New York, 65–101.

——, von Huene, R., Langseth, M., Honza, E. & Bruns, T. in press. Interpretation of seismic records, Japan Trench transect. *Initial Rep. Deep Sea drill. Proj.* **57**.

Piper, D. J. W., von Huene, R. & Duncan, J. R. 1973. Late Quaternary sedimentation in the active eastern Aleutian Trench. *Geology*, **1**, 19–22.

Scholl, D. W. & Marlow, M. S. 1974b. Global tectonics and the sediments of modern and ancient trenches—some different interpetations. *In:* Kahle, C. F. (ed.), Plate tectonics, assessments and reassessments, *Mem. Am. Assoc. Petrol. Geol.* **23**, 255–72.

——, ——, & Cooper, A. K. 1977. Sediment sub-duction and offscraping at Pacific margins *In: Maurice Ewing Series,* **1,** *Island Arcs, Deep Sea Trenches and Back-Arc Basins,* 199–210.

Seely, D. R., Vail, P. R. & Walton, G. G. 1974. Trench slope model. *In:* Burk, C. A. & Drake, C. L. (eds), *The geology of continental margins,* Springer-Verlag, New York, 249–60.

von Huene, R. 1972. Structure of the continental margin and tectonism at the eastern Aleutian Trench, *Bull. geol. Soc. Am.* **83**, 3613–26.

—— & Nasu, N., 1978. Japan Trench transected on Leg 57: *Geotimes,* **23,** 16–21.

—— & Shor, G. G. Jr. 1969. The structure and tectonic history of the eastern Aleutian Trench. *Bull. geol. Soc. Am.* **80,** 1889–902.

R. von Heune, U.S. Geological Survey, Menlo Park, California.

M. Arthur, Deep Sea Drilling Project, Scripps Institute of Oceanography, La Jolla. California.

B. Carson, Le High University, Bethlehem, Pennsylvania.

Geometrical problems and implications of large scale overthrusting in the Banda Arc -Australian margin collision zone

M. G. Audley-Charles

SUMMARY: Inversion of stratigraphical sequences, the presence of high grade metamorphic rocks sitting on serpentinite rafts bounded by unmetamorphosed sedimentary rocks, and zones of imbrication have been cited as evidence of large scale overthrusting in the Outer Banda Arc. Earthquake data reveal a Benioff zone implying intermediate depth and deep focus underthrusting beneath the Banda Arc but there is a paucity of shallow focus shocks with underthrusting mechanisms. Multichannel seismic reflection surfeys between the Outer Banda Arc and the Australian–New Guinea shelf have been interpreted as showing imbrication in the north wall of the Timor Trough and the S wall of the Seram Trough. Quaternary steep angled block faulting post-dates and thus obscures much of the thrust faulting in the Banda Arc.

Many geometrical problems arise in trying to interpret the structural history of this collision zone between Australia and the volcanic (Inner) Banda Arc. They include:– (1) the apparent absence of a subduction trench and accretionary arc-trench gap in the Banda Arc; (2) the location of the surface trace of the Benioff zone before collision; (3) the history of the Benioff zone after the Pliocene oceanic trench was destroyed; (4) the relationship of the developing fold and thrust belt to the pre-collision geometry of the Australia–New Guinea continental margin; (5) the apparent absence of the continental slope and rise in the northern Australia collision zone; (6) the relationship of the crystalline basement of the Outer Banda Arc to the cover rocks and (7) the tectonic significance of the apparent continuity of the stratigraphically and structurally very different Sunda and Banda Arcs.

Continent-arc collision resulted from the convergence of Australia and the Banda volcanic arc. The associated deformation, represented by the folding and local imbrication of the Australian continental rise sediments of the Outer Banda Arcs with the emplacement of overthrust exotic sheets, was accomplished in 2 Ma. It appears to have been caused by the failure of the Benioff zone to accommodate the thick sediment prism of Australian proximal continental rise. Geometrical considerations suggest that, as a consequence, the Benioff zone and most of the approximately 200 km wide arc-trench gap were overridden by the Australian lithospheric plate during the continued plate convergence of the last 3 Ma. An important conclusion is that the Banda Arc fold and thrust belt developed in proximal continental rise deposits at the foot of the Australian continental slope

The Banda Arc of eastern Indonesia comprises a volcanic (inner) arc and an (outer) arc of strongly folded and thrust sedimentary and metamorphic rocks with minor igneous rocks. On the larger islands of the Outer Banda Arc (Timor and Seram) mountains rise to almost 3 km; the inter-arc marine troughs descend to 3 km and locally, in the Weber Deep, to 7 km. The Banda Arc curves through 180°, has a strike length of about 2400 km and a width of about 250 km (Fig. 1). In size (including relief) the Banda Arc is closely comparable to the whole of the European Alpine mountain chain and the two largest islands, Timor and Seram, are each larger than the Swiss Alps.

The late Cenozoic deformation in the Outer Banda Arc resulted from the collision between the northward drifting Australia–New Guinea continent and the volcanic Inner Banda Arc system. The volcanic Inner Banda Arc is related to the subduction of the ocean floor that lay N of northward moving Australia–New Guinea during the Cenozoic.

Earlier geological investigators were led to interpret the presence of large scale overthrusts, which some called nappes, in the Outer Banda Arc islands of Timor (Wanner 1913; Bemmelen 1949) and Seram (Valk 1945; Germeraad 1946) by geomorphological features and structures reminiscent of Alpine thrust zones. More critical evidence in these islands was found by Grunau (1953, 1957), De Waard (1954, 1955a, b 1956, 1957), Lemoine (1959), Audley-Charles (1968), Carter et al. (1976a), Barber et al. (1977), Brunnschweiler (1978) and Audley-Charles et al. (1979). However, partly, because so few major thrust planes have been found exposed, Grady

Thrust and Nappe Tectonics. 1981. The Geological Society of London

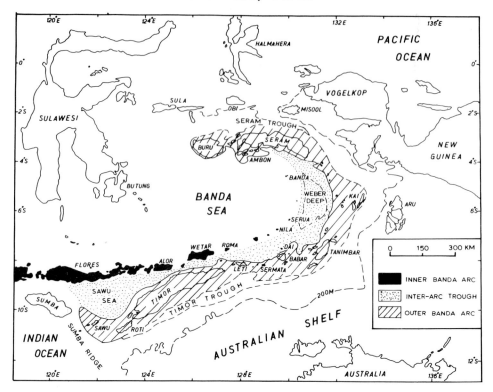

Fɪɢ. 1. Banda Arc of eastern Indonesia.

(1975), Grady & Berry (1977) and Chamalaun & Grady (1978) have argued that Plio-Pleistocene block faulting is the dominant tectonic style. These writers have not accepted the view of Carter *et al.* (1976*a*) and Barber *et al.* (1977) that the Plio-Pleistocene block faulting has displaced the early to mid-Pliocene thrust faults. However, Grady & Berry (1977) admit that their investigations were limited to a small part of northern Timor and they have not checked much of the field evidence cited as evidence for overthrusting.

On the basis of marine geophysical surveys, Bowin *et al.* (in press) followed Cardwell & Isacks (1978), who studied the earthquakes of the Banda region, in concluding that there is evidence to indicate that the India-Australia plate has underthrust the Eurasia plate below the Timor and Seram sectors of the S and N parts (respectively) of the Banda Arc.

This paper is concerned with some problems and implications raised by the mapping of thrust sheets which appear to have moved away from the Banda Sea (4–5 km deep) towards the Australia–New Guinea continent, that is, moved northwards in Seram on the N

side of the Banda Arc and southwards in Timor on the S side. In an attempt to understand the history and mode of development of overthrust tectonics in a continent-island arc collision zone, the simplified geometry of the convergent zone has been reconstructed on a natural scale using recently available geophysical and geological data

Implications of overthrusting for collision tectonics in the Banda Arc

The age of overthrusting and collision in the Banda Arc

On the basis of stratigraphical data (mainly the age of unconformities) the late Cenozoic deformation of the Outer Banda Arc, indicated by folding and emplacement of overthrusts, has been dated by Carter *et al.* (1976*a*) in Timor as zone N 20 or Middle Pliocene (approximately 3 Ma) and by Audley-Charles *et al.* (1979) in Seram as zone N 18 or late Miocene–early Pliocene (approximately

5 Ma). The correlation of radiometric dates with planktonic foraminiferal zonation follows Billman & Scrutton (1976). Carter *et al.* (1976a) argued that the emplacement of thrust sheets in Timor must correlate with the collision between the volcanic Banda Arc and the Australia–New Guinea continental margin over which the thrust sheets travelled towards the continent. Only 20 km now separates the thrust sheets of northern Timor from the volcanic island of Atauru of the Inner Banda Arc. Abbott & Chamalaun (1978) followed Carter *et al.* (1976a) in regarding the emplacement of the Ocussi Volcanics thrust sheet in northern Timor as having occurred when the continental margin of Australia collided with the volcanic Banda Arc in the Middle Pliocene (3 Ma). Bowin *et al.* (in press) also conclude that the collision between the northward drifting Australian continent and the Banda Arc occurred during the Pliocene 3–5 Ma ago.

Location of pre-Pliocene collision Benioff zone

Between the northward drifting Australia–New Guinea continent and the pre-Pliocene volcanic Banda Arc there must have been an ocean trench which accommodated the subducting ocean floor separating these converging plates. The position of this trench with respect to the pre-Pliocene volcanic Banda Arc is not known but, following Abbott & Chamalaun (1978), by comparison with the Sunda Arc, we might expect the trench to have been about 200 km S of the smaller volcanic Banda Arc. The northward moving Australia–

New Guinea continental margin must have collided with this trench before it ceased underthrusting the volcanic arc about 3 Ma ago.

Benioff zone and collision geometry deduced from pre-Pliocene volcanic arc

The evidence of contamination by continental crustal material of the magmas extruded in the volcanic Banda Arc (Whitford *et al.* 1977) indicates that Australian continental margin rocks (probably continental rise sediments—for reasons set out later) were subducted to depths of 100–200 km where they contaminated the rising magmas that erupted in Wetar at least 3 Ma ago (Abbott & Chamalaun 1978).

Using the 7 cm per year plate convergence rate of Bowin *et al.* (in press) and a pre-Pliocene Banda arc-trench gap approximately 200 km wide, the date when the magma contaminating Australian continental rise sediments reached the trench can be estimated as about 7.3 Ma or zone N 17 of late Miocene (Fig. 2). The Kolbano-Betano-Aliambata-Iliomar bathyal sediments of southern Timor are Australian continental rise deposits of late Jurassic to early Pliocene age and now form part of the imbricated para-autochthon (Carter *et al.* 1976a, b; Barber *et al.* 1977). There is no evidence of a stratigraphical break in the N 16–N 18 zone sequences of this facies, but zones N 19 and N 20 are missing. One interpretation that can be placed on this (Fig. 2) is that bathyal sedimentation continued on the foot wall of the trench during N 17 and N 18 times and that, until the end of N 18 times, the

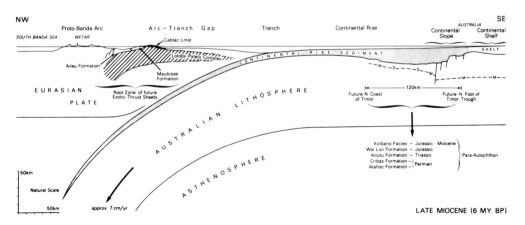

FIG. 2. Reconstruction of the late Miocene northern Australian margin–volcanic Banda Arc convergent zone. Note that about 300 km of Australian distal continental rise deposits must have been subducted before they could contaminate magmas erupted in the volcanic arc.

continental rise deposits were subducted without structural effects on the sediments just entering and outside the trench on the downgoing plate in a manner resembling the 'underthrusting mode' described by Helwig & Hall (1974). The distal part of this continental rise containing these sediments would have already been subducted to depths of 100–200 km below the Pliocene (N 20–3 Ma) volcanic arc. The subducted deposits contaminated the rising magmas about 4.3 Ma after they had accumulated in the region of the trench, thus giving rise to the cordierite-bearing volcanics extruded about 3 Ma ago in the mid-Pliocene. This 3 Ma date appears to be highly significant in the Timor region of the Banda Arc, for it not only coincides with the collision of the Australian proximal continental rise with the volcanic arc-trench gap, as indicated by the emplacement of the overthrusts onto Timor, but also with the cessation of volcanism in this volcanic arc opposite the Timor region (Abbott & Chamalaun 1978). This death of volcanic activity (Fig. 3) has been related to two factors: (a) the consumption of all the oceanic crust between the converging Australian continent and the volcanic arc; most of the oceanic crust had been subducted, but the last remnants, represented perhaps by the Ocussi Volcanics, described as ocean floor tholeiites by Abbott &

Chamalaun (1978), were overthrust onto northern Timor about 3 Ma; (b) with all the ocean crust consumed or overthrust the continental margin of Australia began to be subducted but the buoyancy effect of the density contrast inhibited further underthrusting so that volcanism in the arc died (Fig. 4).

Overthrust stratigraphy implies Benioff zone was overridden by Australian continental rise

The presence of Permian and Mesozoic Australian continental rise deposits now only 20 km from the volcanic Inner Banda Arc (Figs 1 & 4) implies that the volcanic arc-trench gap, probably about 200 km wide during the pre-Pliocene has either suffered extreme shortening, for which there is no evidence, or else it has been overridden by the converging Australian continental rise (Fig. 4). An important question related to the development of the collision margin is how to determine the age of the present configuration of only 20 km between the Inner and Outer Banda Arc in part of the Timor region. The overthrust sheets were emplaced on the Australian margin of Timor about 3 Ma in zone N 20 of the mid-Pliocene when the subduction

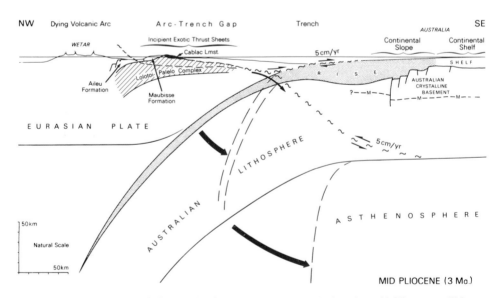

FIG. 3. Reconstruction of the Banda Arc convergent zone during the mid-Pliocene collision. Failure of the Benioff zone to accommodate the thick proximal continental rise deposits led to cessation of shallow focus subduction. Continuation of plate convergence resulted in Australian plate overthrusting the Benioff zone. The upper part of the arc-trench gap, which formed the hanging wall of the subduction zone, sheared and overthrust the continental rise as it rode over the Benioff zone.

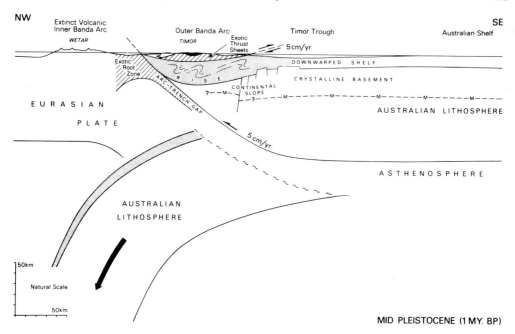

FIG. 4. Mid-Pleistocene reconstruction of the collision zone showing the Australian plate overriding the pre-Pliocene Banda Benioff zone and much of the arc-trench gap resulting in the Australian continental rise arriving only 50 km S of the volcanic Banda Arc. Note that the detached upper part of the arc-trench gap forms the exotic thrust sheets above the continental rise deposits of the para-autochthon. Hamilton (1977, 1978) identified a new trench forming N of the Flores-Alor part of the Wetar volcanic arc initiating southward underthrusting of the Banda Sea below the arc. This accords well with this model but the reversed direction of underthrusting is much less easy to accommodate to the tectonic model of Hamilton (1978), von der Borch (1979) and Bowin *et al.* (in press).

trench, estimated to be then about 200 km S of the volcanic arc, failed to accommodate the underthrusting Australian continental margin. At least 300 km of distal continental rise had already been underthrust to reach 200 km depth below the volcanic arc as outlined in Fig. 2. Plate convergence, estimated at a rate of 5 cm per year (Abbott & Chamalaun 1978), continued after this mid-Pliocene (3 Ma) collision so that the collision suture became deformed by folds and overthrusting. The continuation of this northward component of drift by Australia–New Guinea continent after the mid-Pliocene led to the Australian continental rise riding over most of the 200 km wide volcanic arc-trench gap during the last 3 Ma. Geometrical considerations represented by natural scale cross sections (Figs 2–4) suggest that this continuing plate convergence could only be accommodated by the Australian plate overriding not only the Asian arc-trench gap but also at least 300 km of its own subducted continental rise. Atlantic type rifted continental margins have continental rise deposits that extend up to 500 km or more across the ocean floor (Heezen 1974). The postulated subducted 300 km of northern Australian continental rise would explain why the present continental rise deposits extend for only about 60 km (across Timor). This allows about another 60 km width for continental slope deposits occupying the region between southern Timor and the foot of the N wall of the Timor Trough, which is underlain by Australian shelf according to Bowin *et al.* (in press). These dimensions allow for both considerable shortening in the continental rise following collision and for more than 300 km of rise to have been lost by subduction.

After the main orogenic phase in Timor there is evidence for late Pliocene folding and relatively minor thrusting (Carter *et al.* 1976*a*) and for two Pleistocene folding phases (Kenyon 1974), as well as widespread strong steep angled block faulting during the Pleistocene. These movements appear to be associated with the continuing plate convergence and the buckling response of the collision zone in which the Banda Arc islands have emerged and continued to rise while the interarc troughs and the 'foredeep' between the Outer Banda Arc and the Australia-New Guinea continent have subsided (Veevers *et al.* 1978).

Audley-Charles & Hooijer (1973) argued from the evidence for dwarfing Stegodont populations having wandered back and forth between Timor (Outer Banda Arc) and Flores (volcanic Inner Banda Arc) that there was a land connection between the Inner and Outer Banda Arc during the Pleistocene and that the present Ombai Strait between them is a young subsided feature induced by faulting. The evidence from the stegodonts suggests that the present island configuration in the Timor region was acquired by Middle Pleistocene time (approximately 1 Ma).

Relationship of fold and thrust belt to pre-collision geometry of the Australian continental margin

The dating of the various phases in the development of this Banda Arc orogenesis allows us to investigate the relationship of the location of the fold and thrust belt to the structure of the pre-collision continental margin (Fig. 2). Seismic surveys have revealed that the Australian shelf strata can be traced from the present shelf northwards, below the Timor Trough, as far as the foot of the N wall, where they are overlain by thick deposits lacking

coherent reflectors but which appear to be strongly folded and imbricated (Jacobson *et al.* 1978). This indicates that the Cenozoic, Mesozoic and possibly older shelf deposits extend northwards to about 50 km from the S Timor coast. Thus, only 120 km from the depressed shelf below the present Timor Trough to the N coast of Timor remains to accommodate what is left of the Cenozoic, Mesozoic and Permian Australian continental slope and rise. Taking the average width of 60 km for Atlantic-type rifted continental margin continental slopes (Heezen 1974) means that the present island of Timor approximates to the proximal continental rise extending from the foot of the continental slope located at depth below the S coast of the island. This would mean that in the Timor region the fold and thrust belt of the Banda Arc coincides with what was originally the foot of the continental slope, where the greatest thickness of sediment is trapped (Heezen 1974). Apthorpe (1979) identified the Mesozoic shelf break in the Browse Basin SW of Timor which corresponds with this interpretation. In view of the exceptionally thick sediment (10 km) on the shelf (Robertson *et al.* 1976) we could expect that perhaps at least 15 km of sediment might have been accumulated at the foot of the slope and in the proximal rise. All of the para-autochthonous Cenozoic, Mesozoic and Permian formations of Timor represent deep water slope deposits of the continental rise, locally characterized by various kinds of pelagic sediments, turbidites and sedimentary slumping, which, in the Cribas and Aitutu formations of western Timor, is on a very large scale. The slumping

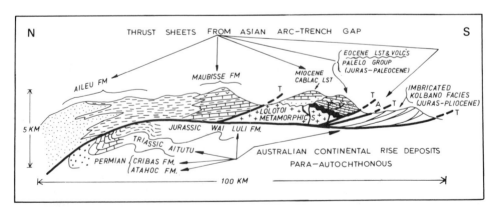

Fig. 5. Diagrammatic sketch across Timor showing the exotic thrust sheets emplaced above the Australian continental rise deposits during the mid-Pliocene collision. A = radiolarian lutites and muds with siltstones of Jurassic–Miocene age containing tiny clasts of metamorphic rocks (Lolotoi Complex?) and Palelo-type volcanic rocks described by Carter *et al.* (1976*b*).

and reworking with local biostratigraphical breaks in the Kolbano facies of Jurassic–Pliocene age has been described in Carter *et al.* (1976*a, b*). The term 'continental shelf unit' applied to these para-autochthonous Permian–Pliocene Australian strata by Barber *et al.* (1977) and others is misleading in this respect; it should have been designated 'continental rise unit'.

Audley-Charles (1978) summarized the evidence for interpreting the Mesozoic–Cenozoic continental slope of the 'Sula Peninsula' (of the Australia–New Guinea continent) to have been situated between N Seram and Misool. A multichannel seismic profile indicates that the Australia–New Guinea shelf deposits of Misool can be traced southwards, where they are depressed below the axis of the Seram Trough, as far as the S wall of the Trough where reflections are obscured below younger deposits (Audley-Charles & Carter 1978). This implies that in the northern part of the Banda Arc, as in the southern part, the fold and thrust belt developed in the continental rise near the foot of the continental slope.

Relation of crystalline basement to cover rocks in the Outer Banda Arc

The coincidence of the Banda Arc fold and thrust belt with the foot of the pre-Middle Pliocene Australian continental slope, where sedimentary accumulations achieved their maximum thickness, explains why no sub-Permian strata nor their crystalline basement have been seen in Timor. The original sediment thickness (probably between 10 and 15 km) in this palaeogeographical zone and the vergence of the fold belt towards the Australian continent, involving displacement of folded and sliced Permian, Mesozoic and Cenozoic strata southwards across Timor, have together provided a very thick pile of cover rocks.

According to Bowin *et al.* (in press) Australian continental crust can be traced by reflection seismic data northwards from the shelf below the Timor Trough where it is about 40 km thick below the trough axis. Chamalaun *et al.* (1976) used gravity data to construct a model that indicates that Australian continental crust continues as far as the north coast of Timor. Their model densities of 2.7 and 2.9 provide for continental crustal thicknesses below Timor of 30 km. These observations and models suggest that most of the distal portion of the Australian continental rise in the Timor

region of the Banda Arc is either missing (subducted) or has been involved in considerable shortening to account for the 30 km crustal thickness below Timor indicated by the gravity model and by the refraction picture of the Trough.

The tectonic style of the Outer Banda Arc islands, Timor ¡ nd Seram, involves strong folding, thrusting and imbrication in the Australian continental rise deposits. This indicates that these strata have become detached from their original crystalline (probably oceanic) basement; hence they are designated as para-autochthonous. They form complex though coherent fold and fault structures which can be mapped in detail if biostratigraphical techniques are employed.

Metamorphic rocks, ranging from granulite to greenschist facies, form a number of massifs in Timor and Seram (Barber & Audley-Charles 1976). These rocks correspond to levels varying from the base of the continental crust to epizonal depths and also include metamorphosed ocean floor materials (Barber 1979). Evidence indicates that these metamorphics have been thrust northwards in Seram and southwards in Timor (Barber & Audley-Charles 1976; Audley-Charles *et al.* 1979). The structural position of the migmatic gneisses in Seram is uncertain; on the available evidence they could be regarded as thrust sheets or upthrust horsts.

Identification of the 'root zone' of the Banda Arc exotic thrust sheets

The tectonic model proposed by Carter *et al.* (1976*a*) suggested the 'root zone' of the exotic thrust sheets was rifted from the Sunda craton in the late Cretaceous and formed the base of the Banda arc-trench gap which migrated southwards from Sulawesi during the late Cretaceous and Palaeocene. Their suggestion that this migration continued by back-arc spreading during the Eocene–Pliocene seems doubtful, in view of the heat flow characters of the southern Banda Sea (Bowin *et al.* in press). Hamilton (1979, fig. 77) followed closely the Carter *et al.* (1976*a*) model but he argued that the main back-arc spreading of the Banda Sea began about 15 Ma in the mid-Miocene. The Carter *et al.* (1976*a*) model can be extended to include the Australian continental rise overthrusting the volcanic arc-trench gap by postulating that the base of the hanging wall of the subduction trench sheared and detached from its basement during the mid-Pliocene deformation (Figs 2, 3, & 4). The failure of the underthrusting mechanism in the upper part of the mid-Pliocene Benioff zone coincided with the arrival at the trench of the great thickness of continental rise sediment near the foot of the Australian continental slope. This composite model (Figs 3 & 4) implies that the 'root zone' of the exotic thrust sheets of the Timor region has been overridden by the Australian continental rise carrying the detached exotic thrust sheets back (northwards) over their own roots.

Tectonic significance of the apparent continuity of the Sunda and Banda Arcs

Bowin *et al.* (in press) argued that the position of the Java Trench relative to the volcanic arc is comparable with the Banda Arc–Timor Trough separation if allowance is made for post-collision compression. They pointed out that both the Java Trench and volcanic arc fit small circles and that the western end of the Timor Trough fits the eastward extrapolation of the Java Trench small circle. They ascribe the progressive divergence of the Timor Trough, from the small circle projection eastward from Timor, to post-collision convergence. They reject the Veevers *et al.* (1978) model for the evolution of the Timor Trough as a downwarping of the Australian margin that migrated towards the continent after collision. However, using the composite Carter *et al.* (1976*a*) and Abbott & Chamalaun (1978) models for the arc-continent collision, it is possible also to combine the Bowin *et al.* (in press) and Veevers *et al.* (1978) models for Timor Trough evolution. This new model would place the mid-Pliocene trench below the western end of the present Timor Trough. The progressive narrowing of the distance between the present volcanic Inner Banda Arc and the Timor–Tanimbar Trough (Fig. 1) could then be attributed to one or more factors: (a) The original (pre-mid Pliocene) width of the arc-trench gap being progressively narrower eastwards from Timor, reflecting the eastwards progressive diminution of the volcanic arc: (b) alternatively the pre-mid Pliocene volcanic arc may have been overridden (as well as the arc-trench gap) E of Wetar and Romang; this would imply that the present small volcanic arc E of Romang is a younger post-mid Pliocene feature, as Bowin *et al.* (in press) suspect.

The small circle fit of the volcanic inner part of both the Sunda and Banda arcs suggests that they evolved as a single tectonic element on the same plate margin associated with the subduction of the Tethys and Indian Oceans as Australia–New Guinea drifted northwards with the Indian Ocean. However, the stratigraphy and structure of the outer part of the Sunda Arc system exemplified by the Mentawai Islands (Moore & Karig in press) are very different from the geology of the Outer Banda Arc, which involves Australian continental margin rocks overlain by exotic thrust sheets.

This fundamental difference in origin of the outer part of the Sunda and Banda Arcs means that, unlike the Mentawai islands of the Sunda Arc system exemplified by the Mentawai Is-Banda Arc islands cannot be regarded as analogous to the 'trench-slope break' of the Pacific arcs, as Cardwell & Isacks (1978) suggested. Neither can the Outer Banda Arc be regarded as an 'accretionary prism' of the hanging wall sitting directly above the underthrusting Australian crust, as Jacobson *et·al.* (1978), Hamilton (1979, fig. 78, 1978, von der Borch (1979) and Bowin *et al.* (in press) suggest. The Australian continental rise deposits in the Outer Banda Arc belong to the footwall that has overridden the Benioff zone and the true accretionary prism to arrive only 20 km from the volcanic arc (Figs 2–4).

Conclusions

1. The region is too complicated and insufficiently known to allow a unique interpretation of the data, nevertheless the Carter *et al.* (1976*a*) tectonic model based largely on stratigraphy of the Outer Banda Arc combines well with the Abbott & Chamalaun (1978) model based mainly on igneous stratigraphy of the volcanic arc. Furthermore, many aspects of the interpretations of Bowin *et al.* (in press) derived largely from marine geophysics and the Veevers *et al.* (1978) model for the Timor Trough can also be combined to form a new composite model that fits the available geological and geophysical data.

2. This composite model involves the accretionary arc-trench gap of the mid-Pliocene volcanic arc being underthrust by about 300 km of the Australian distal continental rise. The arrival at the trench in mid-Pliocene times (3 Ma) of the proximal part of the Australian rise comprising 10–15 km of low density sediments led to the failure of the Benioff zone to accommodate these rocks by underthrusting. Continuing plate convergence re-

sulted in approximately 150 km of the proximal part of the Australian continental rise and slope overriding the trench and the 200 km wide arc-trench gap until, by about Middle Pleistocene times (1 Ma), the proximal continental rise arrived only 20 km from the volcanic arc (then extinct) in the western part of the arc (Timor region). Further E, beyond Romang, this mid-Pliocene volcanic arc seems to have been completely overridden by the Australian continental rise.

3. This model can account for some of the outstanding geological anomalies of this complex arc. These include:- (a) The apparent absence of the Australian continental slope and rise in the northern Australia collision zone. (b) The apparent absence of a subduction trench and an accretionary arc-trench gap in the Banda Arc. (c) The presence of Australian continental rise deposits now only 20 km south of the pre-mid Pliocene volcanic arc. (d) The occurrence above the Australian continental margin of a variety of exotic thrust sheets whose 'root zone' seems most likely to have been the margin of the Sunda craton. (e) The observation that the lowest thrust sheet (Kolbano-Nief) of Timor and Seram comprises Jurassic–Pliocene Australian deep-water continental rise deposits overlain by thrust sheets comprising Eocene and Miocene sediments (Dartollu and Cablac) which were deposited in very shallow water.

4. Implications of this model are: (a) The 100–120 km wide fold and thrust belt of the Banda Arc developed in proximal continental rise deposits at the foot of the Australian continental slope. (b) The only parts of Australian continental crust to be subducted were the sedimentary deposits on the 300 km wide distal portion of the continental rise. (c) The failure of the Benioff zone to accommodate the thick proximal continental rise deposits, and the continuing plate convergence resulted in the collision of the Banda Arc and Australia. The folding, imbrication and overthrusting in this 100 km wide collision suture was accomplished between mid-Pliocene and mid-Pleistocene (about 2 Ma) in the Timor region. (d) Other arc-continent and continent-continent Tethyan collision zones such as the Himalayas may also have involved the Gondwana continental rise or even shelf deposits overridding the Asian arc-trench gap and volcanic arc, leaving little or no trace of their former presence.

5. Predictions for the future of this collision fold belt involve the now deformed and overthrust Australian continental margin (lacking about 300 km of its subducted continental rise) riding over the volcanic Inner Banda Arc if convergence continues. Not only would this remove the volcanic arc from view but it could lead, by erosion of the overthrust volcanic rocks, to little evidence of the volcanic activity remaining.

6. This new composite tectonic model could be tested by a series of seismic refraction lines in the immediate region of the Inner and Outer Banda Arc.

ACKNOWLEDGMENTS. The writer is indebted to A. W. Bally, A. J. Barber, D. J. Carter and N. Schneidermann for discussion.

References

ABBOTT, M. J. & CHAMALAUN, F. H. 1978. New K/Ar age data for Banda Arc volcanics. *Inst. Australas. Geodynamics, Publ.* **78/5,** 1–34.

APTHORPE, M. C. 1979. Depositional history of the Upper Cretaceous of the north-west shelf, based upon foraminifera. *APEA. J.* **19,** 74–89.

AUDLEY-CHARLES, M. G. 1968. The geology of Portuguese Timor. *Mem. geol. Soc. London,* **4,** 1–76.

—— 1978. Indonesian and Philippine Archipelago. *In:* MOULLADE, M. & NAIRN, A. M. (eds), *The Phanerozoic Geology of the World II The Mesozoic A.* Elsevier Publishing Co. Amsterdam. 165–207.

—— & CARTER, D. J. 1978. Interpretation of a regional seismic line from Misool to Seram: Implications for regional structure and petroleum exploration. *Proc. Indones. Petrol. Assoc.* (6th Ann. Conv. Jakarta, 1977), **2,** 3–11.

——, ——, BARBER, A. J., NORVICK, M. S. & TJOK-ROSAPOETRO, S. 1979. Reinterpretation of the geology of Seram: Implications for the Banda Arc and northern Australia. *J. geol. Soc. London,* **136,** 547–68.

—— & HOOIJER, D. A. 1973. Relation of Pleistocene migrations of pygmy stegodonts to island arc tectonics in eastern Indonesia. *Nature London,* **241,** 197–8.

BARBER, A. J. 1979. *Structural interpretations of the island of Timor, eastern Indonesia.* SEAPEX, Singapore, **4,** 9–21.

—— & AUDLEY-CHARLES, M. G. 1976. The significance of the metamorphic rocks of Timor in the development of the Banda Arc. *Tectonophysics,* **30,** 119–28.

——, —— & CARTER, D. J. 1977. Thrust tectonics in Timor. *J. geol. Soc. Aust.* **24,** 51–62.

BEMMELEN, R. W. VAN 1949. *The Geology of Indonesia.* Government Printing Office, The Hague.

BILLMAN, H. G. & SCRUTTON, M. E. 1976. *Stratigraphic Correlation in Indonesia.* SEAPEX, Singapore, **9**, 1–14.

BOWIN, C., PURDY, G. M., JOHNSTON, C., SHOR, C., LAWVER, L., HARTONO, H. M. S. & JEZEK, P. in press. Arc-continent collision in the Banda Sea region. *Bull. Am. Assoc. Petrol. Geol.*

BRUNNSCHWEILER, R. O. 1978. Notes of the geology of eastern Timor. *Bull. Bur. Miner. Resour. Geol. Geophys. Melbourne.* **192**, 9–18.

CARDWELL, R. K. & ISACKS, B. L. 1978. Geometry of the subducted lithosphere beneath the Banda Sea in eastern Indonesia from seismicity and fault plane solutions. *J. geophys. Res.* **83**, 2825–38.

CARTER, D. J., AUDLEY-CHARLES, M. G. & BARBER, A. J. 1976a. Stratigraphical analysis of island arc-continental margin collision in eastern Indonesia. *J. geol. Soc. London*, **132**, 179–98.

——, —— & —— 1976b. Discussion of Stratigraphical analysis of island arc-continental margin collision in eastern Indonesia. *J. geol. Soc. London*, **132**, 358–61.

CHAMALAUN, F. H., LOCKWOOD, K. & WHITE, A. 1976. The Bouguer gravity field and crustal structure of Timor. *Tectonophysics*, **30**, 241–59.

—— & GRADY, A. E. 1978. The tectonic development of Timor: A new model and its implications for petroleum exploration. *APEA J.* **18**, 102–8.

GERMERAAD, J. H. 1946. *Geology of Central Seram.* Amsterdam (de Bussy).

GRADY, A. E. 1975. A reinvestigation of thrusting in Portuguese Timor. *J. geol. Soc. Aust.* **22**, 223–7.

—— & BERRY, R. F. 1977. Some Palaeozoic-Mesozoic stratigraphic and structural relationships in east Timor and their significance in the tectonics of Timor. *J. geol. Soc. Aust.* **24**, 203–14.

GRUNAU, H. R. 1953. Geologie von Portugiesisch Ost-Timor. Eine kurtze Ubersicht. *Eclog. geol. Helv.* **46**, 29–37.

—— 1957. Nueue Daten zur geologie von Portiesisch Ost-Timor. *Eclog. geol. Helv.* **50**, 69–98.

HAMILTON, W. 1977. Subduction on the Indonesian region. *Proc. Indones. Petrol. Assoc.* 2–23.

—— 1978. Tectonic maps of the Indonesian region. *U.S. Geol. Surv. Misc. Invest. Series M I-875-D.*

—— 1979. Tectonics of the Indonesian region. *U.S. Geol. Surv. Prof. Pap.* **1078**, 1–345.

HEEZEN, B. C. 1974. Atlantic-type continental margins. *In*: BURK, C. A. & DRAKE, C. L. (eds), *The Geology of Continental Margins*, 13–24, Springer-Verlag New York.

HELWIG, J. & HALL, G. A. 1974. Steady-state trenches? *Geology*, **2**, 309–16.

JACOBSON, R. S., SHOR, G. G., KIECKHEFER, R. M. & PURDY, G. M. 1978. Seismic refraction and reflection studies in the Timor-Aru Trough system and Australian continental shelf. *Mem. Am. Assoc. Petrol. Geol.* **29**, 209–22.

KENYON, C. S. 1974. *Stratigraphy and Sedimentology of the Late Miocene to Quaternary Deposits of Timor.* Ph.D. Thesis, Univ. of London. (unpubl).

LEMOINE, M. 1959. Un example de tectonique chaotique, Timor: essai de coordination et d'interpretation. *Revue Geogr. phys. Geol. dyn. Paris* **2**, 205–30.

MOORE, G. F. & KARIG, D. E. in press. Structural geology of Nias Island, Indonesia: Implications for subduction zone tectonics. *Am. J. Sci.*

ROBERTSON, G. A., POWELL, D. E. & EDMOND, G. M. 1976. Australian northwest continental shelf: Results of ten years of exploration. *In*: HALBOUTY, M. T., MAHER, J. C. & LIAN, H. M. (eds), *Circum Pacific Energy and Mineral Resources*, Mem. Am. Assoc. Petrol. Geol. **25**, 231–8.

VALK, W. 1944. *Contributions to the Geology of West Seram.* Amsterdam (de Bussy).

VEEVERS, J. J., FALVEY, D. A. & ROBINS, S. 1978. Timor Trough and Australia: Facies show topographic wave migrated 80 km during the past 3 my. *Tectonophysics*, **45**, 217–27.

VON DER BORCH, C. 1979. Continent-island arc collision in the Banda Arc. *Tectonophysics*, **54**, 169–93.

WAARD, D. DE, 1954. Contributions to the geology of Timor. 1 Geological research in Timor, an introduction. *Indones. J. nat. Sci.* **110**, 1–8.

—— 1955a. Contributions to the geology of Timor VII. On the tectonics of the Ofu Series. *Indones. J. nat. Sci.* **111**, 137–43.

—— 1955b. Contributions to the geology of Timor VIII. Tectonics of the Sonnebait overthrust unit near Nikiniki and Basleo. *Indones. J. nat. Sci.* **111**, 144–50.

—— 1956. Contributions to the geology of Timor IX. Geology of a N-S section across western Timor. *Indones. J. nat. Sci.* **122**, 101–14.

—— 1957. Contribution to the geology of Timor XII. The third Timor Geological Expedition preliminary results. *Indones. J. nat. Sci.* **113**, 7–42.

WANNER, J. 1913. Geologie von West Timor. *Geol. Rndsch.* **4**, 136–50.

WHITFORD, D. J., COMPSTON, W., NICHOLLS, I. A. & ABBOTT, M. J. 1977. Geochemistry of late Cenozoic lavas from eastern Indonesia: Role of subducted sediments in petrogenesis. *Geology*, **5**, 571–5.

M. G. AUDLEY-CHARLES, Department of Geological Sciences, Queen Mary College, London.

Neogene thrust emplacement from a frontal arc in New Guinea

J. Milsom

SUMMARY: In northern New Guinea there is clear evidence that at some stage in the Neogene the northern margin of the Australian continent was in collision with a southwards facing island arc. There is still active volcanism along the whole length of this arc and a deep oceanic trench opposite the segment E of the collision zone. The Finisterre Range, a part of the former frontal arc and now part of northern New Guinea, lies up to 50 km S of its expected position with respect to the segments to E and W. Geological and geophysical evidence combine to suggest that this offset is not a deep seated feature, but is the result of movement on a very shallow thrust. Detachment of the thrust sheet from the remainder of the upper crust evidently took place along the line of weakness represented by the volcanic arc.

The mobile segment may have been the part of the frontal arc that first collided with the continental margin; the adjacent segments, which were probably, at the time of collision, opposite largely oceanic, and therefore much deeper, trenches, have not moved in this way.

Since its initial formation, the thrust sheet, or some parts of it, has evidently been involved in movements parallel to the strike of the arc.

Large and relatively thin overthrusts are a feature of many areas where continental crust is thought to have collided with a subduction zone associated either with the margin of another continent or with an island arc system. In some cases, the very existence of a large thrust sheet has been regarded as sufficient evidence that a collision has taken place. However, the geological complexity of such areas has usually hindered efforts to understand the mechanism by which thrusting is initiated. If places can be found where collision has only recently occurred or is still continuing, fresh insights can potentially be gained into emplacement processes. The N coast region of New Guinea would seem to be just such a type area.

N of New Guinea, the islands of the Solomon, New Hebrides and Bismarck archipelagoes form a distinct, though fragmented, geological province in which periods of volcanism in the early and late Tertiary were separated by a long period of quiescence, submergence and sedimentation. The geological unity of the island groups has been recognized in the use of the term 'Outer Melanesian Arc' by a number of authors (e.g. Robinson 1973).

Towards the western end of the island chains, one branch, formed mainly by the island of New Britain, continues without major stratigraphic discontinuity into the northern mainland of New Guinea itself. The major part of New Guinea is clearly continental in character and forms the northern margin of the Australian continental block, but even within the context of the general geological similarities throughout the Outer Melanesian Arc, the detailed parallels which can be drawn between the N coast ranges of New Guinea and the island of New Britain are remarkably close. The segment within which resemblances are strongest extends from the mouths of the Sepik and Ramu rivers, at 144° 30′E, to Wide Bay on New Britain, at 152°E. For convenience, this 1200 km long segment is here termed the Huon zone, the name being taken from the Huon peninsula which forms its centrepiece. It is widely accepted, on the basis of the mapped lithologies, that the mainland section of this zone once formed part of an island arc that has been welded on to the continent by collision (cf. Johnson & Molnar 1972; Jacques & Robinson 1977).

The present paper is concerned principally with the Finisterre and other ranges which form the Huon peninsula and extend for 250 km to the W. The mountain mass, which reaches heights of more than 4000 m, has a maximum width of approximately 100 km, but decreases in elevation and narrows westwards until it finally disappears in the swamps of the Ramu River valley. It is replaced *en echelon* to the NW by the geologically similar but topographically more subdued Adelbert Range. These latter mountains are abruptly terminated at their E end along the Madang coast, a feature of great importance which trends almost due N along the 146th meridian and which offsets the otherwise E–ESE trend of the coastline by more than 100 km.

The entire land area of the Huon zone is characterized by high rainfall, consequent rapid erosion and prolific deposition of clastics along the low-lying margins. Except at the highest levels, where Alpine grasslands are found, the area is covered by dense tropical rain forest interspersed with patches of coarse kunai grass. Exposures of any rocks other than cliff forming limestones are generally confined to the upper reaches of the rivers, where it is often difficult to distinguish between outcrop and massive float.

Geological development of the Huon zone

The development of the Huon zone has been summarized within the general context of the geology of Papua New Guinea by Dow (1977). The Huon peninsula has been discussed in more detail by Robinson (1976) and this and other individual parts of the zone are described in the Explanatory Notes series produced originally by the Australian Bureau of Mineral Resources (BMR) and more recently by the Geological Survey of Papua New Guinea (GSPNG) (Robinson 1974; Jacques & Robinson in press; Robinson et al. 1976. Evidence for the island arc origin of the N coast ranges is discussed by Jacques & Robinson (1977).

The oldest rocks seen in outcrop are the Eocene Baining Volcanics of New Britain and the Gusap Argillite of the mainland. Both formations are sequences of intermixed island arc volcanics and pelagic and hemipelagic sediments, with volcanics predominating on New Britain and sediments on the mainland. On New Britain, there may have been a non-volcanic interlude during the Lower Oligocene (Dow 1977) but on the mainland the Gusap Argillite grades into the overlying Finisterre Volcanics via a steady increase in volcanic component. The latter rocks, and their equivalents on New Britain, are island arc andesites and tholeitic basalts, many of which show signs of submarine extrusion. Comagmatic intrusions are also common on New Britain.

Apparently volcanism ceased abruptly throughout the zone in the earliest Miocene and was followed by a period of calcareous sedimentaion which occupied most of the Middle Miocene. The limestones outcrop most spectacularly in a massive sheet which blankets much of the northern part of the Huon peninsula. Reef corals predominate but some deeper water types have also been reported.

Uplift and emergence of the western part of the zone (i.e. the present-day Adelbert Range) in the latest Middle Miocene resulted in the

start of clastic sedimentation there and this facies extended eastward and became more general during the Pliocene. Deposition was, and is, especially rapid in the narrow marine basin that developed to the N of the Finisterres.

The Pliocene also saw the return of island arc volcanism, with the development of the still active Bismarck arc along the northern margin of the zone. The Pliocene emergence of the frontal arc consisting of New Britain and the N coast ranges of New Guinea was another aspect of the renewal of subduction. A further consequence may have been the extrusion of small amounts of valley-fill basalts in the Finisterres.

The most enigmatic rocks of the zone are the rare ultramafics, chiefly serpentinites and peridotites, found on the Huon peninsula. These have been variously regarded as late Tertiary intrusions or as infaulted blocks of the basement upon which the whole of the Tertiary succession was deposited. Their areas of outcrop are too small to be shown on the simplified geological map (Fig. 1).

Continent–island arc collision

The idea that the Huon zone is an area of collision between continental Australia and an island arc system to the N is virtually as old as the theory of plate tectonics itself. The briefest of glances at the map is sufficient to identify an active island arc, accompanied by a deep oceanic trench, forming the eastern part of the zone. The trench is the surface expression of the subduction process, well attested seismically (Denham 1975), whereby the oceanic crust of the Solomon sea is being absorbed into the mantle beneath New Britain. Since the W end of the trench trends directly towards New Guinea itself, the conclusion that, in that area, an intervening ocean has been recently destroyed and that the trench has then been blocked by the continental margin seems an obvious one. An alternative to this simplest of scenarios relates the collision to the abrupt ending of the lower Tertiary volcanic episode and supposes the Quaternary to have been dominated by deformation of blocks already in contact (cf. Robinson 1973). Some authors have coupled an early collision date with a subsequent complex series of arc reversals to explain points of detail (e.g. Karig 1972). Placement of the collision at the beginning of the Miocene does present a number of difficulties

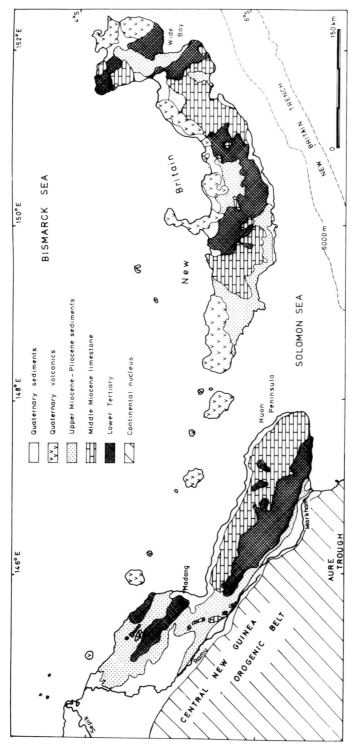

FIG 1. Simplified geological map of the Huon zone, Papua New Guinea, after D'Addario *et al.* 1975.

and some of the evidence in its favour applies only to the N coast ranges W of the Sepik mouth, which may well have attached themselves to New Guinea during this epoch. These western ranges include rocks which are similar to those of the Huon zone but which have been much more extensively tectonized. Significantly, they are not today backed by an active volcanic arc.

One of the problems posed by acceptance of an early date for the collision is that, in order to explain the post-Miocene volcanic activity in the southern Bismarck Sea, it is necessary to suppose that subducted lithosphere which has not produced magma for a considerable period of time can be reactivated even if there is no more ocean to be absorbed. Detachment and further sinking of the material already drawn down into the mantle may be possible, but it would seem a little surprising that over such a great period of time (virtually the whole of the Miocene in this case) the subducted mass has not become thermally and physically integrated with its surroundings. It is also difficult to explain the scarcity of Miocene clastic sediments if, at the time of deposition of the massive limestone sheets, the marine basins which were to become the Adelberts and Finisterres were adjacent to the emergent continental core of New Guinea. Furthermore, if the Ramu and Markham valleys are the surface trace of a collision suture and former Oligocene trench, then the associated volcanics are found unexpectedly far S. Even in New Britain, where the present-day subducted slab is almost vertical at depth (Denham 1975), there is a distance of 100–150 km between the trench axis and the modern volcanic line, whereas the Oligocene volcanics of the Adelberts are only half that distance from the Ramu. Their equivalents in the Finisterres are even further S but in the light of the fault movements proposed below no great significance can be attached to this fact.

Collision W of the Sepik mouth at the start of the Miocene, leaving a narrow belt of oceanic crust further E to be absorbed in the late Tertiary, satisfies most of the constraints imposed by the geological facts as known at present (Jacques & Robinson 1977). The Bismarck Arc only developed in the Pliocene and possibly not before the beginning of the Pleistocene but, if it is the result of an entirely new phase of subduction, well over a hundred kilometres of ocean must presumably have been absorbed before the leading edge of the plate reached depths sufficient to produce calc-alkaline magmas. The more recent date would surely make the Huon zone the world's youngest collision.

The Finisterre Thrust

Despite the stratigraphical continuity of the Huon zone, there are marked structural breaks along the Madang coast and between New Britain and the Huon peninsula. The abrupt truncation of the Adelbert Ranges near Madang and their replacement to the E by a youthful sedimentary basin (Robinson *et al.* 1977) can only be convincingly explained by faulting, although the exact nature of the movements is not clearly established. Normal faulting, with downthrow to the E, is an obvious possibility, but this, while explaining the truncation of the Adelberts, does not explain their relationship to the *en echelon* Finisterres. The roughly equal widths of the two mountain blocks argues rather for some form of lateral movement, with the Finisterres an offset continuation of the Adelberts.

Displacement of one section of an island arc relative to the remainder can be brought about in one of two ways. Either the offsetting faults are deep-seated, meriting the title of arc–arc transforms, or they are of secondary importance and have little extent in depth. In the latter case, a third fault must exist in the form of a shallow thrust upon which a part of the uppermost crust of the arc has moved. The surface patterns produced by the two processes would be rather similar, at least until the outcrops had been dissected by erosion, but the deep structures would be vastly different. Insights into these structures are provided by the gravity field and by the patterns of volcanism and associated seismicity.

The line of the Bismarck volcanic arc which parallels first the Adelberts and then the Finisterres before continuing along the northern coast of New Britain, shows no sign of offset as it passes the line of extension of the Madang coast. There is almost equally little evidence of displacement of the seismic patterns although these, as befits a collision zone, are very complex. Since most evidence suggests, and most current theories assume, that island arc magmas are initially generated at depths of more than 100 km, and may be both modified chemically and physically diverted during ascent into the upper crust, the linearity of the volcanic arc strongly suggests that there is no deep-seated transcurrent faulting, and that any shallow faults do not extend so far N.

A similar deduction can be made from the gravity anomaly maps. Gravity readings have been taken both onshore and offshore throughout the area, although the station spacing is very variable. For the Huon peninsula, the most recent work is still that of St John (1970, but surveys by BMR and GSPNG have added detail in other parts of the onshore area. Offshore, continuous profiles obtained in the Bismarck Sea under a BMR contract have established the main regional pattern (Connelly 1976). Combination of these surveys (Fig. 2) shows that the transition between the oceanic Bismarck Sea and crust of continental thickness is strongly expressed in the gravity field, with a total change in level of more than 200 mgal. In the Adelbert block, the steep rise begins some 30 km inland from the coast, but since the contour lines in the −100 to 0 mgal range run almost straight, along a bearing of about E 30°S, in the Finisterre region the same rise starts about 30 km N of the southwards displaced coastline. The magnitude and position of this gravity gradient indicates that it dominantly reflects changes in crustal thickness and its linearity is clear evidence that any transcurrent faults across it do not extend to the base of the crust.

The gravity patterns S of the main gradient are also extremely interesting. S of the Adelberts the gravity minimum lies in the swampy valley to the SW of Madang. Further E, however, this low splits into two parts, separated by a relative high in the northern part of the Finisterres (Note that all non-zero values marked on contour lines on Fig. 2 are negative). The more northerly low defines the limits of the deep marine sedimentary basin which lies between the mainland and the island volcanoes, while the southern one extends over both the southern fall of the Finisterres and the intermontane trough. The change from a single to a double low occurs quite abruptly along the southward extension of the Madang coast, the very definite gravity break contrasting with the paucity of evidence for this extension in the surface geology. Whereas further N the continuity of a gravity gradient can be used as evidence that there is no deep-seated break in the vicinity of the volcanic arc, the sharp gravity changes along the line S of Madang are evidence that the apparent continuity of the Finisterres across this line is largely superficial. That the Finisterres, homogeneous at the surface, overlie a very heterogeneous basement is still more convincingly demonstrated by the

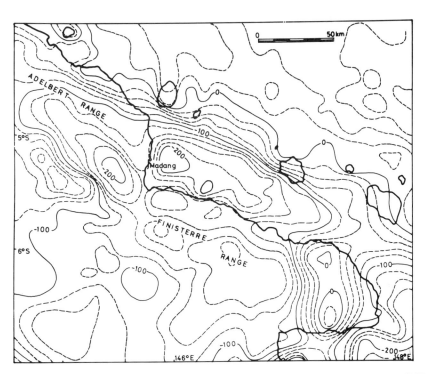

FIG. 2. Gravity variations in the Finisterre region, after Bureau of Mineral Resources (1976). Based on 10 km averages of simple Bouguer anomaly on land and free air anomaly offshore.

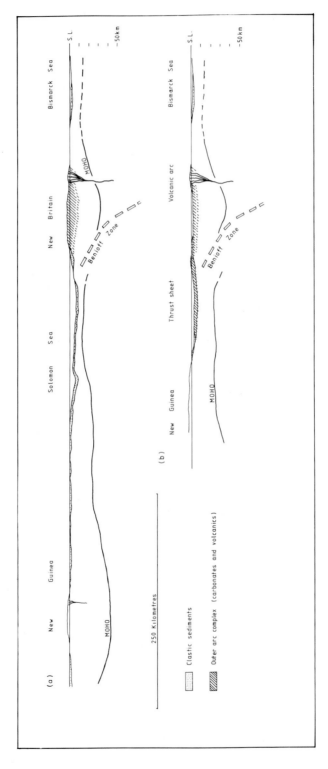

FIG. 3. (a) Present-day geology of the Solomon sea area, the modern analogue of the Pliocene Finisterre region, after Milsom (1974). (b) Geology of the Finisterre region immediately after completion of the initial thrust movements, before uplift of the Finisterre ranges.

pattern at their eastern end. N trending contours define a gravity high which includes in its peak area scattered ultramafic outcrops and which appears to be a continuation of that due to the Papuan Ultramafic Belt further S (Milsom 1973).

All these observations can be simply explained if the Finisterre Ranges are formed by a relatively thin overthrust sheet which broke away from the remainder of the upper crust along the line of weakness represented by the volcanic arc and moved forward into the depression at the collision suture, leaving in its wake a young sedimentary basin. Although the movement was evidently almost directly southward initially, as demonstrated by the Madang coast and the gravity offsets, later westward adjustments shifted parts of the sheet into their present position in front of the Adelbert Range. The heterogeneous gravity field of the Finisterres is a reflection of the heterogeneity of the underlying continental margin and the occurrence of ultramafics on the Huon peninsula suggests that in places the thrust sheet thins to the point of fragmentation. This hypothesis makes a clear distinction between the normal frontal arc, which overthrusts subducted crust along the Benioff Zone, and the Finisterre block which, in addition, has been thrust still further forward on a very flat lying fault plane.

The nature of the proposed movements is shown in the diagrammatic natural scale cross-sections of Fig. 3. The present-day structures of New Britain, the Solomon sea and the Papuan peninsula are shown in Fig. 3a; the Pliocene Finisterres must have looked very similar. Fig. 3b shows the structural pattern after collision between the subduction zone and the continental margin. The trench is rather shallower but has still provided the elevation difference necessary for the uppermost part of the frontal arc to move forward and downwards, with the toe of the thrust advancing a little way up the opposite slope. Later, and well attested, differential uplift not only raised the Finisterres to their present elevation but may also have readjusted the position of the overthrust sheet by further gravity-driven gliding.

Conclusion

The Finisterre range provides strong evidence that, in one case at least, mobilization of an overthrust has been a consequence of a collision between an island arc and a continent. An attempt to reconstruct the earlier shape of the N New Guinea coastline suggests that the relationship between collision and thrusting may be very direct. Immediately S of the Ramu–Markham suture line, the dominant structural trend changes from the northerly of the Papuan peninsula and the Aure trough to the north-westerly general in central New Guinea (Dow 1977). It seems likely that the pre-collision coastline protruded northward in the vicinity of the change in strike, a hypothesis supported by the apparent continuation beneath the Huon peninsula of the N-striking zone of high gravity associated with the Papuan Ultramafic Belt. This, in turn, makes it probable that it was the Finisterre section of the Huon zone which was the first to come in contact with the continental margin. This is a rather unexpected conclusion, since it is easier to imagine that, after a subduction zone has been blocked by collision, parts of the frontal arc on either side may slide down into the trench, than that the arc section immediately opposite the blockage should move down into a presumably much shallower trough. However, gabbro intersected at the bottom of Keram No. 1 borehole between the Sepik and Ramu rivers has been regarded as oceanic crust (Jacques & Robinson 1977) which also argues for the survival of some fragments of ocean between the Adelberts and the continental nucleus. This is one point of detail, amongst many others, which seems to merit further study.

ACKNOWLEDGMENTS. I thank former colleagues in the Geological Survey of Papua New Guinea and particularly L. Jacques for many stimulating discussions and arguments.

References

BUREAU OF MINERAL RESOURCES 1976. *Preliminary Gravity Map of Melanesia.* Geophysical Branch, Canberra.

CONNELLY, J. B. 1976. Tectonic development of the Bismarck sea based on gravity and magnetic modelling. *Geophys. J. R. astron. Soc.* **46,** 23–40.

D'ADDARIO, G. W., DOW, D. B. & SWOBODA, R. 1975. Geology of Papua New Guinea 1:2 500 000 map. *Bur. Miner. Resour. Geol. Geophys. Aust.*

DENHAM, D. 1975. Distribution of underthrust lithospheric slabs and focal mechanisms—Papua New Guinea—Solomon Islands region. *Bull. Aust. Soc. Expl. Geophys.* **6,** 35–7.

J. Milsom

Dow, D. B. 1977. Geological synthesis of Papua New Guinea. *Bull. Bur. Miner. Resour. Geol. Geophys. Canberra*, **201**, 41 p.

Jacques, A. L. & Robinson, G. P. 1977. Continent/island arc collision in northern Papua New Guinea. *J. Bur. Miner. Res. Aust. Geol. Geophys.* **2**, 289–303.

—— & —— in press. Explanatory notes on the Bogia geological map. *Geol. Surv. Papua New Guinea*.

Johnson, R. W. 1976. Late Cenozoic volcanism and plate tectonics at the southern margin of the Bismarck sea, Papua New Guinea. *In:* Johnson, R. W. (ed). *Volcanism in Australasia*. Elsevier, Amsterdam, 101–16.

Johnson, T. & Molnar, P. 1972. Focal mechanisms and plate tectonics of the southwest Pacific. *J. geophys. Res.* **77**, 5000–32.

Karig, D. 1972. Remnant arcs. *Bull. geol. Soc. Am.* **83**, 1057–68.

Milsom, J. 1973. Papuan Ultramafic Belt: gravity anomalies and the emplacement of ophiolites. *Bull. geol. Soc. Am.* **84**, 2243–58.

—— 1974. East New Guinea. *In:* Spencer, A. M. (ed). *Mesozoic–Cenozoic Orogenic Belts*. Spec. Publ. geol. Soc. London, **4**, 463–474.

Robinson, G. P. 1973. Stratigraphy and structure of the Huon peninsula, New Guinea, within the framework of the Outer Melanesian Arc. *In:* Fraser, R. (ed). *Oceanography of the South Pacific*, New Zealand National Commission for UNESCO, Wellington.

—— 1974. Explanatory notes on the Huon–Sag Sag geological map. *Bur. Miner. Resour. Aust. Geol. Geophys.*

—— 1976. Geology of the Huon peninsula *Mem. geol. Surv. Papua New Guinea* **2**, 34 p.

——, Jacques, A. L. & Brown, C. M. 1976. Explanatory notes on the Madang geological map. *Geol. Surv. Papua New Guinea*.

St John, V. P. 1970. Gravity field and structure of Papua New Guinea. *J. Aust. Petrol. Expl. Assoc.* **10**, 41–55.

J. Milsom, 15 Cambridge Road, Wimbledon, London SW 20, England.

IV.
THRUST AND NAPPE REGIMES
B. '*THE NEW WORLD*'

The Americas

The Cordilleran foreland thrust and fold belt in the southern Canadian Rocky Mountains

R. A. Price

SUMMARY: The thick (~40 km) slab of Hudsonian (>1750 Ma) continental crust that extends under western Canada from the Canadian Shield can be followed westward, on the basis of its distinctive magnetic anomalies, its influence on the Bouguer gravity values, the results of deep seismic refraction experiments, and the results of geomagnetic depth sounding of the deep electrical conductivity structure, to the Kootenay Arc. The Kootenay Arc is basically a W-facing monocline of crustal dimensions, across which the change in structural level involves an aggregate stratigraphic thickness of up to 20 km. It marks the western edge of the continental craton over which the displaced supracrustal rocks have been draped.

Balanced structure sections of the thrust and fold belt, which take into consideration the deep crustal structure, as constrained by the geophysical data, show that: (i) in early Campanian time the continental crust that now lies beneath the western Rocky Mountains and the Purcell anticlinorium was covered with the platformal Palaeozoic to Upper Jurassic rocks and the exogeoclinal Mesozoic rocks that now form the northeasterly verging imbricate thrust slices of the eastern Rocky Mountains; (ii) the Cordilleran miogeocline developed outboard from the edge of the continental craton, on tectonically attenuated continental crust, or oceanic crust; and (iii) tectonic shortening of about 200 km in the supracrustal rocks in the Rocky Mountains must be balanced at a deeper level, W of the Kootenay Arc, by the shortening of the oceanic or attenuated continental crust.

The net convergence between the Cordilleran magmatic arc and the autochthonous cover on the continental craton is a type of intra-plate subduction that was antithetic to the SW verging subduction zone marking the boundary of the North American Plate. The basement of the back-arc or marginal basin, in which the miogeocline formed, was consumed; but the adjoining continental margin was not. The foreland thrust and fold belt is a shallow subduction complex that was tectonically prograded over the margin of the continental craton, as the supracrustal cover scraped off the down-going slab was piled up against the overriding mass, and spread laterally eastward under its own weight.

The foreland thrust and fold belt of the North American Cordillera is a zone of easterly verging shallow thrust faulting and décollement folding, up to about 300 km wide, that follows the boundary between the Cordilleran miogeocline and the North American craton from the Yukon Territory of northern Canada to southeastern California (King 1969; Wheeler et al. 1974; Burchfiel & Davis 1972). From whence it may extend across southern Arizona and New Mexico and southwestern Texas into the Sierra Madre Oriental of Mexico (Corbitt & Woodward 1973), and finally into Guatemala and Honduras (de Cserna 1971). Within this zone of 'thin-skinned' deformation, an easterly tapering wedge of supracrustal rocks, comprising parts of the miogeocline, the cover of the cratonic platform, and the overlying exogeoclinal wedge of synorogenic clastic wedge deposits, was horizontally compressed and tectonically thickened, as it was displaced eastward relative to the underlying undeformed craton. The distinctive attributes of structural style and tectonic setting of this belt are characteristic of many other foreland thrust and fold belts, including: the Helvetic and Jura Mountains of the northern Alps (Bernoulli et al. 1974), the Valley and Ridge Province in the western Appalachian Mountains of the United States (Rodgers 1970), the Labrador 'trough' along the boundary between the Churchill Province (Proterozoic–Aphebian) and Superior Provinces (Archean) in the eastern Canadian Shield (Dimroth 1970), and the Asiak fold and thrust belt along the boundary between the Bear Province (Proterozoic–Aphebian) and the Slave (Archean) Province in the northwestern

Canadian Shield (Hoffman 1973; Hoffman *et al.* 1978). Foreland thrust and fold belts appear to represent a geotectonic phenomenon that is widely distributed in space and time, but for which there is, as yet, no simple global explanation.

Foreland thrust and fold belts display obvious similarites in structural geometry to the zones of imbricate thrust faulting and associated folding that occur above subduction zones along the inner slope of trenches in which there is a thick sedimentary fill (Hamilton 1977; Seeley 1977); and some foreland thrust and fold belts have been interpreted as the result of a 'collision' between a passive continental margin and island arc or another continental margin, during which part of the supracrustal cover of the underriding passive margin was scraped off against the overriding plate (Dewey & Bird, 1970). However, many foreland thrust and fold belts cannot be formed in this way because they represent relatively small ($d \times 10^2$ km) displacements distributed within a single physically continuous lithospheric plate (intra-plate displacements), rather than relatively large ($d \times 10^3$ km) displacements across a suture along which one discrete plate has overridden another quite different one (inter-plate displacements).

The foreland thrust and fold belt of the North American Cordillera is a good example of an intra-plate thrust and fold belt. Although there are conspicuous changes in the details of tectonic setting, structural style and history of deformation from one segment to another of the foreland thrust and fold belt of the North American Cordillera, the segment containing the southern Canadian Rocky Mountains is as typical as any. It is a particularly appropriate place for a more detailed analysis of the nature and tectonic significance of this foreland thrust and fold belt, because its essential features are not obscured by younger sedimentary and volcanic deposits, or superimposed deformation of the Basin and Range type, and because it has been relatively thoroughly studied by deep drilling and seismic reflection exploration for hydrocarbon traps (Fox 1959; Dahlstrom 1970; Shaw 1963; Keating 1966; Bally *et al.* 1966) as well as by systematic mapping of surface exposures. The main objective of this paper is to elucidate the geological structure, tectonic evolution, and geotectonic significance of the segment of the Rocky Mountains thrust and fold belt between latitude 48°N and latitude 52°N (Fig. 1), and of the Cordilleran foreland thrust and fold belt in general.

Structure of the southern Canadian Rocky Mountains

The structure of the southern Canadian Rocky Mountains is dominated by thrust faults, almost all of which are easterly verging. Flexural-slip folds have developed in conjunction with the displacements along the thrust faults; and many of the thrust faults die out upward in the cores of anticlines or downward in the cores of synclines, where they mark the centres of curvature for strata that are concentrically folded (Price 1964*b*, 1965). The mechanical anisotropy due to the stratigraphic layering has exerted a profound influence on the style of the deformation. The thrust faults commonly follow bedding glide zones that are linked by ramps along which the faults step across the stratigraphic layering; and the thrust

---

FIG. 1. Geological map of the foreland thrust and fold belt of the North American Cordillera between 49° and 52°N latitude. The lines labelled W–E and SW–NE mark the locations of the structure sections presented in Fig. 2. Symbols identifying the more important faults are as follows: Bo-Bourgeau; BR-Bull River; Ca–Chatter Creek; Co–Columbia River; Fl–Flathead; Ha–Hall Lake; Ho–Hope; Jo–Johnston Creek; Le–Lewis; Li–Livingstone; Mc–McConnell; Moy–Moyie; Mo–Mons; Ne–Newport; Pi–Pipestone Pass; Pu–Purcell; RMT–Rocky Mountain Trench; Ru–Rundle; Sa–Standfast Creek; Si–Simpson Pass; Sm–Sulphur Mountain; StM–St. Mary.

Symbols identifying batholiths are as follows: Ba–Battle Mountain; Bu–Bugaboo; By–Bayonne; F–Fry Creek; H–Horsethief Creek; Ka–Kaniksu; Ku–Kuskanax; N–Nelson; W–White Creek. The Valhalla gneiss complex is identified by the symbol V. The information which is compiled and interpreted in this map is taken from maps by: Balkwill, *et al.* (in press *a, b*); Benvenuto (1978); Bielenstein, *et al.*, (1971); Campbell & Loofbourow (1957); Douglas (1951, 1952, 1958); Fyles (1964, 1967); Fyles & Hewlett (1959); Gilman (1972); Glover (1978); Harrison & Jobin (1963, 1965); Harrison & Schmidt (1971); Henderson (1954); Höy (1977, 1978); Huntting *et al.* (1961); Johns (1970); Leech (1959, 1960); Little (1960); Miller (1974 a–d); Miller *et al.* (1961); Johns (1970); Ollerenshaw (1975, 1978); Park & Cannon (1943); Price (1962); Price & Mountjoy (1978 a–d, 1979 a–b, in press); Price *et al.* (in press); Price *et al.* (in press *a, b*); Balkwill *et al.* (in press *a & b*); Read & Wheeler (1976); Reesor (1973); Ross (1959); Sears (1979); Simony & Wind (1970); Thompson (1972); Wheeler (1963); Williams (1949); Yates (1964, 1971); Zwanzig (1973).

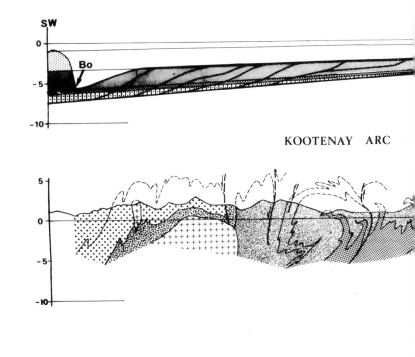

KOOTENAY ARC

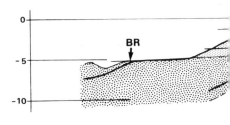

KOOTENAY ARC

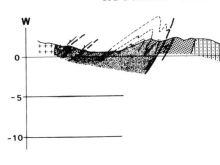

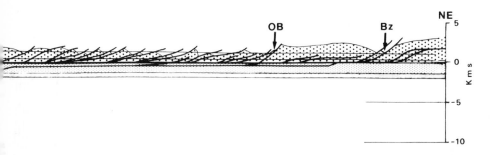

FOOTHILLS

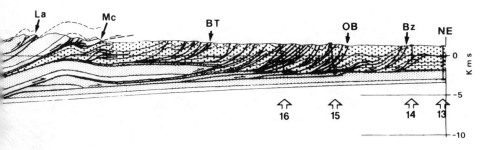

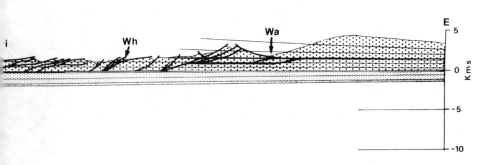

FOOTHILLS   ALBERTA SYNCLINE

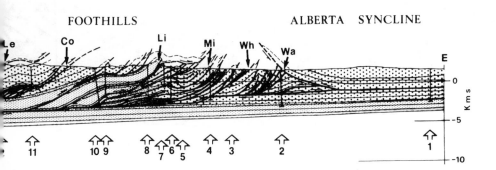

sheets have been folded (and unfolded) as they moved along the stepped fault surfaces (Douglas 1950). Flexural-slip folding and thrust faulting have proceeded concurrently as two different manifestations of the same basic process of horizontal compression and relative northeasterly upward translation of the supracrustal rocks. Many of the thrust faults have been folded together with the beds they cut, because of displacements on other curved faults which developed later, at lower structural levels (Douglas 1950, 1952, 1958; Dahlstrom 1970). Displacements on the thrust faults range up to a maximum of at least 50 km in the case of the Lewis Thrust (Price 1965; Dahlstrom et al. 1962); but nevertheless all the faults die out along the strike, and the rock mass is physically continuous around the ends of each fault. On a regional scale, the faults comprise a penetrative array of discrete, discontinuous overlapping and interfingering slip surfaces; and at this scale, the deformation can be viewed as a kind of compressive plastic flow (Nye 1952) involving both large distortion (E–W compression and vertical thickening) and

large easterly relative translation, without any overall disruption and loss of cohesion (Price 1973).

The tectonically foreshortened easterly tapering wedge of supracrustal rocks is firmly attached in the E to the undeformed supracrustal rocks comprising the platformal and exogeoclinal deposits that cover the western flank of the Canadian Shield. The western part is penetrated by granitic intrusions and intercalated with and overlain by calc-alkaline volcanic rocks comprising a regional calc-alkaline magmatic belt that has been attributed to the easterly subduction of oceanic lithosphere beneath the Cordilleran orogenic belt (Monger et al. 1972; Monger & Price 1979). There are some structures in the deformed supracrustal wedge that reflect an easterly horizontal stretching; but, as will be shown below, the magnitude, location, and timing of this horizontal stretching leave no doubt that the development of the foreland fold and thrust belt involved a large net convergence between the magmatic belt and the North American craton. Therefore, the relative easterly translation of

FIG 2. Structure Sections and palinspastically restored sections through the Cordilleran foreland thrust and fold belt in southern Canada. The locations of section are given in Fig. 1. Symbols identifying equivalent points on the hanging-wall side of the more important faults in each structure section and its palinspastically restored counterpart are listed: Bo–Bourgeau; BR–Bull River; BT–Burnt Timber; Bz–Brazeau; Co–Coleman; HL–Hall Lake; In–Inglismaldie; La–Lac des Arcs; Le–Lewis; Li–Livingstone; Mc–McConnell; Mi–Mill Creek; OB–Old Baldy; RMT–Rocky Mountain Trench; Ru–Rundle; Sm–Sulphur Mountain; Wa–Watson; Wh–Whaleback.

The horizontal sea-level datum for the restored sections is the boundary between marine and non-marine Upper Jurassic rocks. In the overlying synorogenic clastic wedge deposits of the exogeocline the Upper Jurassic and Lower Cretaceous Kootenay Formation is designated–JKk; the Lower Cretaceous Blairmore Group in designated–Kbl, and the Upper Cretaceous marine Alberta Group is designated Kag. The shallow structure shown in the eastern part of Section W–E is adapted, with modifications, from sections by Douglas (1950), Price (1962); that between the Bull River (BR) and Rocky Mountain Trench (RMT) faults is modified after Leech (1958) and Höy (1978); and that in the Kootenay Arc follows Fyles (1967) and Höy (1977). The eastern part of Section SW–NE, above −2400 m, is adapted with modifications from sections at a scale of 1:50 000 by Price & Mountjoy (1970a, 1970b, 1973a, 1973b) and Ollerenshaw (1972a, 1972b) and follows the basic pattern of a section by Bally et al. (1966, plate 1B and plate 3) that is based on seismic reflection data and deep drilling. The shallow structure of the Purcell anticlinorium is adapted with modifications from a section at 1:250 000 by Reesor (1973); and that in the Kootenay Arc follows a section by Fyles (1964).

Locations of wells drilled for oil and gas, from which logs were used in the preparation of the structure sections are shown by heavy lines and identified by number as follows: 1–Spring Point 2-4-10-29W4 (projected 460 m S); 2–Calstan C&E Cow Ck. 76-30-8-1W5 (projected 8400 m S); 3–Marjon Lundbeck No 1. (projected 4100 m S) (log by Douglas 1950); 4–Texaco Wilmont Todd Ck A-1 3-6-10-2W5 (Projected 4100 m S); 5–Union Quaich 10-3 10-3-9-3W5 (Projected 4500 m N); 6–Imperial Quaich 3-3-10-3W5 (Projected 4100 m); 7–Triad Union Quaich 10-21-9-3W5 (Projected 100 m S); 8–Texaco Livingstone East 3-20-9-3W5 (Projected 500 m N); 9–Coseka et al. Coleman 4-23-9-4W5 (Projected 500 mN); 10–Gulf PCP Coleman 7-33-10-4W5 (projected 460 m S); 11–California Standard-Crowsnest 6-14-8-5W5 (Projected 11500 mN); 12–Sinclair et al. Racehouse 15-29-9-5W5 (Projected 2100 m S); 13–Consumer Shell Cremanc 10-21-29-5W5 (projected 1200 m SW); 14–Dome Winchell 10-18-24-5W5 (Projected 1500 m S; 15–Western Imperial wildcat 6-16-18-6W5 (Projected 2400 m SW); 16–Imperial Fina Pacifac Benjamin 3-14-38-W75 (Projected 800 m SW).

The logs of the wells are given in the Schedule of Wells Drilled for Oil and Gas, Province of Alberta, published annually by the Energy Resources Conservation Board, Calgary, Canada.

the magmatic belt, and the attendant horizontal compression of the supracrustal wedge, must be balanced by an equivalent large horizontal displacement and/or compression of a basement of continental or oceanic lithosphere at a deeper crustal level. This raises a number of important questions concerning the foreland thrust and fold belt:

1. What is the minimum amount of net horizontal shortening across it?
2. How is this shortening accommodated at a deep crustal level?
3. What is the significance of the foreland fold and thrust belt in terms of the geotectonic evolution of the whole of the Cordilleran Orogen?

In attempting to answer these questions it is necessary, first, to consider the nature of the northeasterly tapering wedge of supracrustal rocks, in order to provide a framework for interpreting the structures that have developed within it.

Tectonostratigraphic framework

The northeasterly tapering wedge of supracrustal rocks, within which the structures of the foreland fold and thrust belt have developed, consists of a series of distinctive tectonostratigraphic assemblages, each comprising a suite of rock units, the overall characteristics of which imply deposition in a particular tectonic setting. These tectonostratigraphic assemblages record the existence of contrasting eugeoclinal, miogeoclinal and platformal tectonic domains, and of distinct preorogenic and synorogenic stages of tectonic evolution (Fig. 1). The preorogenic stage spans the interval from late Proterozoic to Middle Jurassic, and involves a western eugeoclinal domain characterized by the widespread occurrence of basic to intermediate and acidic volcanic rocks and of immature, wacke-type clastic rocks; and eastern platformal and miogeoclinal domains characterized by mature, shallow-water clastic and carbonate rocks that become thicker and more shaly westward, from the platform to the miogeocline. The synorogenic stage spans the interval from late Jurassic to Palaeogene and is characterized by clastic deposits that are of western or else local provenance. These accumulated mainly in a fore-deep or exogeocline that migrated northeastward from late Jurassic to Palaeocene time (Bally et al. 1966), as the continental lithosphere subsided isostatically in reponse to the load imposed on it by

tectonic thickening and relative northeasterly displacement of the overlying supracrustal rocks (Price 1973).

The Belt-Purcell Supergroup, the oldest assemblage in the supracrustal wedge, has a maximum exposed thickness of about 11 km in the Purcell anticlinorium in southern Canada (Reesor 1973), and about 20–25 km in NW Montana (Harrison 1972). The lower part, which is up to at least 6 km thick in southern Canada, consists mainly of fine-grained quartz-wacke turbidites and dark pelites that grade upward through light grey, green, purple and red shallow-water argillites and sandstones, into the carbonate rocks of the middle part. The great volume of relatively homogeneous fine-grained sediment comprising the very thick lower part of the Belt-Purcell assemblage appears to have been supplied by a very large river system of the size and character of the modern Mississippi, and to have been prograded outboard from the margin of the continent (Price 1964a). From the thickness and volume of the Belt-Purcell sediments, and the fact that they lie athwart the structural grain of the buried crystalline basement complex, one may infer that the basin in which they accumulated formed during the initial stages in the rifting of a former Precambrian continental mass which was eventually severed to produce the Pacific margin of the North American continent (Sears & Price 1978). The middle and upper parts of the Belt-Purcell assemblage consist of shallow-water carbonate and terrigenous clastic, tidal-flat and flood-plain deposits that accumulated over the prograded delta plain. Eastward thinning and convergence of all the units in the Belt-Purcell assemblage is accompanied by the disappearance of the turbidite facies, and by the appearance of coarse feldspathic detritus that apparently came from the nearby margin of the basin (Price 1964a).

The Windermere Supergroup, of late Proterozoic age, provides a sharp contrast with the Belt-Purcell assemblage, which it overlies unconformably. Coarse-grained feldspathic wacke sandstone and quartz-feldspar pebble conglomerates are interbedded with green and grey pelites, and locally with carbonate rocks. Conglomeratic mudstones, some of which have been interpreted as glacial deposits (Aalto 1971), occur on the unconformity at the base of the assemblage, and locally also at various other levels, including the top. The clasts in these conglomerates consist of distinctive rock types that occur in the underlying Belt-Purcell Supergroup. They are of local provenance, and imply high structural relief that exposed Belt-Purcell rocks, whilst Windermere strata accumulated nearby to thicknesses of up to 9 km (Lis & Price 1976). In contrast, the coarse feldspathic wackes had an external provenance and were transported southwestward (Young *et al.* 1973) over the Belt-Purcell rocks to their site of deposition. The Eo-Cambrian quartz sandstones, which form the base of both the overlying Lower Palaeozoic miogeoclinal and platformal assemblage and the eugeoclinal assemblage, unconformably overlap the thickest part of the Windermere Supergroup, and also the Upper and Middle Belt-Purcell strata, in the Purcell anticlinorium in southern Canada. Relationships beneath the unconformity show that the St Mary Fault (Fig. 1, 49°30′N, 116°15′N), which is now an important right-hand reverse fault (Rice 1941; Leech 1958, 1962) and is linked to thrust faults in the western Rocky Mountains, follows the locus of an older NE trending structure across which there were up to 13 km of stratigraphic separation with the northwest side down, during the deposition of the Windermere Supergroup (Lis & Price 1976).

The Lower Palaeozoic platformal sequence consists of about 1 km or less of shallow-water carbonate rock and interbedded shale. It thickens westward in the miogeocline, to about 5 km adjacent to a carbonate bank margin that is now located in the centre of the Rocky Mountains (Fig. 1, 49°40′N, 115°10′W to 52°0′N, 117°20′W). At this carbonate bank margin all the Cambrian and Ordovician formations, except one Upper Cambrian limestone unit and an Upper Ordovician and Lower Silurian dolomite unit undergo a relatively abrupt change in facies to light-coloured shale and argillaceous limestone (Aitken 1971). Farther W, there is a profound change across the Purcell anticlinorium between the light-coloured miogeoclinal shale facies and the coeval eugeoclinal facies. The latter consists mainly of dark graphitic pelites, but contains significant intercalations of basic volcanic rocks and feldspathic grits and wacke-type sandstones (Fyles 1964) that must have had either a western or a local provenance. The Lower Palaeozoic platformal and miogeoclinal strata appear to have accumulated as shelf and slope deposits along a continental margin (Monger *et al.* 1972) that was prograding westward into a back-arc or marginal basin. Repeated basic volcanism punctuates the record of deposition in this basin; and it includes intermittent incursions of igneous clastic detritus, that presumably were derived from a magmatic arc situated

further west, (Monger & Price 1979). Abrupt thickness and facies changes, which occur in the miogeoclinal rocks of the Purcell and western Rocky Mountains, record the tilting of large blocks, perhaps caused by displacements on deep down-to-the-basin listric normal faults.

Important unconformities separate the Lower Palaeozoic and Upper Palaeozoic assemblages. Mississippian and younger eugeoclinal rocks, consisting of dark pelites with intercalated sandstones, limestones and basic volcanic rocks, overlie the Lower Palaeozoic assemblage with angular unconformity. A basal conglomerate, containing clasts among which there is random orientation of a low-grade metamorphic tectonite foliation, shows that the Lower Palaeozoic rocks in the eugeoclinal domain were deformed and metamorphosed prior to late Mississippian time (Read & Wheeler 1976). In the platformal and miogeoclinal domain, Upper Devonian shallow-water carbonate rocks unconformably overlap Silurian, Ordovician and Upper Cambrian formations toward the E (Price & Mountjoy 1970, Figs. 2, 3) across the flank of a broad epeirogenic structure, the Alberta arch (Douglas *et al.* 1970, Fig. VIII–15). However, in the Purcell Mountains and Rocky Mountains near Cranbrook (Fig. 1, 49°30′, 113°30′) relationships beneath the unconformity show that the Moyie-Dibble Creek Fault, another right-hand reverse fault like the St Mary Fault, follows the locus of an older northeasterly trending structure across which there was stratigraphic separation of more than 10 km, with the NW side down, during the deposition of the Lower Palaeozoic assemblage (Leech 1958, 1962; Norris & Price 1966; Price 1972).

The Triassic–Middle Jurassic assemblage is represented on the cratonic platform by about 100 m of Jurassic marine shale; but it is more than 1000 m thick in the miogeocline, where it includes about 600 m of Triassic shallow-water marine shale, siltstone, quartz sandstone, carbonate rock and evaporites. The coeval eugeoclinal assemblage, which is only preserved W of the Purcell anticlinorium and the Kootenay arc (Fig. 2) appears to be more than 10 km thick (Little 1960; Read & Wheeler 1976) and consists of dark pelites, volcanogenic sandstones, and mainly andesitic volcanic rocks. Some of the mid to late Jurassic granitic plutons have been deformed along with the rocks they have intruded, and they may be partially coeval with the Jurassic volcanic rocks; whereas the Cretaceous granitic plutons cut across previously developed folds and faults, and have no obvious extrusive counterparts (Gabrielse & Reesor 1974).

The dramatic changes in thickness and lithofacies that occur along, as well as across, the strike of the northeasterly tapering wedge of Proterozoic–Jurassic supracrustal rocks involve important changes in mechanical properties, and have exerted a profound influence on the nature and orientation of the structures that have developed within it. They account for the development of a series of distinct linear tectonic subprovinces in the Rocky Mountains, including the Foothills (platformal Palaeozoic and exogeoclinal Upper Cretaceous), Front Ranges (platformal to miogeoclinal Palaeozoic and exogeoclinal Jurassic–Lower Cretaceous), Eastern Main Ranges (miogeoclinal carbonate facies) Western Main Ranges (miogeoclinal Cambrian shale facies), and Western Ranges (miogeoclinal Cambro-Ordovician shale facies with Ordovician–Silurian carbonate rocks). Each of these displays distinctive characteristics of structural style and physiography, as well as stratigraphy (North & Henderson 1954; Price & Mountjoy 1970). Most change abruptly along the strike at about 49°20′N latitude because of changes in sedimentary facies and thicknesses resulting from the influence of the transverse, northeasterly trending structures that were active during Proterozoic and Palaeozoic time. For example, SE of this zone, where the thick and relatively homogenous Belt-Purcell assemblage above the Lewis thrust fault is overlain by very thin Lower Palaeozoic and Upper Palaeozoic assemblages that are in the platformal facies, broad open folds in relatively flat-lying beds are carved into castellated mountain massifs, and a structural and physiographic style that is characteristic of the eastern Main Ranges further N, extends out to the edge of the Foothills. The steeply-dipping, moderately thick thrust slices of Palaeozoic platformal to miogeoclinal carbonate rocks, that form the characteristic linear mountain ranges of the Front Ranges subprovince further N, are missing completely. The conspicuous changes in structural trend that occur across this transverse zone can be related, as will be shown below, to changes in the configuration and orientation of the margins of the basin in which the various tectonostratigraphic assemblages accumulated.

Balanced structure sections

Reliable estimates for the minimum net tectonic shortening or convergence across the thrust and fold belt can be obtained from balanced structure sections (Dahlstrom 1969b), in which the deep crustal structure is also considered, and is constrained by the relevant geophysical data. A balanced section is one in which there is geometric compatibility from one level to another. In a thrust faulted terrain the simplest application of this principle is the requirement that the rock units which occur on one side of a thrust fault must have matching counterparts on the other side. Provided that the deformation accompanying the thrust faulting has been accomplished mainly by flexure and interstratal slip, and that the penetrative strain within the beds is so small in comparison with the size of the folds and thrust faults that it can be ignored, a balanced section is one in which there is consistency of stratigraphic markers from one level to another, and in which the lengths of the stratigraphic markers in the deformed state are the same as they were in the undeformed state, only the shape having changed during the deformation. Under these circumstances one test of a balanced section is that it leads to a logical and reasonable palinspastic restoration (Dahlstrom 1969b).

Systematic regional geological mapping and many detailed studies of the stratigraphy and sedimentary petrography of the rocks of the exogeoclinal assemblage and the eastern carbonate facies of the platformal and miogeoclinal assemblages show that stratigraphic units do not change significantly in thickness between the limbs and hinge zones of folds, and also that even the finest details of original sedimentary and organic structures have survived the deformation without significant distortion. This leaves no doubt that intrastratal penetrative strain within these rocks is very low and can be neglected for purposes of constructing balanced sections. Accordingly, the structure sections through the carbonate facies of the platformal and miogeoclinal assemblages (Fig. 2) have been balanced, on the premise that the lengths of the stratigraphic contacts have not been altered significantly in the course of the folding and faulting; and the palinspastic sections have been constructed on the premise that the lengths of the beds in the deformed state are essentially the same as in the undeformed state. In the shale facies of the Lower Palaeozoic miogeoclinal assemblage, widespread development of penetrative cleavage and schistosity, and conspicuous distortion of primary structures (Balkwill 1972; Gardner 1977) preclude the application of this technique except at the highest stratigraphic levels (Middle Ordovician quartz sandstones and

Upper Ordovician and Lower Silurian dolomites), where interstratal penetrative strains are low, and shortening has been accomplished mainly by flexural-slip folding and associated thrust faulting (central parts of Sections NE–SW and E–W, Fig. 2).

In the Proterozoic rocks of the Windermere and Belt-Purcell assemblages, Penetrative intrastratal strain is variable, increasing from relatively low levels in the E to higher levels with progressively higher metamorphic grade toward the W. However, the general structure of the Purcell anticlinorium can be outlined satisfactorily by projecting what occurs at the surface along the northerly and northwesterly plunge into the plane of the sections. The Kootenay Arc, which forms the SW flank of the Purcell anticlinorium, is characterized by high, penetrative strains and complex tectonic overprinting associated with greenschist and amphibolite facies regional metamorphism and coaxial refolding about N and NW trending axes (Fyles 1964, 1967); and the general character of the structures within it can also be outlined on the basis of projections along the plunge (Fyles 1967; Höy 1977). There is a very large change in structural level across the Kootenay Arc, from the lowest part of the Belt-Purcell Supergroup in the core of the Purcell anticlinorium to an extensive tract of exposures of the Triassic–Jurassic eugeoclinal assemblage, which occurs adjacent to the Nelson batholith and the Shuswap Metamorphic Complex. The aggregate thickness of the succession of rock stratigraphic units which occur in superposition between these two horizons is more than 20 km. Lateral variations, involving a westerly decrease in the thickness of older units and an easterly decrease in the thickness of younger units, may account for some of this large change in stratigraphic level, but most of it is an expression of change in structural level. Accordingly, the Kootenay Arc, in spite of the complexity of the detailed structure within it, is basically a simple structure—a westerly facing monocline of crustal dimension. Geophysical investigations of deep crustal structure indicate that this monoclinal structural step in the supracrustal rocks marks the western edge of the thick (~40 km) slab of Hudsonian (>1750 Ma) continental crust that forms the basement of the North American craton in western Canada.

Deep drilling and seismic exploration for hydrocarbons show that the thrust faults flatten with depth within the supracrustal succession, above the Hudsonian basement, at least as far W as the central part of the Rocky Mountains, and probably beyond the Rocky Mountain

Trench beneath the eastern flank of the Purcell anticlinorium (Bally *et al.* 1966). The distinctive pattern of broad, high-amplitude, NE trending magnetic anomalies that is characteristic of the Hudsonian basement, which extends under the cratonic platform from the Churchill Province of the Canadian Shield, can be followed across the whole of the Rocky Mountains into the eastern part of the Purcell anticlinorium, and perhaps as far W as the Kootenay arc (Fig. 3). These relationships corroborate the interpretation from the seismic reflection data. The Hudsonian basement does, indeed, extend under the thrust and fold belt and the Purcell anticlinorium without any apparent disruption of its characteristic NE trending tectonic fabric.

The results of seismic refraction experiments, using explosions in lakes in the interior of the Cordillera (Chandra & Cumming 1972; Berry & Forsyth 1975; Mereu *et al.* 1977), mine blasts in the coalfields of the southern Rocky Mountains and the porphyry copper mines of the interior of the Cordillera (Bennett *et al.* 1975; Spence *et al.* 1977; Cumming *et al.* 1979), show that the change in structural level that occurs in the supracrustal rocks across the Kootenay Arc coincides with a westerly decrease in crustal thicknesses, from a maximum thickness of 50–55 km in the vicinity of the western Rocky Mountains and the Purcell anticlinorium to about 30–40 km beneath the interior of the Cordillera (Monger & Price 1979). The monoclinal step at the Kootenay Arc also coincides with a westerly increase in crustal and upper mantle electrical conductivity as outlined by geomagnetic depth sounding experiments (Caner 1971; Dragert & Clarke 1976); and with a westerly change in the Bouguer gravity anomaly from about −200 mgal, where the crust is thickest, to about −140 mgal in the interior of the Cordillera (Fig. 4). It is worthy of note, that the lowest Bouguer gravity anomaly values occur within the widest part of the foreland fold and thrust belt, where the amount of tectonic thickening of the supracrustal wedge would be expected to be greatest. Morever, the amount of crustal thickening in this area, as indicated by the analysis of the Bouguer anomalies (Stacey 1973) and by the results of the seismic refraction experiments that were cited above, is about that which is required to accommodate the tectonic thickening of the supracrustal wedge that was calculated by Price (1973) from a comparison of structure sections and corresponding palinspastically restored sections by Bally *et al.* (1966) and Price &

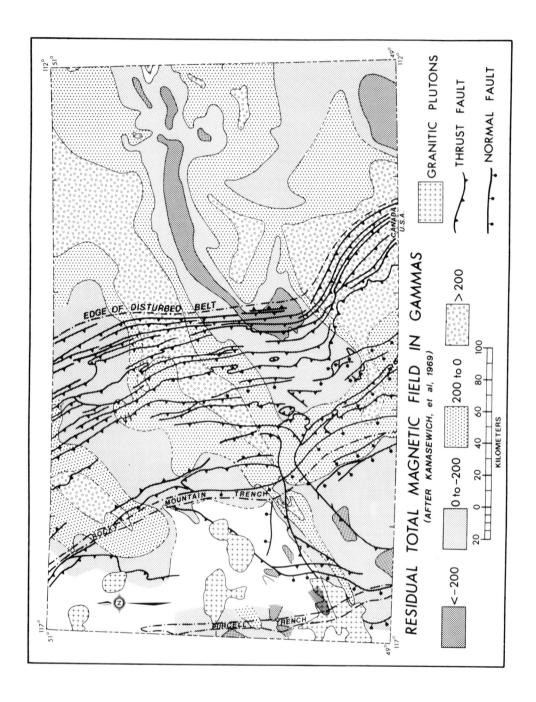

RESIDUAL TOTAL MAGNETIC FIELD IN GAMMAS
(AFTER KANASEWICH, et al, 1969)

GRANITIC PLUTONS

THRUST FAULT

NORMAL FAULT

< -200   0 to -200   200 to 0   > 200

KILOMETERS

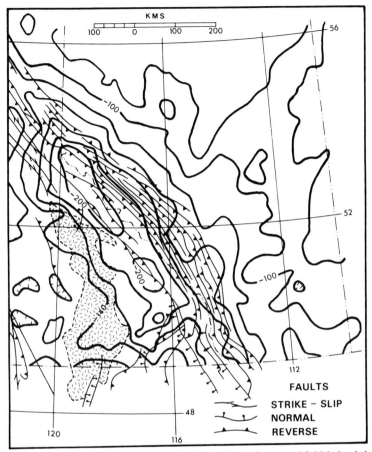

FIG. 4. Relationships between the structures in the foreland thrust and fold belt of the southern Canadian Rocky Mountains and the Bouguer gravity anomalies. The Bouguer gravity anomaly values are after the Earth Physics Branch of Canada (1974). The faults and the limits of the Shuswap Metamorphic Complex are from Fig. 1 and from King (1969).

Mountjoy (1970)—10 km of increase in crustal thickness, of which 2 km stand above sea level. However, it is not enough to balance, at a deep crustal level below the basement surface, the amount of tectonic shortening that occurs in even the eastern part of the thrust and fold belt, where deep drilling and seismic reflection data leave little scope for imagination in interpretations of tectonic shortening in the supracrustal wedge. Thus, a consideration of the deep crustal structure, based on the seismic refraction, magnetic and gravity data leads to the conclusion that the slab of continental crust, about 40 km thick, that underlies the cratonic platform in front of the thrust and fold belt, extends under the deformed wedge of supracrustal rocks, beneath the Rocky Mountains and the Purcell anticlinorium, to the Kootenay Arc, where the supracrustal rocks wrap around the edge of it (Fig. 5). This is contrary to the interpretation of Eisbacher *et al.* (1974) who suggested that the structure in the western Rocky Mountains and beyond is the result of uplift involving both the supracrustal wedge and its Precambrian crystalline basement, and that the flat thrust faults and undeformed basement are limited to the eastern Rocky Mountains. Their interpretation was based on structure sections which cannot be balanced between the supracrustal rocks and the basement because they involve relatively little shortening at the level of the basement,

FIG. 3. Relationships between the structures of the thrust and fold belt of the southern Canadian Rocky Mountains and the Hudsonian structural fabric of the Precambrian basement that extends under it. The magnetic anomaly map is after Kanasewich *et al.* (1969). The thrust faults and normal faults are a simplified portrayal of those in Fig. 1.

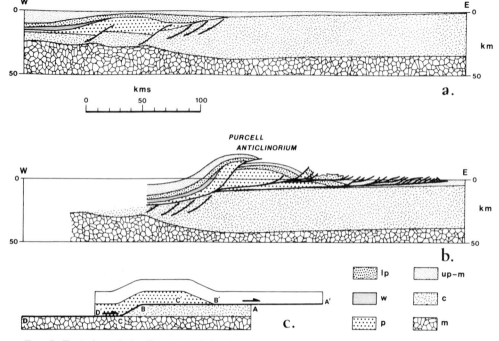

FIG. 5. Evolution of the Purcell anticlinorium a. Restored Section through the southeastern Canadian Cordillera along 49°45′N Latitude (as in Fig. 7). b. Generalized structure of the Cordilleran fold and thrust belt and the Purcell anticlinorium along 49°45′N Latitude (based on Section W–E of Fig. 2; but drawn to eliminate the effects of the erosion of supracrustal rocks that occurred during and after the thrust faulting). c. Schematic representation of the development of the Purcell anticlinorium (Points on the footwall and hanging wall of the zone of detachment, that were initially contiguous, are labelled with the same letters) m—mantle; c—continental crust; p—Belt-Purcell assemblage; w—Windermere assemblage; lp—Lower Palaeozoic assemblages; up-m—Upper Palaeozoic and Triassic–Jurassic assemblages.

whereas tectonic shortening in the supracrustal rocks to the E amounts to 65 km across the Foothills alone (Bally *et al.* 1966, plate 12), and all of this would have to be accommodated within the basement E of the boundary of their postulated basement uplift.

A conspicuous increase in the Bouguer gravity values occurs southward along the Purcell anticlinorium where the transverse northeasterly trending St Mary and Moyie Faults cut across it. Further S, in Montana, at about 48°15′N, Wynn *et al.* (1977), on the basis of their analysis of a gravity and audio-frequency magnetotelluric traverse across the Purcell anticlinorium, concluded that crystalline basement rocks occur in the core of the anticlinorium there. Transported basement rocks could be expected within the deformed wedge of supracrustal rocks at this structural position because suspected basement rocks occur in about the same position above the Purcell thrust fault, to the N, at about 52°30′N (Campbell 1968; Price & Mountjoy 1970).

Structure sections W–E and SW–NE (Fig. 2) have been drawn perpendicular to the local structural trend, in order to facilitate the projection of surface and well data, along the plunge of the structures, into the plane of the section. Errors in estimates of tectonic displacements, introduced by the fact that the structure sections may not be parallel with the direction of net tectonic displacement, vary with the cosine of the angle between the structure section and the direction of net tectonic displacement. The error introduced in this way is normally less than 15%, if the angle between the line of section and the average direction of net tectonic displacement is less than 30°. Both sections are based on the premise that the Hudsonian crystalline basement complex extends under the thrust and fold belt to the centre of the Purcell anticlinorium, and that all the thrust faults lie above it, in the supracrustal wedge, or at the basement surface (Bally *et al.* 1966). In both sections, the depth to the basement, as shown, is the minimum depth that is required to accommodate the total thickness of the supracrustal succession, as it is known from one place to another, and to meet the geometric requirements of a balanced section. The eastern part of Section W–E is relatively tightly constrained by information from deep drilling, and it illustrates several important principles, some of which are portrayed in more detail in Fig. 6. It is a well established empirical rule that the thrust faults cut up through the stratigraphic succession in the direction of relative displacement of the overthrust side, and that they carry older rocks over younger and produce repetitions of the normal stratigraphic succession. Thus, westerly verging thrust faults, such as the Waldron fault, cut up through the stratigraphic succession toward the W; and easterly verging thrust faults, even if folded and E-dipping, cut up through the stratigraphic succession toward the E and carry older rocks over younger. Certain stratigraphic zones are a preferred locus of décollement or bedding glide, and other thrust faults branch away from them as concave upward imbricate splays. The condition of geometric compatibility for a balanced section requires that an extensive bedding glide zone in the hanging-wall of a thrust fault must have its matching counterpart in the footwall. The bedding glide zones in the upper part of the Alberta Group (Kag) in the eastern part of Fig. 6, require matching footwall counterparts to permit the palinspastic reconstruction shown in the lower part of the figure. The thrust faults are commonly stepped, comprising extensive bedding glide zones that are linked by relatively narrow ramps. The external rotation and folding which is inherent in movement along such stepped fault surfaces affects all the overlying rocks, including any thrust faults which occur within them. Thrust faults may merge upwards as well as downwards, as shown by the tectonically thickened wedge of Alberta Group (Kag), Belly River Formation (Kbr) and Bearpaw Formation (Kbp) which is responsible for the easterly dip of the Alberta Syncline, and separates it from the relatively flat-lying strata below (Fig. 6). Elsewhere, as for example in the Coleman Thrust sheet, beneath where it is overlapped at the surface by the Lewis Thrust sheet (Fig. 2, Section W–E), sigmoidal imbricate thrust faults that merge upward with one fault and downward with another result in substantial tectonic thickening of an isolated lenticular mass of rock, as well as a significant transfer of displacement from the lower fault to the upper.

In the Foothills, along and beneath the Livingstone Thrust fault (Li in Section W–E, Fig. 2), extensive bedding glide zones occur in Jurassic marine shales (Fernie Group) and in or at the base of a thick unit of Upper Devonian micritic limestone (Palliser Formation). The condition of geometric compatibility for a balanced section requires that offset counterparts of these bedding glide zones be represented along the opposite side of the same thrust surfaces to the W; and this leads to the conclusion that autochthonous Upper Devonian and Cambrian strata lie on undeformed Hudsonian crystalline basement under the western Rocky Mountains, beneath the Bourgeau (Bo) and Bull River (BR) thrust sheets. It also implies that along this line of section the Lewis Thrust sheet (Le) cannot contain a thick succession of Belt-Purcell strata, as it does further S (Fig. 1), unless there is an abrupt change in the depth to the basement surface to provide the necessary space. Seismic reflection profiling shows no such change; instead, the basement in this area slopes gently W without disruption (P. L. Gordy pers. comm. 1979). Similar arguments, involving the Coleman thrust sheet (Co), the Lewis Thrust sheet (Le), and the Bourgeau Thrust sheet (Bo), indicate that the thick Lower Palaeozoic miogeoclinal shale facies and the underlying thick succession of Belt-Purcell strata that occurs between the Bull River Thrust fault and the Rocky Mountain Trench (RMT) first appears in the Bougeau Thrust sheet. The abrupt westerly increase in the thickness and facies of the supracrustal succession within the Bourgeau thrust sheet, which marks the change from platformal to miogeoclinal supracrustal rocks, must have had a matching counterpart in the 'autochthonous' cover succession on the basement below the Bourgeau thrust fault. Palinspastic reconstruction of only that part of the balanced section W–E (Fig. 2) which lies E of and includes, the Bourgeau Thrust sheet (eastern two-thirds of the Rocky Mountains) indicates that the locus of this matching 'autochthonous' counterpart is along the Kootenay Arc. This corroborates what was concluded from a consideration of the geophysical data—that the western edge of the thick slab of continental cratonic crust lies beneath the Kootenay Arc. It implies that all the thick miogeoclinal strata, including the Lower Palaeozoic shale facies and the underlying Windermere and Belt-Purcell assemblages, accumulated outboard from the edge of the craton on attenuated continental crust or oceanic crust.

The structure in section SW–NE differs in

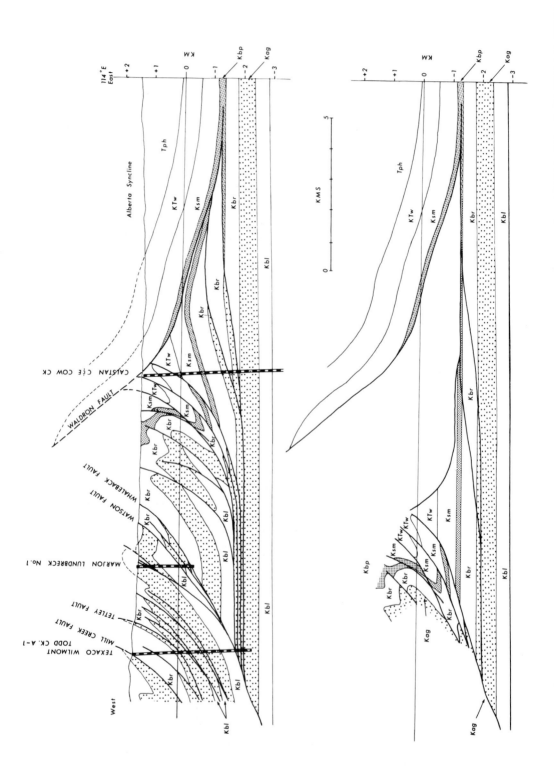

detail from that in Section W–E because of changes in the character of the supracrustal succession, but also because of an increase in the amount of overall tectonic shortening or convergence across the fold and thrust belt. The Lower Palaeozoic platformal and miogeoclinal carbonate facies is substantially thicker and more complete beneath the sub-Devonian unconformity, and extends further W than in Section W–E. It forms a series of five moderately thick, relatively steeply dipping thrust sheets (Mc, La, In, Ru, and Sm in Section SW–NE of Fig. 2) beneath the Bourgeau Thrust fault (Bo); whereas in Section W–E there are only two in the same interval. As in Section W–E, the Bourgeau Thrust fault marks the approximate position of the relatively abrupt increase in thickness of the Lower and Upper Palaeozoic assemblages that defines the boundary between the platform and the miogeocline. It also marks the first appearance of Precambrian rocks, but these belong to the Windermere assemblage rather than the Belt-Purcell assemblage.

A broad, northerly plunging anticlinorium occurs W of the Bourgeau Thrust fault, in the centre of the Rocky Mountains near the Continental Divide. The Simpson Pass Thrust fault follows its crest, and several large thrust faults that develop as northeasterly diverging splays from the Simpson Pass Thrust fault are folded across the anticlinorium and adjacent syncline, and extend far to the NW (Price & Mountjoy 1970).

There are about 2 km of Windermere strata exposed above the Simpson Pass Thrust fault, and these, together with the thicknesses of the overlying formation, define a lower limit on the total thickness of supracrustal rocks that must be accommodated between the crystalline basement and the rocks that are exposed at the surface to the W of the Simpson Pass Thrust fault. This minimum estimate of the depth to the basement is what has been used to construct the section. Because the section is based on the premise that the Hudsonian basement is undeformed and slopes beneath the deformed supracrustal wedge to beyond the Rocky Mountain Trench, the space between the basement surface and the core of this northerly plunging anticlinorium is considered to be occupied by deformed supracrustal rocks, the

specific structure of which is completely hypothetical. The particular interpretation shown in the section follows the style of the structures which occur in a similar setting beneath the Coleman fault and the Livingstone Thrust in Section W–E, where their existence is documented by deep drilling; and beneath the Lewis thrust sheet further S, where they are exposed (Fermor & Price 1976). The choice of the number of thrust faults that occur beneath the Bourgeau Thrust fault and merge upward with it may be arbitrary, but it does have implications regarding the rate at which the stratigraphic succession in the supracrustal wedge thickens westward between the Sulphur Mountain (Sm) and Bourgeau thrust faults. The interpretation shown implies that the thickening is gradual and relatively uniform. If the thickening is abrupt, fewer thrust faults and less shortening between the Sulphur Mountain and Bourgeau thrust sheets would be involved.

The carbonate bank margin, marking the boundary between the Lower Palaeozoic carbonate and shale facies, occurs W of the Simpson Pass fault and is, in part, offset by late listric normal faults (Cook 1975). W of this boundary, there is a profound change in structural style marked by the widespread development of slaty cleavage and high penetrative strain. A conspicuous fan structure is outlined by the orientation of the cleavage and the axial surfaces of the folds, which are northeasterly verging on the NE side and southwesterly verging on the SW side. Locally, it is situated over an anticlinal culmination in underlying Eo-Cambrian quartz sandstones (Balkwill 1972), but elsewhere (Section SW–NE) it coincides with a monoclinal flexure (see also Price & Mountjoy 1979a and b; Price et al. in press). The fan structure can be attributed to décollement above the Eo-Cambrian quartz sandstone succession, in Cambrian slates of the Lower Palaeozoic shale facies, in conjunction with displacement on the Purcell Thrust fault (as shown in Section SW–NE). Cross-cutting relationships amongst northeasterly and southwesterly verging thrust faults on the W flank of the fan structure, under the Purcell Thrust fault, outline two phases of tectonic overprinting. Older northeasterly verging thrust faults were rotated during continued folding, until overturned, together with the beds in which

FIG. 6. Structure of the eastern Rocky Mountain Foothills at 49°45′N Latitude. The line of section is the same as that of Section W–E in Fig. 2, and the sources of information on wells drilled for oil and gas are those given in Fig. 2. The interpretation in the upper part of the section is adapted, with some modifications, from Douglas (1950). The symbols identifying lithostratigraphic units are as follows: Kbl—Blairmore Group; Kag—Alberta Group; Kbr—Belly River Formation; Kbp—Bearpaw Formation; Ksm—St. Mary River Formation; KTw—Willow Creek Formation; Tph—Porcupine Hills Formation.

they occur (Balkwill 1972). They are cut by younger southwesterly verging thrust faults that involve displacements out of the core of the fan structure. These, in turn, are cut by still younger northeasterly verging thrust faults that are spatially related to the Purcell thrust fault which has overridden the W flank of the fan structure. The Lower Palaeozoic shale facies appears to have been 'scraped' off the underlying quartz sandstones, and piled up in front of the Purcell Thrust sheet. The same fan structure extends southward to Section W–E, beyond which it terminates against the northeasterly trending Moyie-Dibble Creek Fault (Moy) that follows the southern margin of the basin in which the Lower Palaeozoic shale facies accumulated. This asymmetric basin, which formed on top of the late Precambrian miogeoclinal prism, was probably controlled by deep-seated listric normal faulting. The steep, E flank forms a natural, local boundary between the miogeocline and platform.

In the Purcell anticlinorium, W of the Purcell fault, the Lower Palaeozoic miogeoclinal succession, which is about 8 km thick in the western Rocky Moutains, occurs as a condensed section that is overlain by Upper Devonian strata, and locally is less than 500 m thick (Reesor 1973). This contrast can be attributed to tectonic foreshortening, across the Purcell thrust fault, of the less steep W flank of the Lower Palaeozoic basin. The structure shown in the upper levels of the Purcell anticlinorium in Section SW–NE is based on projections along the plunge of structures exposed nearby; but the structure at depth is based on the hypothesis that the edge of the undeformed cratonic basement extends to the W flank of the Purcell anticlinorium, and that the Purcell Thrust fault and the décollement above the Eo-Cambrian quartz sandstone succession extends just about as far.

Palinspastic restorations

The tectonic displacements involved in the evolution of the thrust and fold belt can be analyzed most conveniently in terms of a horizontal datum defined by the transition from late Jurassic marine to non-marine deposits, which marks the onset of synorogenic sedimentation; and a reference frame fixed relative to the 'autochthonous' supracrustal rocks that are attached to the Hudsonian basement E of the thrust and fold belt (Price & Mountjoy 1970). The relative horizontal (and vertical) displacements of points in the thrust and fold belt, and the amount of tectonic shor-

tening or convergence between them and the autochthon can be estimated by comparing their position in the restored section with their present position, provided that the angle between the section and the actual direction of net tectonic displacement is not more than about 30°. The minimum total convergence between the leading edge of the Bourgeau thrust sheet and the autochthon estimated in this way is about 170 km in Section SW–NE, and about 105 km in Section W–E. The estimated minimum total shortening up to and including the McConnell Thrust sheet, which stands above the Foothills in Section SW–NE, is about 75 km, whereas that up to and including the Lewis Thrust sheet, which stands above the Foothills in Section W–E, is about 90 km. However, the Lewis thrust fault dies out along the strike to the N within the Rundle Thrust sheet, and the estimated minimum net shortening up to and including the Rundle Thrust sheet in Section SW-NE is about 105 km. Although the total convergence across the fold and thrust belt probably does decrease southward, some of the difference in estimated tectonic convergence between the two sections can be attributed to errors arising from sections that are not parallel with the direction of net tectonic displacement.

The palinspastic restoration based on Section SW–NE, indicates that the Mesozoic exogeoclinal rocks occurring under and E of the McConnell Thrust fault have been horizontally compressed by at least 10 km more than the underlying Upper Palaeozoic platformal rocks from which they are separated by a regionally important bedding glide or décollement zone (Dahlstrom 1969a). A similar relationship in a nearby section has been described by Bally *et al.* (1966, p. 350), and attributed to crosscutting relations involving a younger fault which developed in the Palaeozoic carbonate rocks, under the Mesozoic rocks, after the latter had been horizontally compressed above the décollement. In Section SW–NE, this younger fault is the McConnell Thrust fault, and the tectonic shortening that occurred above the décollement before it was offset by the McConnell Thrust must be related, at a deeper level, to other more westerly thrust faults.

Times of deformation

The record of deformation within the thrust and fold belt in this region spans an interval of almost 100 Ma from late Jurassic to Palaeocene time (Price & Mountjoy 1970).

The first stratigraphic record of deformation, uplift and erosion of the miogeoclinal assemblages occurs in the Upper Jurassic rocks (Kootenay Formation and upper part of Fernie Group). It is marked by an abrupt reversal in the provenance of clastic sediment, from the NE cratonic provenance, that characterized the miogeoclinal assemblages, to the SW Cordilleran provenance that characterized the exogeoclinal assemblage. Although the ages of individual thrust faults cannot be defined precisely, some broad limits can be established. Thrust faults in the western Rocky Mountains, particularly those along the W side of the fan structure that occurs in the Lower Palaeozoic shale facies, are linked spatially and kinematically to NE trending, right-hand reverse faults that cut across the Purcell anticlinorium (Fig. 1). Several of these NE trending, right-hand reverse faults are cut by early to mid-Cretaceous batholiths, and this establishes an upper limit for the times of last displacement on them and on the thrust faults that are linked to them. The Hall Lake fault, which is linked to faults in, and E of, the Rocky Mountain Trench that form part of the same thrust system as the Purcell fault, is cut by the White Creek batholith, for which Rb-Sr and K-Ar whole rock dates of 129 Ma and 111 Ma have been reported (Wanless et al. 1968). The St Mary fault, which is linked to faults in the western Rocky Mountains NE of Cranbrook, is cut by the Bayonne batholith, and K-Ar dates from the Bayonne batholith indicate that it was emplaced prior to 90 Ma (Archibald et al. 1977). Along the Kootenay Arc the late to mid-Cretaceous granitic plutons post-date most, or all, of the penetrative strain in the country rocks and have relatively low pressure thermal aureoles (Glover 1978; Sears 1979), in contrast with the late Jurassic plutons which are associated with intermediate pressure (Barrovian) regional metamorphism, and were deformed along with the enclosing strata (Gabrielse & Reesor 1974; Glover 1978). Thus, deformation in the eugeoclinal rocks W of the Kootenay Arc was underway in late Jurassic time, and thrust faults in the western Rocky Mountains had already developed by mid-early Cretaceous time.

The McConnell and Lewis thrust sheets both overlap Cenomanian to Santonian marine deposits and early Campanian non-marine deposits of the exogeoclinal assemblage (Alberta Group and Belly River and Brazeau Formations, respectively), and this establishes a lower limit for the time of displacement on these faults. An upper limit for the time of displacement on the Lewis Thrust is given by the late Eocene–early Oligocene age of the Kishenehn Formation, which unconformably overlaps the structures in the Lewis thrust sheet along the downthrown side of the Flathead fault (Price 1965), a SW dipping listric normal fault that merges at depth with the Lewis thrust fault (Bally et al. 1966). Thus, a minimum of about 100 km of the total horizontal convergence across the thrust and fold belt occurred between early Campanian and late Eocene time; and if the subsidence and sedimentation in the migrating foredeep was an isostatic response of the lithosphere to the loads imposed by the displacement of the thrust sheets (Price 1973), this amount of convergence must have occurred within less than 30 Ma, the time represented by the thick succession of early Campanian to Palaeocene fluvial sediments that makes up the youngest part of the exogeoclinal assemblage (McLean & Jerzykiewicz 1978). The implications of these conclusions warrant further consideration.

In early Campanian time, prior to displacement on the McConnell, Lewis and Rundle Thrusts, the Precambrian crystalline basement that now extends as an undeformed autochthonous slab under the Rocky Mountains and the eastern part of the Purcell anticlinorium was still covered by a thin sequence of autochthonous, Palaeozoic platformal carbonate rocks with an overlying easterly tapering blanket of autochthonous late Jurassic–Campanian exogeoclinal deposits (Fig. 2). At almost the same time, but perhaps somewhat earlier, prior to the displacement on the Bourgeau thrust fault, the hinge zone between the platform and the miogeocline lay above the edge of this slab of continental crust, and the tectonically compressed miogeocline was situated outboard from it, and was underlain by tectonically attenuated continental crust, and perhaps, in part, oceanic crust. At the end of Middle Jurassic time, prior to the displacements on the thrust faults in the western Rocky Mountains and the the eastern Purcell anticlinorium, and on the NE trending right–hand reverse faults that cut across the Purcell anticlinorium, the miogeocline was essentially undeformed and comprised a series of overlapping and interfingering, unconformity-bounded, tectono-stratigraphic assemblages, for which the aggregate thickness at any one place was about 15–20 km.

Tectonic models

The only obvious actualistic model for this situation seems to be a rifted continental mar-

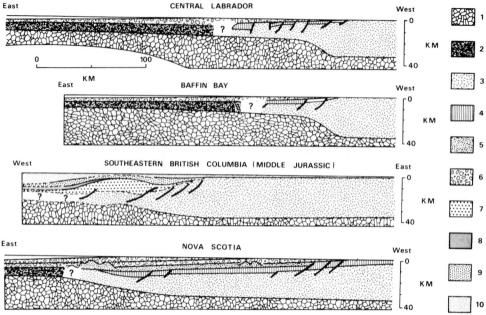

FIG. 7. Comparison of a palinspastically restored section through the foreland thrust and fold belt of southern Canada with crustal sections through the Atlantic margin of Canada. 1—Mantle; 2—oceanic crust; 3—continental crust; 4—continental basement rocks (pre-rifting); 5—early Jurassic and older sediments on the Nova Scotian shelf; 6—post-rifting sediments; 7—Belt-Purcell assemblage; 8—Windermere assemblage; 9—Lower Palaeozoic assemblages; 10—Upper Palaeozoic and Triassic–Jurassic assemblages.

The sections through the Atlantic continental margin are taken from Keen & Hyndman (1979). The palinspastically restored section for the Cordilleran margin in southern British Columbia and Alberta in Middle Jurassic time is based on the Section W–E of Fig. 2, and on the premise that the slab of continental crust approximately 40 km thick, which underlies the craton E of the foreland thrust and fold belt, extends under it to the vicinity of the Kootenay Arc, where it is tectonically attenuated as a result of rifting associated with the development of the western margin of North America in Proterozoic and early Palaeozoic time.

gin of the Atlantic-type. The results of recent investigations of the Atlantic continental margin of Canada (Keen & Hyndman 1979) provide some indication of the possible range in the configurations and relationships among continental and oceanic crust and an overlying, continental terrace wedge of supracrustal rocks (Fig. 7). The abrupt increase in thickness of the supracrustal wedge along section W–E can be compared with the abruptly attenuated continental margins that occur in Baffin Bay or Central Labrador, whereas the apparently more gradual increase in thickness along section SW–NE may be more comparable with gently tapering continental crust off Nova Scotia.

When the evolution of the thrust and fold belt is viewed from this perspective, the origin and significance of the Purcell anticlinorium and Kootenay Arc become obvious (Fig. 5). The Purcell anticlinorium formed in Campanian to early Palaeocene time, as a geometric

consequence of the juxtaposition of the thick northeasterly tapering prism of sediment that had accumulated above the zone of abrupt crustal attenuation, outboard from the continental margin, with relatively flat, planar basement surface on the continental platform. The Kootenay Arc formed at the same time, as a W-facing monoclinal step beyond the crest of the Purcell anticlinorium where the sedimentary prism was draped over the edge of the continental platform. The zone of detachment, along which this juxtaposition occurred, reached the surface far to the E in the thrust and fold belt where it is expressed as a series of stacked imbricate thrust faults in the horizontally compressed supracrustal rocks. The overall structure is a crustal scale version of the stepped thrust faults which control the configuration of structures within the deformed supracrustal wedge (Fig. 5c).

The amount of displacement of the miogeoclinal prism relative to the cratonic basement can be visualized readily on even a regional geological map such as Fig. 1, provided that the map shows the relative distrubutions of the Palaeozoic shale and carbonate facies, and the location of the Kootenay Arc. The boundary between the Lower Palaeozoic shale and carbonate facies formed above, or close to, the edge of the continental craton, and the Kootenay Arc now follows the locus of the edge of this continental craton. Thus, the distance between the Kootenay Arc and the shale-carbonate facies boundary is a measure of how far this boundary has been displaced, and therefore, of the amount of convergence between the miogeocline and the autochthonous cover on the craton to the E. It is worth noting, that adjacent to the International Boundary, where there is a conspicuous right-hand deflection about 50 km long in the otherwise curvilinear N to NW trend of the Kootenay Arc, there is a matching right-hand deflection in the eastern and southern limit of the Lower Palaeozoic shale facies, which lies about 150 km NE of the Kootenay Arc. Moreover, S of 50°N Latitude, where the structural relief across the Kootenay Arc is greatest and the change in level across it is most abrupt, the change from a thin platformal facies of the Lower Palaeozoic assemblage to a very thick shale facies is also most abrupt. It seems clear that the miogeocline formed outboard from the continental craton, on tectonically attenuated continental crust, or on oceanic crust, and has subsequently been juxtaposed with the continental craton.

The idea that foreland thrust and fold belts may develop by lateral gravitational spreading is based on the premise that some other process operates to produce the topographic gradient, and thereby the gravitational potential, that drives the lateral spreading. Price & Mountjoy (1970) ascribed the gravitational potential in the southern Canadian Rockies to the buoyant upwelling of a hot, ductile infrastructure of high-grade metamorphic rocks, the exposed parts of which are represented by the intermediate-pressure (Barrovian) series metamorphic rocks of the Shuswap Metmorphic Complex. However, they left unspecified the processes that had carried the protolith of the metamorphic complex to the depths from which the subsequent upwelling occurred; and they also, mistakenly, placed too much emphasis on a conceptual model involving simple diapiric upwelling without any attendant convergence or crustal shortening. The dominantly flat foliation and mainly northeasterly oriented stretching lineation in the Shuswap Metamorphic Complex can be taken as evidence of large-scale vertical compression and horizontal northeasterly extension (Price & Mountjoy 1970). However, the fact that the less metamorphosed rocks in the suprastructure around the southern (Fig. 1) and northern (Campbell 1973) ends of the metamorphic culminations have a fabric indicative of horizontal compression, and moreover, show no indication of horizontal extension on the scale that is necessary to balance the more than 200 km of horizontal shortening that occurs between the metamorphic complex and the autochthonous cover on the craton, implies that there has been a large net horizontal shortening or convergence across the entire belt, and that the horizontal stretching in the deep infrastructure is a second-order effect associated with the special conditions which existed there. For example, tectonic slides are common around some of the margins of the metamorphic culminations. These are shallow-dipping extension faults (see Fig. 1) across which young rocks are juxtaposed on old rocks, and low-grade metamorphic rocks on high-grade metamorphic rocks. Faults of this type, marked by strong cataclasis, occur along the E side of the Shuswap Metamorphic Complex (Read 1977; Sears 1979), on the flanks of the Valhalla gneiss complex (Reesor 1965; Little 1960); on the W flank of a NNW-trending metamorphic culmination that extends along the Purcell Trench at about 116°30′ to 117°E Latitude (Fyles 1967); and around three-sides of a local structural and metamorphic depression within a U-shaped metamorphic culmination at Newport in northeastern Washington State (Miller 1974 b–d). There is a contrast in structural style across the faults from recumbent folds below, to upright folds above. Some of these faults are cut by early to mid-Cretaceous plutons (Read 1977); others cut early (?) Tertiary rocks (Miller 1974b–d). The basic structural relationships are similar to those around many metamorphic culminations further S in the Cordilleran belt of the United States. The faults around these metamorphic culminations have been interpreted (Davis & Coney 1979) as ductile, normal, growth faults related to Neogene thermal upwelling with horizontal stretching, pinch-and-swell, and mega-boudinage of the crust. However, they occur in the basin-and-range province where evidence of Neogene–Recent crustal extension abounds; and moreover, the displacements on them appear to be much younger than on the comparable faults in S Canada and NE Washington, where the shallow extension faults appear to be related to local diapiric movement involving the buoyant rise of culminations in the metamorphic infrastructure and relative subsidence of parts of the suprastructure. Lateral continuity in nearby rocks indicates that they do not represent a major regional horizontal extension of the crust.

Brown & Tippet (1978) have interpreted the evolution of the Selkirk fan structure, along the eastern margin of the metamorphic complex NW of Golden, as a product of two distinct phases of deformation; and Brown (1978) has concluded that the evolution of the SE Canadian Cordillera involved earlier 'eastward underthrusting from the W', and then 'westward underthrusting of North America from the E'. However, the Selkirk fan structure has also been interpreted as a fan fold (Price & Mountjoy 1970; Zwanzig 1973; Price 1979), like that in the Lower Palaeozoic shale facies of the western Rocky Mountains (Fig. 2), involving a single progressive deformation above a zone of regional décollement, and comprising a local reversal in the vergence of the structures, like that which occurs along the W side of the Alberta syncline (Fig. 6).

The conclusion that there has been a large net horizontal shortening or convergence across the entire tract from the E edge of the thrust and fold belt to the W edge of the Shuswap Metamorphic Complex constrains interpretations of the geotectonic significance of the foreland thrust and fold belt. Convergence between the W flank of the Shuswap Metamorphic Complex and the autochthonous cover on the continental craton appears to be approximately equal to the amount of crustal shortening across the thrust and fold belt—about 200 km (Bally et al. 1966; Price & Mountjoy 1970). The shortening must have been balanced by an equivalent convergence or crustal shortening at a deeper crustal level, and this constitutes a type of subduction. Bally (1975) has called this 'Alpinotype or A-subduction', and has contrasted it with 'Benioff or B-subduction', in which a slab of oceanic lithosphere dips deep into the mantle with décollement or scraping off of suprarustal rocks and imbrication of oceanic crust and upper mantle. He has suggested that it is the shallower conjugate homologue of B-subduction and that it involves the disposal of large amounts of continental crust. In the southern Canadian Rocky Mountains, this A-subduction may have been the conjugate homologue of B-subduction which occurred along the Pacific Margin of the Cordillera from mid-Jurassic to Palaeogene time (Monger &

Price 1979). However, it apparently did not involve the disposal of any significant amount of continental crust, because it occurred outboard from the edge of the continental craton, in an area floored by attenuated continental crust or oceanic crust.

The following scenario is suggested. As the attenuated continental crust and its suprarustal cover of eugeoclinal and miogeoclinal rocks were carried into the subduction zone, they were metamorphosed to relatively high grades in an intermediate pressure (Barrovian) metamorphic facies series, became ductile, rose bouyantly and spread laterally into the overlying shallower suprastructure of less metamorphosed rocks, partly along ductile zones of extension faulting that are now represented by tectonic slides. Easterly verging imbricate thrust faults and related folds developed concurrently, at a higher level, farther to the E in the subduction zone, in a subduction complex that was tectonically prograded eastward up to and over the edge of the continental craton, in much the same way that subduction complexes above sediment-filled oceanic trenches have been tectonically prograded over the adjacent oceanic crust (Hamilton 1977). The topographic slope produced in this way was primarily due to the compression of the supracrustal cover that was scraped off the down-going slab, and therefore, was a second-order effect, rather than the primary cause of the thrust and fold belt (Chapple 1978; cf. Elliot 1976). Thus, the evolution of the foreland thrust and fold belt in the southern Rocky Mountains can be viewed as an example of intra-plate convergence, involving the collapse of a back-arc or marginal basin, behind the main easterly dipping Cordilleran subduction zone. As the supracrustal cover of miogeoclincal rocks was scraped off the down-going slab, it was tectonically prograded over an adjacent continental craton to form a very wide and shallow subduction complex.

ACKNOWLEDGMENTS. This work has been supported by the National Science and Engineering Research Council of Canada, and by the Canada Department of Energy Mines and Resources. It has been made possible by a Canada Council Killam Senior Research Fellowship. Mina Price assisted with the compilation of the maps and the preparation of the sections. Peter Fermor collaborated on the preparation of Section SW–NE in Fig. 2. Most of the figures were drafted by Christopher Peck. A. W. Bally, P. L. Gordy, E. W. Mountjoy, S. S. Oriel and R. I. Thompson reviewed an earlier draft of the manuscript and made helpful suggestions for improving it.

References

AALTO, K. R. 1971. Glacial marine sedimentation and stratigraphy of the Toby conglomerate (Upper Proterozoic) southeastern British Columbia, northwestern Idaho and northeastern Washington, *Can. J. Earth Sci.* **8,** 753–87.

AITKEN, J. D. 1971. Control of Lower Paleozoic sedimentary facies by the Kicking Horse rim, southern Rocky Mountains, Canada. *Bull. Can. Pet. Geol.* **19,** 557–69.

ARCHIBLAD, D. A., ꟿLOVER, J. K. & FARRAR, E. 1977. K-Ar ages from the Bayonne batholith and some nearby plutons in SE British Columbia and their geological implications. *Geol. Assoc. Can. Progs with Abstr.* **2,** 5.

BALKWILL, H. R. 1972. Structural geology, lower Kicking Horse river region, Rocky Mountains, British Columbia. *Bull. Can. Pet. Geol.* **20,** 608–33.

——, PRICE, R. A. & MOUNTJOY, E. W. (in press *a*). Geology, Golden (east half), British Columbia. *Geol. Surv. Can. Map* **1496A.**

——, —— & —— (in press *b*). Geology, Golden (west-half), British Columbia. *Geol. Surv. Can. Map* **1497a.**

BALLY, A. W. 1975. A geodynamic scenario for hydrocarbon occurrences. *9th World Petrol. Cong. (Tokyo),* **2,** 23–44.

——, GORDY, P. L. & STEWART, G. A. 1966. Structure, seismic data and orogenic evolution of southern Canadian Rockies. *Bull. Can. Pet. Geol.* **14,** 337–81.

BENNETT, G. T., CLOWES, R. M. & ELLIS, R. M. 1975. A seismic refraction survey along the southern Rocky Mountain Trench, Canada. *Bull. seismol. Soc. Am.* **65,** 37–54.

BENVENUTO, G. L. 1978. *Structural Evolution of the Hosmer Thrust Sheet, South-Eastern British Columbia.* Queen's Univ. Ph.D. thesis (Unpubl.).

BERNOULLI, D., LAUBSCHER, H. P., TRÜMPY, R. &WENK, E. 1974. Central Alps and Jura Mountains. *In:* SPENCER, A. M. (ed), *Mesozoic-Cenozoic Orogenic Belts.* Spec. Publ. geol. Soc. London, **4,** 83–108.

BERRY, M. J. & FORSYTH, D. A. 1975. Structure of the Canadian Cordillera from seismic refraction and other data. *Can. J. Earth Sci.* **12,** 182–208.

BIELENSTEIN, H. U., PRICE, R. A. & JONES, P. B. 1971. Geology of the Seebe-Kananaskis area, Map. *In:* HALLADAY, I. A. R. & MATHEWSON, D. H. (ed), *A Guide to the Geology of the Eastern Cordillera along the Trans-Canada Highway between Calgary, Alberta and Revelstoke, British Columbia.* Alberta Soc. Petrol. Geol., Calgary.

BROWN, R. L. 1978. Structural evolution of the southeast Canadian Cordillera: A new hypothesis. *Tectonophysics,* **48,** 133–51.

—— & TIPPET, C. R. 1978. The Selkirk fan structure of the southeastern Canadian Cordillera. *Bull. geol. Soc. Am.* **89,** 548–58.

BURCHFIEL, B. C. & DAVIS, G. A. 1972. Structural framework and evolution of the southern part of the Cordilleran orogen, Western United States. *Am. J. Sci.* **272,** 97–118.

CAMPBELL, R. B. 1968. Canoe River, British Columbia. *Geol. Surv. Can. Map* **15–1967.**

—— 1973. Structural Cross-Section and Tectonic Model of the S.E. Canadian Cordillera. *Can. J. Earth Sci.* **10,** 1607–20.

CAMPBELL, I. & LOOFBOUROW, J. S., Jr. Preliminary geologic map and sections of the magnesite belt, Stevens county, Washington, *U.S. Geol. Surv. Map* **MF-117.**

CANER, B. 1971. Quantitive interpretation of geomagnetic depth-sounding data in western Canada. *J. geophys. Res.* **76,** 7202–16.

CHANDRA, N. N. & CUMMING, G. L. 1972. Seismic refraction studies in western Canada. *Can. J. Earth Sci.* **9,** 1099–109.

CHAPPLE, W. M. 1978. Mechanics of thin-skinned fold and thrust belts. *Bull. geol. Soc. Am.* **89,** 1189–98.

COOK, D. C. 1975. Structural style influenced by lithofacies, Rocky Mountain Main Ranges, Alberta-British Columbia. *Bull. geol. Surv. Can.* **233.**

CORBITT, L. L. & WOODWARD, L. A. 1973. Tectonic framework of cordilleran foldbelt in southwestern New Mexico. *Bull. Am. Assoc. Petrol. Geol.* **57,** 2207–16.

CUMMING, W. B., CLOWES, R. M. & ELLIS, R. M. 1979. Crustal structure from a seismic refraction profile across southern British Columbia. *Can. J. Earth Sci.* **16,** 1024–40.

DAHLSTROM, C. D. A. 1969*a.* The upper detachment in concentric folding. *Bull. Can. Pet. Geol.* **17,** 326–46.

—— 1969*b.* Balanced cross sections. *Can. J. Earth Sci.* **6,** 743–57.

—— 1970. Structural geology in the eastern margin of the Canadian Rocky mountains. *Bull. Can. Pet. Geol.* **18,** 332–406.

——, DANIEL, R. E. & HENDERSON, G. G. L. 1962. The Lewis thrust at Fording mountain, British Columbia. *J. Alberta Soc. petrol. Geol.* **10,** 373–95.

DAVIS, G. & CONEY, P. J. 1979. Geological development of the Cordilleran metamorphic core complexes. *Geology,* **7,** 120–4.

DE CSERNA, Z. 1971. Development and structure of the Sierra Madre Oriental of Mexico. *Geol. Soc. Am. (Abstracts with programs),* **3,** Rocky mountain section, 377–78.

DEWEY, J. A. & BIRD, J. M. 1970. Mountain belts and the new global tectonics. *J. geophys. Res.* **75,** 2625–47.

DIMROTH, E. 1970. Evolution of the Labrador geosyncline. *Bull. geol. Soc. Am.* **81,** 2717–42.

DOUGLAS, R. J. W. 1950. Callum creek, Langford creek and Gap map-areas, Alberta. *Mem. geol. Surv. Can.* **255.**

—— 1951. Pincher creek, alberta; preliminary map. *Pap. geol. Surv. Can.* **51–22.**

—— 1952. Waterton Alberta; preliminary map. *Pap. geol. Surv. Can.* **52–10.**

—— 1958. Mount Head map-area, Alberta. *Mem. geol. Surv. Can.* **291.**

—— 1970. in DOUGLAS, R. J. W., GABRIELSE, H., WHEELER, J. O., STOTT, D. F. & BELYEA, H. R. Geology of Western Canada, Chap. VIII of Geology and Economic Minerals of Canada. *In:* DOUGLAS, R. J. W. (ed), *Geol. Surv. Can. Econ. Geology report*, **1**, 396.

DRAGERT, H. & CLARKE, G. K. C. 1976. A detailed investigation of the Canadian cordillera geomagnetic transition anomaly. *J. geophys.* **42**, 373–90.

EARTH PHYSICS BRANCH. 1974. Bouguer anomaly map of Canada. *Dept. Energy Mines & Res., Can. Gravity map series* **74–1**.

EISABACHER, G. H., CARRIGY, M. A. & CAMPBELL, R. B. 1974. Paleodrainage pattern and late-orogenic basins of the Canadian Cordillera. *In:* DICKINSON, W. R. (ed). *Tectonics and Sedimentation.* Spec. Publ. Econ. Paleon. & Min. **22**, 143–66.

ELLIOT, D. 1976. The motion of thrust sheets. *J. geophys. Res.* **81**, 949–63.

FERMOR, P. R. & PRICE, R. A. 1976. Imbricate structures in the Lewis thrust sheet around the Cate Creek and Haig Brook windows. *Pap. geol. Surv. Can.* **76-1B**, 7–10.

FOX, F. G. 1959. Structure and accumulation of hydrocarbons in southern Foothills, Alberta, Canada. *Bull. Am. Assoc. Petrol. Geol.* **43**, 992–1025.

FYLES, J. T. 1964. Geology of the Duncan lake area, Lardeau district, British Columbia. *Bull. Br. Columbia Dep. Mines Petrol. Res.* **49**.

—— 1967. Geology of the Ainsworth-Kaslo area, British Columbia. *Bull. Br. Columbia Dep. Mines Petrol. Res.* **53**.

—— & HEWLETT, C. G. 1959. Stratigraphy and structure of the Salmo lead-zinc area. *Bull. Br. Columbia Dep. Mines.* **41**.

GABRIELSE, H. & REESOR, J. E. 1974. The nature and setting of granitic plutons in the central and eastern parts of the Canadian Cordillera. *Pacific Geology*, **8**, 109–38.

GARDNER, D. A. C. 1977. *Structural Geology and Metamorphism of Calcareous Lower Paleozoic Slates, Blaeberry River-Redburn Creek Area, near Golden, British Columbia.* Queen's Univ., Ph.D. thesis (Unpubl.).

GILMAN, R. A. 1972. Geology of the Clachnacudainn salient near Albert canyon, British Columbia. *Can. J. Earth Sci.* **9**, 1447–54.

GLOVER, J. K. 1978. *Geology of the Summit Creek Map Area, Southern Kootenay Arc, British Columbia.* Queen's Univ. Ph.D. thesis (Unpubl.).

HAMILTON, W. 1977. Subduction in the Indonesian region. *In:* TALWANI, M. & PITMAN, W. C. (ed). *Island Arcs, Deep Sea Trenches and Back-Arc Basins.* Am. geophys. Union. Maurice Ewing series **I**, 15–31.

HARRISON, J. E. 1972. Precambrian Belt basins of northwestern United States: its geometry, sedimentation, and copper occurrences. *Bull. geol. Soc. Am.* **83**, 1215–40.

—— & JOBIN, D. A. 1963. Geology and ore deposits of the Clark Fork quadrangle, Idaho-Montana.

Bull. U.S. geol. Surv. **1141-K**.

—— & —— 1965. Geologic map of the Packsaddle mountain quadrangle, Idaho. *U.S. geol. Surv. Map* **GQ-375**.

—— & SCHMIDT, P. W. 1971. Geologic map of the Elmira quadrangle, Bonner county, Idaho. *U.S. geol. Surv. Map* **I-603**.

HENDERSON, G. G. L. 1954. Geology of the Stanford range of the Rocky mountains. *Bull. Br. Columbia Dep. Mines* **35**.

HOFFMAN, P. 1973. Evolution of an early Proterozoic margin: the Coronation geosyncline and associated aulacogens of the northwestern Canadian Shield. *Philos. Trans. R. Soc. London* **A273**, 547–81.

HOFFMAN, P. F., ST. ONGE, M., CARMICHAEL, D. M. & DE BIE, I. 1978. Geology of the Coronation geosyncline (Aphebian) Hepburn lake sheet (86J), Bear province, district of Mackenzie; current research. *Pap. geol. Surv. Can.* **78-1A**, 147–51.

HÖY, T. 1977. Stratigraphy and structure of the Kootenay arc in the Riondel area, southeastern British Columbia. *Can. J. Earth Sci.* **14**, 2301–15.

—— 1978. Geology of the Estella-Kootenay King area, southeastern British Columbia. *Br. Columbia Dep. Mines prelim. Map* **28**.

HUNTTING, M. T., BENNETT, W. A. G., LIVINGSTON, V. E., JR., & MOENS, W. S. (Compilers). 1961. Geologic map of Washington. Washington Div. Mines and Geology.

JOHNS, W. M. 1970. Geology and mineral deposits of Lincoln and Flathead counties, Montana. *Bull. Montana Bur. Mines Geol.* **79**.

KANASEWICH, E. R., CLOWES, R. M. & McCLOUGHAN, C. H. 1969. A buried Precambrian rift in western Canada. *Tectonophysics*, **8**, 513–27.

KEATING, L. F. 1966. Exploration in the Canadian Rockies and Foothills. *Can. J. Earth Sci.* **3**, 713–23.

KEEN, C. E. & HYNDMAN, R. D. 1979. Geophysical review of the continental margins of eastern and western Canada. *Can. J. Earth Sci.* **16**, 712–47.

KING, P. B. (Compiler) 1969. Tectonic map of North America. *U.S. geol. Surv.* Washington, D.C.

LEECH, G. B. 1958. Fernie map-area, west half, British Columbia. *Pap. geol. Surv. Can.* **58–10**.

—— 1959. Canal Flats, British Columbia. *Geol. Surv. Can. Map* **24–1958**.

—— 1960. Fernie, west half, British Columbia. *Geol. Surv. Can. Map* **11–1960**.

—— 1962. Structure of the Bull river valley near latitude 49°35′. *J. Alberta Soc. petrol. Geol.* **10**, 396–407.

LIS, M. G. & PRICE, R. A. 1976. Large-scale block faulting during deposition of the Windermere supergroup (Hadrynian) in southeastern British Columbia. *Pap. geol. Surv. Can.*, **76-1A**, 135–6.

LITTLE, H. W. 1960. Nelson map-area, west half, British Columbia. *Mem. geol. Surv. Can.* **308**.

McLEAN, J. R. & JERZYKIEWICZ, T. 1978. Cyclicity, tectonics and coal: Some aspects of fluvial sedimentology in the Brazeau-Paskapoo formations, Coal valley area, Alberta, Canada. *Mem. Can. Soc. petrol. geol.* **5**, *Fluvial Sedimentology*, 441–68.

MEREU, R. F., MAJUMDAR, S. C. & WHITE, R. E. 1977. The structure of the crust and upper mantle under the highest ranges of the Canadian Rockies from a seismic refraction survey. *Can. J. Earth Sci.* **14**, 196–208.

MILLER, F. K. 1974a. Preliminary geologic map of the Newport number 1 quadrangle, Pend Oreille county, Washington and Bonner county, Idaho. *Washington Dept. Natural Res. geol. Map* **GM-7.**

—— 1974b. Preliminary geologic map of the Newport number 2 quandrangle, Pend Oreille and Stevens counties, Washington. *Washington Dept. Natural Res. geol. Map* **GM-8**.

—— 1974c. Preliminary geologic map of the Newport number 3 quadrangle, Pend Oreille, Stevens and Spokane counties, Washington. Washington *Ddpt. Natural Res. geol. Map* **GM-9.**

—— 1974d. Preliminary geologic map of the Newport number 4 quadrangle, Spokane and Pend Oreille counties, Washington and Bonner county, Idaho. *Washington Dept. Natural Res. geol. Map* **GM-10.**

——, CLARK, L. D. & ENGELS, J. C. D. 1975. Geology of the Chewelah-Loon Lake area, Stevens and Spokane countries, Washington. *Prof. Pap. U.S. geol. Surv.* **806.**

MONGER, J. W. H. & PRICE, R. A. 1979. Geodynamic evolution of the Canadian Cordillera—progress and problems. *Can. J. Earth Sci.* **16**, 770–91.

——, SOUTHER, J. G. & GABRIELSE, H. 1972. Evolution of the Canadian Cordillera: a plate-tectonic model. *Am. J. Sci.* **272**, 577–602.

NGUYEN, E. K., SINCLAIR, A. J. & LIBBY, W. G. 1968. Age of the northern part of the Nelson batholith. *Can. J. Earth Sci.* **5**, 955–7.

NORTH, F. K. & HENDERSON, G. G. L. 1954. Summary of the geology of the southern Rocky Mountains of Canada. *Alberta Soc. petrol. Geol., Calgary, Guidebook, Fourth Annual Field Conference*, 15–81.

NORRIS, D. K. 1958a. Beehive mountain, Alberta and British Columbia. *Pap. geol. Surv. Can.* **58–5.**

—— 1958b. Livingstone river, Alberta. *Geol. Surv. Can. Map* **5–1958**.

—— & PRICE, R. A. 1966. Middle Cambrian lithostratigraphy of southeastern Canadian Cordillera. *Bull. Can. Pet. Geol.* **14**, 385–404.

NYE, J. F. 1952. The mechanics of glacier flow. *J. Glaciol. London*, **2**, 82–93.

OLLERENSHAW, N. C. 1972a. Geology, lake Minnewanka (east half), Alberta *Geol. Surv. Can. Map* **1347A.**

—— 1972b. Geology, Wildcat Hills (west half), Alberta. *Geol. Surv. Can. Map* **1351A.**

—— (Compiler), 1975. Rocky mountain Foothills and Front ranges; Calgary region. In guidebook,

Savanna creek to Panther river, exploration update W5. *Can. Soc. Pet. Geol.*, Calgary.

—— (Compiler), 1978. Geology, Calgary, Alberta-British columbia. *Geol. Surv. Can. Map* **1457A.**

PARK, C. F., JR & CANNON, R. S., JR. 1943. Geology and ore deposits of the Metaline quadrangle, Washington, *Prof. Pap. U.S. geol. Surv.*, **202.**

PRICE, R. A. 1962. Fernie map-area, east half Alberta and British Columbia. *Pap. geol. Surv. Can.* **61–24.** (includes *Map* **35–1961**).

—— 1964a. The Precambrian Purcell System in the Rocky mountains of southern Alberta and British Columbia. *Bull. Can. Pet. Geol.* **12**, 399–426.

—— 1964b. Flexural-slip folds in the Rocky Mountains, southern Alberta and British Columbia. Seminars on Tectonics IV, Dept. Geol. Sci., Queen's Univ., Kingston, Ont. (Also as Geol. Surv. Can. reprint 78).

—— 1965. Flathead map-area, British Columbia and Alberta. *Mem. geol. Surv. Can.* **336.**

—— 1970. Geology, Canmore (east half) Alberta. *Geol Surv. Can. Map* **1265A.**

—— 1972. Rocky Mountain Trench—Golden to Cranbrook. *In:* PRICE, R. A., BALKWILL, H. R., CHARLESWORTH, H. A. K., COOK, D. G. & SIMONY, P. S. *The Canadian Rockies and Tectonic Evolution of the Southeastern Cordillera.* Guidebook, field excursion AC15, XXIV Inter. Geol. Congress. Montreal, 77–85.

—— 1973. Large-scale gravitational flow of supracrustal rocks, southern Canadian Rockies. *In:* DE JONG, K. A. & SCHOLTEN, R. (ed) *Gravity and tectonics.* Wiley, New York, 491–502.

—— 1979. The Selkirk fan structure of the southeastern Canadian Cordillera: Discussion. *Bull. geol. Soc. Am.* **90**, 695–8.

——, BALKWILL H. R. & MOUNTJOY, E. W. in press. Geology, McMurdo (east half), British Columbia. *Geol. Surv. Can. Map* **1501A.**

——, COOK, D. G., AITKEN, J. D. & MOUNTJOY, E. W. in press a. Geology, Lake Louise, (west half), Alberta-British Columbia. *Geol. Surv. Can. Map* **1483A.**

——, ——, —— & —— in press b. Geology, Lake Louise, (east half), Alberta-British Columbia. *Geol. surv. Can. Map* **1482A.**

—— & MOUNTJOY, E. W. 1970. Geologic structure of the Canadian Rocky Mountains between Bow and Athabasca rcvers—a progress report. *In:* WHEELER, J. O. (ed), *Structure of the Southern Canadain Cordillera.* Spec. Pap. geol. Assoc. Can. **6**, 7–25.

—— & —— 1972a. Geology, Banff, (east half), Alberta-British Columbia. *Geol. Surv. Can. Map* **1294A.**

—— & —— 1972b. Geology, Banff, (west half), Alberta-British Columbia. *Geol. Surv. Can. Map* **1295A.**

—— & —— 1978a. Geology, Hector Lake, (east half), Alberta-British Columbia. *Geol. Surv. Can. Map* **1463A.**

—— & —— 1978b. Geology, Hector Lake, (west half), Alberta-British Columbia. *Geol. Surv.*

Can. Map **1464A.**

—— & —— 1978c. Geology Siffleur River, (east half), Alberta. *Geol. Surv. Can. Map* **1465A.**

—— & —— 1978d. Geology, Siffleur River, (west half), Alberta. *Geol. Surv. Can. Map* **1466A.**

—— & —— 1979a. Geology, Mount Goodsir, (east half), Alberta-British Columbia. *Geol. Surv. Can. Map* **1476A.**

—— & —— 1979b. Geology, Mount Goodsir, (west half), Alberta-British Columbia. *Geol. Surv. Can. Map* **1477A.**

—— & in press. Geology, McMurdo, (west half), British Columbia. *Geol. Surv. Can. Map* **1502A.**

READ, P. B. 1977. Relationship of the Kootenay arc to the Shuswap Metamorphic Complex, Southern British Columbia. *Geol. Assoc. Can. Progs with Abstr.* **2,** 43.

—— & WHEELER, J. O. 1976. Geology of Lardeau west-half map area. *Geol. Surv. Can. open-file Report* **288.**

REESOR, J. E. 1965. Valhalla gneiss complex, British Columbia. *Bull. geol. Surv. Can.* **129.**

—— 1973. Geology of the Lardeau map-area, east half, British Columbia. *Mem. geol. Surv. Can.* **369.**

RICE, H. M. A. 1941. Nelson map-area, east half, British Columbia. *Mem. geol. Surv. Can.* **228.**

RODGERS, J. 1970. *The Tectonics of the Appalachians.* Wiley-Interscience, New York.

ROSS, C. P. 1959. Geology of Glacier National Park and the Flathead region, northwestern Montana. *Prof. Pap. U.S. geol. Surv.* **296.**

SEARS, J. W. 1979. *Tectonic Contrasts between the Infrastructure and Suprastructure of the Columbian Orogen, Albert Peak Area, Western Selkirk Mountains, British Columbia.* Queen's Univ., Ph.D. thesis (Unpubl.).

—— & PRICE, R. A. 1978. The Siberian connection: A case for Precambrian separation of the North American and Siberian cratons. *Geology,* **6,** 267–70.

SEELEY, D. R. 1977. The significance of landward vergence and oblique structural trends on trench inner slopes. *In:* TALWANI, M. & PITMAN, W. C. (eds), *Island Arcs, Deep Sea Trenches and Back Arc Basins.* Am. geophys. Union. Maurice Ewing Series **1,** 187–98.

SHAW, E. W. 1963. Canadian Rockies—orientation in time and space. *In:* CHILDS, O.E. (ed), *Backbone of the Americas.* Mem. Am. Assoc. Petrol. Geol. **2,** 231–42.

SIMONY, P. S. & WIND, G. 1970. Structure of the

Dogtooth Range and adjacent portions of the Rocky Mountain Trench. *In:* WHELLER, J. O. (ed), *Structure of the Southern Canadian Cordillera.* Spec. Pap. geol. Assoc. Can. **6,** 41–53.

SPENCE, G. D., CLOWES, R. M. & ELLIS, R. M. 1977. Depth limits of the M discontinuity in the southern Rocky Mountain Trench, Canada. *Bull. seismol. Soc. Am.* **67,** 543–6.

STACEY, R. A. 1973. Gravity anomalies, crustal structure, and plate tectonics in the Canadian Cordillera. *Can. J. Earth Sci.* **10,** 615–28.

THOMPSON, R. I. 1972. *Geology of the Akolkolex River Area near Revelstoke, British Columbia,* Queen's Univ. Ph.D. thesis (Unpubl.).

WANLESS, R. K., LOVERIDGE, W. D. & MURSKY, G. 1968. A geochronological study of the White Creek batholith, southeastern British Columbia. *Can. J. Earth Sci.* **5,** 375–86.

WHEELER, J. O. 1963. Rogers pass map-area, British Columbia and Alberta. *Pap. geol. Surv. Can.,* **62–32.**

—— & GABRIELSE, H. 1972. The Cordilleran Structural Province. *In:* PRICE R. A. & DOUGLAS, R. J. W. (eds), *Variations in Tectonic Styles in Canada;* Spec. Pap. Geol. Assoc. Can., **11,** 1–81.

——, CHARLESWORTH, H. A. K., MONGER, J. W. H., MULLER, J. A., PRICE, R. A., REESOR, J. E., RODDICK, J. A. & SIMONY, P. S. 1974. Western Canada. *In:* SPENCER, A. M. (ed), *Mesozoic-Cenozoic orogenic belts.* Spec. Publ. geol. Soc. London, **4,** 592–623.

WILLIAMS, E. P. 1949. Preliminary map, Cardston, Alberta. *Pap. geol. Surv. Can.* **49–3.**

WYNN, J. C., KLEINKOPF, M. F. & HARRISON, J. E. 1977. Audio-frequency magnetotelluric and gravity traverse across the crest of the Purcell anticlinorium, northwestern Montana. *Geology,* **5,** 309–12.

YATES, R. G. 1964. Geologic map and sections of the Deep Creek area, Stevens and Pend Oreille counties, Washington. *U.S. geol. Surv. Map* **I-412.**

—— 1971. Geologic map of the Northport quadrangle, Washington. *U.S. geol. Surv. Map* **1-603.**

YOUNG, F. G., CAMPBELL, R. B. & POULTON, T. P. 1973. The Windermere Supergroup of the southeastern Canadian Rockies. *Belt Symposium* **1,** 181–203.

ZWANZIG, H. V. 1973. *Structural Transitions between the Foreland Zone and the Core Zone of the Columbian Orogen, Selkirk Mountains, British Columbia.* Queen's Univ. Ph.D. thesis (Unpubl.).

R. A. PRICE. Department of Geological Sciences, Queen's University, Kingston, Ontario, K7L 3N6, Canada.

The nature and significance of large 'blind' thrusts within the northern Rocky Mountains of Canada

R. I. Thompson

SUMMARY: The northern Canadian Rocky Mountains comprise a rugged, structurally complex Foothills subprovince of large amplitude box and chevron folds, and a structurally diverse Rocky Mountain subprovince in which large mappable thrusts are rare. The boundary between them is, in some regions, defined by the unfaulted E-dipping limbs of an *en echelon* sequence of large mountain-front anticlines. The lack of thrusts, especially along the mountain front, contrasts with the well exposed linearly continuous thrusts of the Front Ranges structural subprovince within the southern Rocky Mountains, and leads to the impression that little lateral displacement has occurred.

Where deep cross-cutting valley erosion combines with increased fold plunge, it is apparent that the frontal anticlines are, in reality, large allochthonous sheets displaced many kilometres eastward relative to the craton on flat thrusts that separate Ordovician shales from underlying Devonian and Mississippian shales. The faults can be traced, in some places, eastward to the mountain front where they cut abruptly through the thick hanging wall successions of carbonate rocks; however, they cannot be mapped further eastward into surface exposures because they terminate within a décollement zone of Devonian and Mississippian shales, where the displacement on them is transformed into disharmonic folds and tectonic thickening of overlying units.

The Devonian and Mississippian shale succession is interpreted as a fundamental décollement zone of regional extent that separates a lower structural level of thrust-faulted carbonate rocks from an upper structural level characterized by folded late Palaeozoic and Mesozoic units. The shortening represented by Foothills folds is interpreted to equal the amount of shortening on 'blind' thrusts beneath the western margin of the Foothills structural subprovince.

A structural reinterpretation across the Muskwa Anticlinorium using the blind thrust interpretation demonstrates that the mountain-front Tuchodi Anticline may represent a large allochthonous thrust sheet folded over a large step in the blind thrust on which it was transported.

The northern Rocky Moutains, narrower and less foreshortened than the southern Rocky Mountains, are interpreted as a thin-skinned tectonic regime similar to but orogenically less mature than the southern Rocky Mountains.

The significant on-strike changes in structural style that affect the Canadian Rocky Mountain thrust and fold belt as it is traced northward beyond the well documented Waterton and Bow Valley regions (e.g. Bally *et al.* 1966; Price & Mountjoy 1970; Dahlstrom 1970) reflect a concomitant and gradual change in the stratigraphic character of the rocks that were deformed (Thompson 1979). The pattern of imbricate thrusts that typifies the structural fabric within the Foothills and Front Ranges in the S is less well developed northward where it is progressively replaced by a compensating pattern of folds and fold complexes in which thrusts are a subordinate tectonic element. Although thrusts and folds are never mutually exclusive, one may traverse some parts of the northern Rocky Mountains and not encounter a single thrust of consequence.

Without the well documented model of thin-skinned detachment tectonics so successfully applied to interpretation of the southern Rockies, and some appreciation for the gradual nature of stratigraphic and structural changes that occur northward along strike, one might be tempted to interpret the northern Rockies as a 'thick-skinned' terrain where vertical basement uplifts controlled the evolution of surface structures. The presence of broad mountain-front anticlines without visible thrusts along their eastern margins, a general lack of well defined imbricate thrust sheets involving large stratigraphic overlap, structural disharmony between major stratigraphic units, and an apparent minor amount of supracrustal shortening, constitute some of the reasons that influenced others (e.g. Taylor 1972; Taylor & Stott 1973) to speculate that the northern Rocky Mountains may differ in a fundamental way from its southern counterpart.

Much of the data and many of the ideas expressed here are taken from an earlier publication (Thompson 1979) that presented a thin-skinned detachment model of structural evolution for part of the northern Canadian Rocky Mountains. The theme of this paper remains unchanged, but its scope has been extended to include a structural reinterpretation across the Muskwa Anticlinorium (Figs 1 & 2), a large southward plunging anticlinorial closure cored by rocks of Middle Proterozoic age that is geologically similar to the Purcell Anticlinorium in the S (see Price, this volume).

FIG. 1. Location of study area in relation to the major tectonic subdivisions of the Canadian Cordillera.

Arguments will be presented that suggest the northern Rocky Mountains are tectonically less mature than the southern Rockies and as such represent a 'preview' of Canadian Rocky Mountain structural evolution prior to development of the spectacular thrust-faulted Front Ranges structural subprovince that now characterizes the eastern portion of the southern Rocky Mountains.

Geological framework

The northern Rocky Mountains consist of three major tectono-stratigraphic assemblages (Fig. 2). On the E, mechanically incompetent clastic rocks of Upper Palaeozoic and Mesozoic age dominate the complexly folded Foothills structural subprovince. Adjacent to the Foothills, a second assemblage of thrust faulted and folded Middle Proterozoic (Helikian) and Palaeozoic rocks is dominated

by thick carbonate successions and forms the large southward plunging Muskwa Anticlinorium (Taylor & Stott 1973); southeastward, beyond the plunge-out if the anticlinorium, Palaeozoic carbonates form a narrow spine of topographically prominent peaks that defines the eastern edge of the Rocky Mountains structural subprovince. On the W is the third major assemblage comprising more penetratively deformed upper Proterozoic (Hadrynian) and Palaeozoic clastic facies (Taylor et al. 1979; Cecile & Norford 1979; Thompson 1976) in which continuity and scale of individual structures are less developed, and the structural styles more diverse.

It is usual to describe the Canadian Rockies in terms of structural subprovinces (North & Henderson 1954), each of which is characterized by distinctive topographic, stratigraphic and structural features separated by major thrusts or thrust systems. In the southern Rockies there are four: Foothills, Front Ranges, Main Ranges and Western Ranges, but as these subprovinces are traced northward to the latitude of the Peace River (56°N) the lateral limits and distinctive features of each become increasingly difficult to distinguish, and only two basic subdivisions remain: the Foothills structural subprovince on the E and the undivided Rocky Mountains structural subprovince on the W (Fig. 2); a small thrust may separate them or, alternatively, the Foothills subprovince may merge laterally with the Rocky Mountains subprovince across a topographically low, densely vegetated valley with no obvious evidence of a structural break between them (Fig. 2). This is in marked contrast with the southern Rockies where large thrusts such as the Lewis and McConnell, with displacements across them measured in tens of kilometres, place massive cliffs of Proterozoic or Palaeozoic carbonate rocks against topographically low Foothills terrain composed of Cretaceous shales.

Unlike the southern Foothills, the northern Foothills subprovince is a mountainous fold terrain comprising large-amplitude box and chevron folds that expose strata mainly of Mesozoic age (Fitzgerald 1968), although large folds of Mississippian through Permian strata occur along the western margin (Fig. 3). Some thrusts are present and are normally associated with tightly folded anticlinal complexes. Similarly, the undivided Rocky Mountains subprovince is in marked contrast with the Front and Main Ranges of the S. Rapid changes in structural style, both along and across the strike, disrupt the topographic and structural grain.

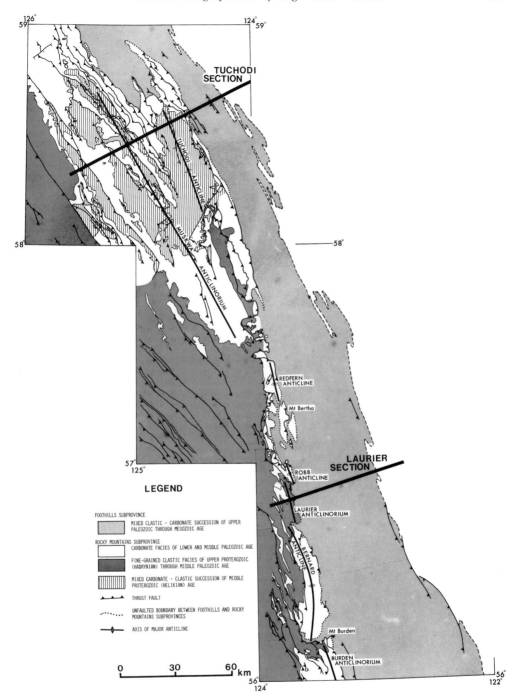

FIG. 2. Generalized tectonic-stratigraphic assemblage map showing the distribution of major thrust faults, the location of major mountain front anticlines, the Muskwa Anticlinorium, and the location of the Laurier and Tuchodi structure cross-sections.

FIG. 3. The eastern half of a large box fold of Mississippian carbonate rocks (as viewed from the NW) located along the western margin of the Foothills structural subprovince. White line highlights layering.

Two features are especially noticeable: (1) there are fewer thrusts, and those present lack the lateral continuity typical of major thrusts within the southern Rocky Mountains, and (2) the mountain front may be defined by the steep E-dipping limb of a large anticline that exposes Lower and Middle Palaeozoic carbonate rocks but with no obvious evidence of lateral transport of the anticline on a thrust (Figs 4 & 5).

Except for the folds within the Foothills, there is little evidence of significant lateral telescoping of the sedimentary prism— certainly nothing to suggest the 200 km or more of shortening calculated for the southern Rocky Mountains (Bally et al. 1966; Price & Mountjoy 1970). It will be argued that the lack of major thrusts is more apparent than real and that the large anticlinal structures within the northern Rocky Mountains have been displaced relatively eastward as much as 10 or more km on flat thrusts—termed blind thrusts here—that do not project into surface exposures.

The on-strike changes in structural style from S to N are closely linked to changes in the stratigraphic character of the miogeoclinal rock prism. Comparison of the cross sections in Fig. 11 illustrates the increased presence, in the N, of thick shale tongues, along with greater proximity of major carbonate to shale facies transitions to the eastern margin of the Rocky Mountain subprovince. Two of the incompetent units illustrated in Fig. 11 have played an important role in subsequent structural evolution: the unit of Cambro-Ordovician age (u€-lO) comprising thin bedded limestone, siltstone and shale is an important bedding glide zone into which thrusts flatten with depth; the Devonian–Mississippian shale succession (D–M_{sh}) is a stratigraphically higher décollement zone of regional extent into which thrusts may merge upward. A further complication is the oblique trend of major facies transitions to the structural strike, with the result that a thrust faulted carbonate succession may pass quickly along strike into a complex of stacked recumbent folds cut by subsidiary thrusts.

Blind thrusts

Blind thrusts played a critical role in the structural development of the northern Rocky Mountains, and are reponsible for some of the important differences in structural style between the northern and southern Rockies. Unlike thrusts which splay upward from a basal detachment zone to intersect the topographic surface, blind thrusts merge and flatten at some point in their upward trajectory into an 'upper' detachment zone(s). Consequently,

FIG. 4. View looking S along the eastern margin of the Bernard Anticline showing the unfaulted E-dipping fold limb which defines the eastern limit of the Rocky Mountain structural subprovince. Silurian and Devonian platform carbonate rocks (S–D) are overlain with apparent conformity by Devonian and Mississippian shales (M–D) of the Besa River Formation.

FIG. 5. View looking S along the eastern margin of the Laurier Anticlinorium showing the overturned limb of a near recumbent mountain front anticline consisting of Silurian (S) and Devonian (D) clastic facies rocks that are more distal clastic facies of the Silurian and Devonian platform carbonate rocks shown in Fig. 4. The white lines outline stratigraphic boundaries. The Laurier cross-section (Fig.9) passes through this structure.

they are rarely observed at surface and can influence the character of the surface geology to the point where one may traverse a low-angle thrust faulted terrain and not know it!

Geometric considerations require that the displacement on a blind thrust be transferred into the overlying (hanging-wall) beds through formation of a complex of disharmonic structures, otherwise balanced shortening from one stratigraphic level to another would not be possible (Dahlstrom 1969). This is illustrated in Fig. 6, a simplified diagrammatic representation of the blind thrust model.

As displacement on the blind thrust is initiated, a second detachment within the overriding sheet forms, and permits incompetent strata to behave independently and disharmonically with respect to the underlying rigid (hanging-wall) carbonates (Fig. 6a). If the amount of shortening caused by disharmonic folding keeps pace with the amount of displacement on the blind thrust, it will not extend laterally beyond the limits of the fold complex. If this balance is not maintained, then a splay from the blind thrust will develop, and break to surface as a kind of 'release valve' that accommodates the shortening imbalance. As displacement continues, the lateral limits of disharmonic folding are extended to keep pace with fault displacement (Fig. 6b).

By superimposing a hypothetical topographic surface onto Fig. 6c, it becomes apparent how misleading the surface geology may be. There is no structural break between the large surface anticline on the left and the fold complex on the right, and no way of determining that the large anticline is actually an allochthonous thrust sheet that is folded over a fault ramp or step at depth. Based on the surface evidence, one might argue in favour of vertical (basement) uplift as the agent responsible for the large anticline and that the fold complex adjacent to it is a consequence of gravitational sliding off the uplifted carbonate terrain.

The field evidence in favour of the blind thrust model is present in those areas where the plunging portion of a mountain-front anticline is cut across-trend by a deep eroded valley in which lower structural levels are exposed. At Mount Burden, illustrated in Figs 7a and b, a flat thrust fault can be traced across the strike for 10 km. Over most of this length, the fault separates relatively flat lying Upper Cambrian–Lower Ordovician shales from underlying Devonian and Mississippian Besa River Shales; at its eastern end the complete Lower and Middle Palaeozoic carbonate suc-

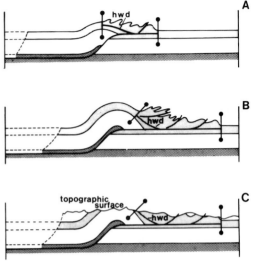

FIG. 6. A diagrammatic representation of the blind thrust model. The patterns define mechanically incompetent strata separated by a rigid carbonate unit with no pattern. (a) Illustrates the onset of displacement across the thrust accompanied by development of a hanging-wall detachment(s) (hwd) which allows the incompetent strata within the hanging-wall plate to deform disharmonically and absorb displacement on the underlying thrust. The thrust ceases to exist at the point where shortening due to folding in the hanging-wall equals displacement on the thrust—hence the pin on the right side of the section. In (b) continued thrust fault displacement increases the width of disharmonically deformed hanging-wall succession. (c) Illustrates the difficulty in deciphering the detached nature of the mountain front anticline using surface exposures. The major thrust remains 'blind', and much of the shortening within the disharmonically deformed incompetent unit may be difficult to assess unless good stratigraphic markers are present.

cession in the hanging-wall dips eastward and is cut-off abruptly against the fault which then has Besa River shales in both the hanging-wall and footwall. Rather than continuing to cut up section, the fault is deflected into the Besa River Shale where it remains concealed from view along the strike of the mountain front. At the Mount Burden locality, some of these shales (and thin carbonates) are preserved within the frontal portion of the thrust plate, where the upper surface of the rigid (hanging-wall) carbonate succession is essentially undeformed and east-dipping whereas the overlying

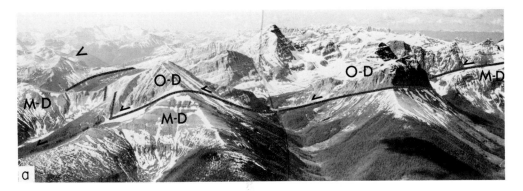

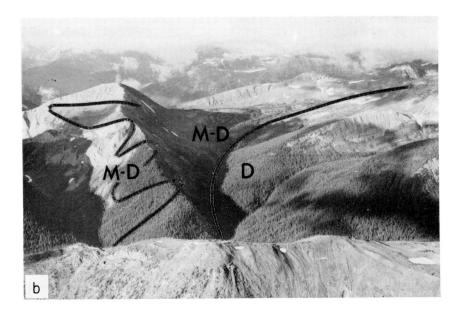

FIG. 7. (a) View toward the SW (oblique to the NW–SE structural grain) of the allochthonous Mt. Burden Anticlinorium. The thrust fault can be traced from W (right) to E (left) over 10 km but cannot be traced eastward beyond the hanging-wall cut-off of the Ordovician through Devonian carbonate succession (O—D) or along the trend of the mountain front. Below the fault trace are shales of Devonian and Mississippian age (M–D). Arrow head points to area shown in detail in Fig. 7b. The dark lines drawn above the fault trace approximate the stratigraphic boundary between Devonian platform carbonate rocks on the right and Devonian through Mississippian shales and argillaceous limestones on the left. (b) Detailed view toward the S, of structural disharmony within the toe region of the Mt. Burden thrust plate. The dark line adjacent to D represents the planar upper stratigraphic boundary of Middle Devonian dolostones; the black line within M–D outlines a succession of stacked recumbent folds within limestone and shale of the Devonian–Mississippian shale succession. This incompetent structural unit within the hanging-wall of the Mt. Burden thrust plate has deformed and shortened disharmonically with respect to the underlying more rigid dolostones (D).

shale succession forms a series of stacked recumbent isoclinal folds (Fig. 7b). Clearly, a
detachment exists between the shales and the
carbonates, and this detachment has served to
allow displacement on the underlying blind
thrust to be compensated, in part, by the fold
complex above the hanging-wall detachment.

Further evidence for the existence of large
blind thrusts is present along the northern limit
of the Robb Anticline: the thrust over which it
was displaced is clearly exposed along its
northern limit as illustrated in Fig. 8a, yet the
fault cannot be mapped southward along the
strike of the Anticline, as illustrated in Fig. 8b.

Knowing the geometric characteristics of
blind thrusts provides a more complete conceptual framework with which to interpret the
surface and subsurface geology of the northern
Rockies. Large surface anticlines of Lower and
Middle Palaeozoic carbonate rocks such as the
Burden and Redfern structures (Fig. 2) can be
interpreted as allochthonous thrust sheets that
have been displaced eastward several
kilometres at least. The fold and fault complexes at higher structural and stratigraphic
levels can be interpreted as large strain absor-
bers that compensate for the displacements on
blind thrusts at depth; and the amount of
bed-length shortening within the fold complex
at surface should equal the amount of displacement across blind thrusts at depth—an important consideration when preparing balanced
structural cross-sections using surface data
(Dahlstrom 1969, 1970; Douglas 1950, 1958).

The generalizations outlined above can now
be used to prepare structural interpretations of
deeper features. To follow, are descriptions of
two regional structure cross-sections (Fig. 9);
one drawn across the Laurier Anticlinorium
(termed the Laurier cross-section) where blind
thrusts can be documented from surface geological relationships, and another drawn across
the Tuchodi Anticline (termed the Tuchodi
cross-section), a much larger structure that has
the surface appearance of a broad upwarp. A
third section drawn across the Bernard Anticline is described in Thompson (1979).

Two representative
structure cross-sections

Laurier section

The Laurier section (Fig. 9) illustrates fold
styles typical of the Foothills subprovince, the
structural disharmony that exists across the
Devonian and Mississippian Besa River Shale

detachment zone, and the stacking of thrust
sheets on blind thrusts at the mountain front.

Foothills folds are box or chevron in character, and conform in most respects to fold styles
described by Faill (1969) from the Appalachian Plateau Province, and Laubscher
(1977) from the Jura. This fold style is especially well developed in Triassic and younger
strata but also typifies folds within the thick
Mississippian carbonate succession (Fig. 3) exposed along the W margin of the Foothills
subprovince. Some workers have interpreted
such fold styles as representing the product of
giant intersecting kink bands (e.g. Faill 1969).
This approach is useful in a purely geometric
sense to facilitate the balancing of bed length
shortening within a single fold because no
space problem is created by a decreasing
radius of curvature, as occurs within concentric
folds.

Deformation beneath the Foothills subprovince 'bottoms out' within the Besa River
Shale (D–M$_{sh}$). The underlying Middle Devonian carbonate succession is represented as an
essentially planar surface for two reasons: first,
beds at the bottoms of large synclines are near
the regional stratigraphic dip projected westward into the line of section from the Plains
region on the E, and second, the Headstone
Creek well, located on a large Foothills Anticline (Fig. 9), failed to intersect Middle Devonian strata despite having been terminated
substantially below the point where Middle
Devonian rocks should have been intersected
had they been intimately involved in the folding. This assumption of an undeformed Middle
Palaeozoic 'basement' beneath the Foothills
should not be accepted too literally (Thompson
1979); it is probably cut by thrusts and is likely
to be broadly folded, but the geometry and
space constraints imposed by the overlying
folded successions dictate that the scale and
intensity of deformation is substantially less
than that within the overlying rocks.

Middle Devonian and older rocks must become structurally involved in a major way
beneath the W margin of the Foothills subprovince because synclines at surface are raised
well above the regional stratigraphic gradient,
with the result that a large 'hole' is generated
between the 'undeformed' Middle Devonian
carbonates projected westward and Mississippian carbonate rocks at surface. Additional
evidence that a significant thrust repetition is
present within this interval can be observed
30 km northward along strike at Mount Bertha
(Fig. 2), where a slice of Middle Palaeozoic
carbonate rocks has overridden Besa River

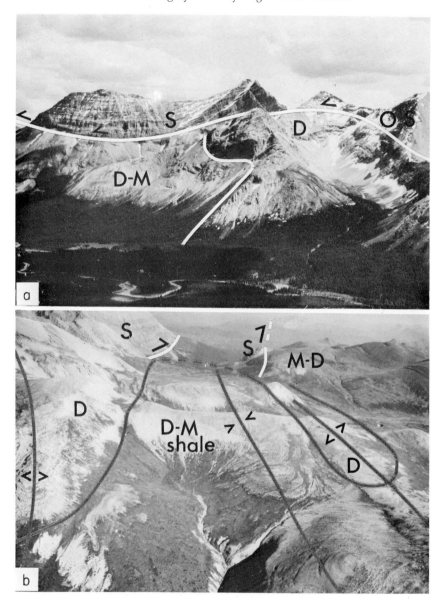

FIG. 8. (a) View toward the S of the up plunge limit of the Robb Anticline showing a thrust that places Ordovician and Silurian carbonate rocks (O, S) onto folded Middle Devonian dolostone (D) and Devonian–Mississippian shale (D–M); minimum lateral displacement is 5 km. (b) View from the S along the eastern flank of the Robb Anticline showing the abrupt termination of the thrust present in Fig. 8a 2 km S of that location. In the foreground are folds of Devonian dolostone (D) and Devonian–Mississippian shale (D–M) which appear unaffected by the major thrust immediately to the N; in the left foreground is the E dipping limb of the Robb Anticline which defines the mountain front. Without the more northerly up-plunge exposures, there would be little reason to suspect the allochthonous nature of the Robb Anticline.

Shales. The thrust cannot be traced laterally for any distance and it is interpreted here as a splay from a blind thrust.

The large volume of shale shown immediately in front of the Laurier Anticlinorium represents tectonically-thickened Besa River shale that has absorbed much of the displacement on the blind thrust over which the anticlinorium was displaced. An example of the style and disharmony of deformation within this interval of incompetent strata is illustrated in Fig. 10 (see also Fitzgerald 1965).

The Laurier Anticlinorium (Fig. 5) comprises a fold complex made up of fine-grained clastic facies that are equivalent in age to the Silurian and Devonian platform carbonate succession mapped to the N and S (Thompson 1976). The anticlinorium is thrust over the time-equivalent carbonate facies exposed within the southward plunging Robb Anticline necessitating that the major carbonate-to-shale facies transition of Silurian and Devonian age must occur within the thrust sheet that forms the Robb Anticline. It is speculated here that the position and geometry of the facies transition exerted an influence on the location of the footwall ramp over which the Laurier Anticlinorium was displaced and folded.

Structure W of the Laurier Anticlinorium consists of tightly folded, faulted and cleaved Upper Cambrian and Lower Ordovician shales and siltstone (€-O). This incompetent Cambro-Ordovician succession comprises an important detachment zone of regional extent. Like the Besa River Shale, it is a zone of structural disharmony between thrust faulted and folded Cambrian rocks below and thrust faulted middle Ordovician through Devonian carbonate rocks above.

Tuchodi section

The purpose of attempting a structural interpretation at the latitude of the Tuchodi section (Fig. 9) is to test the applicability of the blind thrust model as an alternative to the 'thick-skinned' interpretation of Taylor & Stott (1973). In their cross-sections, Taylor and Stott (op. cit.) show thrusts at surface which flatten down-dip into a regional detachment zone at the top of the Proterozoic sedimentary succession. Some of the fault displacement is then transferred onto steep W dipping (70–80°) contraction faults and onto curved convex-up contraction faults that presumably continue to steepen with depth to become subvertical basement controlled structures. The remainder of the displacement shown on faults above the regional detachment is unaccounted for within the underlying Proterozoic succession. The mountain front Tuchodi Anticline (Fig 2) is drawn as a simple upwarp, with no evidence of having undergone lateral W–E displacement, and folds within the adjacent

Fɪɢ 10. Disharmonic folds within argillaceous limestone and shales of Devonian and Mississippian age located adjacent (E) to the Mt. Burden Anticlinorium.

Foothills subprovince are portrayed as open concentric structures that affect the total Palaeozoic as well as the top of the Proterozoic stratigraphic assemblages. This geometric model is fundamentally different from the blind thrust model presented in the Laurier section (and in Thompson 1979) and I question that both 'thick- and thin-skinned' geometric solutions are compatible or even geologically plausible within the confined strike length distance between the Laurier and Tuchodi sections. Comparisons along strike reveal no changes in regional geological structural style that would indicate a fundamental change in the crustal processes that produced the surface structures.

Three important aspects of the Tuchodi section differ from the Laurier section. First, it was drawn with the built-in constraint of an uninvolved crystalline basement (Hudsonian) surface that dips gently westward; second, the dimensions of the Tuchodi Anticline are considerably larger than those of the Laurier Anticlinorium or Robb Anticline; and third, the mechanical character, age and thicknesses of stratigraphic assemblages that comprise the miogeoclinal prism are changed. The Upper Palaeozoic and Mesozic succession is thinner and less competent and lacks the thick Mississippian carbonate unit which separates the Besa River shale detachment zone below from Permian and Triassic shales above. The Lower and Middle Palaeozoic succession is much thinner and does not contain a thick Lower Ordovician shale detachment unit; and the Middle Proterozoic succession, which may or may not exist at the latitude of the Laurier section, is very thick and competent and has exerted an important influence on the structural style.

The depth to basement at the E limit of the Tuchodi section is estimated to be 5.4 km, and the westward dip of the basement surface is drawn to average 5°. These values are based on preliminary results from seismic reflection surveys in a region SE of the line of section (pers. comm. oil company geologists 1979). The depth and gradient estimates should be regarded as 'best guess' approximations that will undoubtedly be revised as the quality and quantity of seismic information improves.

The top of the Middle Palaeozoic carbonate succession (S–D) was projected into the line of cross-section from the undeformed Plains region to the E, and the regional slope maintained beneath the E portion of the Foothills subprovince to the position where thrust faulted Middle Devonian carbonate rocks are intersected above the regional dip by the Dome-Amoco Dunedin well. The thrust which cuts the Middle Devonian and older strata is interpreted as flattening into the detached and tectonically thickened succession of Upper Palaeozoic and Mesozoic shales.

The Tuchodi Anticline was produced by displacing and folding a thick coherent sheet of Proterozoic rocks over a large step on a major blind thrust. The remainder of the section was drawn by projecting surface faults downward into a major detachment at the top of the crystalline basement surface, making sure that bed length shortening was balanced from one stratigraphic level to another.

The essential surface geological constraints discussed by Taylor & Stott (1973) are satisfied by the cross-section. The Tuchodi Anticline appears as a broad surface fold; there is a detachment at the top of the Proterozoic sedimentary succession, and there is structural disharmony between the Rocky Mountains and Foothills structural subprovinces. In addition, the displacement shown at surface is accounted for at all stratigraphic levels down to basement, and there is no necessity to translate vertical uplift at depth into horizontal shortening at surface.

The Tuchodi section is geometrically possible only if the amount of displacement on the blind thrusts shown beneath the Foothills subprovince is compensated by an equal amount of bed length shortening within the disharmonically folded Upper Palaeozoic and Mesozoic rocks within the Foothills subprovince. A major disparity in values would indicate that one or more of the initial assumptions was incorrect. To check for balanced shortening, the cross-sectional area of deformed Upper Palaeozoic through Triassic (uP–T) strata was measured and compared with that of an undeformed strip of equal length (see upper right of Fig. 9). The difference in areas represents the additional amount of rock added to the cross-section as a result of folding and faulting during deformation. This excess area, if cast in terms of a normal stratigraphic thickness, has a length equal to the excess bed length due to shortening. In the Tuchodi section, it amounts to 21 km of Foothills shortening and agrees very well with the 19 km of displacement interpreted on the blind thrusts. It should be stressed that the computation was made after the section was completed and did not influence the initial assumptions used in any way.

Palinspastic restorations

The Laurier and Tuchodi cross-sections were partially restored to their original undeformed lengths (Fig. 9) by measuring along competent marker units, around folds and between faults. The thrust fault trajectories were plotted and keyed by number to faults in the structure sections to show the relative positions of ramps or steps, prior to eastward translation. The upward limit of preserved strata (i.e. the stretched-out surface topography) is also plotted to illustrate the relative effects of individual structures on the quantity of material removed by erosion.

Total shortening across Tuchodi section is 45 km: 20 km across the Foothills subprovince (including the kinematically-linked blind thrusts at depth), and 25 km on structures W of the Tuchodi anticline.

The Laurier section contains 28 km of shortening across the Foothills subprovince. Of this amount, 13 km occurs in Foothills folds W to the axis of the very large box syncline, and this has been balanced by placing an equal amount of displacement on blind thrust no. 1; the remaining 15 km is a minimum estimate of displacement on the blind thrusts at the mountain front.

Comparison of these net supracrustal shortening values, with values across similar segments of the southern Rockies, demonstrates a decrease in the amount of convergence between S and N. The Foothills subprovince together with the first Front Range Thrust (e.g. McConnell thrust) along the Bow Valley transect of the southern Rocky Mountains, has been shortened by 70 km. If this is extended westward to include the remainder of the Front Ranges, shortening exceeds 100 km (Bally *et al.* 1966; Price & Mountjoy 1970).

Despite the difference in amounts of net convergence, the basic structural style of the northern Rocky Mountains is consistent with that shown in cross-sections of the southern Rockies (e.g. Price, this volume; Price & Mountjoy, 1970; Bally *et al.* 1966; Keating 1966). The top of the crystalline basement surface can be interpreted as an undeformed passive planar element, at least to the western limits of the Laurier and Tuchodi sections. Thrust faults cut up stratigraphically from W to E and place older strata onto younger strata. Fault trajectories follow flat bedding glide zones except where they step or ramp upward from a lower to a higher glide zone, and fault displacements are on the scale of kilometres.

A comparison with the southern Rocky Mountains

The differences in structural style between the northern and southern Rocky Mountains reflect a change in the overall mechanical character of the layered rock sequence. In the N there is a greater proportion of incompetent, relative to competent, rock units that provided greater potential for the formation of décollement zones as well as structural disharmony between different stratigraphic levels. However, this explanation is incomplete because it fails to account for the reduction in supracrustal shortening from S to N, the narrower width of the northern Rockies, and the smaller volume of late Cretaceous and early Tertiary foredeep deposits adjacent to it. Changes northward in the lithostratigraphic character of the miogeocline should not have affected the width of the deformed belt or the amount of supracrustal shortening contained within it—only the surface or geometric expression of that shortening.

Comparison of the northern with the southern Rocky Mountains requires first that each belt be placed within a common frame of reference. In Fig. 11 (reproduced from Thompson 1979) the positions of individual structural subprovinces are plotted onto a restored cross-section of the miogeocline for both the northern and southern Rocky Mountains. Each cross-section is then compared graphically using the hinge lines as a common reference datum.

Three interdependent observations are apparent: (1) Deformation in the N did not progress as far craton-ward as in the S. A 20 km width (at least) of cratonic and clastic wedge deposits is deformed in the southern cross-section but remains undeformed in the northern cross-section: (2) the northern Rocky Mountains structural subprovince occupies a cross-section stratigraphic position within the miogeocline equivalent to the Main Ranges (and Western Ranges, not shown in Fig. 11) structural subprovince in the S; and (3) in the N there is no analogue for the closely spaced imbricated sheets of cratonic Palaeozoic carbonate rocks that characterize the southern Rockies Front Ranges structural subprovince because platform carbonate rocks occupying an equivalent cross-section position in the N remain essentially undeformed.

The E limit of deformation in each cross-section (Fig. 11) may be regarded as the preserved external limit of a strain front that passed progressively from W to E through the miogeocline. The narrower width and decreased amount of foreshortening in the N can be related directly to the observation that a narrower width of the sedimentary prism was deformed. If strain had persisted further eastward in the N, the platform carbonate succession that currently forms a basement to

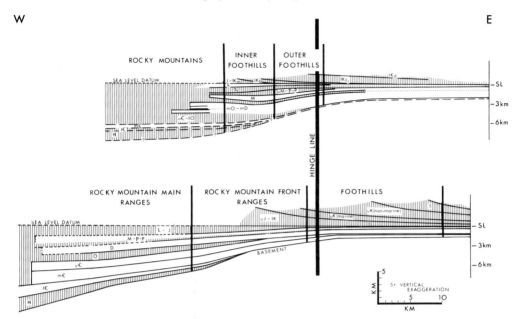

Fig. 11. A comparison of palinspastic reconstructions of stratigraphic sections across the miogeocline for the northern Rockies region near the Laurier section (above) and the southern Rockies (below; adapted from Price & Mountjoy 1970, Figs 2–3). The vertical line pattern is drawn across incompetent units, more rigid quartzites and carbonates are left open. The limits of structural subprovinces are indicated by solid vertical lines. The hinge line shown represents the approximate locus of accelerated thickening of the Lower and Middle Palaeozoic carbonate successions in each section. (Reproduced from Thompson 1979 with permission from the Canadian Journal of Earth Sciences.)

Foothills folds, would have become imbricated and uplifted as deeper décollement surfaces were extended eastward, resulting with a thrust-faulted structural subprovince similar in character to the Front Ranges of the southern Rocky Mountains. The thickness and lateral extent of the young portion of the adjacent clastic wedge deposits would also have been affected. Increased loading of the lithosphere by thrust sheets during late Cretaceous and early Tertiary time would have caused a deepening and enlargement of the adjacent foredeep basin (Price & Mountjoy 1970) and increased the potential for accumulation of a thicker more extensive clastic wedge sequence of that age. Instead, the northern Canadian Rocky Mountains represent a less complete stage in structural development of the foreland belt, a stage that preceded development of a Front Ranges-type structural domain. This does not mean that deformation ended sooner. On the contrary, Lower Cretaceous foredeep deposits form a major component of the Foothills structural subprovince (Stott 1975) which was deformed in late Cretaceous (and early Tertiary?) time, synchronous with the major late Cretaceous–early Tertiary tectonic

pulse to the S. However, the intensity of that pulse decreased northward.

It is not surprising then that a crude symmetry exists between the northern Rocky Mountains structural subprovince and the more internal zones of the southern Rockies. Each contains a large anticlinorium of Middle Proterozoic (Helikian) rocks—the Muskwa Anticlinorium in the N and the Purcell Anticlinorium in the S (see Price, this volume). Along their W margins is a thick, penetratively deformed and metamorphosed clastic sequence of Upper Proterozoic (Hadrynian) age, and along the E border of each is a cleaved succession of shales, siltstones and argillaceous limestones of Lower Palaeozoic age. The anticlinoria are cut by thrusts and high-angle faults that displace coherent rock slices, whereas the surrounding less competent assemblages are more intricately folded and faulted.

Conclusions

The northern Canadian Rocky Mountains are a thin-skinned detachment type structural domain that is fundamentally consistent with structural patterns documented for the southern part of the Rocky Mountain belt. Blind thrusts are an important structural element that disguise the presence of large allochthonous thrust sheets. The amount of supracrustal shortening is less within the northern Rockies and reflects the less intense nature of orogenic activity, especially during the late Cretaceous and early Tertiary.

ACKNOWLEDGMENTS This paper draws from important regional studies by Irish (1970), Taylor & Stott (1973), and Taylor (1979). My interpretation of their data does not necessarily reflect or support their views and sole responsibility for any errors of fact rest with me. I benefited from the comments of D. Cook and A. Okulitch who critically read the manuscript. This synthesis is a product of continuing regional geological studies of the northern Canadian Rocky Mountains by the Geological Survey of Canada. The prompt and efficient work of typist Claudia Thompson is appreciated.

References

BALLY, A. W., GORDY, P. L. & STEWART, G. A. 1966. Structure, seismic data, and orogenic evolution of southern Canadian Rocky Mountains. *Bull. Can. Pet. Geol.* **14**, 337–81.

CECILE, M. P. & NORFORD, B. S. 1979. Basin to platform transition, Lower Paleozoic strata of Ware and Trutch map areas, Northeastern British Columbia. *Pap. geol. Surv. Can.* **79–1A**, 219–26.

DAHLSTROM, C. D. A. 1969. Balanced cross sections. *Can. J. Earth Sci.* **6**, 743–57.

—— 1970. Structural geology in the eastern margin of the Canadian Rocky Mountains. *Bull. Can. Pet. Geol.* **18**, 332–402.

DOUGLAS, R. J. W. 1950. Callum Creek, Langford Creek, and Gap Map-areas, Alberta. *Mem. geol. Surv. Can.* **225**, 124.

—— 1958. Mount Head Map-area, Alberta. *Mem. geol. Surv. Can.* **291**, 241 p.

FAILL, R. T. 1969. Kink band structures in the Valley and Ridge Province, Central Pennsylvania. *Bull. geol. Soc. Am.* **80**, 2539–50.

FITZGERALD, E. L. 1968. Structure of British Columbia Foothills, Canada. *Bull. Am. Assoc. Petrol. Geol.* **52**, 641–64.

—— & BRAUN, L. T. 1965. Disharmonic folds in Besa River Formation, Northeastern British Columbia, Canada. *Bull. Alberta Soc. Petrol. Geol.* **49**, 418–32.

IRISH, E. W. J. 1970. Halfway River Map-area, British Columbia. *Pap. geol. Surv. Can.* **69,-11**, 154 p.

KEATING, L. F. 1966. Exploration in the Canadian Rockies and Foothills. *Can. J. Earth Sci.* **3**, 713–23.

LAUBSCHER, H. P. 1977. Fold development in the Jura. *Tectonophysics*, **37**, 337–62.

NORTH, F. K. & HENDERSON. G. G. L. 1954. Summary of the geology of the southern Rocky Mountains of Canada. *Alberta Soc. Petrol. Geol. Guidebook, 4th Annual Field Conference*, 15–81.

PRICE, R. A. & MOUNTJOY, E. W. 1970. Geologic structure of the Canadian Rocky Mountains between Bow and Athabasca Rivers, a progress report. *In:* WHEELER, J. O. (ed). *Structure of the Southern Canadian Cordillera.* Spec. pap. geol. Assoc. Can. **6**, 7–39.

STOTT, D. F. 1975. The Cretaceous System in Noreastern British Columbia, *In:* CALDWELL W. G. E. (ed). *Cretaceous System in the Western Interior of North America.* Spec. pap. geol. Assoc. Can. **13**, 441–67.

—— & TAYLOR, G. C. 1972. Stratigraphy and structure, Rocky Mountains and Foothills of west-central Alberta and northeastern British Columbia. *24th Int. geol. Cong., Montreal, Guidebook Field Excursion*, **A10**.

TAYLOR, G. C. 1972. The influence of pre-Laramide tectonics on Rocky Mountain structures. *Geol. Assoc. Can. Cordilleran Section, Prog. & Abs.* 36–7.

—— 1979 Trutch (94G) and Ware East Half (94F, E 1/2) Map-areas, Northeastern British Columbia. *Geol. Surv. Can. Open File Report*, **606**.

——, CECILE, M. P., JEFFERSON, C. W. & NORFORD, B. S. 1979. Stratigraphy of Ware (East Half) Map-area, Northeastern British Columbia. *Pap. geol. Surv. Can.* **79–1A**, 227–31.

—— & STOTT, D. F. 1973. Tuchodi Lakes Map-area, British Columbia. *Mem. geol. Surv. Can.* **373**, 37 p.

THOMPSON, R. I. 1976. Some aspects of stratigraphy and structure in the Halfway River map-area (94B), British Columbia. *Pap. geol. Surv. Can.* **76–1A**, 471–77.

—— 1978. Geological maps and sections of Halfway River Map-area, British Columbia (94B). *Geol. Surv. Can., Open File Report*, **536**.

—— 1979. A structural interpretation across part of the northern Rocky Mountains, British Columbia, Canada. *Can. J. Earth Sci.* **16**, 1228–41.

R. I. THOMPSON, Geological Survey of Canada, 100 W Pender St., Vancouver, Canada

Metamorphic complex of SE Canadian Cordillera and relationship to foreland thrusting

R. L. Brown

SUMMARY: The Rocky Mountain miogeocline thickens westward into a basin that was established during the Proterozoic. The western margin of the basin is flanked by a platform that was developed upon Aphebian continental crust. These Aphebian rocks comprise the basement gneisses of the Shuswap Complex that have telescoped onto the cratonic margin of North America. The floor of the basin is assumed to have been transitional or oceanic crust that was subducted westward beneath the Aphebian continental crust of the Shuswap Complex.

Deformation of the platform and western margin of the basin was initiated in the Palaeozoic and culminated in the Jurassic. Development of easterly overturned folds in the basin and thrust faults along its eastern margin occurred during the final stages of ductile shortening of the basin. Thrust faults developed in the western margin of the miogeocline and deformation migrated eastward as the Shuswap Complex encroached upon the cratonic margin of the North American plate.

Eastward displacements of allochthonous cover rocks of the Shuswap Complex are post metamorphic events that are most likely interlocked with thrust faulting in the western margin of the Rocky Mountain miogeocline. Westward underthrusting of the basement of the miogeocline probably ceased by late Eocene and a regime of NE–SW extension was established. Most recent movements of allochthonous cover rocks and late doming of the metamorphic complex are related to this period of Tertiary extension.

The structural geometry of the Rocky Mountain Thrust and Fold Belt in SW Canada (Figs 1 & 2) has been studied extensively and cross sections such as those drawn by Bally *et al.* (1966) and Price & Mountjoy (1970) are accepted as textbook examples of décollement thrusting of a miogeoclinal succession above rigid cratonic basement. The western limit of the décollement is not yet clear. It has been suggested that some thrust faults may root in basement rocks beneath the Main Ranges E of the Rocky Mountain Trench (Campbell 1970, 1973; Eisbacher *et al.* 1974).

Models put forward to account for the deformation (Bally *et al.* 1966; Price & Mountjoy 1970; Elliott 1976; Chapple 1978; Brown 1978) are not well constrained, since available data on the nature of the root zone of the décollement has been limited and ambiguous.

A clear understanding of the relationship to plate boundary interaction is yet to be established. No simple model of subduction at a major plate boundary can be entertained since the Rocky Mountain Belt evolved within the accreted margin of the North American plate. Active subduction of the Pacific plate beneath North America is considered to have been situated some 500 km W of the Rockies adjacent to the present edge of the continent during the main eposide of décollement thrusting (Monger *et al.* 1972; Monger & Price 1979).

On the scale of major plate boundaries, the Rocky Mountain Belt is an intraplate structure that must be viewed in terms of its interaction with the metamorphic complex and the accreted arc and oceanic terranes that lie against its western extremity.

The presence of mantled gneiss domes (Reesor 1965, 1970; Reesor & Moore 1971; Wheeler & Gabrielse 1972) together with extensive terranes with gently dipping foliation, suggested to Price & Mountjoy (1970) and Price (1973) that gravitational upwelling and lateral spreading of the metamorphic complex could have caused décollement thrusting in the Rocky Mountain Belt. Mapping and analysis of approximately 8000 km² of metamorphic terrane in the Selkirk and Monashee Mountains (Figs 1 & 2) by the author and students has led to a different interpretation (Brown & Tippett 1978; Brown 1978). It has been found that a model of lithosphere convergence and underthrusting best explains the observational data. In our view the metamorphic complex is structurally the western extremity of the Rocky Mountain Thrust and Fold Belt. Of significance is the fact that it experienced a protracted history of deformation and metamorphism that predates thrusting in the Rocky Mountain Belt. This terrane was carried northeastward together with the telescoped miogeoclinal wedge. The metamorphic com-

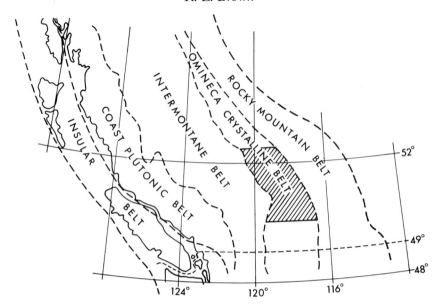

FIG. 1. Structural Belts of the Canadian Cordillera. Diagonal lines drawn over location of Shuswap Metamorphic Complex and limits of study area.

plex was not the cause of the Foreland Thrust and Fold Belt, it was an integral part of it.

The aim of this paper is to demonstrate that the Rocky Mountain miogeocline extended westward into a marine basin, and that a protracted history of deformation and eventual collapse of the basin occurred before initiation of thrust faulting and associated folding in the Rocky Mountain Foreland. Thrust faulting occurred when a terrane underlain by Aphebian continental crust encroached upon, and was underthrust by, the North American cratonic basement of the Rocky Mountain Foreland. The approach is to combine new and published geological data to formulate a structural history of the region. This history is then interpreted to establish a kinematic model.

Structural elements of the Metamorphic Complex

W of the Rocky Mountain Trench, between latitudes 50 N and 53 N, the Omineca Crystalline Belt (Douglas et al. 1976) includes the Selkirk Mountains, Kootenay Arc, and Monashee Mountains (Fig. 2). The terrane of high grade metamorphic rocks exposed in the Monashee Mountains has generally been termed the 'Shuswap Metamorphic Complex' (Jones 1959; Reesor 1970); within this terrane are exposed the gneiss of Frenchman Cap,

Thor–Odin, Pinnacles (Fig. 2), and continuing southward, Valhalla in southern British Columbia and Okanogan Dome in northern Washington. These are part of a sinuous belt of some 25 domes that have been recognized in the North American Cordillera and termed 'Metamorphic Core Complexes' (Coney 1973, 1976, 1978; Crittenden et al. 1978).

Selkirk Mountains and Kootenay Arc are also metamorphic terranes and are included here under the umbrella of 'Metamorphic Complex'. N of Frenchman Cap and within the Metamorphic Complex is also exposed the Malton tectonic slice (Fig. 2; see Campbell 1968; Giovanella 1968; Price & Mountjoy 1970; Ghent et al. 1977) and in this paper it will be considered tectonically related to the dome terrane.

The metamorphic complex in southeastern British Columbia is readily discussed by reference to Shuswap Basement, Autochthonous Cover, and Allochthonous Cover.

Shuswap basement

Samples of gneissic rock within the core of Frenchman Cap have been collected by the author, and have been dated by Armstrong (1979); Rb/Sr whole rock isochrons give an Aphebian age of 2.1 Ga. Gneissic rocks in Thor-Odin dome (Reesor & Moore 1971) have yielded a Rb/Sr whole rock isochron indicative of an age of approximately 3 Ga (Dun-

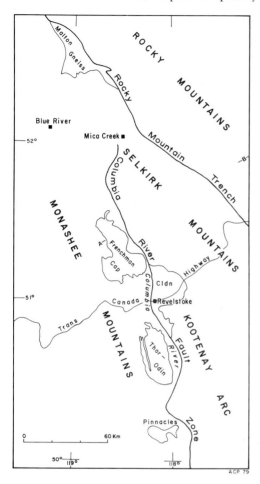

FIG. 2. Location of structural and physiographic features. A–B locates cross section of Fig. 5.

can 1978). Orthogneiss within Thor-Odin has yielded a zircon age of 1.9 Ga (Wanless & Reesor 1975). The Malton gneiss has also yielded old dates (Chamberlain *et al.* 1978) that are indicative of the presence of early Proterozoic or older rocks. The wide distribution of these ages leaves little room to doubt that the metamorphic complex is underlain by an extensive terrane that is at least 2 billion years old.

The basement of Frenchman Cap and Thor-Odin is exposed over an area of approximately 1600 km², and recent work by Read (1980) and Brown (1980) has shown that basement gneisses are countinuous between the domes. An Aphebian age is compatible with the inferred age of cratonic rocks that underlie the

Foreland to the E of the Rocky Mountain Trench, and a conservative view suggests that the Shuswap basement terrane is part of the disrupted western edge of the North American craton.

Autochthonous cover

Aphebian gneisses of Frenchman Cap dome are overlain by an autochthonous cover of 1–3 km of shallow marine clastics and carbonates (Brown & Psutka 1979). Basal quartzite rests with apparent conformity upon the basement gneisses and has been traced around the flanks of the dome (Brown & Psutka 1979; Hoy & McMillan 1979; Brown 1980). The quartzite is clearly 'glued' to the basement. It's thickness varies from a few metres up to as much as 100 m, and at least some of this variation must be attributed to primary deposition rather than deformation.

The platform rocks are at amphibolite grade, but primary features are locally preserved. Cross bedding is well displayed in quartzite at the northern end of Frenchman Cap and is observed infrequently elsewhere. Thin (~ 10 m) carbonate and quartzite beds have been traced for tens of km. Pelitic rocks on the other hand are interdigitated with calcsilicates both above and below the continuous horizons attesting to rapid lateral facies changes. The autochthonous succession extends southwards and outcrops about the domes of Thor-Odin, Pinnacles and Valhalla (Reesor 1965; Reesor & Froese 1969; Reesor & Moore 1971; Read 1979; Brown & Read 1979*b*; Read 1980). The age of these cover rocks is yet to be determined; the presence of quartzites and other platform sediments has led some workers to propose correlation with Cambrian rocks exposed in the miogeocline to the E (Wheeler *et al.* 1972; Reesor 1970; Hoy & McMillan 1979), however, Brown & Psutka (1979) and Brown & Read (1979*b*) have argued, on structural grounds, for an early Proterozoic (Belt-Purcell) age.

Whether the cover rocks turn out to be Proterozoic or Lower Palaeozoic it is important to recognize that a succession of shallow marine platform sediments has been deposited upon an Aphebian or older sialic basement that outcrops W of the Rocky Mountain Foreland.

Allochthonous cover

N of the Frenchman Cap dome the autochthonous cover dips beneath Proterozoic rocks that are tentatively correlated with strata of the Kaza Group as mapped farther N by Campbell (1968). The platform succession of quartzites and calcareous rocks is overlain with sharp contact by a thick succession of pelitic and amphibolitic rocks that are extensively invaded by concordant and discordant pegmatite. At this northern locality there is an abrupt change from coexisting kyanite and sillimanite in pelitic layers of the autochthonous rocks to silliminate grade migmatites. Fault breccia and gouge occur locally and there is no doubt that the contact is tectonic. Mapping by Wheeler (1965), Brown & Psutka (1979) and Brown (1980) indicates that these allochthonous cover rocks extend southward W of Frenchman Cap and occur as fault slices along the eastern flank of the Columbia River fault zone (Fig. 3). Read (1979) has recognized outliers of allochthonous rocks to the S in the Pinnacle Peaks area (Fig. 2) demonstrating that a detachment zone wraps about autochthonous cover at the southern end of the metamorphic complex.

Within the Columbia River Valley the dislocation is marked by a cataclastic zone with average thickness of approximately 1 km; cataclastic foliation dips gently (~25°) generally E–NE and elongation lineations plunge approximately down the dip. The zone is cut by numerous anastomosing shear zones in which the cataclastic foliation is disrupted and commonly reduced to a clay gouge. The shear zones are generally nearly parallel to the preexisting foliation; slickensides, fibrous calcite and quartz, together with cleavage developed within the clay gouge zones give clear evidence of normal to oblique normal displacement. The mylonitic foliation developed at at least greenschist grade; its disruption and the generation of clay gouge is a younger event. The Columbia River fault zone has been traced from S of Mica Dam some 200 km southward (Fig. 1; Brown & Read 1979b; Read 1979). The northern extremity of the fault does not continue in the Columbia River Valley as far as Mica Dam since metamorphic isograds are not disrupted at this point and stratigraphic markers can be extrapolated NW out of the Selkirk terrane into Monashee terrane. (Campbell 1968; Ghent *et al.* 1977). Fig. 3 illustrates relationships between the early décollement and younger movement on the Columbia River Fault. The décollement envelopes the dome terrane, but the younger fault continues northeastward.

Strata of the Selkirk Mountains and Kootenay Arc lie above the hanging wall of the Columbia River fault and have been transported eastward relative to the Shuswap basement rocks exposed in the domes.

Work on the history of this complex fault zone is in progress, but the available information requires that the Shuswap basement with its 'glued' platform cover be detached from the overlying strata that now mainly outcrop to the E in the Selkirk Mountains and Kootenay Arc. The Shuswap 'domes' are simply part of the footwall terrane that have been exposed as structural windows. Documented displacement occurred after the Middle Jurassic regional metamorphism and may have been active as recently as Eocene; eastward dip-slip displacement exceeds 15 km (Read 1979; Brown & Read 1979b; Brown & Psutka 1979), but an upper limit of displacement has yet to be determined.

The Clachnacudainn allochthon (Fig. 3) is a tectonic slice within the allochthonous rocks that was emplaced before the recent movements on the Columbia River fault.

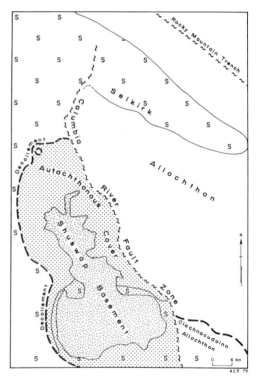

FIG. 3. Tectonic elements in the vicinity of Frenchman Cap Dome. S indicates terrain where metamorphic grade is at or above the first sillimanite isograd. Metamorphic boundary in SW corner from McMillan (1970). See text for further explanation.

Tectonic history

Proterozoic–Palaeozoic

It has been pointed out that shallow marine platform sediments of probable Precambrian age were deposited upon Aphebian gneisses that outcrop as domes within the Omineca Crystalline Belt. E of the Rocky Mountain Trench Proterozoic clastic rocks rest with presumed décollement upon cratonic basement gneisses of the North American plate (Price & Mountjoy 1970). The Proterozoic cover forms a westward thickening wedge that is recognized in the Selkirk Mountains and elsewhere W of the Trench despite the telescoping effects of deformation (Campbell *et al.* 1973; Brown *et al.* 1978). These distal shelf to slope sediments are stratigraphically overlain by Upper Proterozoic–Cambrian shallow marine clastics. It appears that a sedimentary basin lay between the western platform and the distal edge of the Rocky Mountain miogeocline. This basin herein called the Selkirk-Kootenay Basin, was filled with over 10 km of Proterozoic sediments and volcanics, and was then overlapped by a westerly prograding wedge of Cambrian shallow marine clastics (Wheeler 1965; Wheeler & Gabrielse 1972; Brown *et al.* 1978).

The platform was covered by at least 15 km of strata and locally intruded by granitic plutons prior to metamorphism and deformation in Middle Jurassic time. It may have been a positive terrane during the early Palaeozoic, and could have been the source for volcanics and clastic sediments (Lardeau Group) shed into the basin to the E, but more work is required to test this suggestion.

Mineral assemblages in the basement and cover rocks of the Shuswap Terrane imply pressures of at least 5 kb during the peak of metamorphism (cf. Ghent *et al.* 1977). The nature of this cover is unknown, but most likely included Palaeozoic and Mesozoic volcanic rocks. In this light it is reasonable to speculate that the Shuswap Metamorphic Complex may have been the floor of an island arc that was active in late Palaeozoic and Mesozoic time.

The basement that was originally beneath the Selkirk-Kootenay Basin is unknown, but was probably transitional or oceanic rather than continental. Amphibolite dykes and sills occur extensively in the lower part of the Proterozoic Horse Thief Creek Group (Brown *et al.* 1978), and ultramafic pods and lenses have

also been noted (Wheeler 1965; Franzen 1974). Within the Basin in the Selkirk Mountains, the Cambrian Hamill Group is composed of shallow marine clastics that are locally interdigitated with tholeiitic basalt flows (Brown *et al.* 1978; Lane 1977). The presence of Lower Jurassic calc-alkaline volcanics (Rossland Group) in the southern part of the Basin in the Kootenay Arc is interesting in this regard. Beddoe-Stephens & Lambert (1978) have suggested that the petrochemistry of these rocks implies an oceanic origin possibly in a small back-arc basin.

Seismic refraction data (Chandra & Cumming 1972; Cumming 1977; Mereu *et al.* 1977; Spence *et al.* 1977) and gravity data (Stacey 1973) indicate that the crust beneath the Omineca Crystalline Belt is thinner than beneath the Rocky Mountain Belt. These observations have led Monger & Price (1979) to suggest that the present edge of the North American Craton coincides with this boundary. Also if one accepts that the Rocky Mountain Thrust and Fold Belt was telescoped above an essentially undeformed basement, it follows that, relative to the cover of the miogeocline, the edge of the craton was initially E of its present position. The logic of this argument when carried W of the Rocky Mountain Trench supports the contention that the Kootenay-Selkirk Basin was originally underlain by transitional or oceanic crust.

The terrain W of the Shuswap Metamorphic Complex is presumed to have been oceanic crust that developed by rifting and sea floor spreading in the mid-Proterozoic (Monger *et al.* 1972; Stewart 1972; Burchfiel & Davis 1972, 1975; Monger & Price 1979).

There is evidence of tectonic activity in the Proterozoic (Racklan–East Kootenay orogenies), Ordovician (see Okulitch 1979) and Devonian to early Mississippian (Caribooan or Antler orogeny), but very little is known about the kinematic history of these events at this latitude in the orogen. The earliest deformation that has been recognized in the Selkirk-Kootenay terranes is known to have occurred before Middle Mississippian (Read & Wheeler 1975; Read 1975, 1976) and may probably be attributed to Caribooan orogenic events. The evidence for deformation in the Kootenay Arc consists of the presence of disoriented foliation in clasts of the Mississippian Milford Group. The foliation is not observed in the matrix and a few clasts contain folds that are truncated at the clast boundaries. Read (1975) considers early isoclinal folds observed in Palaeozoic rocks below the unconformity to be pre-

Milford in age. Large nappes may have developed at this time along the western flank of Selkirk-Kootenay terrane, but as yet there is insufficient evidence to allow detailed kinematic models to be constructed.

Mesozoic

The southern Canadian Cordillera W of the cratonic margin of North America is a composite terrane consisting of both accreted allochthonous and autochthonous elements (Monger *et al.* 1972; Monger 1977; Davis *et al.* 1978; Irving *et al.* in press). The terrain W of the Shuswap Complex consists of two major tectonic blocks of exotic origin that are thought to have been amalgamated in the late Jurassic or early Cretaceous at a latitude about 13° S of their present position. The blocks were translated northwards, and arrived at their present position relative to cratonic North America between latest Cretaceous and Oligocene time (Irving *et al.* in press).

The Omineca terrane, (Shuswap Complex and Kootenay-Selkirk Basin) was extensively deformed and metamorphosed in the Middle Jurassic; polyphase deformation associated with regional metamorphism occurred across the length and breadth of the terrane. Folds that developed before and during the peak of metamorphism were primarily overturned toward the W; easterly overturned structures developed after the peak of metamorphism and interference of these superimposed structures gave rise to a large fan structure in the Selkirk terrane (Brown & Tippett 1978; Brown 1978). Granitic plutons were emplaced, some truncate the pre-metamorphic structure and are deformed by late to post-metamorphic folding. Recent Rb/Sr dating of post-tectonic intrusive events in this part of the Omineca terrane supply unambiguous evidence for termination of regional ductile deformation by the beginning of the late Jurassic (Duncan *et al.* 1979).

In Selkirk terrane in the vicinity of the Rocky Mountain Trench, late metamorphic to post metamorphic folds are overturned toward the NE and stacked in the hanging-wall of the Purcell thrust (Fig. 5c); it has been argued that these structures are coeval with initiation of thrust faulting in the western margin of the Rocky Mountain Foreland (Brown 1978).

The Shuswap basement terrane and the Selkirk-Kootenay Basin appear to have been telescoped against the Rocky Mountain Foreland in the Middle Jurassic. The terrane that lay to the W of the Shuswap at this time is a mystery; if preserved it presumably might be found in northern British Columbia.

Cenozoic

During Middle Jurassic synmetamorphic deformation, folds overturned toward the W developed penetrative axial surface foliation. This easterly dipping foliation was reactivated after the metamorphic peak and probably after emplacement of early to mid-Cretaceous plutons. Granitic plutons N of Revelstoke are involved in the cataclastic zone of the Columbia River fault; one of these plutons has been dated by the Geological Survey of Canada as early to mid-Cretaceous (Okulitch & Woodsworth, open file 481). This late development of cataclastic fabrics occurred during detachment of the allochthonous cover and its eastward displacement relative to the Shuswap basement.

K/Ar ages on late Jurassic plutonic rocks point to reheating at various times up to the Eocene (Duncan *et al.* 1979). Work by Parrish (1976) in the Wolverine Complex of the Omineca Belt (300 km NW of Frenchman Cap) indicates initial uplift and cooling in late Jurassic to early Cretaceous with renewed uplift associated with an early Tertiary thermal event. These results imply that uplift of the Omineca Belt and displacement along the Columbia River fault zone were coeval and occurred from late Jurassic–Eocene Time.

More work is required to be certain of relationships between movement on the Columbia River fault and thrust faulting in the Rocky Mountain Belt, but it is tentatively proposed that the Columbia River fault flattens eastward and is mechanically interlocked with the system of thrust faults that outcrop in the vicinity of the Rocky Mountain Trench. However, it is important to recognize that thrust faulting in the Rocky Mountains was probably initiated at the time of late to post metamorphic folding in the Selkirk-Kootenay terrane, and that development of cataclastic fabrics and associated displacement along the Columbia River fault appears to be younger than these events; major thrusting in the Rockies started after the Middle Jurassic peak of metamorphism (Craw 1978; Brown 1978) and before deposition of late Jurassic clastics in the Rocky Mountain Foredeep (Price & Mountjoy 1970).

High angle normal faults occur within the metamorphic complex and Rocky Mountain Belt (Price 1965; Bally *et al.* 1966; Leech 1967; Wheeler *et al.* 1972; Brown & Tippett 1978). Some of these faults have been documented to have been active in Upper Eocene to younger times (Price 1965).

Relationship of metamorphic complex to foreland thrusting

A comprehensive analysis of the tectonic evolution of the Southern Canadian Cordillera will not be attempted here; the objective is to establish the kinematic relationship between events in the Metamorphic Complex and the Rocky Mountain Thrust and Fold Belt. For recent reviews of the northern Cordillera the reader is referred to Monger *et al.* (1972), Davis *et al.* (1978), and Monger & Price (1979).

The first major deformation (phase 1) that is recognized in the region is thought to be Palaeozoic, and most likely Devonian. Nappe formation and plutonism affected the Shuswap terrane and western margin of the Selkirk-Kootenay Basin, but does not appear to have involved the Rocky Mountains to the E. The direction of nappe emplacement on a regional scale remains unclear but contrary to an earlier suggestion (Brown & Tippett 1978) their spatial distribution and present westward facing and sense of overturning in the Selkirk Mountains (Brown & Read 1979*a*) implies movement from E to W (see also Ghent *et al.* 1977; Hoy 1977).

Devonian–Mississippian (Antler) Orogeny is well documented to the S in Nevada where the Roberts Mountains thrust belt attests to extensive telescoping and displacement of an assemblage of oceanic sedimentary and volcanic rocks eastward onto the shelf assemblages of the continental margin (Burchfiel & Davis 1972, 1975), but its significance in the Canadian Cordillera is not clear (see Monger & Price, 1969). Devonian plutonism is recognized in the Omineca terrane (Okulitch *et al.* 1975), and Read (1975, 1976) has argued convincingly for a pre-Middle-Mississippian age for phase 1 nappes in the Kootenay terrane.

It is suggested that these early nappes in the Omineca Belt are related to a Palaeozoic period of plate convergence, and that subduction of oceanic crust to the W beneath the Omineca terrane caused plutonism and initiated collapse of the western margin of the Selkirk-Kootenay Basin with probable nappe displacement from the Basin westward across the Shuswap basement terrane (Fig. 4b).

The early nappes were refolded by Middle Jurassic deformation that developed in the Selkirk-Kootenay Basin. Westerly overturned

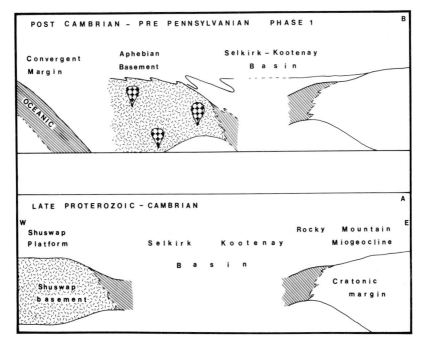

FIG. 4. Early tectonic setting of the region. Diagrams are schematic and not to scale. Tear drops in (b) refer to post Cambrian–pre Pennsylvanian plutonism. See text for further explanation.

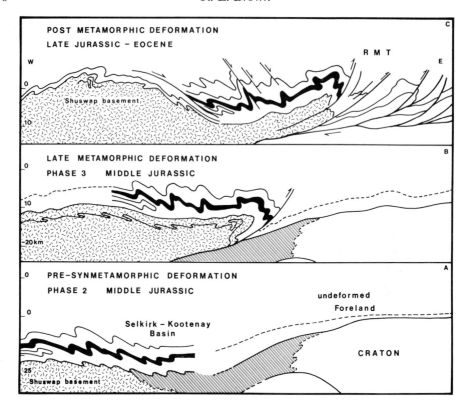

FIG. 5. Middle Jurassic–Eocene kinematic history. Diagrams are drawn with equal horizontal and vertical scale. Diagram (a) is schematic and depths are approximate estimates inferred from metamorphic mineral assemblages; (b) is an approximate reconstruction prior to major eastward displacement of Selkirk-Kootenay allochthone; (c) a simplified cross-section of present structure. Cross-section has been compiled from composite sections drawn along A–B of Fig. 1. Black band is an exaggerated thickness of a calcareous formation within Proterozoic Horsethief Creek Group. Geology east of the Rocky Mountain Trench (RMT) simplified from Wheeler *et al.* (1972).

folds (phase 2) are best developed in the western margin of the Selkirk-Kootenay Basin, and are closely associated in time with developing regional metamorphism (Brown & Tippett 1978; Brown 1978). The peak of metamorphism with pressure in excess of 5 kb. outlasted this deformation implying that significant uplift of the Omineca terrane did not occur until later. The westerly overturned structures may be kinematically accounted for by incipient underthrusting of the Shuswap basement beneath the strata of the Selkirk-Kootenay Basin (Brown & Tippet 1978). Oceanic or transitional crust that may have existed in the Basin would be consumed beneath either the Shuswap basement or the cratonic margin to the E (Fig. 5a).

Continued collapse of the Selkirk-Kootenay Basin brought the Shuswap Terrane toward the cratonic margin. The tectonically thickened mass of the Omineca belt was bouyant relative to the craton, and deformation probably continued by underthrusting of oceanic basement westward beneath the Omineca terrane. Easterly overturned folding (phase 3) in the eastern part of the Basin occurred as the rising terrane was underthrust, first by the basement of the collapsing Basin and eventually by cratonic rocks of the continental margin (Fig. 5b). Décollement thrust faults in the Rocky Mountain Foreland migrated eastward in response to continued underthrusting of the basement and uplift of the tectonically thickened Omineca terrane. Progressive thickening and uplift of the western end of the Foreland wedge would account for the eastward migration of the deformation (Chapple 1978).

Detachment of cover rocks above the Shuswap basement by eastward displacement along the Columbia River fault zone occurred in conjuction with post metamorphic uplift, and early movement may be a distal manifestation of thrust faulting in the Rocky Mountain Foreland (Fig. 5c).

Décollement thrusting was active in the eastern part of the Rocky Mountains into the Paleocene (Price & Mountjoy 1970). By the Eocene a new tectonic pattern is suggested with evidence of NE–SW extension across the Cordillera, together with heating and renewed uplift of the Omineca terrane (see earlier discussion).

The Tertiary evolution of metamorphic core complexes in the North American Cordillera has recently been discussed by Coney (1979). The Omineca terrane of Southern Canadian Cordillera has been included in a synthesis in which he proposes that the complexes are early to Middle Tertiary in age and have been produced by massive extensional tectonics during post-Laramide to pre-Basin and Range time (55–15 Ma). He admits that some of the complexes have been involved in earlier deformation events, but claims that formation of

domes and detachment of cover marked by zones of cataclasis are features that formed in Tertiary times along the length of the Cordillera. The Columbia River fault zone has clearly had a protracted history of deformation, and reactivation in Tertiary times appears to be most likely, but not yet proven.

Since the post metamorphic history of the fault zone records normal displacements on the E dipping zone, it will be difficult to separate movements associated with Laramide thrust faulting from younger movement related to crustal extension.

ACKNOWLEDGMENTS. The project has been funded by grants from the National Research Council of Canada (Operating Grant A2693) and the Department of Energy, Mines and Resources (Research Agreement 2239-4-170/78). During the summers of 1977 and 1978 field work in the Columbia River Valley was supported by the British Columbia Hydro and Power Authority as part of a geological investigation of the Revelstoke reservoir.

References

ARMSTRONG, R. L. 1979. Sr Isotopes in igneous rocks of the Canadian Cordillera and the extent of Precambrian rocks (Abs.). Evolution of the Cratonic Margin and Related Mineral Deposits. *Abs. geol Assoc. Can. Cordilleran section and Abs.* **7**.

BALLY, A. W., GORDY, P. L. & STEWART, G. A. 1966. Structure, seismic data, and orogenic evolution of the Southern Canadian Rocky Mountains. *Bull. Can. Pet. Geol.* **14**, 337–81.

BEDDOE-STEPHENS, B. & LAMBERT, R. ST. J. 1978. The Rossland Volcanics, B. C., Petrochemistry and origin. *Abs. geol. Assoc. Can. Annual Meeting Prog. with Abs.* **3**, 365.

BROWN, R. L. 1978. Structural evolution of the Southeast Canadian Cordillera: A new Hypothesis. *Tectonophysics*, 48, 133–151.

—— 1980. Frenchman Cap Dome, Shuswap Complex, British Columbia: A progress report, *Pap. geol. Surv. Can.* **80–1A**, 47–51.

—— & PSUTKA, J. F. 1979. Stratigraphy of the east flank of Frenchman Cap Dome, Shuswap Complex, British Columbia. *Pap. geol. Surv. Can.*, **79-1A**. 35–6.

—— & READ, P. B. 1979a. Inverted Stratigraphy and Structures, Downie Creek, Southern British Columbia. *Pap. geol. Surv. Can.*, **79–1A**, 33–4.

——, —— 1979b. Basement-cover interaction: Shuswap Metamorphic Complex and the Kootenay Arc-Northern Selkirks. Evolution of the cratonic margin and related mineral deposits. *Abs. geol. Assoc. Can. Cordilleran Section, Prog. and Abs.* 9.

—— & TIPPETT, C. R. 1978. The Selkirk Fan Structure of the Southeastern Canadian Cordillera. *Bull. geol. Soc. Am.* **89**, 548–58.

——, —— & LANE, L. S. 1978. Stratigraphy, facies changes, and correlations in the Northern Selkirk Mountains, Southern Canadian Cordillera. *Can. J. Earth Sci.* **15**, 1129–40.

BURCHFIEL, B. C. & DAVIS, G. A. 1972. Structural framework and evolution of the Southern part of the Cordilleran orogen, Western United States. *Am. J. Sci.* **272**, 97–118.

—— &—— 1975. Nature and controls of Cordilleran orogenesis, Western United States; extensions of an earlier synthesis. *Am. J. Sci.* **275-A**. 363–96.

CAMPBELL, R. B. 1968. Canoe River, British Columbia. *Geol. Surv. Can.* Map 15 (1967).

—— 1970. Structural and metamorphic transitions from infrastructure to suprastructure, Cariboo Mountains, British Columbia. *In:* WHEELER, J. O. (ed). *Structure of the Southern Canadian Cordillera.* Spec. Pap. geol. Assoc. Can. **6**, 67–72.

—— 1973. Structural cross-section and tectonic model of the South-eastern Canadian Cordillera. *Can. J. Earth Sci.* **10**, 1607–19.

—— MOUNTJOY, E. W. & YOUNG, F. G. 1973. Geology of McBride Map-area, British Columbia. *Pap. geol. Surv. Can.* **72–35**. 1–104.

CHAMBERLAIN, V. E., LAMBERT, R. ST. J. & HOLLAND, J. G. 1978. Preliminary sub-divisions of the Malton Gneiss Complex, British Columbia. *Pap. geol. Surv. Can.* **78–1A**. 491–2.

CHANDRA, N. N. & CUMMING, G. L. 1972. Seismic

refraction studies in western Canada, *Can. J. Earth Sci.* **9,** 1099–109.

CHAPPLE, W. M. 1978. Mechanics of thin-skinned fold and thrust belts. *Bull. geol. Soc. Am.* **89.** 1189–98.

CONEY, P. J. 1973. Non-collision tectogenesis in Western North America. *In*: TARLING, D. H. & RUNCORN, S. H. (eds). *Implications of Continental Drift to the Earth Sciences.* Academic Press. New York, 713–27.

—— 1976. Plate tectonics and the Laramide orogeny. *Spec. Publ. New Mexico geol. Soc.* **6,** 5–10.

—— 1978. Mesozoic-Cenozoic Cordilleran plate tectonics. *Mem. geol. Soc. Am.* **152.**

—— 1979. Tertiary evolution of Cordilleran metamorphic core complexes. *In*: *Pacific Coast Paleogeography Symposium,* **3.** Soc. Econ. Pal. and Min. 14–28.

CRAW, D. 1978. Metamorphism, structure and stratigraphy in the Southern Park Ranges British Columbia. *Can. J. Earth Sci.* **15.** 86–98.

CRITTENDEN, M. JR., CONEY, P. J. & DAVIS, G. H. 1978. Penrose Conference Report, Tectonic Significance of metamorphic core complexes in the North American Cordillera. *Geology,* **6.** 79–80.

CUMMING, W. B. 1977. *Crustal Structure from a Seismic Refraction Profile across Southern British Columbia.* M.Sc. Thesis, University of British Columbia, Vancouver, B.C. 82p. (unpubl).

DAVIS, G. A., MONGER, J. W. H. & BURCHFIEL, B. C. 1978. Mesozoic Construction of the Cordilleran 'Collage', Central British Columbia to Central California. *In*: *Mesozoic Sym.* **2–8,** Soc. Econ. Pal. Min. 1–32.

DOUGLAS, R. J. W., GABRIELSE, H., WEELER, J. O., STOTT, D. F. & BELYEA, H. R. 1976. Geology of Western Canada. *In*: DOUGLAS, R. J. W. (ed). *Geology and Economic Minerals of Canada.* Geol. Surv. Can. **B.** 367–546.

DUNCAN, I. J. 1978. Rb/Sr whole-rock evidence for three Precambrian events in the Shuswap Complex, southeast British Columbia (Abs.) *Prog. with Abs. geol. Assoc. Can.* **3,** 392–3.

——, PARRISH, R. R. & ARMSTRONG, R. L. 1979. Rb/Sr geochronology of post-tectonic intrusive events in the Omineca Crystalline Belt, Southeastern British Columbia. Abs. Evolution of the Cratonic Margin and Related Mineral Deposits. *Abs. geol. Assoc. Can. Cordilleran Section, Prog. and Abs.* p. 15.

EISBACHER, G. H., CARRIGY, M. & CAMPBELL, R. B. 1974. Paleodrainage patterns and late-orogenic basins of the Canadian Cordillera. *Spec. Publ. Soc. Econ. Geol. Pal.* **22,** 143–66.

ELLIOTT, D. 1976. The Motion of thrust sheets. *J. geophys. Res.* **31.** 949–1198.

FRANZEN, J. P. 1974. *Structural analysis in the Selkirk Fan Axis near Argonaut Mountain, Southeastern British Columbia.* M.Sc. Thesis, Carleton Univ. Ottawa, Ont. 55 p. (unpubl.).

GHENT, E. D., SIMONY, P. S., MITCHELL, W., PERRY, J., ROBBINS, D. & WAGNER, J. 1977. Structure and metamorphism in southeast Canoe River area, British Columbia *Pap. geol. Surv. Can.* **77–1C,** 7–13.

GIOVANELLA, C. A. 1968. Structural studies of metamorphic rocks along the Rocky Mountain Trench at Canoe River, British Columbia. *Pap. geol. Surv. Can.* **68–1A,** 27–30.

HOY, T. 1977. Stratigraphy and Structure of the Kootenay Arc in the Riondel area, southeastern British Columbia. *Can. J. Earth Sci.* **14,** 2301–15.

—— & MCMILLAN, W. J. 1979. The geology in the vicinity of Frenchman's Cap gneiss dome. *In*: Geological Fieldwork 1978, *British Columbia Dept. Mines and Resc.*

IRVING, E., MONGER, J. W. H. & YOLE, R. W. In press. New paleomagnetic evidence for displaced terranes in British Columbia. *In*: Wilson Symposium, *Geol. Assoc. Can.,* Special Volume.

JONES, A. G. 1959. Vernon map area, British Columbia *Mem. geol. Surv. Can.* 296, 1–186.

LANE, L. S. 1977. *Structure and Stratigraphy, Goldstream River-Downie Creek Area, Selkirk Mountains, British Columbia.* M.Sc. Thesis, Carleton Univ. Ottawa, Ont. 140 p (unpubl.).

LEECH, G. B. 1967. Cretaceous strata in the west face of the Rocky Mountains. *Pap geol. Surv. Can.* **67–1A,** 72–3.

MCMILLAN, W. J. 1970. West flank, Frenchman's Cap gneiss dome, Shuswap Terrane, British Columbia. *In*: WHEELER, J. O. (ed), *Structure of the Southern Canadian Cordillera.* Spec. Pap. geol. Assoc. Can. **6,** 99–106.

MEREU, R. F., MAJUMDAR, S. C. & WHITE, R. E. 1977. The structure of the crust and upper mantle under the highest ranges of the Canadian Rockies from a seismic refraction survey. *Can. J. Earth Sci,* **14,** 196–208.

MONGER, J. W. H. 1977. Upper Paleozoic of the Western Canadian Cordillera and their bearing on Cordilleran evolution. *Can. J. Earth Sci.* **14,** 1832–59.

—— & PRICE, R. A. 1979. Geodynamic evolution of the Canadian Cordillera—progress and problems. *Can. J. Earth Sci.* **16,** 770–91.

——, SOUTHER, J. G. & CABRIELSE, H. 1972. Evolution of the Canadian Cordillera: a plate-tectonic model. *Am. J. Sci.* **272,** 577–602.

OKULITCH, A. V. 1979. The continental Margin and mineral deposits of the eastern Cordillera in the Paleozoic Era. Abs. Evolution of the cratonic margin and related mineral deposits. *Geol. Asoc. Canada, Cordilleran Section. Prog. and Abs.* **22.**

——, WANLESS, R. K. & LOVERIDGE, W. D. 1975. Devonian plutonism in south central British Columbia. *Can. J. Earth Sci.* **12,** 1760–9.

PARRISH, R. R. 1976. *Structure, Metamorphism, and Geochronology of the Northern Wolverine Complex near Chase Mountain, Aiken Lake Map-Area. British Columbia.* M.Sc. Thesis, Univ. British Columbia, (unpubl.).

PRICE, R. A. 1965. Flathead Map-area, British Columbia and Alberta. *Mem. geol. Surv. Can.* **336.**

—— 1973. Large-scale gravitational flow of supracrustal rocks, southern Canadian Rockies. *In*: DE JONG, K. A. & SCHOLTEN, R. (eds). *Gravity and Tectonics*, Wiley, New York, 473–91.

—— & MOUNTJOY, E. W. 1970. Geologic Structure of the Canadian Rocky Mountains between Bow and Athabasca Rivers—a progress report. *In*: WHEELER, J. O. (ed). *Structure of the Southern Canadian Cordillera*. Spec. Pap. geol. Assoc. Can. **6,** 7–39.

READ, P. P. 1975. Lardeau Group, Lardeau map-area, west half, British Columbia. *Pap. geol. Surv. Can.* **75–1A,** 28.

—— 1976. Lardeau map-area (82K west-half), British Columbia. *Pap. geol. Surv. Can.* **77–1A,** 95–6.

—— 1979. Relationship between the Shuswap Metamorphic Complex and Kootenay Arc, Vernon east-half, Southern British Columbia. *Pap. geol. Surv. Can.* **79–1A,** 37-40.

—— 1980. Stratigraphy and structure: Thor-Odin to Frenchman Cap 'domes', Vernon east-half, southern British Columbia; *Pap. geol. Surv. Can.* **80–1A.**

—— & WHEELER, J. O. 1975. Lardeau west-half geology. *Geol. Surv. Can. Open File,* **288.**

REESOR, J. E. 1965. Structural evolution and plutonism in Valhalla Gneiss Complex, British Columbia. *Bull. Surv. Can.* **129,** 1–128.

—— 1970. Some aspects of structural evolution and regional setting in part of the Shuswap Metamorphic Complex. *In*: WHEELER, J. O. (ed). *Structure of the Southern Canadian Cordillera*. Spec. Pap. geol. Assoc. Can. **6,** 73-86.

—— FROESE, E. 1969. Structural and Petrological study of Pinnacle Peaks gneiss dome, British Columbia. *Pap. geol. Surv. Can.* **69–1A,** 139–40.

—— & MOORE, J. M. 1971. Petrology and structure of Thor-Odin Gneiss Dome, Shuswap Metamorphic Complex, British Columbia. *Bull. geol. Surv. Can.* **195,** 1–149.

SPENCE, G. D., CLOWES, R. M. & ELLIS, R. M. 1977. Depth limits on the M. discontinuity in the southern Rocky Mountain Trench, Canada. *Bull. Seism. Soc. Am.* **67,** 543–6.

STACEY, R. A. 1973. Gravity enomalies, crustal structure, and plate tectonics in the Canadian Cordillera. *Can. J. Earth Sci.* **10,** 615–28.

STEWART, J. H. 1972. Initial deposits in the Cordilleran geosyncline; evidence of a late Precambrian (850 m.y.) continental separation. *Bull. geol. Soc. Am.* **83,** 1345–60.

WANLESS, R. K. & REESOR, J. E. 1975. Precambrian zircon age of orthogeneiss in the Shuswap Metamorphic Complex, British Columbia, *Can. J. Earth Sci.* **12,** 326–32.

WHEELER, J. D. 1965. Big Bend map-area, British Columbia (82M east-half). *Pap. geol. Surv. Can.* **64–32,** 1–37.

——, CAMPBELL, R. B., REESOR, J. E. & MOUNTJOY, E. W. 1972. Structural style of the Southern Canadian Cordillera. *24th Int. Geol. Congr. Guidb. Field Excursion* X01-A01.

—— & GABRIELSE, H. 1972. The Cordilleran structural province. *In*: PRICE, R. A. & DOUGLAS, R. J. W. (eds). *Variations in Tectonic Styles in Canada*. Spec. Pap. geol. Assoc. Can. **11,** 9–81.

R. L. BROWN, Department of Geology, Carleton University, Ottawa, Ontario K1S KB6, Canada.

Thrust nappes in the Rocky Mountain Foothills near Mountain Park, Alberta

H. A. K. Charlesworth & W. E. Kilby

SUMMARY: In 200 km² of W central Alberta, the thrusts associated with seven nappes cut up section to the NE at about 5° through 1000 m of Upper Jurassic and Lower Cretaceous strata whose overall dip is gentle and to the SW. The thrusts, whose horizontal spacing ranges from 0 to 4 km, have a combined displacement of about 12 km. Most folds affecting the nappe assemblage originated through bending over steps in the thrusts against which they end downwards. Up plunge to the NW the upper nappes, most of which involve older strata, are apparently truncated by the McConnell Nappe, whereas three of the thrusts underlying the lower nappes appear to run into the Miette thrust which to the NW replaces the McConnell as the SW boundary of the Foothills. Down plunge to the SE the thrusts merge in an Upper Cretaceous décollement zone whose 15 km of movement are dissipated in the Foothills to the NE by low-angle thrusts splaying into the overlying strata. The décollement and associated thrusts are cut by a younger generation of faults that include the McConnell, Nikanassin and Folding Mountain.

The Canadian Rocky Mountains with a NW–SE trend developed from a NE tapering sedimentary prism which during orogenesis moved outwards over an intact cratonic platform. In the process the prism thickened vertically and shortened horizontally, partly as the result of folding but mainly by movement along thrusts which dip SW and merge at depth with the basal zone of décollement. On a large scale these thrusts cut up section to the NE at low angles, but on a smaller scale are commonly stepped, being approximately parallel or at a 30° angle to bedding. During orogenesis deformation within the prism appears to have migrated NE, so the lower of any two thrusts is generally the younger.

The stratigraphic succession within the sedimentary prism is divisible into an older miogeoclinal sequence, Precambrian–Middle Jurassic in age, and a younger clastic wedge sequence of late Jurassic–Palaeocene age. The older sequence, dominated by Palaeozoic carbonates, is generally resistant to erosion and gives rise to the well exposed Main and Front Ranges. Rocks belonging to the more recessive clastic wedge sequence underlie much of the poorly exposed Foothills at the frontal part of the prism. Whereas most thrust nappes of the Main and Front Ranges consist only of the older sequence, those of the foothills generally contain both sequences. Excellent exposures in the Main and Front Ranges and good seismic reflections from the top of the Palaeozoics beneath the foothills have meant that nappe structure in the miogeoclinal sequence is well documented. In contrast poor exposures and seismic reflections from much of the Mesozoics of the Foothills and the smaller scale of the structures there have prevented the characteristics of nappes in the clastic wedge sequence from becoming as well known.

The purpose of this paper is to describe and discuss the major structural features of the clastic wedge sequence in 200 km² of the Foothills near the former coal mining community of Mountain Park (Fig. 1). Here good outcrop, drill hole and topographic data, combined with detailed mapping and computerized analysis, have enabled the essential characteristics of seven thrust nappes to be determined. These characteristics represent an interesting variation to the pattern usually exhibited by faults of this type (see Bally *et al.* 1966; Dahlstrom 1970).

Stratigraphy

The clastic wedge sequence in W central Alberta consists of one shale and two molasse units. At Mountain Park the lower molasse unit comprises the Upper Jurassic–Lower Cretaceous Nikanassin Formation (425 m of thinly interbedded marine and non-marine sandstone and shale) and the Lower Cretaceous Cadomin (8 m of conglomerate), Luscar (340 m of non-marine sandstone, shale and coal, thinly interbedded towards the base, thickly towards the top) and Mountain Park (200 m of non-marine sandstone with some shale) Formations. The overlying marine shale unit contains the Cretaceous Blackstone (430 m of shale) and Cardium (75 m of sandstone with some shale)

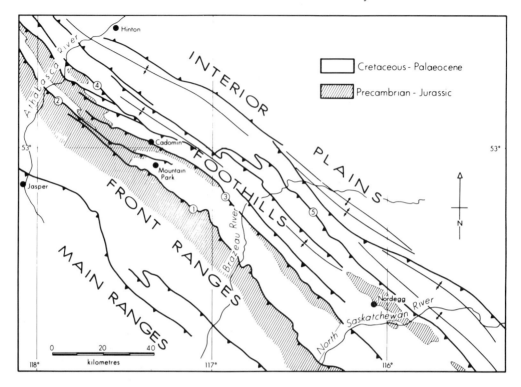

FIG. 1. Geological map of the Rocky Mountain Foothills between the North Saskatchewan and Athabasca Rivers, Alberta. (1) McConnell, (2) Miette, (3) Nikanassin–Bighorn, (4) Folding Mountain and (5) Brazeau Thrust faults. (after Price & Mountjoy 1970, fig. 2-1).

Formations. These formations increase in competence from the very incompetent Blackstone, through the moderately incompetent Nikanassin and Luscar and the moderately competent Mountain Park, to the very competent Cadomin and Cardium (see e.g. McCrossan & Glaister 1964).

Method of study

Many structural data were stored, retrieved, displayed and processed with the aid of the computer. It was used, for example, to calculate fold-axes and establish domains within which folding is cylindrical. Structural cross-sections were drawn using a computerized version of the downplunge projection technique. This involved instructing the computer to prepare plots that show the positions of outcrops and drill hole intersections projected parallel to the fold-axis onto the plane of the plot. On these plots each outcrop is represented by a line parallel to the trace of bedding and each drill hole intersection by a cross. Guided by

these symbols and by accompanying letters designating stratigraphic position, the traces of stratigraphic horizons and longitudinal faults can be drawn fairly objectively. Where two or more cylindrically folded domains exist within an area, each domain is first rotated separately, again using the computer, so that the entire area has a common fold-axis by the time a composite plot is obtained (Charlesworth *et al.* 1976; Langenberg *et al.* 1977).

Structure

The strata at Mountain Park, although involved in seven thrust nappes, have an overall gentle dip to the SW. They rest on the miogeoclinal sequence of the Nikanassin Thrust nappe, while to the SW they are overthrust by the Palaeozoics of the McConnell Nappe which at this latitude form the first of the Front Ranges of the Rocky Mountains (Fig. 1).

In general the basal thrust of each nappe is traceable only from the point where it cuts the resistant Cadomin Conglomerate in the foot-wall to where it enters the Blackstone Shale in the hanging-wall (Fig. 2). Once within the monotonous Nikanassin or highly recessive Blackstone Formations, the thrusts are lost to view. Within the area studied all but the most northerly fault seem to 'root' in the Nikanassin Formation, i.e. only the northernmost thrust appears to penetrate the highest unit of the miogeoclinal sequence, the 300 m Fernie Shale of Jurassic age. However, the gradational nature of the contact between this unit and the overlying Nikanassin, the scarcity of outcrop and the low angle between the faults and bedding meant that the contact could not be traced at all confidently, so more than one fault may involve the Jurassic shales N of Mountain Park. This is particularly likely in the NW part of the area and indeed this interpretation is shown in Fig. 4. As discussed below no thrust nappe involves the overlying Cardium Sandstone. Both the strata in the nappes and the associated faults have apparently been folded together about axes which plunge SE at about 15°.

Nappe 1

Nappe 1, the highest or most south-westerly of the seven, rests on a basal thrust which has one splay (Fig. 2). In the NW both faults thrust Nikanassin and Cadomin strata over the Luscar Formation. Traced SE, i.e. down plunge, the faults cut up section through the Luscar Formation, duplicating and in one place triplicating the 11 m Kennedy coal seam. East of Mountain Park the basal thrust repeats the Mountain Park Formation before entering the Blackstone Shale. Geophysical drill hole logs show that a shale interval in the Kennedy coal seam thins abruptly from 10 m in the nappe to 3 m in the footwall, which suggests considerable movement on the part of the nappe.

In order to estimate this movement and the angle between the thrusts and bedding, a profile similar to part of the cross-section of Fig. 3 was constructed using the downplunge projection method mentioned above. From it the angle between the traces of the faults and bedding was found to be about 4°. This angle may be taken as the true angle between bedding and the faults only if both are normal to the plane of the profile, i.e. if the folds in bedding are coaxial with those in the faults. Most folds in the Rocky Mountains are either buckle or kink folds related to the same stress field responsible for the thrusts, or bending folds related to the stepped configuration of

these thrusts, so one could argue from general considerations that the two sets of fold-axes are likely to coincide. Fortunately the plans of the abandoned underground mine at Mountain Park provide evidence of a more tangible kind to support this conclusion. On them the underground workings in the Kennedy and another seam in the hanging-wall of the basal thrust end along lines with orientations of 139° 12° and 155° 19°. Since these lines appear to mark the intersections of the seams with the thrust, and since the fold-axis has an orientation of 146° 17°, we can conclude that the fault as well as the coal seams parallel the axis of folding in bedding.

The apparent displacements in a direction normal to the fold-axis can be determined from the profile, using the Kennedy coal seam as marker, to be about 2.7 and 2.6 km for the basal thrust and its splay. If the direction of displacement was oblique to the fold-axis the true displacements would be somewhat larger. However, slickenside striae observed on mesoscopic fault planes are generally normal to the associated fold-axis, and large grooves in the base of the Cadomin Conglomerate where it is cut by the basal thrust make an angle of 90° with the fold-axis, so the probable direction of displacement was approximately normal to the fold-axis.

Strata within nappe 1 contain several macroscopic folds. The prominent overturned syncline, some of whose SW limb is cut out by a thrust fault, probably resulted from drag associated with emplacement of the McConnell Thrust nappe. The nappe 1 thrusts appear to be older than this fold. The other folds in nappe 1 affect one or more of the underlying nappes and thus are also younger than the thrusts.

Nappe 2

The basal thrust of the underlying nappe 2 is readily identified in the NW by its duplication of the Cadomin Conglomerate. A profile constructed in the same way as for Nappe 1 suggests that it makes an angle of about 10° with bedding and that its displacement is about 2.3 km. Just E of Mountain Park the thrust becomes lost to view in poorly exposed ground underlain by complexly deformed Luscar and Mountain Park strata. Once the thrust enters the Luscar Formation in the hanging-wall. some of its displacement appears to be taken up by small scale deformation and by movement along several splays of which only one is shown in Figs 2 and 3. Up section, the splay, which developed after folding of the basal

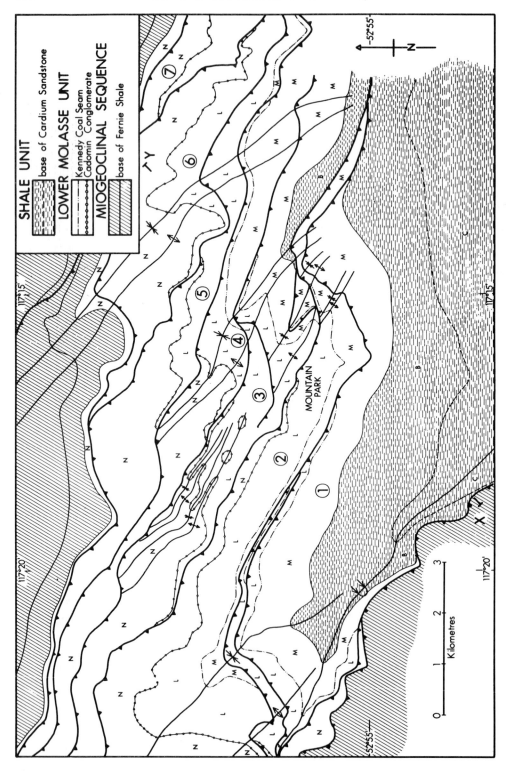

SHALE UNIT
base of Cardium Sandstone

LOWER MOLASSE UNIT
Kennedy Coal Seam
Cadomin Conglomerate

MIOGEOCLINAL SEQUENCE
base of Fernie Shale

MOUNTAIN PARK

Kilometres
0   1   2   3

117°15'
117°20'
52°55'

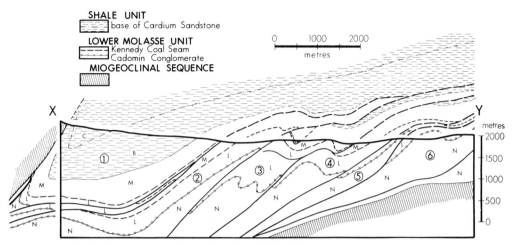

SHALE UNIT
base of Cardium Sandstone

LOWER MOLASSE UNIT
Kennedy Coal Seam
Cadomin Conglomerate

MIOGEOCLINAL SEQUENCE

FIG. 3. Vertical structural section across the Mountain Park area prepared by downplunge projection using data from within the area of Fig. 2. The numbers 1–6 identify the nappes referred to in the text. N—Nikanassin, L—Lower Luscar, M—Upper Luscar and Mountain Park, B—Blackstone, C—Cardium Formations. In the SW, the steepness of the McConnell Thrust results from its not being coaxial with folds in the underlying Mesozoics.

thrust, rejoins it to thrust Luscar and Mountain Park over Blackstone strata before entering the Blackstone Shale.

Three anticline-syncline pairs occur in nappe 2 just E of Mountain Park. The western two folds end downwards against a step in the basal thrust and were generated by a step in the basal thrust; the original bending folds were subsequently tightened, some of the tightening having occurred through displacement along joints. The middle two folds, continuous with an anticline-syncline pair in nappe 3, have been displaced by the splay mentioned above.

Nappe 3

Nikanassin, Cadomin and Lower Luscar strata have been folded to a greater extent in nappe 3 than in any of the other nappes (Figs 2 & 3). The folds, which in places are overturned to the NE, do not extend into the W part of the area and presumably end downwards against the basal thrust. Whether they are tightened bending folds or owe their existence entirely to buckling is uncertain. The horizontal shortening accomplished by these folds is considerably greater than that of the overlying Kennedy coal seam in the upper Luscar Formation. Much of the folding in the older strata

must therefore die out upwards against a zone of décollement or thrust fault which connects with the basal thrust of nappe 3. This thrust has a displacement of about 1 km, using the Kennedy coal seam as marker, and makes an overall angle of about 5° with bedding.

Nappes 4–7

Displacements along the basal thrusts of nappes 4–6 using the Cadomin Conglomerate as marker add up to about 2.4 km. These thrusts, like those discussed above, all make low angles with bedding. Two prominent folds in nappe 4 just N of Mountain Park extend upwards into nappe 3 and perhaps as high as nappe 1. Nappes 2–6 are all affected by a gentle anticline-syncline pair which can be traced into the Palaeozoics of the Nikanassin Range. Little is known about nappe 7 except that, to judge from the separation of the Cadomin Conglomerate W of the area mapped, the displacement along its low-angle basal thrust is about 1.3 km.

Discussion

The thrusts associated with the Mountain Park nappes all cut up section to the NE at an

FIG. 2. Geological map of the Mountain Park area. The numbers 1–7 identify the nappes referred to in the text. F—Fernie, N—Nikanassin, L—Lower Luscar, M—Upper Luscar and Mountain Park, B—Blackstone, C—Cardium Formations. XY—line of cross-section of Fig. 3. In the E, the fault underlying Nappe 1 thrusts Mountain Park and Blackstone over basal Blackstone strata too thin to show on a map of this scale.

average angle of about 5° through the 1000 m thick lower molasse unit, and their horizontal spacing ranges from 0 to 4 km. The cumulative displacement along these thrusts is about 12 km. Most large folds end downwards against a thrust fault and affect strata in two or more of the overlying nappes. Thus the nappes appear to obey the general rule in having developed from SW to NE, so that nappe 1 is the oldest and nappe 7 the youngest. The sole exception to this appears to be the splay in the basal thrust of nappe 2 which displaces two folds formed during the emplacement of nappe 3. In addition to macroscopic folding, strata in the nappes have experienced considerable mesoscopic deformation. Although the small size of most outcrops prevented us from learning much about this deformation, there are two reasons why it may be significant: (1) strata at many outcrops are cut by faults of unknown displacement and are mesoscopically folded about axes subparallel to those of the associated macroscopic folds, and (2) the apparent thicknesses of formations such as the Nikanassin and Luscar in profiles of cylindrically folded domains are commonly considerably greater than the stratigraphic thicknesses.

Let us now examine what happens to the nappes as they are traced away from Mountain Park (Fig. 4). Up plunge to the NW the thrusts underlying the nappes become lost to view in the monotonous Nikanassin Formation. From the 1 : 63 360 geological map of the area (MacKay 1929) we can make the following observations. (1) The highest two thrusts, i.e. those associated with nappe 1, still located in Nikanassin strata, are truncated either by the McConnell fault or by the thrust in the SW limb of the underlying overturned syncline. (2) The basal thrust of nappe 2 cuts into the Jurassic shales at the top of the miogeoclinal sequence before being truncated by the McConnell Thrust as the boundary fault of the nappe 3 appears to penetrate both the Jurassic shales and the underlying Triassic strata before it too is truncated by the McConnell thrust. From these observations we conclude that nappes 1–3 are older than the McConnell nappe. The thrusts underlying nappes 4–6 appear to merge down section to become the Miette fault, which 50 km to the NW has replaced the McConnell Thrust as the boundary fault of the Front ranges (Fig. 1). It thrusts Palaeozoics over strata in structural continuity with those in nappe 7. The basal thrusts of all nappes in the upper part of the miogeoclinal sequence appear to make the same low angle with bedding as they do in the lower molasse unit.

Down plunge to the SE the faults underlying all the nappes become lost to view in the recessive and practically unexposed Blackstone Shale. That the faults flatten and merge in this formation is indicated by their failure to cut the overlying Cardium Sandstone which continues unbroken for a distance of 50 km to the SE, much of it down plunge (Fig. 4). Thus each nappe terminates up section against a décollement zone in the Blackstone Shale. How much displacement is associated with this décollement? The answer at first would appear to be the cumulative displacement along all seven thrust faults, i.e. about 12 km. But to this figure must be added the displacement associated with the dying out upwards against the décollement of all the macroscopic folding and mesoscopic deformation to affect the Kennedy seam, probably another 3 km, making a total of about 15 km. This displacement appears to continue within the Blackstone Shale into the Foothills NE of Mountain Park where it becomes distributed among numerous low-angle thrust-faults affecting Cardium and younger strata. Such faults have long been known occur there (Hake *et al.* 1942). The Nikanassin and Folding Mountain thrusts appear to displace the Blackstone décollement zone (Fig. 4), in which case they belong with the McConnell to a younger generation of faults, a situation similar to that already postulated for the Foothills to the SE (Bally *et al.* 1966, fig. 6).

Thus the thrusts associated with the seven Mountain Park nappes generally have the following characteristics: (1) they cut up section to the NE at an angle of about 5° through about 1500 m of fairly incompetent strata at the top of the miogeoclinal and base of the clastic wedge sequences; (2) they have an average displacement of nearly 2 km; (3) they differ from the thrusts in the Palaeozoic part of the miogeoclinal sequence in their closer spacing, smaller displacement and greater internal deformation; (4) they flatten & merge in the Blackstone décollement zone to reappear as low-angle thrusts in the upper part of the clastic wedge sequence in the outer Foothills; (5) the décollement zone and associated faults appear to be older than such major thrusts as the McConnell, Nikanassin and Folding Mountain.

Earth scientists have often tended to allow intuition to decrease the objectivity of their observations and the rationality of their thinking. Nowhere is this more striking than in the field of tectonics where we find ourselves dealing with physical quantities involving length,

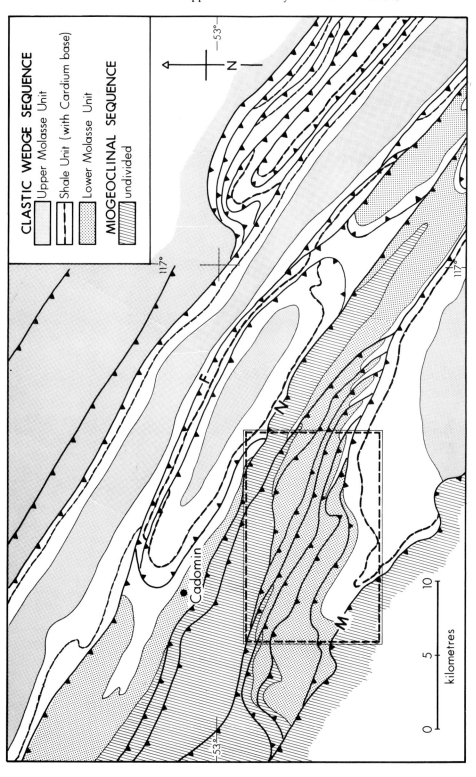

Fig. 4. Geological map showing the setting of the area of Fig. 2 in adjacent Foothills (after MacKay 1943). M—McConnell, N—Nikanassin, F—Folding Mountain thrusts.

mass and time so different from our every day experience as to be beyond our comprehension. Some of us have been obsessed with the strength of rocks and refused to believe the evidence for continental drift which long before the advent of plate tectonics was virtually unassailable. Others, convinced of the weakness of sedimentary assemblages refused to consider the validity of Buxtorf's décollement hypothesis and regarded the sedimentary cover as an inert blanket passively accommodating itself to the underlying basement. Today, however, most of us are prepared to believe that sedimentary thrust-nappes have a life of their own, although perhaps with such provisos as (1) the nappe must have a competent backbone, or (2) the pore pressures must have been high, or (3) gravity must have played an important role. The authors do not know how the backboneless structures discussed in this paper came into existence, to what extent gravity was involved or to what extent they were pushed from behind. All that we ask is that intuitive arguments concerning rock strength not be allowed to question their existence.

ACKNOWLEDGMENTS. We thank the Consolidation Coal Company of Canada for providing access to field and drill hole data, many of which were collected by W. E. K. while an employee. We acknowledge the award of a Graduate Teaching Assistantship by the University of Alberta (W. E. K.) and of research grants by the National Sciences and Engineering Research Council and Geological Survey of Canada (H. A. K. C.). We also thank Ron Swaren, Scott Anderson, Chris Gold, Dave Flint and Bruce Vincent for helping with fieldwork and computing. Kathy Berndt digitized map data and verified computer files and Frank Dimitrov drafted the text-figures.

References

BALLY, A. W., GORDY, P. L. & STEWART, G. A. 1966. Structure, seismic data and orogenic evolution of southern Canadian Rocky Mountains. *Bull. Can. Pet. Geol.* **14**, 337–81.

CHARLESWORTH, H. A. K., LANGENBERG, C. W. & RAMSDEN, J. 1976. Determining axes, axial planes and sections of macroscopic folds using computer-based methods. *Can. J. Earth Sci.* **13**, 54–65.

DAHLSTROM, C. D. A. 1970. Structural geology in the eastern margin of the Canadian Rocky Mountains. *Bull. Can. Pet. Geol.* **18**, 332–406.

HAKE, B. F., WILLIS, R. & ADDISON, C. C. 1942. Folded thrust-faults in the Foothills of Alberta. *Bull. geol. Soc. Am.* **53**, 291–334.

LANGENBERG, C. W., RONDEEL, H. E. & CHARLESWORTH, H. A. K. 1977. A structural study in the Belgian Ardennes with sections constructed using computer-based methods. *Geol. Mijnbouw.* **56**, 145–54.

MACKAY, B. R. 1929. Mountain Park, Alberta. *Geol. Surv. Can.* Map 208A.

—— 1943. Foothills belt of central Alberta. *Pap. geol. Surv. Can.* **43–3**.

McCROSSAN, R. G. & GLAISTER, R. P. (eds). 1964. *Geological History of Western Canada.* Alberta Soc. Pet. Geol. 264 pp.

PRICE, R. A. &. MOUNTJOY, E. W. 1970. Geologic structure of the Canadian Rocky Mountains between Bow and Athabasca Rivers—a progress report. *In*: WHEELER, J. O. (ed). *Structure of the Southern Canadian Cordillera*. Spec. Pap. geol. Assoc. Can. **6**, 7–25.

H. A. K. CHARLESWORTH & W. E. KILBY, Department of Geology, University of Alberta, Edmonton, Canada T6G 2E3.

Deformational styles in two Mesozoic fault zones, western Washington, USA

D. S. Cowan & R. B. Miller

SUMMARY: The Navaho Divide and Lopez fault zones record sub-greenschist facies, brittle fragmentation and tectonic mixing at an active Mesozoic continental margin. Displacement directions across these zones are interpreted as partly or wholly dip-slip, although unambiguous criteria in these and many other Cordilleran fault zones are lacking. The moderate to high-angle Navaho Divide zone, which is part of the ophiolitic Ingalls Complex, contains variously sized elongate fragments of serpentinized ultramafic rocks, gabbro, and related rock types set in a voluminous matrix of foliated, scaly serpentinite. The moderately dipping Lopez zone comprises larger slices of turbidites, pebbly mudstone, and minor mafic metavolcanic rocks separated by faults and narrow fault zones locally filled with mudstone that apparently flowed during thrusting. In both complexes, the elongate slices and subparallel faults define an imbricate or schuppen structure geometrically similar to the macroscopic fabric of intracratonic, Rocky Mountain-type imbricate zones. However, the Navaho Divide and Lopez zones are fundamentally different in that they both juxtapose and contain rock units that are difficult, or impossible, to restore palinspastically to a pre-faulting configuration.

Thrust faults and fault zones are common structures in the Mesozoic orogenic belts of western North America. Most attention to date has been focussed on the classic Rocky Mountain fold and thrust belt (for example, Bally *et al.* 1966; Price & Mountjoy 1970; Price this volume) where a stratigraphic layercake has been peeled from Precambrian crystalline basement and imbricated in a series of stacked thrust plates. Many moderate-angle faults of Mesozoic age in the westernmost Cordillera, which stretches along much of the Pacific Coast from Alaska to California, are significantly different in several respects. They commonly affect stratigraphically complex 'eugeo-synclinal' sequences, including ophiolitic rocks, which are difficult to restore palinspastically, and juxtapose structural units with contrasting deformational and metamorphic histories. Many such faults record complex plate interactions along broadly convergent plate boundaries (B-subduction of Bally, this volume) in contrast to intracratonic shortening in Rocky Mountain-type orogens, although it is often difficult to assess displacement directions and tectonic setting. We describe here two well-exposed fault-zone complexes in western Washington State, which together illustrate some of the most important characteristics of these distinctive 'West-Cordilleran' fault zones.

The Ingalls Complex & Navaho Divide fault zone

The late Jurassic Ingalls Complex (Fig. 1) is a highly disrupted ophiolitic sequence which has been thrust onto medium-grade pelitic schists of the Skagit crystalline core of the North Cascades. The Mesozoic geology of the North Cascades is described by Misch (1966, 1977), and a brief overview of the geological setting of the Ingalls is in Miller & Frost (1977). The late Cretaceous Mount Stuart batholith truncates the major structures of the complex and physically separates it into two outcrop areas. The larger of these areas lies S of the batholith and is dominated by two extensive fault zones, separated by a coherent body of relatively unserpentinized, high-grade ultramafic tectonites of upper mantle type (Fig. 2). These fault zones strike W–WNW, dip steeply to the N, and are characterized by generally elongate tectonic blocks in a steeply-dipping sheared serpentinite matrix. Most of these blocks consist of ophiolitic rocks, including gabbro, diabase, basalt, high-grade ultramafic tectonites, and several types of sedimentary rocks. Blocks that consist of exotic rock types, mostly well-foliated amphibolites, are a minor constituent and cannot be readily correlated with the ophiolitic rocks or any other unit. Despite some differences in block types, the two fault zones exhibit the same structural style and were probably formed by similar processes. Both appear to pre-date thrust emplacement of the complex. The overall petrologic and structural features of the ophiolitic complex suggest that these fault zones may represent parts of a former oceanic fracture zone. The evidence for this interpretation is presented elsewhere (Miller 1980).

The southern fault zone, known as the

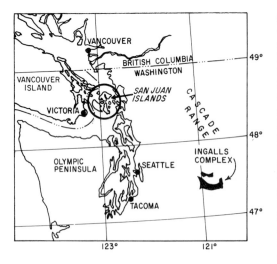

Navaho Divide fault zone, has been better studied and will be described in some detail. This fault zone is exposed for about 35 km, and its width ranges from 1.3 to at least 8 km; at some places part of the zone is covered or intruded by younger rocks. Primary changes in width commonly occur over short distances. In any individual cross-section, the overall amount of matrix ranges from about 5% to approximately 30%. The distribution of blocks and proportion of individual types vary considerably along and across the strike of the fault zone. Thousands of fault-bounded blocks are exposed. The larger ones have been mapped on a scale of 1:24 000. Where exposures are

sufficient, but blocks are too small to be individually mapped, they have been grouped into rock units which are delineated on the basis of lithologically similar block types (Fig. 3). All of these units have a sheared serpentinite matrix, making up from about 10 to 40% or so of the total volume, and contain pods of massive serpentinite which generally are less than 2 m long. Four units, which differ in the types of non-ultramafic ophiolitic blocks present, have been delineated in the Navaho Divide fault zone: (1) *ultramafic units*—all blocks are ultramafic; (2) *gabbro units*—blocks are mainly gabbro and minor diabase; (3) *mixed-mafic units*—gabbro, diabase and basalt blocks occur in varying proportions, and some blocks consist of two or more of these rock types; and (4) *mixed-ophiolitic units*—composed of blocks of all of the mafic and ultramafic rocks listed above and also containing blocks of sedimentary rocks.

Individual tectonic blocks range from 1 cm^2 to 15 km^2 in area, although most are less than 300 m^2. Most blocks are lenticular, and length-to-width ratios range from about 1.5:1 to more than 20:1. This geometry can be seen on all scales; for example, the largest structural block is approximately 12 by 1.2 km, and ratios on the order of 4:1 to 8:1 are common for the smaller slices, many of which are seen to approximate oblate ellipsoids in excellent 3-dimensional exposures.

Serpentinite matrix

The matrix of the fault zone is composed almost entirely of sheared serpentinite which has

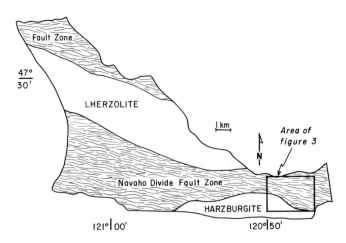

FIG. 2. Simplified geological map of part of the Ingalls Complex, showing the setting of the fault zones described in the text.

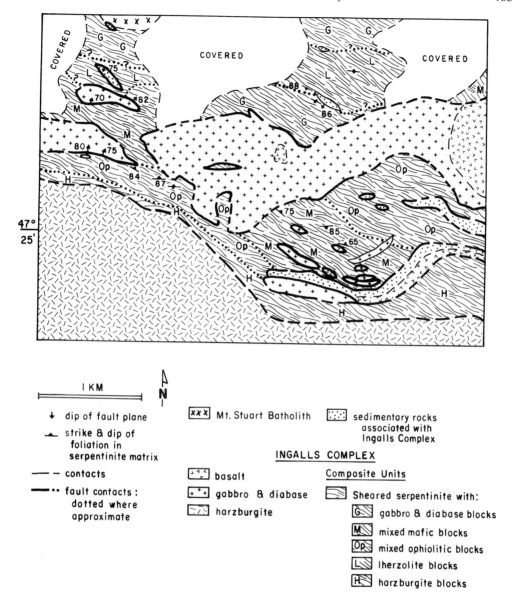

FIG. 3. Detailed map of a small, well-exposed part of the Navaho Divide fault zone. The larger tectonic blocks are individually shown, but smaller blocks have been grouped into composite lithologic units. Contacts between these units are approximate. For further discussion, see text.

been derived from high-grade ultramafic tectonites. Chrysotile and/or lizardite appear to be the predominant serpentine minerals, indicating that the matrix formed at very low temperatures, probably in the prehnite-pumpellyite facies. The intensity of foliation developed in the matrix varies, as is best seen at the boundaries of the fault zone where, in places, fairly massive, fractured peridotite grades into highly schistose serpentinite. These fairly massive peridotites at the edge of the fault zone are cut by thin, serpentine-filled shear fractures which generally are curved and are only very approximately parallel. These fractures are heterogeneously distributed and are separated by massive domains, generally more than 2 m in thickness. Farther into the fault zone, shear fractures are more uniformly distributed, and massive domains are thinner. Here many of the 'fractures' are actually zones of cleaved serpentinite averaging a few cms in thickness. In the central part of the fault zone, the foliation is still more penetrative and is defined by moderately strongly aligned fibrous serpentines which wrap around thin lenses of more massive ultramafite. In some zones of apparently high strain, generally less than 2 m thick, the less strongly foliated lenticular domains are of microscopic dimensions only. These strongly schistose serpentinites presumably represent the most intense deformation attained within the gradational sequence from weakly to strongly foliated ultramafites.

On a microscale, the serpentinites range from fairly massive to well-foliated. The former varieties are characterized by mesh texture, but are cut by minor thin foliated zones. Aligned fibrous, wispy serpentine grains define a strong foliation in some serpentinites that, in hand sample, have a highly sheared appearance. These serpentines have been flattened around, and in some places have cut, highly strained elongate bastite pseudomorphs which commonly have been cataclastically drawn out into subparallelism with the elongate serpentines. The bastites usually display extension fractures, and commonly are bent and folded; some have been completely pulled apart. Locally, a spaced shear foliation, across which there has been minor offset, cuts the dominant foliation of the serpentinite matrix.

The most striking characteristic of the serpentinite matrix, regardless of how strongly foliated it is, is that it anastomoses around lenses of less sheared rock on all scales. Although anastomosing, the foliation is statistically planar, striking W–WNW and dipping steeply to the north. Furthermore, it is parallel to the strike of the fault zone and to the fault contacts of elongate tectonic blocks. This statistically planar fabric represents the one obvious element of order within the otherwise chaotic appearing heterogeneous fault zone. Folds are extremely rare, and penetrative lineations are absent; only slickensides, which lack strong preferred orientation, have been observed.

Most of the strain within the fault zone is probably concentrated in the foliated serpentinite matrix. However, at least some of the non-ultramafic tectonic blocks display structures apparently related to movement within the fault zone. Brittle shear zones, generally less than 2 m thick, and tectonic breccias occur in many of these blocks, and some presumably formed at about the same time as the foliation in the serpentinite matrix.

Displacement

The amount of displacement within the fault zone is unknown, but may be considerable. Rocks of the Navaho Divide fault zone are not in sharp fault contact with adjacent rock units but rather grade into unsheared ultramafites in places, as described above. However, several features suggest substantial displacement. Different types of ultramafic rocks occur on either side of the fault zone: coarse-grained dunites and harzburgites on the S side, and coarse-grained lherzolites and fine-grained, blastomylonitic hornblende peridotites and lherzolites on the N. Within the fault zone, exotic amphibolite-facies blocks are in fault contact with low-grade serpentinites, and in one place with argillite and chert.

The displacement directions across the fault zone are also uncertain, owing to the scarcity of diagnostic small-scale structures and to the lack of restorability of the rocks to a pre-faulting configuration. Circumstantial evidence suggests that both strike-slip and dip-slip movements occurred. Widespread tectonic mixing generally does not occur during normal faulting but is compatible with reverse or convergent strike-slip faulting, i.e. transpression (Harland 1971; Saleeby 1979). The steepness of the faults implies that strike-slip displacement was important. Diapiric movement of serpentinite may also have been significant and might be partially responsible for the juxtaposition of serpentinite with other ophiolitic rocks formed at higher 'stratigraphic' levels. This juxtaposition suggests considerable dip slip displacement, regardless of whether it was due to diapirism.

The Lopez fault zone

The NW striking, NE dipping Lopez fault zone, in the southern San Juan Islands (Figs 1 & 4), has a maximum exposed width of 3 km and length of 13 km. It differs from the Navaho Divide fault zone in that it contains predominantly sedimentary and volcanogenic, rather than ophiolitic, rocks. However, both tectonic complexes have planar fabrics at map and outcrop scales defined by elongate to lenticular slices surrounded by a statistically parallel, anastomosing network of faults and, in the case of the Ingalls Complex, zones of highly deformed matrix. The Lopez consists of variously sized slices of thinly to massively bedded sequences of graywacke and mudstone, pebbly mudstone, pillow lava, radiolarian chert, and meta-igneous breccia composed of altered gabbro and diabase, amphibolite, and

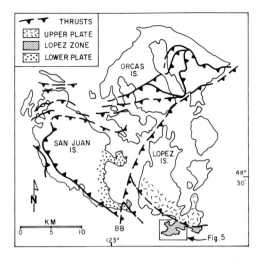

FIG. 4. Major low- to moderate-angle thrusts in the San Juan Islands. Based on Vance (1977) and unpublished mapping by Cowan & M. Brandon. Only a narrow band of the 'upper plate' that is structurally above the projected, NE dipping Lopez is shown, although related rocks crop out elsewhere on Lopez Island and smaller islands to the E. The 'lower plate' is in contact with the Lopez zone only on the SE tip of San Juan Island. Lithologically similar rocks are depicted W of the Buck Bay fault (BB), which truncates the Lopez zone and the upper plate.

quartz-albitite. These fault-bound lenses, which range from less than a metre to about 0.7 km in thickness, strike NW and dip NE, parallel to the fault zone itself (Fig. 5). Many of the faults shown on Fig. 5 are not exposed, but their locations are constrained by abrupt changes in rock types. Slices grouped together as 'sedimentary rocks' can also be differentiated into several types on the basis of sedimentological features and sandstone petrology.

Some fault zones on Johns Point and Iceberg Point contain discontinuous lenses, less than a metre thick, of black mudstone with fragments of chert, metavolcanic rock and sandstone that were locally derived from adjacent slices. Similar, narrow zones occur sporadically within large fault-bound slices throughout the Lopez, but they are not mappable at a scale of 1 : 24 000. Displacements along these intra-slice faults were probably minor, and they may represent the finer scale, incipient fragmentation and disruption of their hosts. The mudstone was apparently mobilized from clastic sequences rather than derived from tectonic

fragments by *in-situ* cataclasis, as was the matrix in the Navaho Divide fault zone. Other evidence attests to the mesoscopic mobility of mudstone during deformation. On the S side of Johns Point, for example a slab of pillow basalt has been juxtaposed with pebbly mudstone, which locally flowed into brittle fractures <2 mm wide and into larger, irregular re-entrants in the lower surface of the basalt slab.

The P-T conditions attending deformation in the Lopez zone are loosely constrained, but we feel it is likely that brittle fragmentation and faulting occurred at low temperatures and perhaps before mobile mudstone-rich rocks were fully consolidated and dewatered. Much of the mudstone still contains clay minerals, and secondary minerals in metabasalt slices typically include chlorite, albite, calcite, and pumpellyite. In addition, a penetrative foliation is locally superimposed upon the earlier features recording fault-related fragmentation. The foliation is defined by a mesoscopic slaty cleavage in mudstone and a fracture cleavage in sandstone and chert but it is unevenly developed and locally absent, even within the area of Fig. 5 which depicts the most highly disrupted part of the Lopez. Slaty mudstones display oriented, recrystallized phyllosilicates and the domainal microstructure typical of slates in general (Hobbs *et al.* 1976). The foliation, which is approximately parallel to the macroscopic, faulting-related fabric, is interpreted to record a heterogeneous, ductile flattening of the entire fault-zone complex.

Structural setting and displacement history

The Lopez fault zone is part of a system of folded, late Mesozoic thrusts in the San Juan Islands (Fig. 4). These thrusts may be related to an extensive thrust system of mid-Cretaceous age in the North Cascades 40–60 km to the E (Misch 1966), but the Mesozoic tectonic setting of these structures is as yet unclear. The San Juan archipelago is underlain by several lithologically heterogeneous formations and igneous complexes ranging in age from early Palaeozoic to Lower Cretaceous (Whetten *et al.* 1978) and comprising graywacke, mudstone, chert, mafic to intermediate volcanogenic rocks, and minor amounts of ultramafic rocks. To date, it has not been possible to restore all the mappable rock units into an original stratigraphic succession. Rather, it seems that stratigraphically

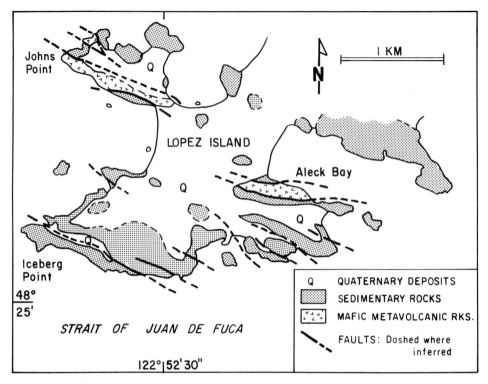

FIG. 5. Simplified geological map of the S part of Lopez Island. 'Sedimentary rocks' includes several petrologically distinct units comprising sandstone and mudstone turbidites and pebbly mudstones. Inferred extensions of some faults are shown to emphasize the lenticularity of slices.

unrelated tectonic elements have been juxta-posed, probably in a convergent setting near the late Mesozoic continental margin.

The Lopez zone illustrates why it is difficult to interpret and unravel this style of thrusting. The 'upper plate' (Fig. 4) comprises a mid-Jurassic ophiolite suite covered by a complex sequence of Jurassic–Cretaceous turbidites and volcanogenic rocks (Brown et al. 1979). Most of the structurally lowest slices in the fault zone are inferred to have been derived from the 'lower plate,' an extensive unit of volcanic-lastic sandstone and siltstones, with minor in-terbedded volcanic rocks and chert, which is also of Jurassic–Cretaceous age. Most of the rock unit correlative with these slices lies W of a younger thrust (BB in Fig. 4); the entire Lopez zone is truncated by this fault and was proba-bly displaced from its original location. Rocks in the upper and lower plates have not been observed in depositional contact, and their original stratigraphic relation, if any, is un-known. Some slices of meta-plutonic breccia and chert-granule sandstone in the Lopez zone are petrologically identical to rocks in the overlying unit, from which they apparently were derived, but many slices, such as strongly light rare-earth enriched pillow lavas of mid-Cretaceous age (Vance et al. 1980) have no known counterparts in either adjacent struc-tural unit. Thus, although the lithologic heterogeneity of the Lopez may partly reflect complex depositional patterns and facies rela-tions in overlying and underlying plates, other lithologic units, that are now represented only within the Lopez, have become imbricated and tectonically mixed as well.

Efforts to reconstruct the displacement di-rections across the Lopez fault zone are ham-pered by these stratigraphic uncertainties, and we have yet to discover unequivocal criteria in the complexly deformed rocks of the San Juan Islands. In the Lopez zone, flexural folds in bedded clastic sedimentary rocks and chert are rare, but most hinges trend approximately parallel to the fault zone and plunge 20°, or less, NW or SE. Overturning, where observed, is toward the SW. The low to moderate dips of faults throughout the archipelago suggest that dip-slip displacements were predominant.

Summary and discussion

The Navaho Divide and Lopez units typify some features of major Mesozoic fault zones in the westernmost North American Cordillera. They each contain and juxtapose diverse rock units interpreted either to constitute, or to have been deposited on, broadly ophiolitic basement. Field and petrographic evidence suggests that brittle deformation, at sub-greenschist facies conditions, accompanied faulting in the 'elastico-frictional regime' of Sibson (1977). The right half of Fig. 6 schematically illustrates one of the conspicuous differences between the Lopez zone and fault zones in the Ingalls Complex: the ratio of fine-grained, pervasively deformed 'matrix' to lenticular tectonic slices. Each fault zone represents an end member of an idealized spectrum in which the size of tectonic slices, or schuppen, decreases as the proportion of deformable matrix increases. The geometry and fabric in this diagram are scale-independent. Detailed, large-scale maps and cross-sections of parts of the Ingalls Complex, consisting of both voluminous cataclastically derived serpentinite matrix and slices too small to be shown at the scale of Fig. 3, would resemble the far right-hand side of Fig. 6. Similar tectonic complexes in California (Saleeby 1979) and the Alpine-Himalayan Orogen (Knipper 1971; Gansser 1974) have been termed 'serpentinite melanges,' a term which descriptively conveys an abundance of fine-grained, deformed matrix and a chaotic 'block-in-matrix' mesoscopic fabric imparted by dispersed tectonic inclusions.

In both the Lopez and Navaho Divide fault zones, the lenticularity of tectonic slices and the subparallel, anastomosing network of faults and fault zones recall similar geometric features of Rocky Mountain-type imbricate, or schuppen, zones. In spite of this similarity, there are important differences, depicted diagrammatically in Fig. 6. The imbricate zone in the left half of the figure consists of systematically repeated, geometrically simple slices derived from an orderly stratigraphic sequence. Each slice can be restored to its original position if the thicknesses of stratigraphic units, dips of listric faults, and the depth to authochthonous 'basement' are known. The fault zone in the right diagram comprises a varied suite of rock types. Although some of them may have been derived from adjacent stratigraphically and structurally complex 'eugeo-synclinal' sequences of turbidites, chert, and mafic and ultramafic rocks, others have exotic ages, lithologies, metamorphic assemblages, or deformational histories and are palinspastically non-restorable. Such fault zones typically occur sandwiched between stratigraphically unrelated structural units rather than as internally imbricated wedges detached from an underlying, regionally extensive basement as in the Canadian Rockies (Bally *et al.* 1966; Price & Mountjoy 1970). In the Rockies, the directions of dip-slip displacements and amounts of shortening can be reliably estimated by constructing balanced cross-sections, restoring systematically imbricated strata, and measuring the hinge lines of flexural folds genetically related to thrust faults. In our examples, summarized in the right diagram of Fig. 6, conventional techniques are not applicable, and the possibility that the imbricate structure itself

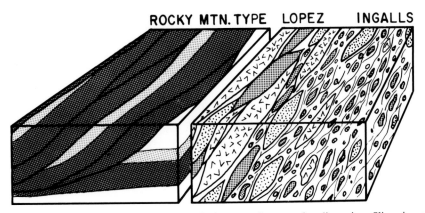

FIG. 6. Deformational styles in Cordilleran fault zones. See text for discussion. Slices in some imbricate zones (left block diagram) are systematically derived from stratigraphic layercakes; other fault zones are lithologically heterogeneous (right diagram) and slices are difficult to restore. Anastomosing lines represent foliation in deformed matrix.

results in part from strike-slip displacements across high-angle zones such as the Navaho Divide must be entertained as a working hypothesis.

ACKNOWLEDGMENTS. Research in the San Juan Islands by D. S. C. is supported by National Science Foundation Grants EAR 7613127 and 7910827.

Some of the work reported here was done by R. B. M. as part of a doctoral thesis under the supervision of P. Misch. This thesis work was supported by Geological Society of America Penrose Grants, the Department of Geological Sciences and the Graduate School at the University of Washington, the Amoco Foundation, and the Society of the Sigma Xi. We thank M. Brandon, P. Misch, and two anonymous reviewers for comments on an earlier version of the manuscript.

References

BALLY, A. W., GORDY, P. L. & STEWART, G. A. 1966. Structure, seismic data, and orogenic evolution of southern Canadian Rockies. *Bull. Can. Pet. Geol.* **14**, 337–81.

BROWN, E. H., BRADSHAW, J. Y. & MUSTOE, G. E. 1979. Plagiogranite and keratophyre in ophiolite on Fidalgo Island, Washington. *Bull. geol. Soc. Am.* **90**, 493–507.

GANSSER, A. 1974. The ophiolite melange, a worldwide problem on Tethyan examples. *Eclog. geol. Helv.* **67**, 479–507.

HARLAND, W. B. 1971. Tectonic transpression in Caledonian Spitsbergen. *Geol. Mag.* **108**, 27–42.

HOBBS, B. W., MEANS, W. D. & WILLIAMS, P. F. 1976. *An Outline of Structural Geology*. John Wiley & Sons, New York.

KNIPPER, A. L. 1971. Constitution and age of serpentinite melange in the Lesser Caucasus. *Geotectonics.* **5**, 275–82.

MILLER, R. B. 1980. *Structure, Petrology, and Emplacement of the Ingalls Complex, Central Washington Cascades.* Ph.D. dissertation, Univ. of Washington, Seattle (unpubl.).

—— & FROST, B. R. 1977. Geology of the Ingalls complex and related pre-late Cretaceous rocks of the Mount Stuart uplift, Central Cascades, Washington. *In*: BROWN, E. H. & ELLIS, R. C. (eds). *Geological Excursions in the Pacific Northwest.* Western Washington University, Bellingham, 283–91.

MISCH, P. 1966. Tectonic evolution of the northern Cascades of Washington State—a west Cordilleran case history. *Can. Inst. Ming. Metall. Spec.* **8**, 101–48.

—— 1977. Bedrock geology of the North Cascades. *In*: BROWN, E. H. & ELLIS, R. C. (eds). *Geological Excursions in the Pacific Northwest.* Western Washington University, Bellingham, 1–62.

PRICE, R. A. & MOUNTJOY, E. W. 1970. Geologic structure of the Canadian Rocky Mountains between Bow and Athabasca Rivers—a progress report. *Spec. Pap. geol. Assoc. Can.* **6**, 7–25.

SALEEBY, J. 1979. Kaweah serpentinite melange, southwest Sierra Nevada foot-hills, California. *Bull. geol. Soc. Am.* **90**, 29–46.

SIBSON, R. H. 1977. Fault rocks and fault mechanisms. *J. geol. Soc. London,* **133**, 191–213.

VANCE, J. A. 1977. The stratigraphy and structure of Orcas Island, San Juan Islands. *In*: BROWN, E. H. & ELLIS, R. C. (eds). *Geological Excursions in the Pacific Northwest.* Western Washington University, Bellingham, 170–203.

——, DUNGAN, M. A., BLANCHARD, D. P. & RHODES, J. M. 1980. Tectonic setting and trace element geochemistry of Mesozoic ophiolitic rocks in Western Washington. *Am. J. Sci.* **280A,** 359–88.

WHETTEN, J. T., JONES, D. L., COWAN, D. S. & ZARTMAN, R. E. 1978. Ages of Mesozoic terranes in the San Juan Islands, Washington. *In*: HOWELL, D. G. & McDOUGALL, K. A. (eds). *Mesozoic Paleogeography of the Western United States.* Pacific Sec., Soc. Econ. Paleo. Miner. Los. Angeles, California, 117–132.

D. S. COWAN, R. B. MILLER, Department of Geological Sciences, University of Washington, Seattle, Washington, 98195, U.S.A.
Present address of R. B. MILLER, Department of Geology, University of Kansas, Lawrence, Kansas, 66045, U.S.A.

Thrusts and nappes in the North American Appalachian Orogen

R. D. Hatcher Jr.

SUMMARY: The Appalachian Orogen in North America was subjected to three major deformational-thermal events: the Taconic (Ordovician–Silurian), Acadian (late Devonian), and Alleghanian (Permian). Each event involved large-scale horizontal transport of thrust-nappes ranging from tens to hundreds of kilometres in different parts of the orogen. Transport was dominantly westward although major Acadian-generated eastward transport occurred in southern New England.

There is a direct relationship between chronological proximity to a thermal peak and numbers of thrusts. Thrusts were produced during the Taconic and Acadian events which pre- and post-dated the thermal peak, as well as being synchronous with it. Transport of the Bay of Islands ophiolites and other large masses along the western margin of the orogen occurred before Taconic metamorphism, but probably only immediately before. Many large thrusts of the Appalachians were active during two or even three of the deformational-thermal events, and more than once within a single event. This is particularly true for the Blue-Ridge-Inner Piedmont mega-nappe, which involves at least 225 km of horizontal transport.

Compressional tectonics were probably the dominant process responsible for all thrusts in the Appalachians, except the Taconic klippes. The Alleghanian décollement Valley and Ridge thrusts are overridden by crystalline Alleghanian and older thrusts of the Blue Ridge in the southern Appalachians. The same mechanism must apply to the central Appalachians.

Thrusting and formation of crystalline thrust-nappes in the Appalachians and other mountain chains may be an adiabatic process which functions to dissipate much of the thermal energy produced during subduction (both A and B types) and collision events.

The Appalachian Orogen (Fig. 2) provides an excellent laboratory for the study of thrusts and nappes. Moreover, it has been a fertile area which has yielded some of the classic and fundamental principles of foreland thrusting (for example, Rich 1934; Rodgers 1949). It also contains some of the classical examples of large crystalline thrust sheets (e.g. in the Blue Ridge) as well as some of the best preserved ophiolites (Bay of Islands, Newfoundland) in the world (Fig. 3).

Some of the early attempts to model thrusts and associated folds were based upon studies of the Appalachian foreland by Willis (1893). More recent investigations have been aimed at resolution of tectonic elements of the core and studies of the mechanics of foreland thrusting.

The orogen is remarkably dissimilar from end to end, both with respect to geometry and timing of thrusting (Fig. 1), which is doubtless a function of the Precambrian eastern continental margin of North America, its early Palaeozoic depositional history, and the Palaeozoic history and mechanics of closing of small oceans and the Iapetus Ocean.

At least three major thermal-metamorphic events have affected the Appalachian Orogen (Fig. 1). Each, however, occurred at different intensity and, to some degree, in a different position along the length of the chain. Formation of thrusts is directly correlative with each thermal peak, some forming before, others near the peak and still others after. The process of thrusting in each case was accompanied by intrusions of plutons, predominantly of granitic, but also of mafic compositions.

The orogen has been divided into northern and southern halves for purposes of discussion. However, the division is real in a physical sense, because the dividing line is the region where the orogen reaches its narrowest point of 100–125 km wide at the New Jersey–New York border. It is here that the foreland thrust belt of the southern and central Appalachians is lost and few of the features of the crystalline Appalachians may be easily traced N or S across this narrow zone.

Southern and central Appalachians

The southern and central Appalachian foreland consists of a series of overlapping, westward-directed thrust sheets in the S which give

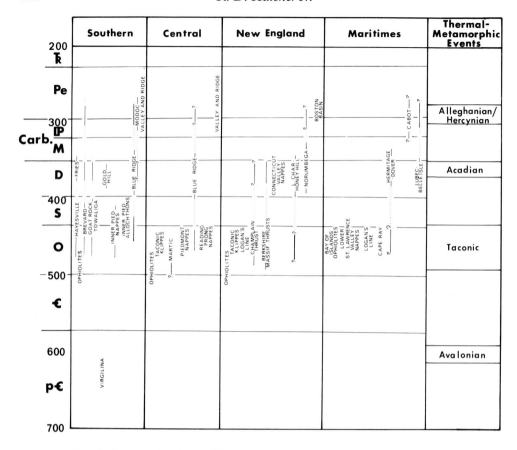

FIG. 1. Distribution of major Appalachian thrusts, other faults and thermal metamorphic events through time. Dotted lines indicate probable recurrent movement. Compiled from Dixon & Lundgren (1968); Thompson *et al.* (1968); Drake (1970); Rodgers (1970); Wise (1970) and Williams (1973, 1978).

way northward to westward-verging folds (Figs 2, 4 & 5). These structures were formed during Carboniferous and Permian times. While a controversy over basement involvement or non-involvement raged for a number of years (Rodgers 1949, 1964; Cooper 1961, 1964, 1968), drilling in the Plateau of the central Appalachians revealed that many of the anticlines pass downward into blind thrusts (Gwinn 1964). This interpretation of blind thrusts over a regional décollement has been projected into the central Appalachian Valley and Ridge (Gwinn 1964, 1970).

More recently, interpretation of seismic data from the Valley and Ridge of Pennsylvania and Tennessee leads to the conclusion that the thin-skinned deformational style prevailed in the deformation of the foreland (Jacobeen & Kanes 1974; Harris 1976; Harris & Milici

1977; Tegland 1978). Additional seismic data from the southern Appalachian Valley and Ridge, Blue Ridge and Piedmont indicate that the thin-skinned deformational style extends beneath major portions of the crystalline Appalachians as well (Cook *et al.* 1979).

An unresolved controversy in the Appalachian foreland, as in other similar terranes, is whether the driving mechanism is gravity or compression. Gwinn (1964, 1970), Milici (1975) and Dennison (1976) have proposed gravity mechanisms for deformation of the southern and central Appalachian foreland. Milici (1975) concluded from the overlap pattern of successive thrust sheets in Tennessee and Virginia that a gravity mechanism produced a W–E old-to-young overlap sequence of thrusts. Problems are encountered in the transition from Valley and Ridge to Blue

Ridge thrusts. Thrusts occur in the Blue Ridge which have been shown independently to be much older, rather than younger, than Valley and Ridge thrusts. Dennison's (1976) gravity mechanism is based upon uplift of the Blue Ridge and the sliding-off of its cover. This, and other similar gravity mechanisms, (e.g. Gwinn 1964) have been brought into serious question by Geiser (1978) where he pointed out that deformation involving crystalline basement rocks in the Blue Ridge has been tied in several places to Valley and Ridge deformation.

Appalachian foreland thrusts are characteristically sharp surfaces containing only thin zones of cataclasis, unless two competent units of similar or slightly different strengths have been brought together. Extensive breccia zones several metres or tens of metres thick may result where thick sandstones, limestones and dolostones are juxtaposed.

Thrusts of the Blue Ridge are more complex than those of the foreland. Décollement thin-skinned thrusts occur in the western Great Smoky Mountains of Tennessee and N Georgia (King 1964). In the central Appalachians and as far S as northeastern Tennessee, westward transport of crystalline basement rocks has occurred along thrusts on the western edge of the Blue Ridge. However, the Blue Ridge thrust becomes discontinuous from about Buchanan, Virginia, northward (Spencer 1968) and the Blue Ridge continues as an anticlinorium. The thrust reappears at Front Royal (Wickham 1972) and near Waynesboro, Virginia (Gathright *et al.* 1977). These thrusts are also sharp breaks but generally have cataclastic zones 1–20 cm or more thick associated with them. The same style of deformation prevails in the Linville Falls fault, which frames the Grandfather Mountain Window. Farther N, in Pennsylvania, New Jersey and New York, basement rocks have been transported W in a series of thrusts/recumbent folds in the Reading Prong and Hudson Highlands (Drake 1970). This zone marks a possible northern continuation of the Blue Ridge.

There exist a number of older major faults in the Blue Ridge and Piedmont whose movement histories precede the Taconic metamorphic peak. The Greenbrier fault of the Great Smoky Mountains (Hadley & Goldsmith 1963; King 1964) has been known for many years. The Hayesville and Shope Fork faults have been demonstrated to be pre-metamorphic faults (Hatcher 1978, Hatcher *et al.* 1979). Most of these faults occur in high grade terranes and are probably tectonic slides recognized by truncation of stratigraphic units. Most

have relatively insignificant mylonite or cataclastic zones associated with them, unless they were reactivated later (most were not).

The Hayesville fault is a fundamental boundary which separates a terrane of mafic volcanic and ultramafic rocks, metasedimentary rocks, granite plutons and rare continental basement rocks to the E from a metasedimentary nonvolcanic terrane which is easily tied to continental basement (Hatcher 1978). Part of this thrust has been reactivated toward the NE (Fries fault) and has a post-metamorphic history (Rankin *et al.* 1973).

The Martic line of Maryland and Pennsylvania is another of these early thrusts which was emplaced before Taconic metamorphism, then deformed but not reactivated later (Wise 1970).

The Blue Ridge Thrust of the Carolinas, Tennessee, SW Virginia and Georgia appears to be a major sole thrust from which several other thrusts have risen at different times. Aeromagnetic and gravity data suggest this is a single large thrust sheet which includes the western Piedmont (Chauga belt, Inner Piedmont and Kings Mountain belt) of the southern Appalachians (Hatcher & Zietz 1978, 1979). The Brevard zone becomes a splay off the main sole and the Towaliga and Goat Rock faults expose the sole in the SW Piedmont of Georgia and Alabama (Figs 2 & 3). Seismic reflection data (Clark *et al.* 1978; Cook *et al.* 1979) strongly support this concept.

The Brevard zone is probably the most intensively studied structure in the southern Appalachians. It consists of a complex assemblage of mylonitic and cataclastic rocks formed from various rock units that occur along its length. One of its attributes is that it is extensively localized in particular stratigraphic units. Its movement history spans much of the Palaeozoic and consists of early (Taconic, pre-to synmetamorphic) and intermediate phases of ductile movement (Acadian), then later brittle (Alleghanian) phases of movement. The brittle phases probably served to ramp the fault zone into the Blue Ridge Thrust sheet as one of the last movement events (Hatcher 1978). The earlier ductile phase may be related to the formation of the great sole thrust which resides beneath the Blue Ridge and western Piedmont.

Several high-angle compressional faults exist in the Piedmont. The Gold Hill-Silver Hill fault of the central Piedmont of N Carolina has been shown to have an Acadian age (Butler & Fullagar 1978). Several faults farther E extending from Georgia to Virginia have been called the Eastern Piedmont Fault System (Hatcher *et al.* 1977). These have been shown to have formed during the Hercynian event (Kish *et al.* 1978). Most of these faults contain extensive zones of mylonite and cataclasite indicating a polyphase history and have a dominant dip-slip component of movement. However, they probably also had a significant strike-slip component of movement.

Early, large-scale recumbent nappes reside in the Inner Piedmont (Griffin 1971, 1974) and Blue Ridge (Hatcher 1973, 1977). These structures formed near the Taconic metamorphic-thermal peak, rode on tectonic slides and are responsible for large-scale horizontal transport (Hatcher 1972). The final emplacement of these nappes is post-thermal peak, since they truncate metamorphic isograds, yet characteristically do not have mylonite (or cataclasite) zones associated with them. The Alto and Smith River allochthons of Georgia and North Carolina/Virginia respectively represent large remnants of some of these nappes is post-thermal peak, since they truncate metamorphic isograds, yet characteristically do not have mylonite (or cataclasite) zones associated with them. The Alto and Smith River allochthons of Georgia and North Carolina/Virginia respectively represent large remnants of some of these nappes which occur near the Brevard zone.

The southern and central Appalachian Orogen contains its oldest thrusts and nappes in the core and the youngest on its flanks (Hatcher & Odom 1980). It is an orogen deformed from the inside out. Its deformational history is not unlike other classic orogens, such as the western Alps and Canadian Cordillera.

New England and Maritime Appalachians

The New England and Maritime Appalachians contain several large thrusts along their western edge and a number of high angle reverse faults along the eastern edge (Fig. 3). The central core of southern New England and Newfoundland contains thrusts and nappes involving high grade metamorphic rocks (Fig. 6).

Thrusts of the western margin were emplaced during the Taconic event. They all are E vergent toward the craton. Logan's line thrust, the thrusts in the Quebec Appalachians (St. Julien & Hubert 1975) and those of western Newfoundland fall into this group. The Champlain Thrust has a movement history that probably began during the Taconic Orogeny but movement may have occurred again later in the Acadian Orogeny (Rodgers 1970). These thrusts along the western margin behave as décollement thrusts and are confined to the Palaeozoic cover rocks.

Taconic klippes extend northward from Pennsylvania to Newfoundland. These are detachment masses of eugeoclinal rocks which appear to be without roots and to have been emplaced by gravity (Zen 1967, 1972; Rodgers 1970). However, a compressional mechanism may be implied by the work of Kidd & Delano (1979).

The Humber Arm allochthon of western Newfoundland appears to be a typical Taconic allochthon emplaced in Ordovician time. However, the Bay of Islands ophiolite sheets were then emplaced on top of this and other allochthons in this region (Williams 1973). If the Humber Arm allochthon was emplaced by a gravity mechanism, perhaps it was shed from

---

FIG. 2. Map showing the principal subdivisions of the Appalachian Orogen. AA-Alto allochthon. GMW-Grandfather Mountain window. SRA: Smith River allochthon. Heavy straight lines in the southern, central and New England Appalachians are the locations of cross-sections. Compiled from maps by Rodgers (1970), Williams (1978), and other published sources.

FIG. 3. Map of the Appalachians showing the principal thrusts and other major faults. Compiled from Rodgers (1970), St. Julien & Hubert (1975), Hatcher (1978), and Williams (1978).

FIG. 4. Cross-section through the southern Appalachians. Extensively modified and revised from Hatcher (1972, fig. 1). p€b: Grenville basement rocks. p€sv: Upper Precambrian metasedimentary and metavolcanic rocks. p€d: Upper Precambrian Ocoee series. p€–€msv: Upper Precambrian to Cambrian metasedimentary and metavolcanic rocks. p€–PZmsv: Upper Precambrian to Lower Palaeozoic metasedimentary and metavolcanic rocks. €–p€sv: Cambrian to Upper Precambrian metasedimentary to metavolcanic rocks. €s–€ch: Cambrian Chilhowee Group and Shady Dolomite, undivided. €r: Rome Formation. O€k–€c: Conasauga and Knox Groups, undivided. M.O.: Middle Ordovician rocks. PZi: Palaeozoic intrusive rocks. KTs: Cretaceous and Tertiary sedimentary rocks. HF: Hayesville fault. CBS: Central Blue Ridge suture. BZ: Brevard zone. CPS: Central Piedmont suture. MF: Modoc fault.

the rising ocean floor prior to the obduction of the ophiolite sheets. Other ophiolites, such as the Mings Bight, Point Rousse and Betts Cove complexes of the Burlington Penninsula, were emplaced farther into the orogen and then overprinted by Taconic metamorphism (Williams *et al.* 1977).

Taconic thrusts involve continental basement rocks in the Berkshire Massif, Hudson Highlands and Reading Prong of western Massachusetts, New York, and New Jersey respectively (Ratcliffe & Harwood 1975; Drake 1970). Many of the thrusts of the Berkshire Massif are involved with Taconic recumbent folding and merge eastward with W vergent nappes of Acadian age (Ratcliffe & Harwood 1975; Osberg 1975; Stanley 1975).

Large-scale nappes associated with gneiss domes in the Connecticut River valley have been described by Thompson *et al.* (1968) and Hepburn (1975). These structures were formed during the Acadian Orogeny and involve rocks as high as the second sillimanite zone (Thompson *et al.* 1968). These structures plunge NE and are no longer recognizable in the low grade Silurian cover of central to northern Maine (Williams 1978).

A large system of W and NE dipping thrusts has been identified in eastern Connecticut by Dixon & Lundgren (1968) and Lundgren & Ebblin (1972). Connection of the NE-Dipping Honey Hill fault with the W-dipping Lake Char and Tatnic faults is indicated by work by Wintsch (1979). Wintsch has also recognized a fault encircling the Willimantic dome farther W and suggests that these are part of the same E-vergent system, implying a minimum eastward horizontal transport of about 34 km. This

system of faults is a ductile fault system in which extensive mylonites were formed and faulting took place at conditions ranging from greenschist to upper amphibolite or granulite facies and must have an Acadian age (Wintsch 1979).

Several large high-angle faults and associated extensive mylonite zones exist in eastern Massachusetts (Fig. 3). These fault zones appear to have experienced much of their movement histories during the Acadian Orogeny (Nelson 1976). One, or more, may be connected to the Lake Char Thrust farther SW (Skehan 1969), to the Lubec-Bellisle fault system (Brown & Helmstaedt 1970) and possibly the other large faults (e.g. the Norumbega) of the Maine coast farther NE. Some of the deformation and high angle faulting in the eastern New England and Maritime Appalachians has a late Palaeozoic age (Skehan 1969). The Cabot and related faults are part of a major strike-slip system that probably can be correlated to the British Isles (Belt 1969; Phillips *et al.* 1976). Rast & Grant (1973) suggest that these strike-slip faults, principally the Chedabucto fault, offset the Variscan front, so it is not observed in Newfoundland but comes ashore in New Brunswick and Massachusetts as the large Variscan fault system of thrusts and strike-slip faults.

Several E-vergent thrusts (e.g. the Dover fault) exist in central Newfoundland (Figs 2 & 3; Williams, 1978). These are either Acadian or later structures. Recumbent and reclined E-vergent folds occur in the Gander zone west of the Dover fault and are probably Acadian structures (Kennedy 1976).

Deformation of the New England and

FIG. 5. Cross-section through the Appalachians in Pennsylvania and Maryland. Extensively modified from sections in Gray (1960) and Weaver (1968). pCb: Grenville basement rocks. pCsv: Upper Precambrian metasedimentary and metavolcanic rocks (Catoctin volcanics). pC–PZmsv: Upper Precambrian and Lower Palaeozoic metasedimentary and metavolcanic rocks. PZ–pCms: Palaeozoic to Upper Precambrian metasedimentary rocks. um: ultramafic rocks. Cch: Chilhowee Group rocks. C: Cambrian rocks undivided. O: Ordovician rocks, undivided. Om: Martinsburg Formation (Middle to Upper Ordovician). S: Silurian rocks. D: Devonian rocks. C: Carboniferous rocks. PZ: Palaeozoic metasedimentary and metavolcanic rocks. PZi: Palaeozoic intrusive rocks. TrJ: Triassic–Jurassic sedimentary rocks.

FIG. 6. Cross-section through part of the New England Appalachians. Modified from published sections by Skehan (1968), Thomson *et al.* (1968), Ratcliffe & Harwood (1975) and data from geological maps by Zen (1967), Hatch (1975) and other published sources. pCb: Grenville basement rocks. pCv: Upper Precambrian (Avalonian) metavolcanic and metasedimentary rocks. C: Cambrian rocks, undivided. CO: Cambrian and Lower Ordovician rocks. OC: Upper Cambrian and Ordovician rocks. O: Ordovician rocks, undivided. Og: Oliverian gneisses (Ordovician and older). Om: Middle Ordovician rocks. OD: Ordovician, Silurian and Devonian rocks. SD: Silurian and Devonian rocks. S: Silurian rocks, undivided. D: Devonian rocks, undivided. Si: Silurian intrusive rocks. Di: Devonian intrusive rocks. C: Carboniferous rocks TrJ: Triassic–Jurassic sedimentary and volcanic rocks.

Maritime Appalachians proceeded along a W to E plan. Oldest structures rode onto the Precambrian/early Palaeozoic continental margin. Younger deformation in the core appears to have reactivated crust produced during the Taconic Orogeny while the late Palaeozoic deformation in the E may deform either a reactivated Taconic crust or one produced during the Acadian Orogeny (Osberg 1978).

Discussion

The Appalachians is an orogen of contrasting deformational styles. Perhaps the most striking contrast is the lack of an extensive foreland in New England and the Maritimes. It is interesting that the foreland is terminated just SW of the Adirondack uplift. There must however, be a relationship of foreland thrusting to stratigraphy NE and SW of the Adirondacks. Toward the SW exist extensive Palaeozoic platform and deltaic/molasse successor sequences. NE of the Adirondacks, the platform sequences are principally of the Cambro-Ordovician carbonate bank which overlie the Precambrian basement (Rodgers 1968). Thrusts forming in these rocks do not have the extensive décollement zones high in the sequences that are available in the S.

There is a decrease in total number of thrusts from S to N (Fig. 3). The deformational style of the southern Appalachians is dominated by large thrusts, (Fig. 4), whereas only the western part of the New England and Maritime Appalachians, with the exception of eastern Connecticut and Massachusetts, is dominated by thrusts (Fig. 6). However, gravity data (McGinnis *et al.* 1979) suggest that the western half of the central Appalachians may be allochthonous in the same manner as the southern Appalachians.

The mechanism by which thrusting occurs deserves additional consideration. Elliott (1976*a*) has concluded that the relative strengths of rocks involved in foreland thrusting are such that gravity forces seem favoured for emplacement of thrust sheets. However, Chapple (1978) considers a model in which the detachment exhibits plastic behaviour, is much weaker than the overlying sedimentary section, and involves a high fluid pressure. As a result, Chapple showed that compressive flow is a more likely driving mechanism in foreland thrust belts. This may solve the problem that deformation of crystalline basement rocks of the central Appalachian Blue Ridge has been temporally and spatially connected with defor-

mation in the foreland in Virginia and Maryland (Cloos 1971). A similar connection may be made in the southern Appalachians. Mechanisms, such as the gravitational spreading concept (Price & Mountjoy 1970; Price 1971, 1974), should probably be modified or abandoned in light of Chapple's conclusions.

Elliott (1976*b*) has considered the energy involved in thrusting in the form of mechanical work expended in the emplacement of the McConnell Thrust in Alberta. Bird *et al.* (1975) have attempted to model the thermal effects of continent-continent collision and conclude that metamorphism and anatexis are produced by frictional heating or by radioactive heating if plates are in contact for more than 30 Ma. This poses a fundamental question regarding thrust faults: the ultimate source of energy for both crystalline and foreland thrusts. Armstrong & Dick (1974) concluded that crystalline thrusts are generated at the ductile-brittle interface behind a subducting mass. Their conclusions, and those outlined above, indicate that the ultimate generator must be thermal, so we are also concerned with the heat source for thermal processes in orgenic belts.

Consider the possibility that mountain chains, and particularly the metamorphic core zones, are essentially thermally closed systems. The process of thrusting could, therefore, be an adiabatic process if thermal energy is used to generate and drive thrust sheets. All mechanical work would be carried out in the emplacement of thrusts, and a thermal/metamorphic event could be self-consuming in the sense that the thrusts remove heat from the core of the orogen thereby terminating the event. The Appalachians may serve very well as a model for this process.

Conclusions

1. The southern and central Appalachians were deformed from the inside out; the New England and Maritime Appalachians were deformed W–E.

2. The broad Appalachian foreland terminates in New York because of fundamental changes in stratigraphy, buttressing by the basement and original differences in the configuration of the ancient continental margin of North America.

3. The southern Appalachians is a thrust-dominated terrane. Differences farther N are caused by similar differences as those outlined in conclusion 2 and the history of opening and closing of small oceans and Iapetus along the orogen.

4. The only gravity-generated thrusts in the Appalachian Orogen may be the Taconic klippes. Gravity (sliding or spreading) as the principal deformation mechanism in the foreland or crystallines suffers from difficulties with timing and a means to uplift and break crystalline rocks gravitationally. A compressional mechanism is therefore appropriate.

5. Close association of thrusting with thermal events may mean that the process of thrusting is adiabatic. Thrusts may terminate thermal events by using heat energy to carry out mechanical work within an essentially closed system.

References

ARMSTRONG, R. L. & DICK, H. J. B. 1974. A model for the development of thin overthrust sheets of crystalline rocks. *Geology*, **1**, 35–40.

BELT, E. S. 1969. Newfoundland Carboniferous stratigraphy and its relation to the Maritimes and Ireland, In: KAY, G. M. (ed). *North Atlantic—Geology and Continental Drift*, International Conf., Gander, Newfoundland 1967, Symposium. Mem. Am. Assoc. Petrol. Geol. **12**, 737–53.

BIRD, P., TOKSOZ, M. N., & SLEEP, N. H. 1975. Thermal and mechanical models of continental-continent convergence zones. *J. geophys. Res.* **80**, 4405–16.

BROWN, R. L. & HELMSTAEDT, H. 1970. Deformational history in part of the Lubec-Belleisle zone of southern New Brunswick. *Can. J. Earth Sci.* **7**, 748–67.

BUTLER, J. R. & FULLAGAR, P. D. 1978. Petrochemical and geochronological studies of plutonic rocks in the southern Appalachians III. Leucocratic adamellites of the Charlotte belt near Salisbury, North Carolina. *Bull. geol. Soc. Am.* **89**, 460–66.

CHAPPLE, W. M. 1978. Mechanics of thin-skinned fold-and-thrust belts. *Bull. geol. Soc. Am.* **89**, 1189–98.

CLARK, H. B., COSTAIN, J. K. & GLOVER, III, 1978. Structural and seismic reflection studies of the Brevard ductile deformation zone near Rosman North Carolina. *Am. J. Sci.* **278**, 419–41.

CLOOS, E. 1971. Microtectonics along the western edge of the Blue Ridge, Maryland and Virginia. *Johns Hopkins Univ. Studies in Geology*, **9**, 206 p.

COOK, F. A., ALBAUGH, D. S., BROWN, L. D., KAUFMAN, S. OLIVER, J. E. & HATCHER, R. D. JR. 1979. Thin-skinned tectonics in the crystalline southern Appalachians; COCORP seismic-reflection profiling of the Blue Ridge and Piedmont. *Geology*, **7**, 563–7.

COOPER, B. N. 1961, Grand Appalachian field excursion. *Va. Engr. Exper. Sta. Exten. Ser. Geol. Guidebook* **1**, 187 p.

—— 1964. Relations of stratigraphy to structure in the southern Appalachians, In: LOWRY, W. D. (ed). *Tectonics of the Southern Appalachians*. Mem. Virginia Poltech. Inst. Dept. Geol. Sci. **1**, 81–114.

—— 1968. Profile of the folded Appalachians of West Virginia. *UMR Jour.* **1**, 27–64.

DENNISON, J. M. 1976. Gravity tectonic removal of cover of Blue Ridge actictinorium to form Valley and Ridge province. *Bull. geol. Soc. Am.* **87**, 1470–6.

DIXON, H. R. & LUNDGREN, L. W., Jr. 1968. Structure of eastern Connecticut, In: ZEN, E-AN, WHITE, W. S. & HADLEY, J. B. (eds). *Studies of Appalachian Geology: Northern and Maritime.* Interscience, New York, 219–30.

DRAKE, A. A., Jr. 1970. Structural geology of the Reading Prong, In: FISHER, G. W., PETTIJOHN, F. J., REED, J. C., Jr. & WEAVER, K. N. (eds). *Studies of Appalachian Geology. Central and Southern.* Interscience, New York, 271–91.

ELLIOTT, D. 1976a. The motion of thrust sheets. *J. geophys. Res.* **81**, 949–63.

—— 1976b. The energy balance and deformation mechanisms of thrust sheets. *Philos. Trans. R. Soc. London*, **A283**, 289–312.

GATHRIGHT, T. M., II, HENIKA, W. S. & SULLIVAN, J. L. 1977. Basement cataclasis and nappe formation in the Blue Ridge of central Virginia. *Geol. Soc. Am. Abs. with Prog.* **9**, 138–9.

GEISER, P. 1978. Gravity tectonic removal of cover of Blue Ridge anticlinorium to form Valley and Ridge province: Discussion. *Bull. geol. Soc. Am.* **89**, 1429–30.

GRAY, C. 1960. *Geologic map of Pennsylvania.* Pennsylvania Top. and Geol. Survey, scale 1/250,000.

GRIFFIN, V. S. Jr. 1971. Inner Piedmont belt of the southern crystalline Appalachians: *Bull. geol. Soc. Am.* **82**, 1885–98.

—— 1974. Analysis of the Piedmont in northwest South Carolina. *Bull. geol. Soc. Am.* **85**, 1123–31.

GWINN, V. E. 1964. Thin-skinned tectonics in the Plateau and northwestern Valley and Ridge provinces of the central Appalachians. *Bull. geol. Soc. Am.* **75**, 863–99.

—— 1970. Kinematic patterns and estimates of lateral shortening, Valley and Ridge and Great Valley provinces, central Appalachians, south-central Pennsylvania, In: FISHER, G. W., PETTIJOHN, F. J., REED, J. C. Jr. & WEAVER, K. N. (eds). *Studies of Appalachian Geology: Central and Southern.* Interscience, New York, 127–46.

HADLEY, J. B. & GOLDSMITH, R. 1963. Geology of the eastern Great Smoky Mountains, North Carolina and Tennessee. *Prof. Pap. U.S. geol. Surv.* **349-B**, 118 p.

HARRIS, L. D. 1976. Thin-skinned tectonics and potential hydrocarbon traps-illustrated by a seismic profile in the Valley and Ridge province of Tennessee. *J. Res. U.S. geol. Surv.* **4**, 379–86.

—— & MILICI, R. C. 1977. Characteristics of thin-skinned style of deformation in the southern Appalachians, and potential hydrocarbon traps. *Prof. Pap. U.S. geol. Surv.* **1018,** 40 p.

HARWOOD, D. S. & ZIETZ, I. 1977. *Geologic Interpretation of an Aeromagnetic Map of Southern New England.* U.S. Geol. Surv. Map GP-906, scale 1/250,000.

HATCH, N. L., Jr., 1975. Tectonic, metamorphic, and intrusive history of part of the east side of the Berkshire Massif, Massachusetts, *In:* HARWOOD, D. S. (ed). *Tectonic Studies of the Berkshire Massif, Western Massachusetts, Connecticut and Vermont.* Prof. Pap. U.S. geol. Surv. **888,** 51–62.

HATCHER, R. D. Jr. 1972. Developmental model for the southern Appalachians. *Bull. geol. Soc. Am.* **83,** 2735–60.

—— 1973. Basement versus cover rocks in the Blue Ridge of northeast Georgia, northwestern South Carolina and adjacent North Carolina. *Am. J. Sci.* **273,** 671–85.

—— 1977. Macroscopic polyphase folding illustrated by the Toxaway Dome, eastern Blue Ridge, South Carolina-North Carolina. *Bull. geol. Soc. Am.* **89,** 1678–88.

—— 1978. Tectonics of the western Piedmont and Blue Ridge: Review and speculation. *Am. J. Sci.* **278,** 276–304.

—— ACKER, L. L., BRYAN, J. G. & GODFREY, S. C. 1979. The Hayesville thrust of the central Blue Ridge of North Carolina and nearby Georgia: A pre-metamorphic, polydeformed thrust and cryptic suture within the Blue Ridge thrust sheet. *Geol. Soc. Am. Abs. with Prog.* **11,** 181.

—— & ODOM, A. L. 1980. Timing of thrusting in the southern Appalachians, USA: Model for orogeny? *J. geol. Soc. London,* **137,** 321–7.

—— HOWELL, D. E., TALWANI, Pradeep. 1977. Eastern Piedmont fault system: Speculations on its extent. *Geology,* **5,** 636–40.

—— & ZIETZ, I. 1978. Thin crystalline thrust sheets in the southern Appalachian Inner Piedmont and Blue Ridge; interpretation based upon regional aeromagnetic data. *Geol. Soc. Am. Abs. with Prog.* **10,** 417.

—— & —— 1979. Interpretation of regional aeromagnetic and gravity data from the southeastern United States, Part II—Tectonic implications for the southern Appalachians. *Geol. Soc. Am. Abs. with Prog.* **11,** 181–2.

HEPBURN, J. C. 1975. Tectonic and metamorphic chronology of the Devonian and Silurian rocks in the Guilford dome area, southeastern Vermont, *In:* HARWOOD, D. S. (ed). *Tectonic Studies of the Berkshire Massif, Western Massachusetts, Connecticut and Vermont.* Prof. Pap. U.S. geol. Surv. **888,** 33–50.

JACOBEEN, F. Jr. & KANES, W. H. 1974. Structure of the Broadtop synclinorium and its implications for Appalachian structural style. *Bull. Am. Assoc. Petrol. Geol.* **58,** 362–5.

KENNEDY, M. J. 1976. Southeastern margin of the northeastern Appalachians: Late Precambrian orogeny on a continental margin. *Bull. geol. Soc. Am.* **87,** 1317–25.

KIDD, W. S. F. & DELANO, L. L. 1979. Two "black-green" boundaries in the northern Taconic allochthon. *Geol. Soc. Am. Abs. with Prog.* **11,** 19.

KING, P. B. 1964. Geology of the central Great Smoky Mountains, Tennessee. *Prof. Pap. U.S. geol. Surv.* **349-C,** 148 p.

KISH, A., FULLAGAR, P. D., SNOKE, A. W. & SECOR, D. T., Jr. 1978. The Kiokee belt of South Carolina (Part 1): Evidence for late Paleozoic deformation and metamorphism in the southern Appalachian Piedmont. *Geol. Soc. Am. with Prog.* **10,** 172–3.

LUNDGREN, L. W., Jr. & EBBLIN, C. 1972. Honey Hill fault in eastern Connecticut: Regional relations. *Bull. geol. Soc. Am.* **83,** 2773–94.

McGINNIS, L. D., WOLFE, M. G., KOHSMANN, J. J. & ERVIN, C. P. 1979. Regional free air gravity anomalies and tectonic observations in the United States. *J. geophys. Res.* **84,** 591–601.

MILICI, R. C. 1975. The structural patterns in the southern Appalachians: evidence for a gravity slide mechanism for Alleghanian deformation. *Bull. geol. Soc. Am.* **86,** 1316–20.

NELSON, A. E. 1976. Structural elements and deformational history of rocks in eastern Massachusetts. *Bull. geol. Soc. Am. Bull.* **87,** 1377–83.

OSBERG, P. H. 1975. Recumbent folding of the Goshen and Waits River Formations, western Massachusetts, *In:* HARWOOD, D. S. (ed). *Tectonic Studies of the Berkshire Massif, Western Massachusetts, Connecticut and Vermont,* Prop. Pap. U.S. geol. Surv. **888,** 63–8.

—— 1978. Synthesis of the geology of the northeastern Appalachians, USA, *In:* TOZER, E. T. & SCHENK, P. E. (eds). *Caledonian-Appalachian Orogen of the North Atlantic Region.* Pap. geol. Surv. Can. **78-13.** 137–47.

PHILLIPS, W. E. A., STILLMAN, C. J. & MURPHY, T. 1976. A Caledonian plate tectonic model. *J. geol. Soc. London,* **132,** 579–609.

PRICE, R. A. 1971. Gravitational sliding and the foreland thrust and fold belt of the North American Cordillera: Discussion. *Bull. geol. Soc. Am.* **82,** 1133–88.

—— 1974. Large scale gravitational flow of supracrustal rocks, southern Canadian Rockies, *In:* DEJONG, K. A. & SCHOLTEN, R. (eds). *Gravity and Tectonics.* New York, John Wiley and Sons, Inc., 491–502.

PRICE, R. A. & MOUNTJOY, E. W. 1970. Geologic structure of the Canadian Rocky Mountains between Bow and Athabaska Rivers—progress report. *Spec. Pap. Geol. Assoc. Can.* **6,** 7–25.

RANKIN, D. W., ESPENSHADE, G. H. & SHAW, K. W. 1973. Stratigraphy and structure of the metamorphic belt in northwestern North Carolina and southwestern Virginia: A study from the Blue Ridge across the Brevard zone to the Saruratown Mountains anticlinorium. *Am. J. Sci.* **273-A,** 1–40.

RAST, N. & GRANT, R. 1973. Transatlantic correlation of the Variscan-Appalachian orogeny. *Am. J. Sci.* **273,** 572–9.

RATCLIFFE, N. M. & HARWOOD, D. S. 1975. Blastomylonites associated with recumbent folds and overthrusts at the western edge of the Berkshire Massif, Connecticut and Massachusetts—a preliminary report, *In:* HARWOOD, D. S. (ed). *Tectonic Studies of the Berkshire Massif, Western Massachusetts, Connecticut, and Vermont.* Prof. Pap U.S. geol. Surv. **888,** 1–20.

RICH, J. L. 1934. Mechanics of Low-Angle overthrust faulting as illustrated by the Cumberland thrust block, Virginia, Kentucky, Tennessee. *Bull. Am. Assoc. Petrol. Geol.* **18,** 1584–96.

RODGERS, J. 1949. Evolution of thought on structure of Middle and Southern Appalachians. *Bull. Am. Assoc. Petrol. Geol.* **33,** 1643–54.

—— 1964. Basement and no-basement hypotheses in the Jura and the Appalachian Valley and Ridge, *In:* LOWRY, W. D. (ed). *Tectonics of the Southern Appalachians.* Mem. Virginia Polytech. Inst. Dept. Geol. Sci. **1,** 71–80.

—— 1968. The eastern edge of the North American continent during the Cambrian and early Ordovician, *In:* ZEN, E-AN, WHITE, W. S. & HADLEY, J. B. *Studies of Appalachian Geology: Northern and Maritime.* Interscience, New York, 141–49.

—— 1970. *The Tectonics of the Appalachians.* Wiley-Interscience, New York, 271 p.

SKEHAN, J. W. 1968. Fracture tectonics of southeastern New England as illustrated by the Wachusett-Marlborough Tunnel, east-central Massachusetts, *In:* ZEN, E-AN, WHITE, W. S. & HADLEY, J. B. (eds). *Studies of Appalachian Geology: Northern and Maritime.* Interscience, New York, 281–90.

—— 1969. Tectonic framework of southern-New England and eastern New York, *In:* KAY, G. M. (ed). *North Atlantic-Geology and Continental Drift.* Mem. Am. Assoc. Petrol Geol. **12,** 793–814.

SPENCER, E. W. 1968. Geology of the Natural Bridge, Sugarloaf Mountain, Buchanan and Arnold Valley Quadrangles, Virginia. *Virginia Div. Min. Res. Dept. Inv.* **13,** 35 p., map scale 1/24,000.

STANLEY, R. S. 1975. Time and space relationships of structures associated with the domes of southwestern Massachusetts and western Connecticut, *In:* HARWOOD, D. S. (ed). *Tectonic Studies of the Berkshire Massif, Western Mas*sachusetts, *Conneticut and Vermont.* Prof. Pap. U.S. geol. Surv. **888,** 69–96.

ST. JULIEN, P. & HUBERT, C. 1975. Evolution of the Taconian orogen in the Quebec Appalachians. *Am. J. Sci.* **275-A,** 337–62.

TEGLAND, E. R. 1978. Seismic investigations in eastern Tennessee. *Bull. Tennessee Div. Geol.* **78,** 68 p.

THOMPSON, J. B., Jr., ROBINSON, P. CLIFFORD, T. N. & TRASK, N. J., Jr., 1968. Nappes and gneiss domes in west-central New England, *In:* ZEN, E-AN, WHITE, W. S. & HADLEY, J. B. (eds). *Studies of Appalachian Geology: Northern and Maritime.* Interscience, New York, 203–18.

WEAVER, K. N. 1968. *Geologic Map of Maryland* Maryland Geol. Survey, scale 1/250,000.

WICKHAM, J. S. 1972. Structural history of a portion of the Blue Ridge, northern Virginia. *Bull. geol. Soc. Am.* **83,** 723–60.

WILLIAMS, H. 1973. Bay of Islands map-area, Newfoundland. *Pap. geol. Surv. Can.* **72–34,** 7 p., map scale 1/125,000.

—— 1978. *Tectonic-lithofacies Map of the Appalachian Orogen.* Memorial Univ. Newfoundland, scale 1/1,000,000.

——, HIBBARD, J. P. & BURSNALL, J. T. 1977. Geological setting of asbestos-bearing ultramafic rocks along the Baie Verte lineament, Newfoundland. *Pap. geol. Surv. Can.* **77–1A,** 351–60.

WILLIS, B. 1893. The mechanics of Appalachian structure. *U.S. Geol. Survey, 13th Ann. Rept.,* Pt. 2, 211–81.

WINTSCH, R. P. 1979. The Willimantic fault: A ductile fault in eastern Connecticut. *Am. J. Sci.* **279,** 367–93.

WISE, D. U. 1970. Multiple deformation, geosynclinal transitions, and the Martic problem in Pennsylvania, *In:* FISHER, G. W., PETTIJOHN, F. J., REED, J. C., Jr. & WEAVER, K. N. (eds). *Studies of Appalachian Geology: Central and Southern.* Interscience, New York, 317–33.

ZEN, E-AN. 1967. Time and space relationships of the Taconic Allochthon and autochthon. *Spec. Pap. geol. Soc. Am.* **97,** 107 p.

—— 1972. The Taconide zone and the Taconic orogeny in the western part of the northern Appalachian orogen. *Spec. Pap. geol. Soc. Am.* **135,** 72 p.

R. D. HATCHER, JR., Department of Geology Florida State University, Tallahassee, Florida 32306, U.S.A.

COCORP seismic reflection profiling
across thrust faults

J. A. Brewer, F. A. Cook, L. D. Brown, J. E. Oliver,
S. Kaufman & D. S. Albaugh

SUMMARY: It is very important to have good subsurface data in order to understand
the nature and behaviour of thrust faults. Deep crustal seismic reflection profiling is the
best technique currently available to make detailed subsurface studies of such important
problems as the attitude and extent at depth of major faults, and hence deduce the mode
of deformation and tectonic forces producing them. The Consortium for Continental
Reflection Profiling (COCORP) is collecting large quantities of seismic reflection data
from the deep crust and upper mantle in many parts of the U.S.A. Areas of major
thrusting which have been profiled so far by COCORP include the Wind River
Mountains in Wyoming and the Southern Appalachians of Georgia and Tennessee.
Seismic profiles have been very successful in delineating a major thrust fault of moderate
dip underlying the Wind River Mountains, thus demonstrating that compressional
tectonics were dominant in their formation. In Georgia and Tennessee the seismic
profiles demonstrate that the major tectonic feature of the Southern Appalachians is a
relatively thin overthrust sheet, which may have moved at least 260 km. Deep crustal
seismic reflection profiling thus appears to be an indispensable tool for the study of areas
in which thrusting and nappe formation have occurred.

The programme of the Consortium for Continental Reflection Profiling is the major effort
to explore the continental basement in this
manner. Scientists from industrial, governmen-
tal and academic laboratories serve on the
project in a variety of capacities. Cornell University is the operating institution and prime
contractor, and other universities carry out
related research. Conventional hydrocarbon
seismic exploration techniques are used, with
field configurations modified to image deep
crustal structures. The Vibroseis* technique is
used because it offers the best quality data with
maximum economy of operation, while
minimizing environmental impact. COCORP
has operated successfully in a wide variety of
areas and geological environments (Oliver et
al. 1976; Oliver & Kaufman 1976; Brown et
al. 1979). For a detailed description of field
techniques used and the data processing steps
involved in producing a typical COCORP seismic profile, see Schilt et al. 1979. This paper
describes the result of profiling in two areas of
thrust faulting; the Wind River Mountains
(Smithson et al. 1978, 1979; Brewer et al.
1980), and the Southern Appalachians (Cook
et al. 1979). At the two sites described here,
data were recorded to 20 sec two-way-travel
time (1 sec two-way-travel time approximately
equals 3 km depth in crystalline basement) i.e.

giving a capability for recording data from as
deep as about 60 km. The COCORP data presented here are displayed as time sections, and
important preliminary interpretations can be
made from them. In making detailed studies of
areas of complex geology, depth conversions
and geometric corrections (migration) must be
calculated in order to extract the maximum
structural information from these sections (see
e.g. Dobrin 1976).

The Wind River Mountains,
Wyoming

During the late Cretaceous–early Tertiary
Laramide Orogeny, distinctive uplifts of Precambrian basement rock were formed in the
foreland of the Cordillera of the W United
States. These uplifts, best developed in Wyoming, were formed 800–1000 km E of the North
American plate margin, and do not fit into
standard plate tectonic orogenic patterns.
There is no obvious suture zone, and there was
a lack of igneous activity during their formation (Burchfiel & Davis 1975; Dickinson &
Snyder 1978). They have diverse trends and
may be flanked by reverse faults (Fig. 1).
Whether these uplifts were produced primarily
by horizontal or vertical movements of the
earth's crust has been much debated (e.g.
Prucha et al. 1965; Sales 1968; Stearns 1978;
Smithson et al. 1978). An important constraint

---

* Registered Trade Mark of Continental Oil Company.

FIG. 1. Map of Wyoming showing Laramide basement uplifts (shaded). 'A' marks the surface position of the Wind River Thrust; other letters denote other main flanking faults (after Berg 1962).

on theories of their formation is provided by the knowledge of the geometry at depth of the flanking faults; a steeply-dipping fault at depth would indicate predominantly vertical movements, while a shallowly-dipping fault would indicate horizontal compressional movements. COCORP has collected over 150 km of deep crustal seismic reflection profiles across the largest of these basement uplifts, the Wind River Mountains, in order to determine the attitude at depth of the Wind River Thrust which flanks these mountains on their SW side.

Fig. 2 shows the location of 3 COCORP seismic lines in this area and Fig. 3 shows the unmigrated seismic sections. Fig. 4 shows an interpreted drawing of these seismic sections, also unmigrated.

The Wind River Thrust can be traced as a continuous series of reflections from its known subcrop position deep into the crust. The reflections can be followed to at least 8 sec (about 24 km) and possibly as deep as 12 sec (about 36 km) (Figs 3 & 4). Where Precambrian basement is thrust over sediments of the

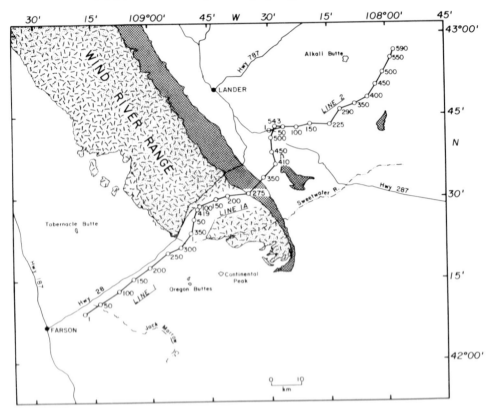

FIG. 2. Map of SE end of Wind River uplift showing location of 3 COCORP seismic profiles. Precambrian basement is marked by coarse stipple pattern and Palaeozoic rocks by fine stipple pattern.

Green River basin, the thrust zone is well defined. Below the base of the sediments, (about 3.9 sec) the zone thickens and becomes more complex. The thickness varies from 1 to 3 km, and the zone appears to be made up of several strands. The smallest of these strands which can be resolved is about 75–150 m wide. Cross cutting relationships along the thrust indicate a complex history of movements. Migration of the thrust using the changes in line direction indicates an average dip of 30–45°, generally to the E–NE. Details of complex deformation in the sediments of the Green River basin underlying the over-thrust wedge of Precambrian may be disting-uished (Figs 3 & 4). 'Back thrusts' in the sedimentary rocks, conjugate to the main thrust, may possibly exist, presumably formed in response to movements along the main thrust (Brewer *et al.* 1980). From the trunca-tion of reflectors in the sedimentary section, at least 21 km of horizontal movement, (and at least 13 km of vertical movement) can be measured from the seismic profiles.

For such a large amount of shortening to occur on one thrust so far into the middle of the North American craton, compressional forces must have been active on a regional scale, and probably regional compression was the dominant tectonic element of the Laramide Orogeny (Grose 1972; Brewer *et al.* 1980). The diversity of trends of the basement uplifts sug-gests that inhomogeneities may have existed in the stress field producing them, or in the crust of the Wyoming region (Sales 1968). The fact that these basement uplifts were formed so far away from the North American plate margin makes it difficult to suggest satisfactory plate tectonic frameworks. One possible model in-vokes a shallowly dipping, subducted, oceanic plate (Farallon plate) dragging along the base of the overriding continental plate (Dickinson & Snyder 1978). Compressive stresses may have been localized in the overriding plate

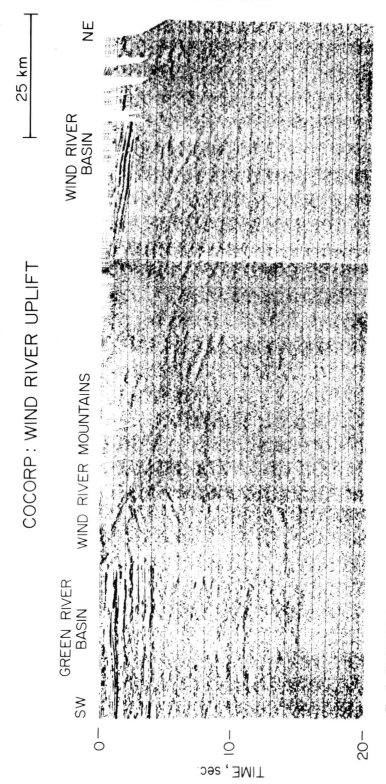

Fig. 3. COCORP Wind River uplift seismic sections (unmigrated). Line 1 on the left, Line 1A in the middle and Line 2 on the right.

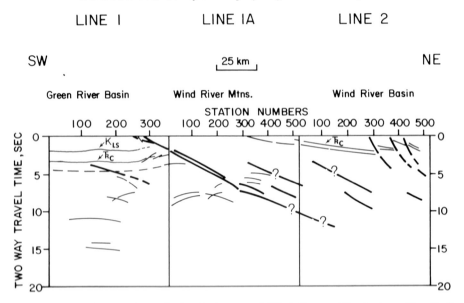

FIG. 4. Line drawing (unmigrated) of main features of Wind River uplift seismic profiles. Faults dipping to the NE to 8 sec and possibly as deep as 12 sec. K_{LS} = Cretaceous Lewis Shale. R_C = Triassic Chugwater Formation.

over the area where the Farallon plate steepened its dip into the mantle (Brewer *et al.* 1980).

The Wind River thrust can be traced to depth because it has created a sufficient acoustic impedance contrast (i.e. a change in rock velocities and/or densities) for direct fault plane reflections to be detected at the surface. This impedance contrast could be generated solely by juxtaposing rocks of different velocities or densities. The complex character of the fault suggests that this impedance contrast might also be produced by zones of fault rocks. Cataclastic processes dominating in the upper, brittle part of the crust would result in zones of fault gouge, and these would give way to mylonites generated in ductile shear zones at greater depths. Either these individual zones have a sufficient impedance contrast with the surrounding rock, or possibly local structural tuning within the zones (i.e. a resonant spacing of reflectors) gives rise to a strong reflected signal. The fault zones probably resemble shear zones in Precambrian rocks, such as those described by Escher & Watterson (1974), Sibson (1977) and Grocott (1977). Quartz microstructure studies and field studies indicate that the lower limit of brittle fracturing occurs at about 10–15 km depth (Sibson 1977; D. L. Kohlstedt, pers. comm. 1978). Thus, much of the observed length of the Wind

River Thrust should lie in the zone of ductile deformation. Movements at depth may have occurred by ductile faulting mechanisms such as those observed by Post (1977) in laboratory experiments on dunites. In these experiments, carried out at pressures and temperatures typical of the lower crust and upper mantle, Post observed penetrative ductile shear zones developed at angles of 25–45° to the direction of principal compression. Dunite is not representative of the lower crust (it probably consists of granulite facies metamorphic complexes, Smithson 1978) and it is important to consider such factors as the presence of fluids and strain rates when applying these experimental results to the behaviour of lower crustal rocks. However, discrete, penetrative, ductile shear zones which propagated within the lower crust provide a reasonable explanation for the reflections seen from the deeper parts of the Wind River Thrust.

A present-day analogy to the Wyoming area of the W United States in the early Tertiary may exist in N Peru and central Chile where the Nazca plate underthrusts South America at a shallow angle (Barazangi & Isacks 1976; Dickinson & Snyder 1978). Earthquakes are observed in the crust of the South American plate in these areas down to depths of 30–40 km, and focal mechanisms indicate thrust faulting (Stauder 1975; Langer *et al.* 1979).

Possibly such deep crustal earthquakes were also associated with movements on the Wind River Thrust.

Many theories of crustal faulting require that the faults steepen to descend deep into the crust at high angles (e.g. Hafner 1951; Sanford 1959; Couples 1977; Stearns 1978). One may infer from the relatively moderate and constant dip of the Wind River Thrust, both at brittle and ductile levels, that other models for crustal fracture may be necessary in order to understand stresses involved in its formation.

The Southern Appalachians

COCORP profiling in the Southern Appalachians of Georgia and Tennessee has revealed that the major tectonic feature in this region is an allochthonous sheet of crystalline rocks which has apparently overthrust sedimentary rocks over a distance of greater than 260 km. Fig. 5 shows the locations of the COCORP profiles superimposed on the major geological features of the Southern Appalachians. Fig. 6 shows a portion of the seismic data form Line 1, Georgia, and Fig. 7 shows a line drawing of the seismic sections collected to date.

The following is a brief summary of the main features of the COCORP Southern Appalachians data: for a more detailed description and tectonic interpretation see Cook *et al.* 1979. General descriptions of Southern Appalachian geology, are given by Rodgers (1970), and Hatcher (1972; this volume).

Studies of surface geology show that the

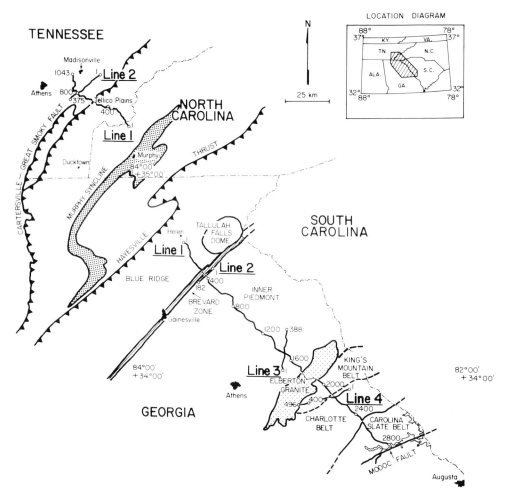

FIG. 5. Map of portion of Southern Appalachians showing COCORP seismic profiles and the main geological provinces crossed by them (from Cook *et al.* 1979).

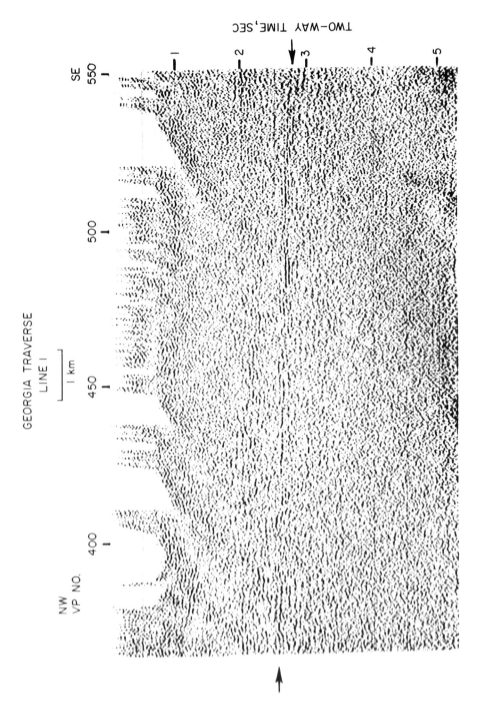

Fig. 6. Portion of COCORP Southern Appalachians traverse (unmigrated). The profile, from Line 1, Georgia, shows the reflection horizons marked by arrows which are correlated with sedimentary rocks of the Valley and Ridge. They underlie crystalline rocks of the Inner Piedmont Province in the area of this Figure (from Cook *et al.* 1979).

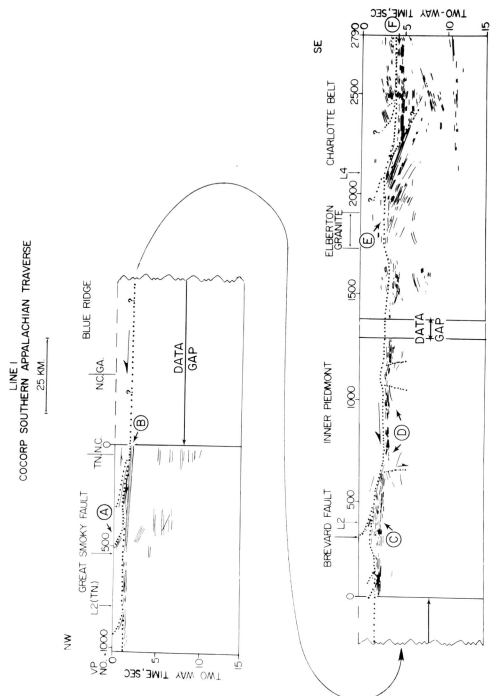

Fig. 7. Line drawing (unmigrated) of main features of COCORP Southern Appalachians seismic profiles. See text for discussion of the interpretation. (After Cook *et al.* 1979).

contact between the Valley and Ridge province (which is characterized by thin-skinned fold and thrust tectonics) and the crystalline Blue Ridge is a thrust fault (the Cartersville–Great Smoky Thrust) dipping at 20–40° to the SE (Roeder *et al.* 1978), Fig. 7A. This thrust surface may be traced on the COCORP sections, soon flattening to near horizontal and overlying a layered sequence of reflecting horizons at about 1.7–2.0 sec (about 5.0–6.5 km), Fig. 7B. These horizons are correlated with similar events in the Valley and Ridge Province which have been identified, seismically and by well data, as Cambrian and Ordovician sedimentary rocks (Harris & Milici 1977). The reflecting horizons may be followed to the SE under the Blue Ridge and Inner Piedmont, with their thickness varying between 1 and 3 km (Cook *et al.* 1979), (Fig. 7C). One may infer from discontinuities in these horizons that pre-thrusting topography and faulting exists (Fig. 7D). On the SE edge of the Inner Piedmont the COCORP profile crosses a large granite body, the Elberton granite. The granite appears to be seismically transparent, with the reflecting horizons continuous beneath it. To the SE of the granite these horizons increase in thickness to about 6 km, and dip easterly (Fig. 7E). From station 2300 to the SE end of the traverse, they appear horizontal and relatively undisturbed (Fig. 7F).

On the basis of geology, gravity and magnetic data Hatcher & Zietz (1978) suggest that the root zone of this overthrust sheet lies in the Kings Mountain belt (Fig. 5). Our results indicate, however, that the thrust may extend much further to the SE, and if the continuity and correlation of the layered events under the Elberton granite is accepted, then the interpreted sedimentary succession underneath the allochthon SE of the Inner Piedmont is remarkably similar to seismic profiles across the Atlantic margin (Cook *et al.* 1979). This implies that most, or all, of the Southern Appalachians is allochthonous, and was thrust over a passive continental margin with apparently little deformation of the underlying continental slope and shelf sediments. The thickness of the allochthon varies from 6 to 15 km, and it has moved at least 260 km. It therefore appears that the concepts of thin-skinned tectonics, well demonstrated in the sedimentary rocks of the Valley and Ridge (Harris & Milici 1977), may be applicable to the crystalline rocks of the Southern Appalachians as a whole. A detailed plate tectonic model for the formation of the Southern Appalachians which incorporated these results is presented in Cook

et al. 1979. This model envisages westward directed thrusting resulting from possibly three stages of plate collision involving a continental fragment, an island arc and the proto-African continent. 348 km of COCORP profiles have already been recorded, and further profiles will be collected, extending the present line to the coast, to determine the extent of this allochthon and find the position of its root zone, possibly the late Palaeozoic suture between North America and the proto-African continent.

The Cartersville–Great Smoky fault produces a fault plane reflection near its outcrop. For most of its length, the position of the thrust plane is inferred on the basis of reflecting horizons continuous with sediments of the Valley and Ridge. How was this great amount of overthrusting accomplished? Did gravity spreading mechanisms play an important role (e.g. Elliott 1976), or were horizontally directed compressional forces, with a mechanism such as Chapple's (1978), more important? If the allochthon represents a crustal flake thrust over onto the North American margin, then what has happened to the crust originally beneath it? One of the striking aspects of Appalachian geology is the continuity along strike of many of the geological provinces (cf. Williams 1978). Does this imply that much of the Appalachians subsurface geology resembles that profiled by COCORP? If so, then the area of sedimentary rocks which are overthrust is extremely large.

If compressional forces have played an important role in the overthrusting of the Southern Appalachians, then it is interesting to note the different fault plane geometries in this area and in the Wind River Mountains. In the Southern Appalachians, thin-skinned thrusting of crystalline basement was probably ultimately caused by continental collision. In the Wind Rivers, regional compression in the continental interior has caused the crust to deform as though it were a fairly rigid block, resulting in a fault zone of moderate dip.

General Considerations

Comparisons of COCORP profiles across major faults show that, taking into account the as yet limited data set, very good results are obtained from areas of thrust movements. In the two areas studied so far there are probably two main contributing factors for this:

(1) The structures have a shallow or moderate dip so that a high proportion of the

reflected energy may be collected by the seismic array;

(2) In the case of the Wind River Mountains, thrusting has produced a sufficient impedance contrast for the major structures to be delineated. Whether this reflects the mode of deformation along the fault or the juxtaposition of different rock types is, at present, undetermined. In the case of the Southern Appalachians, the actual thrust surface is usually not observed, but it is the continuity and correlation with sedimentary rocks of reflecting horizons beneath a sequence of rocks of a predominantly crystalline nature which establishes its presence.

Conclusions

These COCORP deep seismic data have clearly demonstrated the necessity of having good detailed subsurface control in order to understand the structure of thrust regions, and to begin to understand the forces that produced them. The results raise important questions about how continental crust deforms and fractures under stress. By determining the geometry of faults at depth and combining the seismic data with known surface geology, COCORP has shown that the Wind River Mountains were produced by horizontal compressive forces, and that the major part of the Southern Appalachians is allochthonous.

ACKNOWLEDGMENTS. This research is part of the COCORP project, funded by the National Science Foundation as part of the US Geodynamics Project. Primary support came from NSF grants EAR 77-14674, EAR 78-23672 and EAR 78-23673. This paper is Cornell contribution to geology No 649.

References

BARAZANGI, M. & ISACKS, B. L. 1976. Spatial distribution of earthquakes and the subduction of the Nazca plate beneath South America. *Geology*, **4**, 686–92.

—— & —— 1979. Subduction of the Nazca plate beneath Peru: Evidence from spatial distribution of earthquakes. *Geophys. J. R. astron. Soc.* **57**, 537–55.

BERG, R. R. 1962. Mountain flank thrusting in Rocky Mountain foreland of Wyoming and Colorado. *Bull. Am. Assoc. Petrol. Geol.* **46**, 2019–32.

BREWER, J. A., SMITHSON, S. B., OLIVER, J. E., KAUFMAN, S. & BROWN, L. D. 1979. The Laramide orogeny: Evidence from COCORP deep crustal seismic profiles in the Wind River mountains, Wyoming. *Tectonophysics*, **62**, 165–89.

BROWN, L. D., KRUMHANSL, P. A., CHAPIN, C. E., SANFORD, A. R., KAUFMAN, S. & OLIVER, J. E. 1979. Deep structure of the Rio Grande rift from seismic reflection profiling. *In:* RIECKER, R. E. (ed). *The Rio Grande Rift: Tectonism and Magmatism.* Spec. Publ. Am. Geophys. Union. 169–84.

BURCHFIEL, B. C. & DAVIS, G. A. 1975. Nature and controls of Cordilleran orogenesis, western United States; extension of an earlier synthesis. *Am. J. Sci.* **275-A**, 363–40.

CHAPPLE, W. M. 1978. Mechanisms of thin-skinned fold and thrust belts. *Bull. geol. Soc. Am.* **89**, 1189–98.

COOK, F. A., ALBAUGH, D. S., BROWN, L. D., KAUFMAN, S., OLIVER, J. E. & HATCHER, R. D., JR. 1979. Thin-skinned tectonics of the crystalline Appalachians: COCORP seismic reflection profiling of the Blue Ridge and Piedmont, *Geology*, **7**, 563–7.

COUPLES, G. 1977. Stress and shear fracture (fault) patterns resulting from a suite of complicated boundary conditions. *Pageophys.* **115**, 113–33.

DICKINSON, W. R. & SNYDER, W. S. 1978. Plate tectonics of the Laramide orogeny. *Mem. geol. Soc. Am.* **151**, 355–66.

DOBRIN, M. B. 1976. *Introduction to Geophysical Prospecting.* McGraw-Hill, New York. 3rd Edition, 630 pp.

ELLIOTT, D. 1976. The motion of thrust sheets. *J. geophys. Res.* **81**, 949–63.

ESCHER, A. & WATTERSON, J. 1974. Stretching fabrics, folds and crustal shortening. *Tectonophysics*, **22**, 223–31.

GROCOTT, J. 1977. The relationship between Precambrian shear belts and modern fault systems. *J. geol. Soc. London*, **133**, 257–62.

GROSE, L. T. 1972. Tectonics. *In: Geological Atlas of the Rocky Mountain Region.* Rocky Mountain Association of Geologists, Denver.

HAFNER, W. 1951. Stress distribution and faulting. *Bull. geol. Soc. Am.* **62**, 373–98.

HARRIS, L. D. & MILICI, R. C. 1977. Characteristics of thin-skinned style of deformation in the Southern Appalachians, and potential hydrocarbon traps. *Prof. Pap. U.S. geol. Surv.* **1018**, 40 pp.

HATCHER, R. D. 1972. Developmental model for the Southern Appalachians. *Bull. geol. Soc. Am.* **81**, 933–40.

—— & ZIETZ, I. 1978. Thin crystalline sheets in the Southern Appalachians, Inner Piedmont and Brevard Zone: Interpretation based on aeromagnetic data. *Geol. Soc. Am. Abstr. with Prog.* **10**, 417.

LANGER, C. J., ALGERMISSEN, S. T., BOLLINGER, G. A. & CASTANO, J. C. 1979. Aftershocks of the western Argentina earthquake of November 23, 1977. *Abstr. 74th Ann. Mtg. Seism. Soc. Am.*

OLIVER, J. E., DOBRIN, M., KAUFMAN, S., MEYER, R.

& PHINNEY, R. 1976. Continuous seismic reflection profiling of the deep basement, Hardeman County, Texas. *Bull. geol. Soc. Am.* **78,** 1537–46.

—— & KAUFMAN, S. 1976. Profiling the Rio Grande rift. *Geotimes,* **21,** 20–3.

POST, R. L. 1977. High temperature creep of Mt Burnet dunite. *Tectonophysics,* **42,** 75–110.

PRUCHA, J. J., GRAHAM, J. A. & NICKELSEN, R. P. 1965. Basement controlled deformation. *In: Wyoming Province of Rocky Mountains Foreland.* Bull. Am. Assoc. Petrol. Geol. **49,** 966–92.

RODGERS, J. 1971. *The Tectonics of the Appalachians.* Wiley, New York. 271 pp.

ROEDER, D., GILBERT, O. E., JR. & WITHERSPOON, W. D. 1978. Evolution and macroscopic structure of Valley and Ridge thrust belts, Tennessee and Virginia. *University of Tennessee studies in Geology,* **2,** 25 pp.

SALES, J. K. 1968. Crustal mechanics of Cordilleran foreland deformation: A regional and scale model approach. *Bull. Am. Assoc. Petrol. Geol.* **52,** 2016–44.

SANFORD, A. R. 1959. Analytical and experimental study of simple geological structures. *Bull. geol. Soc. Am.* **70,** 19–52.

SCHILT, S., OLIVER, J., BROWN, L., KAUFMAN, S., ALBAUGH, D., BREWER, J., COOK, F., JENSEN, L., KRUMHANSL, P., LONG, G. & STEINER, D.

1979. The heterogeneity of the continental crust: Results of deep crustal seismic reflection profiling using the Vibroseis* technique. *Rev. Geophys. Space Phys.* **17,** 354–68.

SIBSON, R. H. 1977. Fault Rocks & Mechanisms. *J. geol. Soc. London,* **133,** 191–213.

SMITHSON, S. B. 1978. Modelling continental crust: Structural and chemical constraints. *Geophys. Res. Lett.* **5,** 749–52.

SMITHSON, S. B., BREWER, J. A., KAUFMAN, S., OLIVER, J. E. & HURICH, C. 1978. Nature of the Wind River thrust, Wyoming from COCORP deep reflection data and from gravity data. *Geology.* **6,** 648–52.

SMITHSON, S. B., BREWER, J. A., KAUFMAN, S., OLIVER, J. E. & HURICH, C. 1979. Structure of the Laramide Wind River uplift from COCORP deep reflection data and gravity data. *J. geophys. Res.* **84,** 5955–72.

STAUDER, W. 1975. Subduction of the Nazca plate under Peru as evidenced by focal mechanisms and by seismicity. *J. geophys. Res.* **80,** 1053–64.

STEARNS, D. W. 1978. Faulting and forced folding in the Rocky mountains foreland. *Mem. geol. Soc. Am.* **151,** 1–37.

WILLIAMS, H. 1978. *Tectonic Lithofacies Map of the Appalachian Orogen.* Memorial University of Newfoundland.

J. A. BREWER, F. A. COOK, L. D. BROWN, J. E. OLIVER, S. KAUFMAN, D. S. ALBAUGH, Department of Geological Sciences, Kimball Hall, Cornell University, Ithaca, New York 14853, U.S.A.

Mechanisms for basement shortening in the Andean foreland fold belt of southern South America

Margaret A. Winslow

SUMMARY: A mechanism for basement shortening underneath allochthonous foreland fold and thrust belts is reverse faulting along inherited normal faults. Normal faulting of basement rocks beneath much of southernmost South America indicates that up to 30–40% extension occurred before sedimentation in a subsiding foredeep. The basement is divided into blocks of similar dimensions to those in the Basin and range of Nevada, U.S.A. Post-depositional reverse motion along some of these high-angle block boundaries under the foreland can account for the 20–40 km of shortening observed in the cover rocks, without showing upthrust wedges of basement rocks.

The folds in the cover rocks of the foreland fold-belt are asymmetric, open to closed with over-steepened to overturned limbs which are frequently truncated by high-angle reverse faults. These faults attain a shallower dip with depth toward a décollement plane above a basal volcanic section. Basement involvement in thrusts (0.5–1.5 km vertical displacement) is suggested where basal volcanics are involved in thrust wedges, as revealed by drilling and seismic reflection data. Block faults have been observed beneath many forelands and have always been assumed to be pre-orogenic and passive with respect to deformation of the cover. The block dimensions, fault angles, vertical displacements and other parameters from the southern Andes are inserted to calculate pre-depositional extension and syn-orogenic shortening that can occur without producing obvious basement upthrusting. The results are compared with data from the Appalachians and Canadian Rockies.

Careful palinspastic restorations of foreland fold and thrust belts indicate that the area of continental basement directly beneath the unfolded cover rocks is insufficient, if there is no basement shortening. The location of the 'missing' basement has long undergone intense discussion (e.g. Bally et al. 1966; Bally 1975, this volume; Elliott 1973). Models for direct involvement of crystalline basement were largely abandoned when it became obvious that foreland folds are disharmonic and that amplitudes decrease with depth toward a plane of décollement (see Rodgers 1964). The lack of superimposed fabrics and reset radiometric ages in the basement do not support remobilization. High angle reverse faults, listric in profile, are found decreasing in dip with depth toward a plane of décollement along a mechanically weak layer above the basement. As a result of these characteristic features, researchers in foreland fold belts began to search for mechanisms other than horizontally directed homogeneous layer-parallel shortening of the entire crust to explain the large percentage of shortening documented in foreland cover rocks. Moreover, the problem of transmitting stresses hundreds of kilometres through unconsolidated cover sediments has continued to plague gravity spreading and sliding models.

Two mechanisms proposed in other foreland fold belts for dealing with insufficient or lost basement are examined in the light of evidence from the S Andes (Fig. 1). The two mechanisms are 1: upthrusting of basement along inherited normal faults, and 2: underthrusting of continental basement beneath the metamorphic belt or 'internal zone'.

The first mechanism was proposed for the cover folds in the Basin and Range Province, USA, where passive folds are 'draped' over basement blocks defined by high-angle boundaries (Foose 1973). Basement block control of cover rocks, or vertical tectonics, continues to be a popular concept in Soviet literature (e.g. Artemjev & Artyushkov 1971). More recently, direct basement involvement in low angle thrusts (up to 200 km long), previously undocumented in most foreland fold belts, has been supported by new data from the Front Ranges of the Canadian Rocky Mountains and the Appalachians (e.g. Hatcher, this volume).

The second mechanism, so-called A-type subduction, involves low angle underthrusting of continental basement beneath orogenic belts (Bally et al. 1966; Bally 1975 and this volume) first suggested for the Alps (Ampherer & Hammer 1910). Basement beneath allochthonous forelands generally dips toward the highly deformed zone of high grade metamorphism (cordillera in this paper) with a slope of less than 5°. If the basement continues with a shallow dip, then the limit of underthrusting in

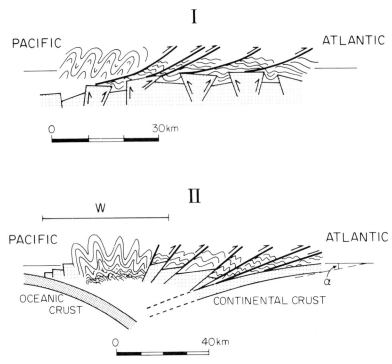

FIG. 1. Mechanisms of basement shortening beneath the fold and thrust belt. Interpretative sketches not to scale. Approximately 2x vertical exaggeration on each. I = Upthrusting along inherited faults with décollement tectonics above the basement blocks. II = Underthrusting of continental basement on an Andean margin. Limit of the continental basement underthrusting is approximately the width (W) of the forearc and cordillera. With increasing dip of the descending continental slab, the limit of underthrusting is W/cos α.

kilometres will be approximately the width of the cordillera (Fig. 1). If, however, the basement slab steepens in its descent, a greater amount of shortening may be possible. On an Andean margin, however, there is a space problem created by the coeval underthrusting of oceanic crust, as will be discussed below. Neither of the above mechanisms necessarily conflicts with 'thin skinned' tectonic models. However, décollement features, known in cover rocks of foreland fold and thrust belts, are now also known to involve the upper several kilometres of basement (e.g. Hatcher ibid).

Following a brief review of the tectonic setting and history of the fold and thrust belt of the S Andes, the general structures will be summarized in order to discuss preliminary evidence for basement involvement in this region. Several calculations are put forward along with suggestions for future work. Because the tectonic provinces can be traced offshore with marine geophysical data and the tip of the South American continent is extremely nar-

row, this region is uniquely suited to studies of basement behaviour beneath foreland fold belts.

Geotectonic setting

The South American Plate is bounded on its W margin by the Nazca and Antarctic Plates (Fig. 2). The Chile Rise intersects the continent at about 46°S latitude. N of this ridge-trench-trench triple junction, the Nazca Plate is actively underthrusting South America at 9 cm/yr (Herron & Hayes 1969). S of the triple junction there is nearly E–W convergence of 1–2 cm/yr between the Antarctic Plate and South America.

Since about 30 Ma ago, the Chile Rise has collided with, and been consumed beneath, the South American margin (Herron & Tucholke 1976; Herron et al. 1977). From the time of collision, Farallon (ancestral Nazca)-South America rapid convergence was transferred S of the triple junction to much slower Antarctic–South America convergence progressing from S to N. The present tectonic

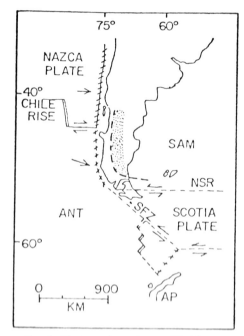

FIG. 2. Geotectonic setting modified from Forsyth (1975). Pacific-ward limit of known crystalline rocks is shown as dashed line with stipple. Inactive trench is indicated by X's. SAM = South American Plate; ANT = Antarctic Plate; NSR = North Scotia Ridge; SFZ = Shackleton Fracture Zone' AP = Antarctic Peninsula.

the Pacific margin to the Atlantic, the Cordilleran province consists of uplifted and deformed Palaeozoic-Lower Mesozoic and Upper Mesozoic metasedimentary and igneous rocks. The Andean foothills consist of deformed Lower Cretaceous through Tertiary sedimentary rocks constituting a classic foreland fold and thrust belt. The continental basement underlying the foreland fold belt S and W of the Precambrian shield yields pre-Jurassic metamorphic ages (Halpern & Carlin 1971).

The foreland fold and thrust of S Patagonia and Tierra del Fuego forms the Atlantic foothills, an arcuate belt 50–80 km wide, of the Andean Cordillera. The fold and thrust belt S of 52°S can be divided into three domains (from the Cordillera toward the craton) which aer physiographically, and stratigraphically distinct: the cordilleran margin, central fold belt, and lowlands (Fig. 3). These domains consist of Upper Jurassic and Lower Cretaceous, Upper Cretaceous through Palaeogene, and Neogene rock units, respectively. The rocks of the cordilleran margin experienced uplift and were deformed with those of the adjacent Cordillera during the mid-Cretaceous and are more intensely deformed than the rocks of the central fold belt and lowlands, deformed in late Palaeogene times.

Tectonic history

Two major orogenies are recognized in the S Andes: the Gondwanian Orogeny (? latest Palaeozoic–early Mesozoic, Dalziel & Elliot 1971) and the Andean Orogeny (late Mesozoic–Cenozoic, Dalziel & Cortés 1972). Two main deformational phases of the Andean orogeny are recognized: a mid-Cretaceous phase affecting the rocks of the Andean Cordillera and a late Palaeogene deformation which affected the sedimentary rocks of the Atlantic foothills (cf. Dalziel & Cortés 1972; Katz 1972; Winslow, in press, 1979).

Following uplift and erosion of the continent, widespread extension of the southern South American continent occurred in Middle to late Jurassic time (Bruhn *et al.* 1977). Thick sequences of silicic and intermediate volcanic rocks including ignimbrites were deposited unconformably on the block faulted metamorphic basement (Fig. 4). Abrupt thickness variations are recorded from drillholes throughout the southern continent, with up to 3000–4000 m of ash and tuff beds in the graben and less than 500 m on the horsts (Empresa Nacional del Petroleo, ENAP, unpubl. data; see summary in Natland *et al.* 1974). Hence, the deposition of

setting is further complicated by transform boundaries with the Scotia plate. Displacements along transcurrent faults during the Cenozoic and possibly late Mesozoic have displaced structural units S of the transform boundary toward the E, accentuating the oroclinal bend of southern South America (Winslow, in press, 1979). The foreland fold belt of the S Andes was initiated before the collision of the Chile Rise, in a setting similar to the central Andes of today.

The W limit of known Precambrian shield in southern South America strikes N–S to about 50°S latitude, where it curves sharply eastward (Fig. 2). The Andean Cordillera and Atlantic foothills parallel the Pacific margin of the shield for thousands of kilometres, then S of 52°S abruptly curve toward the E (Fig. 3). The Cordillera and foothills disappear as topographic features into the South Atlantic Ocean and the Scotia Sea, where they can be traced bathymetrically and by marine geophysical data for at least 1200 km. Several major tectonic provinces are represented in the Cordillera and foothills from 52 to 56°S. From

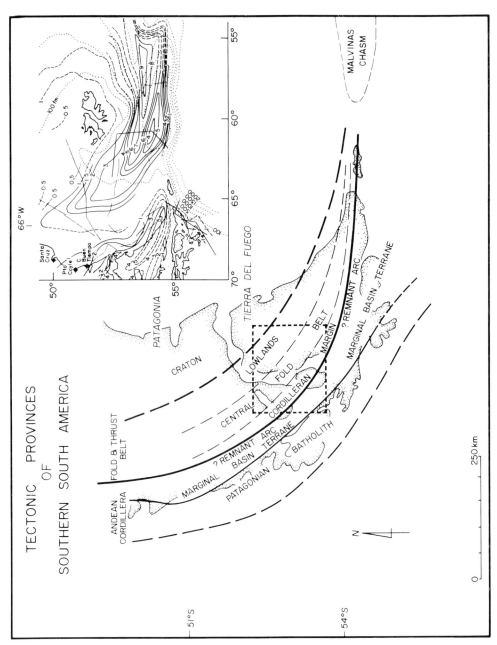

Fig. 3. Tectonic provinces of southern South America. Heavy solid line is the Cordillera-foothills boundary. Dashed lines separate structural domains. Dotted line indicates western limit of known Precambrian basement. Boxed in area refers to geological map Fig. 5.

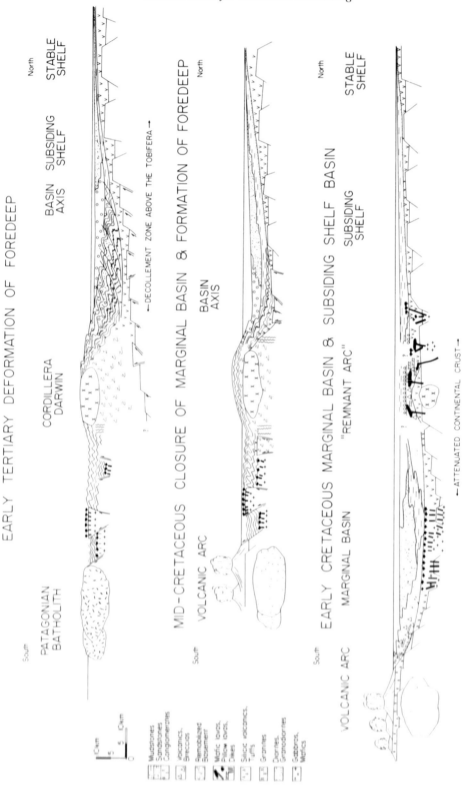

FIG. 4. Tectonic reconstructions. Data include all known water depths, sediments thicknesses and tectonic relationships. Sources are from Katz (1963); Natland *et al.* (1974); Bruhn & Dalziel (1977); Winslow, in press, and ENAP, unpubl. reports. Structure of Cordillera Darwin is schematic (see Nelson *et al.* 1979).

Upper Jurassic volcanic rocks was partly coeval with faulting. Sedimentary rocks overlying the volcanics, however, evenly blanket the faulted terrane.

The W margin of the continent was the site of a late Mesozoic and Cenozoic magmatic arc, presently represented by the outcrops of the Patagonian batholith (Figs 3 & 4; Dalziel & Elliott 1973; Bruhn & Dalziel 1977). The E edge of the continent was a stable platform which received sub-aerial and shallow marine deposits during the late Jurassic, followed by shallow marine deposition during the Cretaceous and Cenozoic (Natland *et al.* 1974). Toward the Pacific, the shelf edge subsided and received shallow to deep water sediments during the early Cretaceous. Lower Cretaceous ophiolitic and sedimentary rocks outcropping between the batholith and the Jurassic volcanics are interpreted to be the floor and infilling of a quasi-oceanic marginal basin which opened between the magmatic arc and the remnant arc-continent edge (Fig. 4; Dalziel & Cortés 1972; Dalziel *et al.* 1974; Bruhn & Dalziel 1977).

The marginal basin and remnant arc were deformed and uplifted to form a proto-cordillera in the mid-Cretaceous (pre-80–90 Ma., Bruhn & Dalziel 1977; Dalziel & Palmer 1979). The resultant land mass shed sediments eastward onto the continental shelf edge that was subsiding to form a deep trough, the Magallanes Basin, parallel to the cordillera (Fig. 4). Rapid subsidence near the shelf edge during the early Cretaceous is indicated by the much greater thicknesses of Lower Cretaceous sedimentary rocks near the present Andean Cordillera (Winslow, in press, 1979). The beginning of uplift of the cordillera is documented by slump folds and the arrival of large volumes of coarse, poorly-sorted sediments whose clasts and sedimentary structures identify which parts of the source terrane were being uplifted at different times (Scott 1966; Dott 1976; Winslow in press, 1979). Rapid subsidence of the shelf from shallow to deep water conditions occurred during the mid-Cretaceous preceding sedimentary loading (Natland *et al.* 1974). Such subsidence history suggests mechanical coupling of basement between the uplifting Cordillera and the adjacent foredeep. During the late Cretaceous and Palaeogene, the foredeep received up to 9 km of sediments in its deepest parts (Natland *et al.* 1974). The foredeep was progressively uplifted and deformed during the Palaeogene, accompanied by a migration of the basin axis toward the Atlantic (Fig. 4). Progressive involvement of younger sediments in folds and thrusts toward the craton occurred over a 50-70Ma period. Shortening in the cover ceased diachronously from S to N from Eocene to Pliocene times (Winslow, in press, 1979).

Structures of the fold and thrust belt

The cordilleran margin domain, central fold belt, and lowlands domains are distinguished by structural contrasts and separated by stratigraphic unconformities. The ages of the rocks involved in folds and thrusts decrease from the Pacific toward the Atlantic. The entire Upper Jurassic volcanic section and the overlying Lower Cretaceous sedimentary rocks are steeply upwarped and locally overturned along the border with the Cordillera (Dalziel *et al.* 1974; Dalziel & Palmer 1979). A few kilometres toward the craton, the Lower Cretaceous sedimentary rocks and underlying volcanic rocks dip toward the central fold belt. This craton-ward dip of the volcanics reverses beneath the central fold belt to a shallow Pacific-ward dip (ENAP, unpublished data).

The central fold belt is composed of allochthonous Upper Cretaceous and Lower Tertiary sedimentary rocks (Figs 3 & 5). Within this belt, the topography is structurally controlled. Numerous thrusts and high angle reverse faults separate long, narrow (usually anticlinal) ridges (Fig. 6). The lowlands are underlain mainly by Neogene rocks which crop out Atlantic-ward of all exposed thrusts Figs 3 & 5).

Folds

The general fold styles consist of open to tight, asymmetric folds. Axial surfaces are planar, dip moderately to steeply toward the Cordillera, and are similar in azimuth and dip direction to mapped thrust faults. Folds generally become tighter toward the Cordillera, with more pronounced cratonward overturn. Axial planes and thrust surfaces dip at increasingly shallow angles toward the Cordillera (Fig. 6). The folds are disharmonic and decrease in amplitude with depth toward a plane of décollement above the Jurassic volcanics. Thus, the regional structures have a predominant vergence toward the craton. The degree of shortening revealed by fold style and presence of cleavage within the cover rocks decreases toward the craton. Sub-isoclinal folds and schistose fabrics are present along the cordilleran margin, in contrast to the more open folds of the central fold belt.

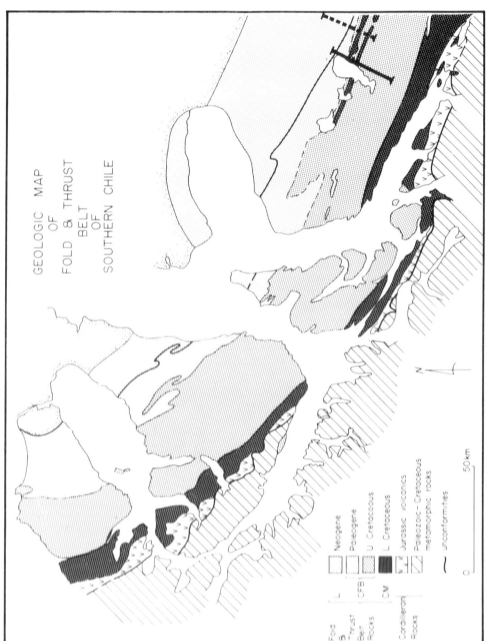

Fɪɢ. 5. Geological map of the fold and thrust belt of southern Chile. L = lowlands; CFB = central fold belt; CM = cordilleran margin. These rocks are the deformed infilling of the Mesozoic-Cenozoic Magallanes Basin, the southern Andean foredeep. Solid line indicates cross section location for Fig. 6. Broken line indicates location of cross section for Fig. 8.

TIERRA DEL FUEGO

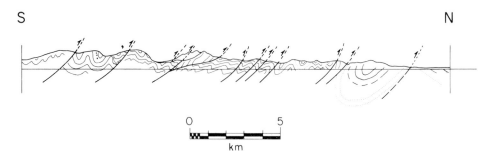

FIG. 6. Cross section from Tierra del Fuego in the central fold belt. No vertical exaggeration. Minimal extrapolation to depth. Based on mapping by the author. Location of cross section on Fig. 5.

Faults

Thrust and high-angle reverse faults, some of which are traceable along strike for 30 km, are directly related in geometry and timing to the folding of the cover rocks of the foredeep. At the surface, fault planes dip moderately to steeply 45–85°) toward the Cordillera, decreasing in dip angle toward the cordilleran margin. Vertical displacements of up to 1600–3800 m can be stratigraphically determined along several major faults. The fault surfaces are planar in cross-section or curviplanar with the convex side toward the craton (Fig. 6). In the central fold belt, thrust faults frequently truncate the overturned limbs of asymmetric anticlines (Fig. 6). Upward steepening faults appear to control fold wavelengths under the lowlands. In other words, asymmetric anticlines with faulted limbs are separated by nearly flat-lying beds (Fig. 6).

Limited subsurface data indicate repetition of rock units and decrease of dip of fault planes with depth, suggesting imbrication above a plane of décollement (ENAP, unpublished data). This imbrication results in greatly increased apparent thicknesses of sediments in the Magallanes basin. The surface of décollement under the central fold belt is the contact between the Jurassic volcanics and the Lower Cretaceous sedimentary rocks.

In addition to the imbricate thrust faults above a décollement surface, drillhole data and seismic reflection studies (ENAP, unpublished data) reveal 8–15 km wide fault-bounded basement blocks. Reverse motion on some of these pre-Cretaceous normal faults is supported by drilling and recent subsurface seismic reflection data (ENAP, unpublished data). In addition, drilling has revealed a few areas in which the

volcanics are thrown up along high-angle faults beneath the central fold belt.

In conclusion, listric reverse faults throughout the fold and thrust belt are geometrically related to folding. These faults are responsible for a large percentage of the shortening within the cover rocks by imbrication of thrust slices. The basement beneath the fold and thrust belt shows block faulting with some evidence of basement wedging. A surface of décollement is found beneath most of the allochthonous fold and thrust belt toward which fold amplitudes decrease and thrust surfaces become tangential. Hence, the overall appearance of the fold and thrust belt fits 'thin-skinned' models, as shortening within the cover rocks is not directly reflected in the basement, except in the localities described below.

Cover shortening

The deformation of the foredeep and shelf to form the fold and thrust belt of the S Andes resulted in stratal shortening above the pre-Jurassic basement. However, basement involvement in cover folds and thrusts is supported by evidence in a few areas, as is discussed below. Palinspastic restoration of the foredeep stratigraphy was undertaken for a section in central Tierra del Fuego (Fig. 7). The datum separates the Lower Cretaceous shallow marine sedimentary rocks from the Upper Cretaceous foredeep sedimentary section. The Lower Tertiary section reflects migration of the foredeep basin axis toward the craton. The restoration was done by 1. unfolding folds, 2. estimating bulk shortening due to cleavage development, and 3. rolling back

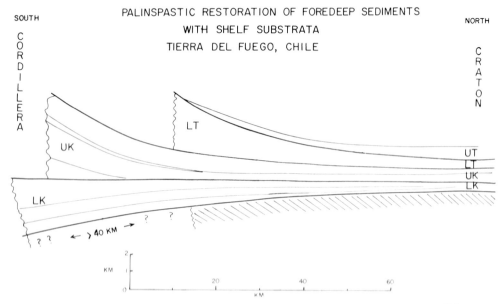

FIG. 7. Palinspastic restoration of foredeep sediments with shelf substrata from central Chilean Tierra del Fuego. Lower Cretaceous section reveals a subsiding shelf. The Upper Cretaceous section shows the Andean foredeep sedimentary rocks. The Lower Tertiary section represents craton-ward migration of foredeep basin axes and the formation of successor basins.

thrusts to restore stratigraphy. The basis for calculating stratal shortening for each domain of the fold and thrust belt is given below, along with the uncertainties involved.

Cordilleran margin

At least 70% shortening, with a sub-horizontal maximum shortening direction, occurred across the cordilleran margin. In addition, sub-vertical shear zones with a mylonitic foliation may contribute a further component of bulk strains, but they are only locally present and the contribution is impossible to evaluate from present data. A continental basement zone, with a width of several kilometres, is exposed across strike along the cordilleran border. Detachment of the shelf edge cover-rocks near the Cordillera, from their underlying continental basement, is inferred from the high angle contact with, and proximity to, marginal basin and remnant arc rocks; and also by the elimination of the angular unconformity (Nelson *et al.* 1979). In addition, several kilometres of basement and cover-rocks may have been lost by imbrication of shallow dipping thrusts along the cordilleran boundary (Figs 1 & 4).

Central fold belt

The allochthonous cover rocks are deformed into asymmetric folds cut by listric faults. The contribution of stratal shortening by imbrication of thrusts can be determined only if there is 1. subsurface control of faults and 2. stratigraphic control. Drillhole data, seismic profiling, and electrical log work has not been conducted in this region, except in the less deformed lowlands. Good stratigraphic thickness control is available for areas near the lowlands (ENAP, unpubl. data) which helps in calculating shortening by folding and faulting for the rest of the central fold belt. However, thickness and lithological data alone are insufficient when attempting palinspastic calculations of units telescoped by imbricated thrusts. The dominantly deep water turbidite assemblages do not allow accurate palinspastic reconstructions which are possible with sedimentary facies data.

The average contribution of shortening, by folding alone, is 30–40%. This is inferred from the concentric and chevron fold styles and from the lack of evidence for flexural flow. Less than 20% layer-parallel shortening has occurred by cleavage development. This may be inferred from the lack of intragranular strain and the thickness of clay selvages relative to the percentage of clay in the whole rock.

Lowlands

In the lowlands, open warps with no obvious cleavage suggest bulk strains of a few percent. However, the presence of narrow anticlines in foreland, especially near the craton, may be due to thrusts rather than buckle phenomena (Foose 1973; Gwinn 1964; Harris 1970), especially where asymmetric fold trains are found with tight anticlines and broad, flat-bottomed synclines. Thus, an unknown percent of shortening in the cover can be accomplished by thrusting in the lowlands without obvious surface buckling, and the limit of allochthonous units cannot be determined in this area.

In conclusion, over the entire 80–100 km width of the foreland fold and thrust belt, at least 40 km of sub-horizontal shortening has occurred in the cover rocks (Fig. 7). This value should be taken as an absolute minimum. At least 10–15 km of shortening has occurred along the cordilleran margin and at least 15–25 km has occurred in the central fold belt with several kilometres of additional shortening in the lowlands.

Basement shortening

There are three mechanisms which can be invoked to explain the differences in estimated cover and basement shortening (at least 40 km) 1. gravity spreading or sliding; 2. basement uplift along inherited high angle faults; and 3. underthrusting of continental lithosphere beneath the Cordillera.

Gravity spreading or sliding

There is abundant evidence for initial tectonic uplift of the S Andean Cordillera at the same time as rapid subsidence and sedimentation in the Magallanes Basin (Dott et al. in press, 1979; Dalziel & Palmer 1979; Winslow in press, 1979). The lifting up of the cordillera, the migrating clastic wedge and progressive deformation toward the craton, fit well into a gravity sliding or spreading model. Along the S margin of the Magallanes Basin, Cordillera Darwin, a structural culmination, was being uplifted during the Palaeogene and resulted in large-scale sedimentary slumping off its N flank. However, this terrane was not present when most of the fold and thrust belt developed and thus, the source terrane of de-

nuded basement is not available for foreland tectonics models. Furthermore, the timing of uplift in the Cordillera generally coincides with subsidence and deposition in the foredeep and not with shortening.

Reverse motion along inherited faults

Shortening and shearing of the Jurassic volcanics, which immediately underlie the surface of décollement in the central fold belt, are only seen in outcrop along the cordilleran margin of the fold belt. Further evidence comes from drillhole and seismic reflection data (ENAP, unpublished data) which discloses the presence of 8–14 km wide uplifted basement blocks beneath the lowlands and central fold belt. The Jurassic volcanics and basement are locally involved in thrusts in the central and lowlands area . One drillhole actually penetrates a basement wedge then re-enters cover-rocks (Fig. 8).

Direct field evidence for basement upthrusting along inherited faults exists in the central fold belt in Tierra del Fuego, where Lower Cretaceous inliers are found within the Upper Cretaceous and Lower Tertiary section (Fig. 5). The Lower Cretaceous rocks crop out as an anticlinorial ridge, bounded on the N and S by reverse faults, and are thrust up 800 m, relative to the rocks on the N and S sides. The sense of overturn of folds on the N side is toward the N, while on the S side overturn is toward the S (Fig. 8). Nearby, wells in the lowlands indicate 'paired', asymmetric anticlines whose steep limbs face towards or away from one another (Fig. 8). Other data, though less compelling, indicate that abrupt thickness variations of late Jurassic volcanic and sedimentary rocks observed in the undeformed part of the lowlands are often reversed in the central fold belt. In other words, thicker sequences are sometimes found on horsts instead of in grabens.

Bruhn (1976) suggested that the spacing, orientation, and location of sub-vertical shear zones in the marginal basin rocks have been directly controlled by such buried horsts and grabens. The most compelling evidence for reverse motion along inherited normal faults comes from the deformed marginal basin. At least 5 km of reverse movement can be inferred along an original marginal basin-remnant arc contact (Bruhn & Dalziel 1977). Elsewhere in the marginal basin, undeformed ophiolites sit on horsts 300–500 m above highly deformed basin infill, indicating that 500–5000 m of differential uplift has occurred in these areas

CENTRAL TIERRA DEL FUEGO, CHILE

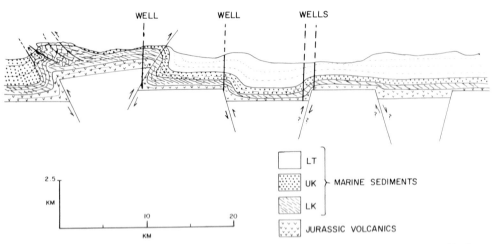

FIG. 8. Interpretative section from central Tierra del Fuego. Note the upthrust basement block control of folds, and thickness variations of the Jurassic volcanics. Published sources of well data are from Thomas (1949); Sass & Neff (1962); and Natland *et al.* (1974).

(Fig. 4). Similarly, these zones which continue under the foredeep and shelf, may have been exploited during Cretaceous and Tertiary and have shortened the basement 13% underneath the foreland fold belt by reverse displacements, (Fig. 9). Also they may have been exploited locally by the major transcurrent faults of Mesozoic and Cenozoic ages. Such narrow shear zones would divide basement blocks which show no post-Gondwanian fabrics, except in the shear zone itself.

If the above data for central Tierra del Fuego are taken at face value, calculations of basement shortening can be made for this area

BASEMENT FAULTING ALONG INHERITED BLOCK FAULTS

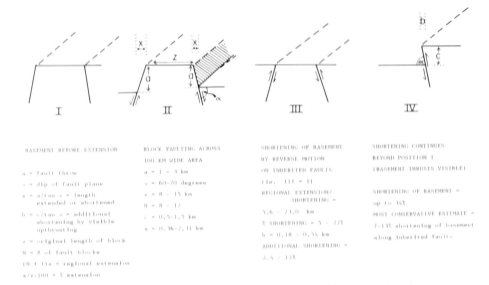

FIG. 9. Basement faulting along inherited block faults. Note: I and II precede deposition of cover sediments. I–II – II–III. See text for the explanation of assumptions.

(Fig. 9). These estimates result in up to 40 km or 13–50% basement shortening by reverse motion on previously normal faults, which were initiated prior to deposition of the sedimentary cover. If we then speculate that these calculations are valid for the fold and thrust belt, 40 km of basement shortening can be explained by this model. Although this can account for the absolute minimum value of stratal shortening, it cannot explain the amounts of shortening that are possibly much larger and which are not documented by facies control.

Continental underthrusting

The possibility of crustal attenuation and decoupling under the cordilleran margin cannot be ruled out. Progressive underthrusting of the continental basement (Bally *et al.* 1966; Coney 1971, 1973) could also be a major mechanism for basement 'disposal' in the sub-Andean fold and thrust belt. Bruhn & Dalziel (1977) suggested that inherited faults (Fig. 4) of the mid to late Jurassic volcano-tectonic rift terrane could have provided pathways for the transport of upper mantle fluids to produce oceanic crust. This initial rifting phase attenuated, but did not breach, the continental crust underneath the continental shelf and craton (Winslow in press, 1979). There may have been some quasi-oceanic crust underlying the cover rocks of the present cordilleran margin.

Furthermore, it is possible that the extremely attenuated continental basement beneath the Magallanes Basin could have decoupled near the shelf-marginal basin boundary, as also occurred along the remnant arc-marginal basin boundary (Bruhn & Dalziel 1977). Incipient underthrusting, along a S dipping plane, might have occurred beneath the cordilleran margin (Fig. 4). There is direct evidence to support this hypothesis, as may be inferred from following the axis of the foredeep eastward along a pronounced negative gravity anomaly offshore into the Atlantic Ocean (Figs 10 & 11). The eastern part of the Malvinas Chasm, the seaward extension of the Magallanes Basin, is floored by oceanic crust. 'Basement' underthrusting of several kilometres of crust has occurred from N to S in the Malvinas Chasm (Barker 1976; Ludwig *et al.* 1978; J. LaBrecque, pers. comm.).

If one follows the transition of the Magallanes Basin along its strike from N to S and then to the E, one observes changes in basin type; from a subareal basin on continental crust to a shallow water marine basin, to a dominantly deep water basin on continental (?) crust into a deep water trough on unquestioned oceanic crust. If underthrusting of continental basement can be proved, then this fold belt may be a unique example of A-type subduction transferring to at least limited B-type subduction with a descending (oceanic?) slab over a distance of a few hundreds of kilometres.

Conclusions

From drillhole and seismic reflection data it can be shown that continental basement is block-faulted, throughout southern South America. These basement blocks control Mesozoic and Cenozoic structures of the deformed cover rocks of the foothills and Cordillera. The foothills of the southernmost Andes are composed of deformed Cretaceous and Tertiary rocks in a well exposed foreland, fold and thrust, belt. The overall structural geometry and vergence are characteristic of other fold belts with thrust planes and axial surfaces of folds dipping toward the Cordillera. A major décollement surface is present above the metamorphic basement, the main thrust surface is often located above the overlying Upper Jurassic volcanic section. Thus, the southern Andean fold and thrust belt is similar in geometry and profile to other forelands, with the exception of the major fault blocks. Present-day reactivation of high angle faults in the basement beneath a foreland has been recently documented seismically in the Zagros fold belt (Jackson *et al.* this volume). These normal faults were active before deposition of the sedimentary cover and subsequent reverse motion has resulted in 20–50 km of shortening.

There is compelling evidence in the central fold belt of S Chile for basement upthrusting of 300–500 m along inherited normal faults. Coring of individual basement blocks will probably not reveal reset radiometric ages, except along the actual fault surfaces. During the deformation and uplift of the Cordillera and foothills, some of these block boundaries were sites of concentrated strain and reverse movement (Bruhn 1976; Bruhn & Dalziel 1977). If taken at face value, basement shortening by uplifting along discrete blocks beneath the foreland does not exceed 13% over the foothill belt. However, if one envisages reverse motion that elevates the former graben, but does not yet begin to form obvious upthrust wedges (Fig. 9, stage II–III), up to 30% shortening can occur without altering the appearance of a passive continental basement.

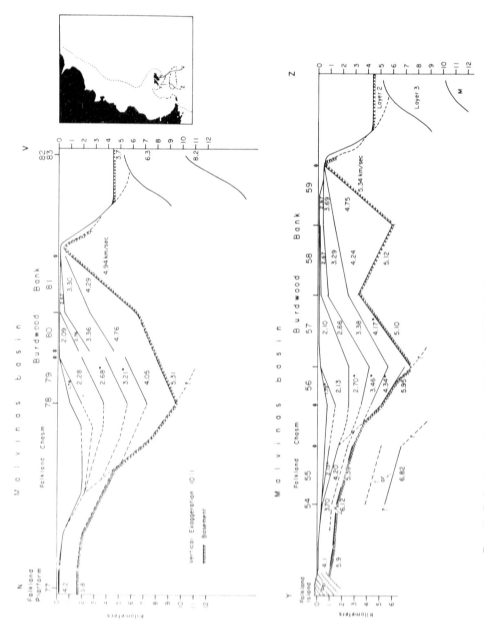

Fig. 10. Reflection profiles across Malvinas (Falkland) Chasm and Basin. Localities are shown on the inset. The Malvinas Chasm is the offshore equivalent of the Magallanes Basin. The Burdwood Bank is the probable offshore equivalent of the Andean Cordillera. Vertical exaggeration is 10:1.

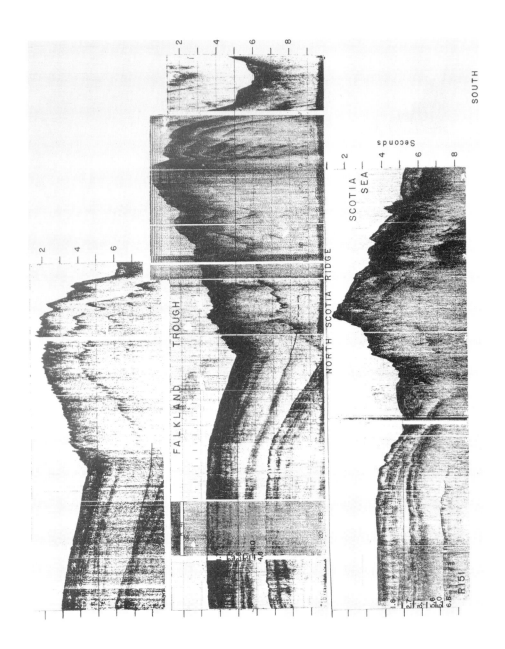

In other words, an equal amount of shortening can occur in the basement (Fig. 9, shortening of Stage II–III = extension in Stages I–II). It is very important to note that extension preceded deposition of the sedimentary cover. It is from these calculations that an estimate of up to 40 km of shortening can occur in the foreland fold belt. These ideas can be tested when further drillhole and seismic reflection data are available in the deformed rocks of the foothills.

Evidence for underthrusting of continental basement is difficult to prove directly in most foreland fold belts, without extensive geophysical data. The dip of the foreland basement is toward the Cordillera (or 'internal' zones) in most fold belts. Basement 'disposal' is possible by detaching the basement at the Cordillera-foreland contact and underthrusting the foreland basement at a shallow angle. In the S Andes, continental crust may have decoupled at the marginal basin continental boundary or along the remnant arc-continental shelf contact following rapid sedimentation and tectonic loading in that zone (Fig. 4). Basement could then be underthrust up to (W)/cos α km (Fig. 1).

The actual basement 'problem' is partly an artifact of modelling. When the foreland fold belt is unfolded and restored, the basement block directly beneath is of insufficient length (Elliott 1973). However, now that the more deformed cordilleras are known to be partly or wholly allochthonous, the 'missing' basement of foreland fold belts may be simply underlying the allochthonous part of the cordillera. In an Andean setting, the amount of underthrusting beneath the orogen may be limited by the presence of a subducting oceanic slab, which creates a space problem (Fig. 1). In other words, low angle continental underthrusting cannot exceed the width of the forearc and cordillera.

The unique aspect of the orogen discussed in this paper is that the offshore equivalents of the Andean tectonic provinces are known from marine geophysical data. These offshore data support underthrusting of foredeep basement beneath the Cordillera, although in the oceanic section the foredeep is floored by oceanic crust. Future studies in the S Andes and in the South Atlantic and Scotia Sea will result in a better understanding of basement behaviour *vis a vis* rifting, deposition, and shortening on a narrow continental margin.

ACKNOWLEDGMENTS. The field and laboratory work for this project was supported by Department of Polar Programs grant DPP-21415, with Ian W. D. Dalziel as principal investigator. The manuscript benefitted greatly from critical discussions with Drs Dalziel, adviser, T. Engelder, C. Scholz, and G. King. Furthermore, I would like to thank Srs. B. Bergman, S. Harambour, and R. Cortés for use of the laboratory and library facilities at the Empresa Nacional del Petroleo, Punta Arenas, Chile during the austral summers of 1974–1978. Preparation of the manuscript and figures was greatly aided by the diligence and support of R. A. Baroody, D. Breger, A. Lewis, and L. Zappa.

References

AMPFERER, O. & HAMMER, W. 1911. Geologischer Querschnitt durch die Ostalpen von Allgau zum Gardasee. *Jahrb. geol. Reichsandstalt*, **61**, 531–710.

ARTEMIEV, M. E. & ARTYUSHKOV, E. V. 1971. Structure and isostasy of the Baikal rift and the mechanism of rifting. *J. geophys. Res.* **76**, 1197–210.

BALLY, A. W. 1975. A geodynamic scenario for hydrocarbon occurrences. *World Petrol. Cong. Tokyo*, 33–44.

——, GORDY, P. L. & STEWART, G. A. 1966. Structure, seismic data, and orogenic evolution of southern Canadian Rocky Mountains. *Bull. Can. Pet. Geol.* **14**, 337–81.

BARKER, P. F. 1976. Correlations between sites on the eastern Falkland Plateau by means of seismic reflection profiles, leg 36, DSDP. *In:*

BARKER, P. F. et al. (eds). *Initial Rep. Deep Sea drill. Proj.* **36**, 971–90. U.S. Govt. Printing Office, Washington.

BRUHN, R. L. 1976. *Middle Cretaceous Deformation in the Andes of Tierra del Fuego: an Example of Aborted Obduction.* Ph.D. Thesis, Columbia University, New York, 76 p. (unpubl.).

—— 1977. Destruction of the early Cretaceous marginal basin in the Andes of Tierra del Fuego. *In:* TALWANI, M. & PITMAN, W. J., III (eds). *Maurice Ewing Series*, **1** *Island Arcs, Deep Sea Trenches and Back-Arc Basins.* 395–406.

——, DEWIT, M. J. & PALMER, K. F. in press, 1979. Destruction of the early Cretaceous back-arc basin in the southern Andes. *In: Third Symposium on Antarctic Geology and Geophysics.* 1977. Madison, Wisconsin.

FIG. 11. Single-channel seismic reflection profiles of Falkland plateau, Falkland trough, and N Scotia ridge from Ludwig et al. (1978). Note that acoustic basement (the deepest reflector recorded) is not true metamorphic basement.

CONEY, P. J. 1971. Cordilleran tectonic transactions and motion of the North American plate. *Nature*, **233**, 462–5.

—— 1973. Non collision tectogenesis in western North America. *In*: TARLING, D. H. & RUNCORN, S. K. (eds). *Implications of Continental Drift to the Earth Sciences*. Academic Press, New York.

DALZIEL, I. W. D. & CORTES, R. 1972. Tectonic style of the southernmost Andes and the Antarctandes. *24th Int. geol. Congr.* **3**, 316–27. Montreal, Canada.

——, DEWIT, M. J. & PALMER, K. F. 1974. Fossil marginal basin in the southern Andes. *Nature* **250**, 291–4.

—— & ELLIOT, D. H. 1971. Evolution of the Scotia Arc. *Nature* **233**, 246–52.

—— & —— 1973. The Scotia Arc and Antarctic margin. *In*: NAIRN, A. E. & STEHLI, F. G. (eds). *The Ocean basins and Margins*: **1**. *The South Atlantic*. 171–245. Plenum Press, New York.

—— & PALMER, K. F. 1979. Progressive deformation and orogenic uplift at the southern extremit of the Andes. *Bull. geol. Soc. Am.* **90**, 259–80.

DOTT, R. H., JR. 1976. Contrasts in tectonic history along the eastern Pacific rim. *In*: SUTTON, G. H., MANGHNANI, M. H. & MOBERLY, R. (eds). *The Geophysics of the Pacific Ocean basin and its Margin*. 299–308. Am. geophys. Union Mon. 19.

——, WINN, R. D., JR. & SMITH, C. H. L. in press, 1979. Relationships of late Mesozoic and early Cenozoic sedimentation to the tectonic evolution of the southernmost Andes and Scotia Arc. *In*: *Third Symposium on Antarctic Geology and Geophysics*. 1977. Madison, Wisconsin.

ELLIOTT, D. 1973. Plate tectonics and the problem of too much granitic basement. *Geology*, **1**, 111.

FOOSE, R. M. 1973. Vertical tectonism and gravity in the Big Horn Basin and surrounding ranges of the middle Rocky Mountains. *In*: DEJONG, K. A. & SCHOLTEN, R. (eds). *Gravity and Tectonics*. 443–55. J. Wiley & Sons, New York.

FORSYTH, D. W. 1975. Fault plane solutions and tectonics of the South Atlantic and Scotia Sea. *J. geophys. Res.* **80**, 1429–43.

GWINN, V. E. 1964. Thin-skinned tectonics in the Plateau and northwestern Valley and ridge provinces of the central Appalachians. *Bull. geol. Soc. Amer.* **75**, 863–900.

—— 1970. Kinematic patterns and estimate of lateral shortening, Valley and Ridge and Great Valley provinces, central Appalachians, south-central Pennsylvania. *In*: FISHER, G. W. *et al.* (eds). *Studies of Appalachian Geology: Central and Southern*. 127–46. Interscience, New York.

HALPERN, M. & CARLIN, G. M. 1971. Radiometric chronology of crystalline rocks from southern Chile. *Antarctic J. U.S.* **6**, 191–3.

HARRIS, L. D. 1970. Details of thin-skinned tectonics in parts of Valley and Ridge and Cumberland Plateau provinces of the southern Appalachians. *In*: FISHER, G. W. (eds.). *Studies of Appalachian Geology: Central and Southern*. 161–74. Interscience, New York.

HERRON, E. M., BRUHN, R., WINSLOW, M. &. CHAQUI, L. 1977. Post Miocene tectonics of the margin of southern Chile. *In*: TALWANI, M. & PITMAN, W. C., III (eds). *Maurice Ewing Series*, **1**, *Island arcs, Deep Sea Trenches and Back-Arc Basins*, 273–84.

—— & HAYES, D. E. 1969. A geophysical study of the Chile Ridge. *Earth planet Sci. Lett.* **6**, 77–83.

—— & TUCHOLKE, B. E. 1976. Sea-floor magnetic patterns and basement structure in the southeastern Pacific. *In*: *Initial Rep. Deep Sea drill. Proj.* **35**, 263–78. U.S. Govt. Printing Office, Washington.

KATZ, H. R. 1972. Plate tectonics-orogenic belts in the southeast Pacific. *Nature*, **237**, 331.

—— 1963. Revision of Cretaceous stratigraphy in Patagonian Cordillera of Ultima Esperanza, Magallanes Province, Chile. *Bull. Am. Assoc. Petrol. Geol.* **47**, 506–24.

LUDWIG, W. J., WINDISCH, C. C., HOUTZ, R. E. & EWING, J. I. 1978. Structure of the Falkland Plateau and offshore Tierra del Fuego Argentina. *In*: *Geological and Geophysical Investigations of Continental Margins*. Mem. Am. Assoc. Petrol. Geol. **29**, 125–37.

NATLAND, M. L., GONZALEZ, E., CANON, A. & ERNST, M. 1974. A system of stages for correlation on Magallanes Basin sediments. *Mem. geol. Soc. Am.* **139**, 1–126.

NELSON, E., DALZIEL, I. W. D. & MILNES, A. G. 1979. Deformation in Cordillera Darwin, southernmost Chilean Andes: A metamorphic core complex? *Abs. geol. Soc. Am. Cordilleran Section Meeting, San Jose, California*, 119.

RODGERS, J. 1964. Basement and no-basement hypotheses in the Jura and the Appalachian Valley and Ridge. *In*: *Tectonics of the Southern Appalachians*, Virginia Polytech. Inst., Dept. Geol. Sci. **1**, 71–80.

SASS, L. C. & NEFF, C. H. 1962. Petroleum developments in South America and Caribbean area, *Bull. Am. Assoc. Petrol. Geol.* **46**, 1077–140.

SCOTT, K. M. 1966. Sedimentology and dispersal pattern of Cretaceous flysch sequence, Patagonian Andes, southern Chile. *Bull. Am. Assoc. Petrol. Geol.* **50**, 72–107.

THOMAS, C. R. 1949. Geology and Petroleum exploration in Magalanes Province, Chile, *Bull. Am. Assoc. Petrol. Geol.* **33**, 1553–78.

WINSLOW, M. A., in press, 1979. The structural evolution of the Magallanes Basin and neotectonics in the southernmost Andes. *In*: *Third Symposium on Antarctic Geology and Geophysics*. 1977. Madison, Wisconsin.

M. A. WINSLOW, Lamont Doherty Geological Observatory, Pallisades, New York, U.S.A.

Subject Index

Orogenic belt (*contd*)
  Moine Thrust Zone, 246–7
  role of gravity, 125–40
Outer crystallines nappes, Himalaya, 385, 386
Overthrust,
  Banda Arc, 407–16
  definition, 7–9
  mechanics, 2
    Haute-Savoie, 159–65
  see also Thrust

Pakistan, Chaman transform zone, tectonic setting, 363–4
Palinspastic restorations, 440–2, 459–61, 520, 521
Palwan trench, seismic section, 16
Papua-Ophiolite thrust, 99
Pelvoux massif, 329, 330
Penninic Nappes, 293
Perfect plastic, model, 2 ·
  see also frictional plastic
Photoelastic model, thrust faulting, 67–8
Physical models,
  clay, 3, 68–75
  and secondary faulting, 68–75
  silicone putty, 136
  photoelastic, 67–8
  wax, 114
Piedmont, 493–4
Pine Mountain
  thrust sheet deformation, 55–63
    results, numerical consequences, 56–7
Plasticity, models, 79–80, 86–88
Plastico-viscous theory, 35
Plate tectonics, 27–8, 199, 267–74, 358, 363, 365–9, 390, 393–406, 483, 514–5
  Canadian Cordillera, 427–8, 441–4, 469–471
  convergence, 270
  Japan Trench transect data, 393–406
  movements, Caledonides, 267–74
  tectonic reconstructions, 27–8
  Variscan Arc, W. Europe, 358
Platé Massif, 159–65
Poisson's ratio, 66, 117
Pole figures, calcite tectonites, 152
  discussion of, 153–7
  quartz, 189, 190
Pore pressure, 2, 3, 34–7, 41–54, 86, 87, 88, 100, 101, 107, 115, 118, 254, 332, 351, 402, 405, 482
  and basal layer weakness, 102
  control of step-bedded plane thrusts, 87–8
  discontinuities and overthrusts, calculations, 35–7
  high fluid, subduction zones, 115
  high and low angle discontinuities, 34–5
  hydrostatic, 43
Post-Cambrian intrusives, Moine Thrust Zone, 246
Prandtl's solution, 82
Precambrian plate remnants, preserved, 28, 29
Pressure, fluid *see* Fluid Pressures
  pore, *see* Pore pressures
Pressure solution, *see* Deformation mechanisms
Pseudotachylyte, 200, 201
  age data, 218

distribution, New Zealand, 202–3
fault/injection vein complex, 200
friction melt, 200
flow banding and spherulite devitrification texture, 200–1
localities (N.Z.), 198
Purcell anticlinorium, 430–1, 436, 440–4
Push from rear (behind), 2, 101
  fluid welt model, 111–124

Ramps, 8, 55–63, 106–7, 114, 179–81, 298, 316, 320, 324, 325, 339, 343
  Alps Maritime, 350
  definition, 8
  generation zones in salt glacier, 179–81
  rock mechanics, toe affects, 106–7
  thrust sheet formation, 55–63
    mathematical model, 55–6
    Pine Mountain block, 56–7
    principal stresses, 57–63
Rangitata Orogeny, 197, 202, 212, 214–7
Recrystallization, salt, 178
  see also Deformation mechanisms
Reversed metamorphic gradient, 126, 159–65
Rheintal Jura, 311–317
Rhinegraben, 311, 312, 313, 316
Roberts Thrust, 99
Rock mechanics of thrust and nappe formation, 3, 4, 99–109
  see also Thrusts
  basal thrust fault, formation, mechanics, 107–8
  crustal thickening, 106–7
  deformation of thrust block, 105
  degree of rigidity, 100
  details of large thrusts, 99
  forces causing movement, 99
  forces resisting movement, 99
  gravity gliding, 103–4
  moving up-slope, 102–3
  propulsion of block from rear, 101–3
  ramping, 106–7
  stability of thrust block calculations, 100–1
  toe-effect, 49–50, 57–58, 106–7
  wedge-shaped block, 104, 114–9
Rocky Mt. Trench, 433, 437
  strike-slip faulting, 26
  see also Canadian Rocky Mountains
'Roll-over' Anticlines, 51, 52
Roof thrust, 8, 244, 249, 250, 320
Rossberg-Goldau slide, 99
Roya Nappe, 339, 341, 343–6
  amounts of displacement, 339–43
  listric normal fault, 339

Saline horizons, Damara orogen, 167–72
  Naukluff Nappes, 167–72
Salt diapirs
  Hormuz formation, S. Iran, 173–83, 377
Santis Nappe, 297, 319, 320
Scandinavian Caledonides—Central
  see Caledonides, Central Scandinavia
Scotland, NW Highlands
  Moine Thrust Zone, 241–60